How Consciousness Became the Universe

Quantum Physics, Cosmology, Relativity, Evolution, Neuroscience, Parallel Universes

2nd Edition

Deepak Chopra, Roger Penrose, Henry P. Stapp, Stuart Hameroff, Menas Kafatos, Rudolph E. Tanzi, Subhash Kak, Chris King, Walter J. Christensen Jr., Chris J. S. Clarke, Roger Nelson, Hans Liljenström, John Smythies, Andrea Nani, Andrea E. Cavanna, John T. Furey, Vincent J. Fortunato, Steven Bodovitz, Franz Klaus Jansen, Francois Martin, Federico Carminati, Giuliana Galli Carminati, Horace W. Crater, R. Joseph, Stan V. McDaniel, Brandon Carter, Michael B. Mensky, Gordon Globus, York H. Dobyns, Shan Gao, Fred Kuttner, Bruce Rosenblum, Michael Nauenberg, Antonella Vannini, Ulisse Di Corpo,

Science Publishers

Copyright © 2017

Published by: Science Publishers

2nd Edition

ISBN-10. 1-938024-45-1
ISBN-13. 978-1-938024-45-0

Contents

How Consciousness Became the Universe

Quantum Physics, Cosmology, Relativity, Evolution, Neuroscience, Parallel Universes

by

Deepak Chopra, Roger Penrose, Henry P. Stapp, Stuart Hameroff, Menas Kafatos, Rudolph E. Tanzi, Subhash Kak, Chris King, Walter J. Christensen Jr., Chris J. S. Clarke, Roger Nelson, Hans Liljenström, John Smythies, Andrea Nani, Andrea E. Cavanna, John T. Furey, Vincent J. Fortunato, Steven Bodovitz, Franz Klaus Jansen, Francois Martin, Federico Carminati, Giuliana Galli Carminati, Horace W. Crater, Stan V. McDaniel, Brandon Carter, Michael B. Mensky, Gordon Globus, York H. Dobyns, Shan Gao, Fred Kuttner, Bruce Rosenblum, Michael Nauenberg, Antonella Vannini, Ulisse Di Corpo,

****

****

****

I: How Consciousness Became the Universe

****

****

****

1. How Consciousness Becomes the Physical Universe

Menas Kafatos[1], Rudolph E. Tanzi[2], Deepak Chopra[3]

[1]Fletcher Jones Endowed Professor in Computational Physics, Schmid College of Science, Chapman University, One University Dr. Orange, California, 92866,

[2]Joseph P. and Rose F. Kennedy Professor of Neurology, Harvard Medical School Genetics and Aging Research Unit Massachusetts General Hospital/ Harvard Medical School 114 16th Street Charlestown, MA 02129

[3]The Chopra Center for Wellbeing, Carlsbad, CA 92009

Abstract

Issues related to consciousness in general and human mental processes in particular remain the most difficult problem in science. Progress has been made through the development of quantum theory, which, unlike classical physics, assigns a fundamental role to the act of observation. To arrive at the most critical aspects of consciousness, such as its characteristics and whether it plays an active role in the universe requires us to follow hopeful developments in the intersection of quantum theory, biology, neuroscience and the philosophy of mind. Developments in quantum theory aiming to unify all physical processes have opened the door to a profoundly new vision of the cosmos, where observer, observed, and the act of observation are interlocked. This hints at a science of wholeness, going beyond the purely physical emphasis of current science. Studying the universe as a mechanical conglomerate of parts will not solve the problem of consciousness, because in the quantum view, the parts cease to be measureable distinct entities. The interconnectedness of everything is particularly evident in the non-local interactions of the quantum universe. As such, the very large and the very small are also interconnected. Consciousness and matter are not fundamentally distinct but rather are two complementary aspects of one reality, embracing the micro and macro worlds. This approach of starting from wholeness reveals a practical blueprint for addressing consciousness in more scientific terms.

1. Introduction

We realize that the title of our paper is provocative. It is aimed at providing a theory of how the physical universe and conscious observers can be integrated. We will argue that the current state of affairs in addressing the multifaceted issue of consciousness requires such a theory if science is to evolve and encompass the phenomenon of consciousness. Traditionally, the underlying problem of consciousness has been excluded from science, on one of two grounds. Either it is taken as a given that it has no effect on experimental data, or if consciousness must be addressed, it is considered subjective and therefore unreliable as part of the scientific method. Therefore, our challenge is to include consciousness while still remaining within the methods of science.

Our starting point is physics, which recognizes three broad approaches to studying the physical universe: classical, relativistic, and quantum. Classical Newtonian physics is suitable for most everyday applications, yet its epistemology (method of acquiring knowledge) is limited -- it does not apply at the microscopic level and cannot be used for many cosmic processes. Between them, general relativity applies at the large scale of the universe and quantum theory at the microcosmic level. Despite all the attempts to unify general relativity with quantum theory, the goal is still unreached. Of the three broad approaches, quantum theory has clearly opened the door to the issue of consciousness in the measurement process, while relativity admits that observations from different moving frames would yield different values of quantities. Many of the early founders of quantum mechanics held the view that the participatory role of observation is fundamental and the underlying "stuff" of the cosmos is processes rather than the construct of some constant, underlying material substance.

However, quantum theory does not say anything specific about the nature of consciousness -- the whole issue is clouded by basic uncertainty over even how to define consciousness. A firm grasp of human mental processes still remains very elusive. We believe that this indicates a deeper problem which scientists in general are reluctant to address: objective science is based on the dichotomy between subject and object; it rests on the implicit assumption that Nature can be studied ad infinitum as an external objective reality. The role of the observer is, at best, secondary, if not entirely irrelevant.

2. Consciousness and Quantum Theory

In our view, it may well be that the subject-object dichotomy is false to begin with and that consciousness is primary in the cosmos, not just an epiphenomenon of physical processes in a nervous system. Accepting this assumption would turn an exceedingly difficult problem into a very simple one. We will sidestep any precise definition of consciousness, limiting ourselves for now to willful actions on the part of the observer. These actions, of course, are the outcome of specific choices in the mind of the observer. Although some mental actions could be automated, at some point the will of conscious observer(s) sets the whole mechanical aspects of observation in motion.

The issue of observation in QM is central, in the sense that objective reality cannot be disentangled from the act of observation, as the Copenhagen Interpretation (CI) clearly states (cf. Kafatos & Nadeau 2000; Kafatos 2009; Nadeau and Kafatos, 1999; Stapp 1979; Stapp 2004; Stapp 2007). In the words of John A. Wheeler (1981), we live in an observer-participatory universe. The vast majority of today's practicing physicists follow CI's practical prescriptions for quantum phenomena, while still clinging to classical beliefs in observer-independent local, external reality (Kafatos and Nadeau 2000). There is a critical gap between practice and underlying theory. In his Nobel Prize speech of 1932, Werner Heisenberg concluded that the atom "has no immediate and direct physical properties at all." If the universe's basic building block isn't physical, then the same must hold true in some way for the whole. The universe was doing a vanishing act in Heisenberg's day, and it certainly hasn't become more solid since.

This discrepancy between practice and theory must be confronted, because the consequences for the nature of reality are far-reaching (Kafatos and Nadeau, 2000). An impressive body of evidence has been building to suggest that reality is non-local and undivided. Non-locality is already a basic fact of nature, first implied by the Einstein-Podolsky-Rosen thought experiment (EPR, 1935), despite the original intent to refute it, and later explicitly formulated in Bell's Theorem (Bell, 1964) and its relationship to EPR – for further developments, see also experiments which favor QM over local realism, e.g. Aspect, Grangier, and Roger, 1982; Tittel, Brendel, Zbinden & Gisin, 1998. One can also cite the Aharonov-Bohm (1959) effect, and numerous other quantum phenomena.

Moreover, this is a reality where the mindful acts of observation play a crucial role at every level. Heisenberg again: "The atoms or elementary particles themselves . . . form a world of potentialities or possibilities rather than one of things or facts." He was led to a radical conclusion that underlies our own view in this paper: "What we observe is not nature itself, but nature exposed to our method of questioning." Reality, it seems, shifts according to the observer's conscious intent. There is no doubt that the original CI was subjective (Stapp, 2007). However, as Bohr (1934) and Heisenberg (1958) as well as the other developers of CI stated on many occasions, the view that emerged can be summarized as, "the purpose is not to disclose the real essence of phenomena but only to track down... relations between the multifold aspects of our experience" (Bohr, 1934). Stapp (2007) restates this view as "quantum theory is basically about relationships among conscious human experiences" (Stapp 2007). Einstein fought against what he considered the positivistic attitude of CI, which he took as equivalent to Berkeley's dictum to be is to be perceived (Einstein 1951), but he nevertheless admitted that QM is the only successful theory we have that describes our experiences of phenomena in the microcosm.

Quantum theory is not about the nature of reality, even though quantum physicists act as if that is the case. To escape philosophical complications, the original CI was pragmatic: it concerned itself with the epistemology of quantum world (how we experience quantum phenomena), leaving aside ontological questions about the ultimate nature of reality (Kafatos and Nadeau, 2000). The practical bent of CI should be kept in mind, particularly as there is a tendency on the part of many good physicists to slip back into issues that cannot be tested and therefore run counter to the basic tenets of scientific methodology.

To put specifics into the revised or extended CI, Stapp (2007) discusses John von Neumann's different types of processes. The quantum formalism eloquently formalized by von Neumann requires first the acquisition of knowledge about a quantum system (or probing action) as well as a mathematical formalism to describe the evolution of the system to a later time (usually the Schrödinger equation). There are two more processes that Stapp describes: one, according to statistical choices prescribed by QM, yields a specific outcome (or an intervention, a "choice on the part of nature" in Dirac's words); the second, which is primary, preceding even the acquisition of knowledge, involves a "free choice" on the part of the observer. This selection process is not and cannot be described by QM, or for that matter, from any "physically described part of reality" (Stapp, 2007).

These extensions (or clarifications) of the original orthodox CI yield a profoundly different way of looking at the physical universe and our role in it (Kafatos and Nadeau, 2000). Quantum theory today encompasses the interplay of the observer's free choices and nature's "choices" as to what constitute actual outcomes. This dance between the observer and nature gives practical meaning to the concept of the participatory role of the observer. (Henceforth we won't distinguish between the original CI and as it was extended by von Neumann— referring to both as orthodox quantum theory.) As Bohr (1958) emphasized, "freedom of experimentation" opens the floodgates of free will on the part of the observer. Nature responds in the statistical ways described by quantum formalism.

Kafatos and Nadeau (2000) and Nadeau and Kafatos (1999) give extended arguments about these metaphysically-based views of nature. CI points to the limits of physical theories, including itself. If any capriciousness is to be found, it should not be assigned to nature, rather to our mindset about how nature ought to work. As we shall see, there are credible ways to build on quantum formalism and what it suggests about the role of consciousness.

3. Quantum Mechanics and the Brain

It is essential that we avoid the mistake of rooting a physical universe in the physical brain, for both are equally rooted in the non-physical. For practical purposes, this means that the brain must acquire quantum status, just as the atoms that make it up have. The standard assumption in neuroscience is that consciousness is a byproduct of the operation of the human brain. The multitude of processes occurring in the brain covers a vast range of spatio-temporal domains, from the nanoscale to the everyday human scale (e.g. Bernroider and Roy, 2004). Even though they differ on certain issues, a number of scientists accept the applicability of QM at some scales in the brain (cf. Kafatos 2009).

For example, Penrose (1989, 1994) and Hameroff and Penrose (1996) postulate collapses occurring in microtubules induced by quantum gravity. In their view, quantum coherence operates across the entire brain. Stapp (2007) prefers a set of different classical brains that evolve according to the rules of QM, in accordance with the uncertainty principle. He contends that bringing in (the still not developed) quantum gravity needlessly complicates the picture.

In order for an integrative theory to emerge, the next step is to connect the quantum level of activity with higher levels. As a specific example of applying quantum-like processes at mesoscale levels, Roy and Kafatos (1999b) have examined the response and percept domains in the cerebellum. They have built a case that complementarity or quantum-like effects may be operating in brain processes. As is well known, complementarity is a cornerstone of orthodox quantum theory, primarily developed by Niels Bohr. Roy and Kafatos imagine a measurement process with a device that selects only one of the *eigenstates* of the observable A and rejects all others. This is what is meant by selective measurement in quantum mechanics. It is also called filtration because only one of the *eigenstates* filters through the process. In attempting to describe both motor function and cognitive activities, Roy and Kafatos (1999a) use statistical distance in setting up a formal Hilbert-space description in the brain, which illustrates our view that quantum formalism may be introduced for brain dynamics.

It is conceivable that the overall biological structures of the brain may require global relationships, which come down processes to global complementarity — every single process is subordinated to the whole. Not just single neurons but massive clusters and networks communicate all but instantaneously. One must also account for the extreme efficiency with which biological organisms operate in a holistic manner, which may only be possible by the use of quantum mechanical formalisms at biological, and neurophysiological relevant scales (cf. Frohlich, 1983; Roy and Kafatos, 2004; Bernroider and Roy, 2005; Davies, 2004, 2005; Stapp, 2004; Hameroff et. al., 2002; Hagan et. al., 2002; Hammeroff and Tuszynski, 2003; Mesquita et. al., 2005; Hunter, 2006; Ceballos et al., 2007).

Stepping into the quantum world doesn't produce easy agreement, naturally. The issue of decoherence (whereby the collapse of the wave function brings a quantum system into relationship with the macro world of large-scale objects and events) is often brought up in arguing against relevant quantum processes in the brain. However, neuronal decoherence processes have only been calculated while assuming that ions, such as $K+$, are undergoing quantum Brownian motion (e.g. Tegmark, 2000). As such, arguments about decoherence (Tegmark, 2000) assume that the system in question is in thermal equilibrium with its environment, which is not typically the case for bio-molecular dynamics (e.g. Frohlich, 1986; Pokony and Wu, 1998; Mesquita et. al., 2005).

In fact, quantum states can be pumped like a laser, as Frohlich originally proposed for biomolecules (applicable to membrane proteins, and tubulins in microtubules, see also work by Anirban, present volume). Also, experiments and theoretical work indicate that the ions themselves do not move freely within the ion-channel filter, but rather their states are pre-selected, leading to possible protection of quantum coherence within the ion channel for a time scale on the order of 10-3 seconds at 300K, ~ time scale of ion-channel opening and closing (e.g. Bernroider and Roy, 2005). Similar timescales apply to microtubular structures as pointed out by Hameroff and his co-workers. Moreover, progress in the last several years in high-resolution atomic X-ray spectroscopy from MacKinnon's group (Jang et al. 2003) and molecular dynamics simulations (cf. Monroe 2002) have shown that the molecular organization in ion channels allows for "pre-organized" correlations, or ion trappings within the selectivity filter of K+ channels. This occurs with five sets of four carbonyl oxygens acting as filters with the K+ ion, bound by eight oxygens, coordinated electrostatic interactions (Bernroider and Roy 2005). Therefore, quantum entangled states of between two subsystems of the channel filter result.

Beyond the brain, evidence has mounted for quantum coherence in biological systems at high temperatures, whereas in the past coherence was thought to apply to systems near absolute zero. For proteins supporting photosynthesis (Engel, et.al., 2007), solar photons on plant cells are converted to quantum electron states which propagate or travel through the relevant protein by all possible quantum paths, in reaching the part of the cell needed for conversion of energy to chemical energy. As such, new quantum ideas and laboratory evidence applicable to the fields of molecular cell biology and biophysics will have a profound impact in modeling and understanding the process of coherence within neuro-molecular systems.

4. Bridging the Gap: A Consciousness Model

Our purpose here is not to settle these technical issues – or the many others that have arisen as theorists attempt to link quantum processes to the field of biology – but to propose that technical considerations are secondary. What is primary is to have a reliable model against which experiments can offer challenges. Such a model isn't available as long as we fail to account for the disappearance of the material universe implied by quantum theory. This disappearance is real. There is at bottom no strictly mechanistic, physical foundation for the cosmos. The situation is far more radical than most practicing scientists suppose. Whatever is the fundamental source of creation, it itself must be uncreated. Otherwise, there is a hidden creator lying in the background, and then we must ask who or what created that.

What does it mean to be uncreated? The source of reality must be self-sufficient, capable of engendering complex systems on the micro and macro scale, self-regulating, and holistic. Nothing can exist outside its influence. Ultimately, the uncreated source must also turn into the physical universe, not simply oversee it as God or the gods do in conventional religion. We feel that only consciousness fits the bill, for as a prima facie truth, no experience takes place outside consciousness, which means that if there is a reality existing beyond our awareness (counting mathematics and the laws of physics as 1 part of our conscious experience), we will never be able to know it. The fact that consciousness is inseparable from cognition, perception, observation, and measurement is undeniable; therefore, this is the starting point for new insights into the nature of reality.

What is the nature of consciousness in our model? We take it as a field phenomenon, analogous to but preceding the quantum field. This field is characterized by generalized principles already described by quantum physics: complementarity, non-locality, scale-invariance and undivided wholeness. But there is a radical difference between this field and all others: we cannot define it from the outside. To extend Wheeler's reasoning, consciousness includes us human observers. We are part of a feedback loop that links our conscious acts to the conscious response of the field. In keeping with Heisenberg's implication, the universe presents the face that the observer is looking for, and when she looks for a different face, the universe changes its mask.

Consciousness includes human mental processes, but it is not just a human attribute. Existing outside space and time, it was "there" "before" those two words had any meaning. In essence, space and time are conceptual artifacts that sprang from primordial consciousness. The reason that the human mind meshes with nature, mathematics, and the fundamental forces described by physics, is no accident: we mesh because we are a product of the same conceptual expansion by which primordial consciousness turned into the physical world. The difficulty with using basic terms like "concept" and "physical" is that we are accustomed to setting mind apart from matter; therefore, thinking about an atom isn't the same as an atom. Ideas are not substances. But if elementary particles and all matter made of them aren't substances, either, the playing field has been leveled. Quantum theory gives us a model that applies everywhere, not just at the micro level. The real question, then, isn't how to salvage our everyday perception of a solid, tangible world but how to explore the mysterious edge where micro processes are transformed into macro processes, in other words, how Nature gets from microcosm to macrocosm. There, where consciousness acquires the nature of a substance, we must learn how to unify two apparent realities into one. We can begin to tear down walls, integrating objects, events, perceptions, thoughts, and mathematics under the same tent: all can be traced back to the same source.

Physics can serve a pivotal role in transitioning to this new model, because the entire biosphere operates under the same generalized principles we described from the quantum perspective, as does the universe itself. This simple unifying approach must be taken, we realize, as a basic ontological assumption, since it cannot be proven in an objective sense. We cannot extract consciousness from the physical universe, despite the fervent hope of materialists and reductionists. They are forced into a logical paradox, in fact, for either the molecules that make up the brain are inherently conscious (a conclusion to be abhorred in materialism), or a process must be located and described by which those molecules invent consciousness -such a process has not and never will be specified. It amounts to saying that table salt, once it enters the body, finds a way to dissolve in the blood, enter the brain, and in so doing learns to think, feel, and reason.

Our approach, positing consciousness as more fundamental than anything physical, is the most reasonable alternative: Trying to account for mind as arising from physical systems in the end leads (at best) to a claim that mathematics is the underlying "stuff" of the universe (or many universes, if you are of that persuasion). No one from any quarter is proposing a workable material substratum to the universe; therefore, it seems untenable to mount a rearguard defense for materialism itself. As we foresee it, the future development of science will still retain the objectivity of present-day science in a more sophisticated and evolved form. An evolved theory of the role of the observer will be generalized to include physical, biological, and most importantly, awareness aspects of existence. In that sense, we believe the ontology of science will be undivided wholeness at every level. Rather than addressing consciousness from the outside and trying to devise a theory of everything on that basis, a successful Theory Of Everything (TOE) will emerge by taking wholeness as the starting point and fitting the parts into it rather than vice versa. Obviously any TOE must include consciousness as an aspect of "everything," but just as obviously current attempts at a TOE ignore this and have inevitably fallen into ontological traps.

The time has come to escape those traps. An integrated approach will one day prevail. When it does, science will become much stronger and develop to the next levels of understanding Nature, to everyone's lasting benefit.

References

Aharonov, Y., and Bohm, D. (1959) Significance of Electromagnetic Potentials in the Quantum Theory, Phys. Rev., 115, 485-491.

Aspect, A., Grangier, P. and Roger, G. (1982) Experimental Realization of Einstein-Podolsky-Rosen-Bohm Gedankenexperiment: A New Violation of Bell's Inequalities, Phys. Rev. Lett., 49, 91-94.

Bell, J.S. (1964) On the Einstein-Podolsky-Rosen paradox, Physics, 1, 195.

Bernroider, G. and Roy, S. (2004) Quantum-classical correspondence in the brain: Scaling, action distances and predictability behind neural signals. FORMA, 19, 55–68.

Bernroider, G. and Roy, S. (2005) Quantum entanglement of K+ ions, multiple channel states, and the role of noise in the brain. In: Fluctuations and Noise in

Biological, Biophysical, and Biomedical Systems III, Stocks, Nigel G.; Abbott, Derek; Morse, Robert P. (Eds.), Proceedings of the SPIE, Volume 5841-29, pp. 205-214.

Bohr, N. (1934) Atomic Theory and the Description of Nature, Cambridge, Cambridge University Press. Bohr, N. (1958) Atomic Physics and Human Knowledge, New York: Wiley.

Ceballos, R., Kafatos, M., Roy, S., and Yang, S., (2007) Quantum mechanical implications for the mind-body issues, Quantum Mind 2007, G. Bemoider (ed) Univ. Salzburg, July, 2007.

Davies, P. (2004) Does Quantum Mechanics play a non-trivial role in Life? BioSystems, 78, 69–79.

Davies, P. (2005) A Quantum Recipe for Life, Nature, 437, 819.

Einstein, A. (1951) In: Albert Einstein: Philosopher-Physicist, P.A. Schilpp (Ed.) New York, Tudor.

Einstein, A., Podolsky, B., and Rosen, N. (1935) Can Quantum-Mechanical Description of Physical Reality Be Considered Complete?, Phys. Rev., 47, 777-780.

Engel, G.S., Calhoun, T.R., Read, E.L., Ahn, T.K., Mancal, T., Cheng, Y.C., Blankenship, R.E., and Fleming, G.R. (2007) Evidence for wavelike energy transfer through quantum coherence in photosynthetic systems, Nature, 446, 782-786.

Fröhlich, H. (1983) Coherence in Biology, In: Coherent Excitations in Biological Systems, Fröhlich, H. and Kremer, F. (Eds.), Berlin, Springer-Verlag, pp. 1-5.

Fröhlich, H. (1986) In: Modern Bioelectrochemistry, F. Gutman and H. Keyzer (Eds.) Springer-Verlag, New York.

Hagan, S., Hameroff, SR., and Tuszynski, JA. (2002) Quantum computation in brain microtubules: Decoherence and biological feasibility, Physical Review E., 65(6), Art. No. 061901 Part 1 June.

Hameroff, S. and Penrose, R. (1996) Conscious Events as Orchestrated Space-Time Selections, Journal of Consciousness Studies, Vol 3, No. 1, 36-53.

Hameroff, S. and Tuszynski, J. (2003) Search for quantum and classical modes of information processing in microtubules: Implications for the living state, In: Bioenergetic organization in living systems,Eds. Franco Mucumeci, Mae-Wan Ho, World Scientific, Singapore.

Hameroff, S., Nip, A., Porter, M. and Tuszynski, J. (2002) Conduction pathways in microtubules, biological quantum computation, and consciousness, Biosystems, 64(1-3), 149-168.

Heisenberg, W. (1958) Physics and Philosophy, New York, Harper.

Hunter, P. (2006) A quantum leap in biology. One inscrutable field helps another, as quantum physics unravels consciousness, EMBO Rep., October, 7(10), 971–974.

Jiang, Y.A., Lee, A., Chen, J., Ruta, V., Cadene, M., Chait, B.T., and MacKinnon, R. (2003) X-ray structure of a voltage-dependent K+ channel, Nature, 423, 33-41.

Kafatos, M. and Nadeau, R. (1990; 2000). The Conscious Universe: Parts and Wholes in Physical Reality, New York: Springer-Verlag.

Kafatos, M. (2009) Cosmos and Quantum: Frontiers for the Future, Journal of Cosmology, 3, 511-528.

Mesquita, M.V., Vasconcellos, A.R., Luzzi, R., and Mascarenhas, S. (2005) Large-scale Quantum Effects in Biological Systems, Int. Journal of Quantum Chemistry, 102, 1116–1130.

Monroe, C. (2002) Quantum information processing with atoms and photons, Nature, 416, 238-246.

Nadeau, R., and Kafatos, M. (1999) The Non-local Universe: The New Physics and Matters of the Mind, Oxford, Oxford University Press.

Penrose, R. (1989) The Emperor's New Mind, Oxford University Press, Oxford, England. Penrose, R. (1994) Shadows of the Mind, Oxford University Press, Oxford, England.

Pokorny, J., and Wu, T.M. (1998) Biophysical Aspects of Coherence and Biological Order, Springer, New York.

Rosa, L.P., and Faber, J. (2004) Quantum models of the mind: Are they compatible with environment decoherence? Phys. Rev. E, 70, 031902.

Roy S., and Kafatos, M. (1999a) Complemetarity Principle and Cognition Process, Physics Essays, 12, 662-668.

Roy, S., and Kafatos, M., (1999b) Bell-type Correlations and Large Scale Structure of the Universe, In: Instantaneous Action at a Distance in Modern Physics: Pro and Contra, A. E. Chubykalo, V. Pope, & R. Smirnov-Rueda (Eds.), New York: Nova Science Publishers.

Roy, S., and Kafatos, M. (2004) Quantum processes and functional geometry: new perspectives in brain dynamics. FORMA, 19, 69.

Stapp, H.P. (1979) Whiteheadian Approach to Quantum Theory and the Generalized Bell's Theorem, Found. of Physics, 9, 1-25.

Stapp, H. P. (2004) Mind, Matter and Quantum Mechanics (2nd edition), Heidelberg: Springer-Verlag.

Stapp, H.P. (2007) The Mindful Universe: Quantum Mechanics and the Participating Observer, Heidelberg: Springer-Verlag.

Tegmark, M. (2000) Importance of quantum decoherence in brain processes, Phys Rev E Stat Phys Plasmas Fluids Relat Interdiscip Topics, 2000 Apr, 61(4 Pt B), 4194-206.

Tittel, W., Brendel, J., Zbinden, H. and Gisin, N. (1998) Violation of Bell Inequalities by Photons More Than 10km Apart, Phys. Rev. Lett., 81, 3563-3566.

Wheeler, J.A. (1981) Beyond the Black Hole, In: Some Strangeness in the Proportion, H. Woolf (Ed.), Reading, Addison-Wesley Publishing Co.

2. Perceived Reality, Quantum Mechanics, and Consciousness

Subhash Kak[1], Deepak Chopra[2], and Menas Kafatos[3]

[1]Oklahoma State University, Stillwater, OK 74078
[2]Chopra Foundation, 2013 Costa Del Mar Road, Carlsbad, CA 92009
[3]Chapman University, Orange, CA 92866

Abstract:

Our sense of reality is different from its mathematical basis as given by physical theories. Although nature at its deepest level is quantum mechanical and nonlocal, it appears to our minds in everyday experience as local and classical. Since the same laws should govern all phenomena, we propose this difference in the nature of perceived reality is due to the principle of veiled nonlocality that is associated with consciousness. Veiled nonlocality allows consciousness to operate and present what we experience as objective reality. In other words, this principle allows us to consider consciousness indirectly, in terms of how consciousness operates. We consider different theoretical models commonly used in physics and neuroscience to describe veiled nonlocality. Furthermore, if consciousness as an entity leaves a physical trace, then laboratory searches for such a trace should be sought for in nonlocality, where probabilities do not conform to local expectations.

Keywords: quantum physics, neuroscience, nonlocality, mental time travel, time

Introduction

Our perceived reality is classical, that is it consists of material objects and their fields. On the other hand, reality at the quantum level is different in as much as it is nonlocal, which implies that objects are superpositions of other entities and, therefore, their underlying structure is wave-like, that is it is smeared out. This discrepancy shows up in the framework of quantum theory itself because the wavefunction unfolds in a deterministic way excepting when it is observed which act causes it to become localized.

The fact that the wavefunction of the system collapses upon observation suggests that we should ask whether it fundamentally represents interaction of consciousness with matter. In reality this question is meaningful only if we are able to define consciousness objectively. Since consciousness is not a thing or an external object, its postulated interaction with matter becomes paradoxical. If we rephrased our question we could ask where our personal self is located and if it is just some neural structure that exists in the classical world, why is it that its activity (observation) collapses the wavefunction?

The human observer interacts with the quantum system through apparatus devised by him and, therefore, the actual interaction is between physical systems. If the human were directly observing the system, then also the interaction is within the human brain that consists of various neural structures. The observation is associated with a time element since the apparatus must first be prepared and then examined after the interaction with the quantum system has occurred. The observer's self-consciousness is also the product of life experience, and therefore the variable of time plays a central role in it.

Neuroscience, which considers brain states in terms of electrical and chemical activity in the interconnection of the neurons, that somehow gives rise to awareness, cannot explain where the aware self is located. Since each neuron can only carry a small amount of information, no specific neuron can be the location of the self. On the other hand, if the self is distributed over a large area of the brain, what is it that binds this area together? Furthermore, since we have different inner senses of self in different states of mind, are these based on recruitment of different set of neurons, and why is it that behind each such sense of selfhood, ostensibly associated with different parts of the brain, is the certitude that it corresponds to the same individual? What integrates all these different senses into one coherent and persisting sense of self? Behind these questions lie a whole set of complementarities. Thus in some contexts it is appropriate to view the self as located at some point in the brain, whereas in other contexts it is distributed all over the body.

The question whether mental states are governed by quantum laws is answered in the affirmative by those who accept a quantum basis of mind (von Neumann, 1932/1955; Wigner, 1983; Penrose, 1994; Nadeau and Kafatos, 1999; Roy and Kafatos, 2004; Hameroff and Penrose, 2003; Stapp, 2003; Freeman and Vitiello, 2006). Recent findings in support of quantum models for biology (e.g., Lambert et al., 2013) lend additional support to this position. We add a point of caution here: mind as a random quantum machine as suggested by some theories may be an advance but not the complete picture since it will not be able to account for the individual's freedom and agency; and it cannot imply an objective reality independent of observation.

The question related to the limitations on what can be known by the mind has a logical component related to Gödel's Incompleteness Theorem and logical paradoxes (Davis, 1965), which can also apply to limits of knowing in physics and biology (Herrnstein, 1985; Grandpierre and Kafatos, 2012; Kak, 2012; Buser et al., 2013).

In this article, we focus on the relationship between reality and our conceptions of it as mediated by consciousness. This mediation may be seen through the lenses of neuroscience and physics. We first show how the mind constructs reality; later we discuss how the nonlocality inherent in quantum theory and, therefore, in physical process, is veiled by consciousness so that it appears to be local (Kak, 2014; Kafatos and Kak, 2014). This veiling is a characteristic of consciousness as process and it mirrors the way quantum theory conceals all the details of the state of a single particle by means of the Heisenberg Uncertainty Principle. Finally, we consider how indirect evidence in terms of anomalous probabilities in certain events can be adduced as evidence in support of reality being quantum-like at a fundamental level.

Interpretations of Quantum Theory

The Copenhagen Interpretation of quantum mechanics separates the physical universe in two parts, the first part is the system being observed, and the second part is the human agent, together with his instruments. The extended agent is described in mental terms and it includes not only his apparatus but also instructions to his colleagues on how to set up the instruments and report on their observations. The Heisenberg cut (also called the von Neumann cut) is the hypothetical interface between quantum events and an observer's information, knowledge, or conscious awareness. Below the cut everything is governed by the wave function; above the cut a classical description applies.

In the materialist conception, which leaves out quantum processes since they were until recently thought not to play a role in brain processes, consciousness is an epiphenomenon with biology as ground. But, although this is the prevalent neuroscience paradigm, there is no way we can justify the view that material particles somehow acquire consciousness on account of complexity of interconnections between neurons. There is also the panpsychist position that consciousness is a characteristic of all things, but in its usual formulation as in the MWI position that will be discussed later it is merely a restatement of the materialist position so as to account for consciousness (Strawson, 2006). On the other hand is the position that consciousness is a transcendent phenomenon – since it cannot be a thing – which interpenetrates the material universe. The human brain, informed by the phenomenon of consciousness, has self-awareness to contemplate its own origins.

We do know that mental states are correlated with activity in different parts of the brain. With regard to mental states several questions may be asked:

1. Do mental states interact with the quantum wavefunction?
2. Are mental states governed by quantum laws?
3. Are there limitations to what the mind can know about reality?

There is considerable literature on research done on each of these questions. The question of interaction between mental states and the wavefunction was addressed by the pioneers of quantum theory and answered in the affirmative in the Copenhagen Interpretation (CI) (von Neumann, 1932/1955). In CI, the wavefunction is properly understood epistemologically, that is, it represents the experimenter's knowledge of the system. Upon observation there is a change in this knowledge. It postulates the observer without explaining how the capacity of observation arises (Schwartz et al., 2005; Stapp, 2003). Operationally, it is a dualist position, where there is a fundamental split between observers and objects. There is the added variance or interpretation of CI followed by von Neumann in his discussion of the quantum cut which implies that although the separation between observers and objects has to be brought into actual experimental setups, that it is not fundamental.

In the realistic view of the wavefunction as in the Many Worlds Interpretation (MWI), there is no collapse of the wavefunction. Rather, the interaction is seen through the lens of decoherence, which occurs when states interact with the environment producing entanglement (Zurek, 2003). By the process of decoherence the system makes transition from a pure state to a mixture of states that observers end up measuring.

In the MWI interpretation, which may be called the ontic interpretation, the wavefunction has objective reality. The problem of collapse of the wavefunction is sidestepped by speaking of interaction between different subsystems. But since the entire universe is also a quantum system, the question of how this whole system splits into independent subsystems arises. Furthermore, if the wavefunction has objective reality, then consciousness must be seen to exist everywhere (Tegmark, 1998). Actually, this particular point was again implied by von Neumann's extension of CI who held that the wave function collapses upon observation, that the wave function is real, and that the world is quantum, which is decidedly contrary to MWI and Tegmark's recent interpretation but in agreement with the works of Wigner and Stapp, as well as our own. We emphasize that the MWI resolution is not helpful because it sees consciousness only as a correlate without any explanation for agency and freedom. There are other interpretations of quantum mechanics not as popular as either CI or MWI that will not be considered in this paper.

Construction Of Reality By The Mind
If we side-step for now the question of where the self is located and focus on the question of how the self relates to reality, we come up with several issues: First, we note that the mind is an active participant, together with the sensory organs, in the construction of reality (e.g. Wheeler, 1990: Kafatos and Nadeau, 2000; Gazzaniga, 1995; Chopra, 2014). An example of this is the phantom limb phenomenon in which there is a sensation of pain in a missing or amputated

limb (Melzack, 1992). There are other cases where the phantom limb does not even correspond to anatomical reality. A recent research paper reported the case of a 57-year-old woman who was born with a deformed right hand consisting of only three fingers and a rudimentary thumb. After a car crash at the age of 18, the woman's deformed hand was amputated, which gave rise to feelings of a phantom hand that was experienced as having all five fingers (McGeoch and Ramachandran, 2012).

In the case of injury to the brain, the construction of reality by mind seen most clearly in terms of deficits that persist even though the related sensory information is reaching the brain. Consider agnosia, which is failure of recognition that is not due to impairment of the sensory input or a general intellectual impairment. A visual agnosic patient will be unable to tell what he is looking at, although it can be demonstrated that the patient can see the object. Prosopagnosic patients are neither blind nor intellectually impaired; they can interpret facial expressions and they can recognize their friends and relations by name or voice, yet they do not recognize specific faces, not even their own in a mirror. Electrodermal recordings show that the prosopagnosic responds to familiar faces although without awareness of this fact. It appears that the patient is subconsciously registering the significance of the faces.

In a recent study (Rezlescu et al., 2014) of prosopagnosia the authors consider the role of the face-specific and the expertise (information processing) aspects in the recognition mechanism. According to the face-specific theory, upright faces are processed by face-specific brain mechanisms, whereas the expertise hypothesis claims faces are recognized by fine-grained visual processing. The authors used greebles, which are objects designed to place face-like demands on recognition mechanisms, in their experiments. They present compelling evidence that performance with greebles does not depend on face recognition mechanisms. Two individuals with acquired prosopagnosia displayed normal greeble learning despite severely impaired face performance. This research supports the theory that face- specific mechanisms are essential for recognition of faces.

Similar counterintuitive behavior of the mind includes the following: in alexia, the subject is able to write while unable to read; in alexia combined with agraphia, the subject is unable to write or read while retaining other language faculties; in acalculia, the subject has selective difficulty in dealing with numbers.

There are anecdotal accounts of blind people who can see sometime and deaf people who can likewise hear. Some brain damaged subjects cannot consciously see an object in front of them in certain places within their field of vision, yet when asked to guess if a light had flashed in their region of blindness, the subjects guess right at a probability much above that of chance.

One may consider that the injury in the brain leading to blindsight causes the vision in the stricken field to become automatic. Then through retraining it might be possible to regain the conscious experience of the images in this field. In the holistic explanation, the conscious awareness is a correlate of the activity in a complex set of regions in the brain. No region can be considered to be producing the function by itself although damage to a specific region will lead to the loss of a corresponding function (Kak, 2000).

Split Brains

The corpus callosum connects the two hemispheres of the brain and each eye normally projects to both hemispheres. By cutting the optic-nerve crossing, the chiasm, the remaining fibers in the optic nerve transmit information to the hemisphere on the same side. Visual input to the left eye is sent only to the left hemisphere, and input to the right eye projects only to the right hemisphere.

Experiments on split-brain human patients raise questions related to the nature and the seat of consciousness. For example, a patient with left-hemisphere speech does not know what his right hemisphere has seen through the right eye. The information in the right brain is unavailable to the left brain and vice versa. The left brain responds to the stimulus reaching it whereas the right brain responds to its own input. Each half brain learns, remembers, and carries out planned activities and it is as if each half brain works and functions outside the conscious realm of the other.

Roger Sperry and his associates performed a classic experiment on cats with split brains (Sperry et al., 1956; Sperry, 1980). They showed that such cats did as well as normal cats when it came to learning the task of discriminating between a circle and a square in order to obtain a food reward, while wearing a patch on one eye. This showed that one half of the brain did as well at the task as both the halves in communication. When the patch was transferred to the other eye, the split-brain cats behaved different from the normal cats, indicating that their previous learning had not been completely transferred to the other half of the brain.

It appears that for split brains nothing is changed as far as the awareness of the patient is considered and the cognitions of the right brain were linguistically isolated all along, even before the commissurotomy was performed. The procedure only disrupts the visual and other cognitive-processing pathways.

The patients themselves seem to support this view. There seems to be no antagonism in the responses of the two hemispheres and the left hemisphere is able to fit the actions related to the information reaching the right hemisphere in a plausible theory. For example, consider the test where the word "pink" is flashed to the right hemisphere and the word "bottle" is flashed to the left. Several bottles of different colors and shapes are placed before the patient and he is asked to choose one. He immediately picks the pink bottle explaining that pink is a nice color. Although the patient is not consciously aware of the right eye having seen the word "pink" he, nevertheless, "feels" that pink is the right choice for the occasion. In this sense, this behavior is very similar to that of blindsight patients.

The brain has many modular circuits that mediate different functions. Not all of these functions are part of conscious experience. When these modules related to conscious sensations get "crosswired," this leads to synesthesia. One would expect that similar joining of other cognitions is also possible. A deliberate method of achieving such a transition from many to one is a part of some meditative traditions. It is significant that patients with disrupted brains never claim to have anything other than a unique awareness.

If shared activity was all there was to consciousness, then this would have been destroyed or multiplied by commissurotomy. Split brains should then represent two minds just as in freak births with one trunk and two heads we do have two minds. But that is never the case.

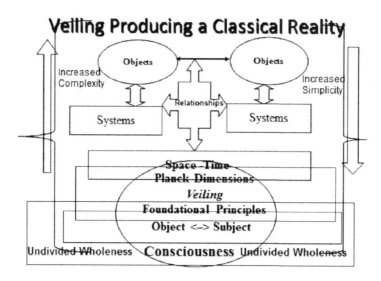

Figure 1. Universe as projection of a transcendent principle (broad arrow is projection; narrow arrow is full representation)

The experiments of Benjamin Libet showed how decisions made by a subject arise first on a subconscious level and only afterward are translated into the conscious decision (Libet, 1983). Upon a retrospective view of the event, the subject arrives at the belief that the decision occurred at the behest of his will.

In Libet's experiment the subject was to choose a random moment to flick the wrist while the associated activity in the motor cortex was measured. Libet found that the unconscious brain activity leading up to the conscious decision by the subject began approximately half a second before the subject consciously felt that he had taken his decision. But this is not to be taken as an example of retrocausation; rather, this represents a lag in the operation of the conscious mind in which this construction of reality by the mind occurs.

Orthodox Quantum Mechanics And Complementarity

As shown in Figure 1, we have dealt with models of reality constructed by the mind, and theories of physics, both of which are at the bottom layer of reality. Now we consider the next higher layer and see how we make observations. To record an observation in a laboratory requires a certain conception of the components of the system and a hypothesis related to the process. The observations are inferred from the readings on instruments or photographic traces. More direct observations register directly with our senses and here the intention in that the sense organ, such as the eye, focuses on a specific object to the exclusion of the remainder of the visual scene indicates that there is some kind of an interaction between consciousness and matter that leads to the observation.

Within the Copenhagen Interpretation, von Neumann provided a mathematical treatment (von Neumann, 1932; Bohr, 1934; Heisenberg, 1958) of this question by speaking of two different processes at work and doing so made one look for the interaction of consciousness with matter in the first process: *Process 1*. This is a non-causal, thermodynamically irreversible process in which the measured quantum system ends up randomly in one of the possible eigenstates (physical states) of the measuring apparatus together with the system. The probability for each eigenstate is given by the square of the coefficients c_n of the expansion of the original system state $|\varphi\rangle$

$$c_n = \langle \varphi_n | \phi \rangle$$

This represents the collapse of the wavefunction.

Process 2. This is a reversible, causal process, in which the system wave function evolves deterministically. The evolution of the system is described by a unitary operator $U(t_2, t_1)$ depending on the times t_1 and t_2, so that

$$|\varphi_2\rangle = U(t_2, t_1) |\varphi_1\rangle$$

The evolution operator is derived from the Schrödinger equation

$$i\hbar \frac{d|\varphi\rangle}{dt} = H|\varphi\rangle$$

When the Hamiltonian H is time independent, U has the form:

$$U(t_2, t_1) = e^{-\frac{i}{\hbar}H(t_2 - t_1)}$$

Von Neumann was guided by the principle of psycho-physical parallelism which requires that it must be possible to describe the extra-physical process of the subjective perception as if it were in reality in the physical world. This principle is not appreciated much nowadays but it is justified since psychological states must have a corresponding physical correlate. von Neumann described the collapse of the wave function as requiring a cut between the microscopic quantum system and the observer. He said it did not matter where this cut was placed:

> The boundary between the two is arbitrary to a very large extent. ... That this boundary can be pushed arbitrarily deeply into the interior of the body of the actual observer is the content of the principle of the psycho-physical parallelism -- but this does not change the fact that in each method of description the boundary must be put somewhere, if the method is not to proceed vacuously, i.e., if a comparison with experiment is to be possible. Indeed experience only makes statements of this type: an observer has made a certain (subjective) observation; and never any like this: a physical quantity has a certain value. (von Neumann, 1932).

To the extent that the collapse provides a result in a statistical sense, there appears to be a choice made by Nature. The other choice is made by the observer whose intention sets the measurement process in motion.

These two processes are an instance of complementarity of which the wave-particle duality of the Copenhagen Interpretation is a more commonly stated example. In reality, complementarity is a general principle that characterized all experience. Although it is sometimes seen as emerging out of complexity (Theise and Kafatos, 2013), here we view it as a fundamental principle that organized reality.

The question of complementarity was matter of debate in Greek thought. Thus reality was taken as change by Heraclitus and as things and relationships by Parmenides. In Indian thought several fundamental dichotomies such as matter and consciousness, physical reality and its descriptions, and analysis and synthesis are given. Some of the complementarities that are part of the contemporary discourse are:

- Waves and particles – quantum theory
- Being and time – in philosophy (Heidegger, 1962)
- Law and freedom – in physics and psychology
- Holistic and reductionist views – in system theory
- Matter and consciousness.

If we take complementarity as the common thread in phenomena that are described at different levels, then one might suspect that quantum theory should also underlie consciousness.

Veiled Monlocality

According to quantum mechanics reality is nonlocal and objects separated in time and space can be strongly correlated. Thus for a pair of entangled particles billions of miles apart, an observation on one particle causes an instant collapse of the wavefunction of the twin particle. Entanglement also persists across time and an observation made now can change the past as in Wheeler's delayed choice experiment (Wheeler, 1990). Yet there is no way one can confirm such an entanglement for a specific pair of particles for any attempt at verification will be defeated by the collapse of the wavefunction. Probability experiments for ensembles of particles to separate classical from quantum effects do exist (Bell, 1964).

If reality is nonlocal why does it appear to our senses as local and separated? The idea of veiled nonlocality is that consciousness disguises its wholeness and nonlocality in order to produce local processes. This idea arose out of the experimental fact that no loophole free test of nonlocality has yet been found (Kak, 2014). It can be seen as quite like the Heisenberg's Uncertainty Principle which places limits on the description of the state of a specific particle.

This filtering process allows for specific observations and thoughts in a classical world of everyday experience, while keeping quantum and general relativistic processes out of sight. Another example of veiled nonlocality in gravitation is the hypothesis of cosmic censorship (Penrose, 1999), which describes the inability of distant observers to directly observe the center of a black hole, or "naked singularity." (Kafatos and Kak, 2014)

Veiled nonlocality is like a fuzzification that breaks up a whole system into several locally connected subsystems. We illustrate below in Figure 2 the general idea.

The breakup of a whole into subsystems can be shown through simple observation. The five senses cannot perceive the quantum world, and yet perception depends upon it. The quantum world is hidden from us the way the operation of the brain is hidden. If you think the word "elephant" and see an image of the animal in your mind's eye, you aren't aware of the millions of neurons firing in your brain in order to produce them. Yet those firings -- not to mention the invisible cellular operations that keep every part of your body alive -- are the foundation of the brain's abilities.

Just as the image of an elephant is the visible end point of veiled processes, the material world is founded on a veiled reality. Moreover, to produce a single mental image, the whole brain must participate. Specific areas, mainly the visual cortex, produce mental pictures, but they are coordinated with everything else the brain does, such as sustaining the cerebral cortex, which recognizes what an image is, and maintaining a healthy body. This points to a profound link between the brain and the cosmos. The two are inseparable. In fact, in our view, complementarity assures that they appear as separate and one causing the other but in fact they are aspects of undivided wholeness brought about by consciousness, which is undivided, nonlocal and whole (see also below).

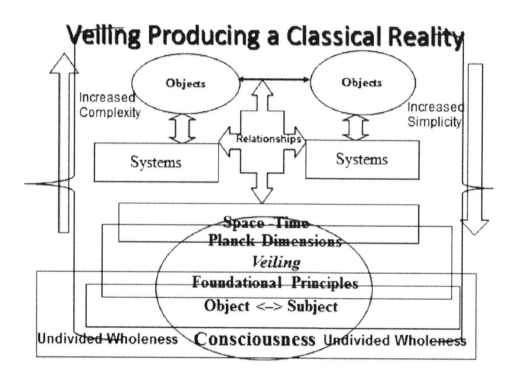

Figure 2: Breakup of the undivided wholeness of consciousness and implied quantum wholeness through the veiling process.

The veiling of reality is in consonance with the idea of the mind constructing its reality. Such a veiling even occurs in the scientific process which filters out and discards a huge portion of human experience -- almost everything one would classify as subjective. Its model is just as selective, if not more so, than the model which shapes a religious or metaphysical reality. As far as the brain is concerned, neural filtering is taking place in all models, whether they are scientific, spiritual, artistic, or psychotic. The brain is a processor of inputs, not a mirror to reality.

If our brains are constantly filtering every experience, there is no way anyone can claim to know what is "really" real. You can't step outside your brain to fathom what lies beyond it. Just as there is a horizon for the farthest objects that emit light in the cosmos, and a farthest horizon for how far back in time astronomy can probe, there is a farthest horizon for thinking. The brain operates in time and space, having linear thoughts that are the end point of a selective filtering process. So whatever is outside time and space is inconceivable, and unfiltered reality would probably blow the brain's circuits, or simply be blanked out.

Consciousness as Foundational Principle of Reality

We propose, as shown in Figure 2, that consciousness-based reality limited by a fundamental veiling provides meaning and the appearance of what we say is objective reality, systems, objects and relationships at all levels of organization. The quantum and the classical worlds aren't separated merely by a physical gap. On one side the behavior of the quantum is meaningless, random, and unpredictable. A subatomic particle has no purpose or goal. On the other side, in the classical world, it goes without saying that each of us lives our life with purpose and meaning in mind. To accept this as self-evident is crucial to getting up every morning, so arcane disputations about free will and determinism are, pragmatically speaking, not relevant to the more fundamental question: Can randomness produce meaning, and if so, how?

To lead a meaningless existence is intolerable, so it's ironic that quantum physics bases the cosmos on meaningless operations, and doubly ironic when you consider that physics itself is a meaningful activity. The phrase "participatory universe," sums up how the very process of observation changes the outcome (Wheeler, 1990). Observation not only changes the outcome in a random sense, but it can actually be used to steer to unfolding of a physical system to whichever way one chooses by the quantum Zeno effect (Misra and Sudarshan, 1974; Kak, 2007).

By definition reality is complete; therefore, whatever purpose and meaning we find in it, using limited human capacities, is a fragment of a pre-existing state, which we term the state of infinite possibilities. The fragment cannot be the whole, although in what may appear as strange, the part implies the whole (Kafatos and Nadeau, 2000; Nadeau and Kafatos, 1999). And the whole is more than the sum of the parts, because no amounts of parts, no matter how many, form the whole. This state is veiled from us, just as the existence of every possible subatomic particle is hidden from us. The concept of a field contains within it this relationship between the whole and its parts. There is no reason to exclude the field of consciousness from exhibiting the same relationship to its parts, whence the insight that there can be only one consciousness, not many (Schrödinger, 1974).

In a matter–alone conception of the universe, we cannot conceive of a reality that has no objects in it, and only pure consciousness. However, such a matter alone conception goes against the very nature of a quantum universe as quantum theory contains observation through measurement. Yet without awareness, nothing can be perceived. Having placed its trust in "reality as given," science overlooks the self- evident fact that nothing can be experienced without consciousness. It is a more viable candidate for "reality as given" than the physical universe. Even if the materialist position is accepted that claims consciousness is an epiphenomenon, one cannot escape the fact that consciousness existed from the very beginning although it may have been in a latent form.

If enlightenment consists of seeing beyond the veiling that accompanies a commonsensical view of the universe, it too isn't some sort of obscure mysticism but recognition that self-awareness can know itself. The mind isn't only the thoughts and sensations constantly streaming through it. There is a silent, invisible foundation to thought and sensations. Until that background is accounted for, individual consciousness mistakes itself, and in so doing it cannot help but mistake what it observes. This is expressed in a Vedic metaphor about the wave and the ocean: A wave looks like an individual as it rises from the sea, but once it sinks back, it knows that it is ocean and nothing but ocean.

Cosmic consciousness, then, isn't just real -- it's totally necessary. It rescues physics and science in general from a dead end -- the total inability to create mind out of matter -- and gives it a fresh avenue of investigation. We exist as creatures with a foot in two worlds that are actually one, divided by appearance and reality. Consciousness as a transcending principle provides a way to bridge the two processes of quantum theory. We emphasize that this view is the only one that is ultimately self-consistent. Material views of reality ultimately run into unanswerable conundrums and inconsistencies or the need of strange views such as the MWI which is founded on the existence of real outcomes without the agency of consciousness.

Conclusion

Quantum theory has reached the point where the source of all matter and energy is a vacuum, a nothingness that contains all the possibilities of everything that has ever existed or could exist. These possibilities then emerge as probabilities before "collapsing" into localized quanta, manifesting as the particles in space and time that are the building blocks of atoms and molecules.

Where do the probabilities exist? Where is the exquisite mathematics that we have at our disposal to be found? Some sort of "real space", or material-like space? That of course makes no sense. The probability of an event (even an event like winning the lottery or flying on the day a blizzard strikes) only exists as long as there is someone to ask the question of what may happen and to measure the outcomes when they occur. So probabilities and other mathematical expressions, which are the foundation of modern quantum physics, imply the existence of observation. Countless acts of observation give substance and reality to what would otherwise be ghosts of existence. This solves the so-called "measurement problem" of quantum theory which is there if one assumes a reality independent of observation.

It is more elegant, self-consistent and far easier to accept as a working hypothesis that sentience exists as a potential at the source of creation, and the strongest evidence has already been put on the table: Everything to be observed in the universe implies consciousness. Some theorists try to rescue materialism by saying that information is encoded into all matter, but "information" is a mental concept, and without the concept, there's no information in anything, since information by definition must ultimately contain meaning (even if it is a sequence of 0s and 1s as in computer language), and only minds grasp meaning. Besides, assuming that this kind of bit information is an encoded property of matter implies hidden variables (the bits) which have been ruled out by the Bell (1964) Theorem and laboratory experiments related to it (Aspect, Dalibard and Roger, 1984). Does a tree falling in the forest make no sound if no one is around to hear it? Obviously not. The crash vibrates air molecules, but sound needs hearing in order for these vibrations to be transformed into perception.

We've proposed that consciousness creates reality and makes it knowable -- if there's another viable candidate, it must pass the acid test: Transform itself into thoughts, feelings, images, and sensations. Science isn't remotely close to turning the sugar in a sugar bowl into the music of Mozart or the plays of Shakespeare. Your brain converts blood sugar into words and music, not by some trick of the molecules in the brain, since they are in no way special or privileged. Rather, your consciousness is using the brain as a processing device, moving the molecules where they are needed in order to create the sight, sound, touch, taste, and smell of the world.

In everyday life, we get to experience the miracle of transformation that causes a three-dimensional world, completed by the fourth dimension of time, to manifest before our eyes. The great advantage of experience is that it isn't theoretical. Reality is never wrong, and all of us are embedded in reality, no matter what model we apply to explain it.

The indirect examination of consciousness through the process of veiling as sketched in this paper can be tested by means of experiments. For example, the proposed theory can be refuted if loophole-free tests to confirm nonlocality are devised. On the other hand, cognitive processes with anomalous probabilities would lend support to our thesis.

We finally note that the cut of Heisenberg/von Neumann does not exist anywhere: The observer must be one, all observers are appearances of distinct or independent entities, taking on an apparent "reality" through the veiling action. As stated above, our thesis resolves the measurement problem. In reading von Neumann, there is a strong hint that he also held this view.

REFERENCES

Aspect, A., Dalibard, J., Roger, G. (1981). Physical Rev. Letters, 47, p. 460.

Bell, J. (1964) On the Einstein Podolsky Rosen paradox. Physics 1 195–200.

Bohr, N. (1934) Atomic theory and the description of nature. Cambridge: Cambridge University Press.

Buser, M., Kajari, E., and Schleich,, W.P. (2013). Visualization of the Gödel universe. New Journal of Physics 15, 013063.

Chopra, D. (ed.) (2014). Brain, Mind, Cosmos. Trident Media, New York.

Davis, M. (1965). The Undecidable: Basic papers on undecidable propositions, unsolvable problems and computable functions. Raven Press, New York.

Freeman, W. and Vitiello, G. (2006) Nonlinear brain dynamics as macroscopic manifestation of underlying many-body dynamics. Physics of Life Reviews 3: 93-118.

Gazzaniga, M.S. (1995) The Cognitive Neurosciences. Cambridge, MA The MIT Press. Hameroff, S. and Penrose, R. (2003) Conscious events as orchestrated space-time selections. NeuroQuantology 1: 10-35.

Heidegger, M. (1962) Being and Time, trans. by John Macquarrie & Edward Robinson. London: SCM Press.

Heisenberg, W. (1958) Physics and Philosophy: The Revolution in Modern Science, London: George Allen & Unwin.

Herrnstein, R.J. (1985). Riddles of natural categorization. Phil. Trans. R. Soc. Lond. B 308: 129-144.

Kafatos, M. and Nadeau, R. (2000) The Conscious Universe. Springer.

Kafatos, M. and Kak, S. (2014) Veiled nonlocality and cosmic censorship. arXiv:1401.2180

Kak, S. (2000) Active agents, intelligence, and quantum computing. Information Sciences 128: 1-17

Kak, S. (2007) Quantum information and entropy. International Journal of Theoretical Physics 46, 860-876.

Kak, S. (2012) Hidden order and the origin of complex structures. In Swan, L., Gordon, R., and Seckbach, J. (editors), Origin(s) of Design in Nature. Dordrecht: Springer, 643- 652.

Kak, S. (2014) From the no-signaling theorem to veiled non-locality. NeuroQuantology 12: 1- 9.

Lambert, N. et al, (2013) Quantum biology. Nature Physics 9, 10–18.

Libet, B. et al. (1983) Time of conscious intention to act in relation to onset of cerebral activity (readiness-potential) - The unconscious initiation of a freely voluntary act. Brain 106: 623–642.

McGeoch, P., and Ramachandran, V., (2012), The appearance of new phantom fingers post- amputation in a phocomelus, Neurocase, 18 (2), 95-97.

Melzack, R. (1992). Phantom limbs. Scientific American (April): 120–126.

Misra, B. and Sudarshan, E. C. G. (1977). The Zeno's paradox in quantum theory. Journal of Mathematical Physics 18, 758–763.

Nadeau, R. and Kafatos, M. (1999). The Non-local Universe: The New Physics and Maters of the Mind, Oxford University Press, Oxford.

Penrose, R. (1994) Shadows of the Mind. New York: Oxford.

Penrose, R. (1999) The question of cosmic censorship. J. Astrophys. Astr. 20: 233–248.

Roy, S. and Kafatos, M. (2004). Quantum processes and functional geometry: new perspectives In brain dynamics. FORMA, 19, 69.

Rezlescu, C., Barton, J. J. S., Pitcher, D. & Duchaine, B. (2014) Normal acquisition of expertise with greebles in two cases of acquired prosopagnosia. Proc Natl Acad. Sci. USA http://dx.doi.org/10.1073/pnas.1317125111.

Schrödinger, E. (1974). What is Life? and Mind and Matter. Cambridge University Press.

Schwartz, J.M., Stapp, H.P., Beauregard, M. (2005) Quantum physics in neuroscience and psychology. Phil. Trans. Royal Soc. B 360: 1309-1327.

Sperry, R. (1980) Mind-brain interaction: Mentalism, yes; dualism, no. Neuroscience 5 (2): 195–206

Sperry, R. W., Stamm, J. S., and Miner, N. (1956) Relearning tests for interocular transfer following division of optic chaism and corpus callosum in cats. J. Compar. Physiol. Psych. 49: 529-533.

Stapp, H.P. (2003) Mind, Matter, and Quantum Mechanics. New York: Springer-Verlag. Strawson, G. (2006) Realistic monism: Why physicalism entails panpsychism. Journal of Consciousness Studies 13: 10–11, 3–31.

Tegmark, M. (1998) The interpretation of quantum mechanics: many worlds or many words? Fortsch. Phys. 46: 855-862.

Theise, N.D. and Kafatos, M. (2013) Complementarity in biological systems: a complexity view. Complexity 18: 11-20.

Von Neumann, J. (1932/1955) Mathematical Foundations of Quantum Mechanics, translated by Robert T. Beyer, Princeton, NJ: Princeton University Press.

Wheeler, J.A. (1990). Information, physics, quantum: the search for links. In Complexity, Entropy, and the Physics of Information, W.H. Zurek (Ed.). Addison-Wesley, pp. 3- 28.

Wigner, E. (1983). "The Problem of Measurement", In: Quantum Theory and Measurement, J.A. Wheeler, & W.H. Zurek (Eds.), Princeton University Press, Princeton.

Zurek, W.H. (2003) Decoherence, einselection, and the quantum origins of the classical. Rev. Mod. Phys. 75: 715-775

3. Quantum Reality and Mind

Henry P. Stapp

Lawrence Berkeley Laboratory, University of California, Berkeley, California

Abstract

Two fundamental questions are addressed within the framework of orthodox quantum mechanics. The first is the duality-nonduality conflict arising from the fact that our scientific description of nature has two disparate parts: an empirical component and a theoretical component. The second question is the possibility of meaningful free will in a quantum world concordant with the principle of sufficient reason, which asserts that nothing happens without a sufficient reason. The two issues are resolved by an examination of the conceptual and mathematical structure of orthodox quantum mechanics, without appealing to abstract philosophical analysis or intuitive sentiments.

Key Words: Quantum Reality, Mind, Mind-Matter, Free Will, Duality, Mental monism

1. Introduction

The first purpose of this article is to explain the nature of the connection between mind and matter and how orthodox quantum mechanics is both dualistic and nondualistic: it is dualistic on a pragmatic, operational level, but is nondualistic on a deeper ontological level.

The second purpose is to reconcile a meaningful concept of human freedom with the principle of sufficient reason; with the principle that nothing happens without a sufficient reason.

To lay a framework for discussing these two issues I shall begin by describing some contrasting ideas about the nature of reality advanced by three towering intellectual figures, Rene Descartes (1596-1650), Isaac Newton (1642-1727), and William James (1842-1910).

René Descartes conceived nature to be divided into two parts: a mental part and a physical part. The mental part, which he called "res cogitans", contains our thoughts, ideas, and feeling, whereas the physical part, called "res extensa", is defined here to be those aspects of nature that we can describe by assigning mathematical properties to space-time points. Examples of physical aspects of our understanding of nature are trajectories of physical particles, the electric field $E(x,t)$, and the quantum mechanical field (operator) $A(x,t)$. Descartes allowed the mental and physical aspects to interact with each other, but only for those physical parts that are located inside human brains. This is the classic Cartesian notion of duality.

Isaac Newton built the foundations of "modern physics" upon the ideas of Descartes, Galileo, and Kepler. The astronomical observations of Tycho Brahe led to Kepler's three laws of planetary motion. These laws, coupled to Galileo's association of gravity with acceleration, led directly to Newton's inverse square law of gravitational attraction, and his general laws of motion. Newton extended these dynamical ideas, with tremendous success, down to the scale of terrestrial motions, to the tides and falling apples etc.. He also conjectured an extension down to the level of the atoms. According to that hypothesis, the entire physically described universe, from the largest objects to the smallest ones, would be bound by the precept of physical determinism, which is the notion that a complete description of the values of all physically described variables at any one time determines with certainty the values of all physically described variables at any later time. This idea of universal physical determinism is a basic precept of the development of Newtonian dynamics into what is called "classical physics".

1a. The Omission of the Phenomenal Aspects of Nature. The dynamical laws of classical physics are formulated wholly in terms of physically described variables: in terms of the quantities that Descartes identified as elements of "res extensa". Descartes' complementary psychologically described things, the elements of his "res cogitans", were left completely out: there is, in the causal dynamics of classical physics, no hint of their existence. Thus there is not now, nor can there ever be, any rational way to explain, strictly on the basis of the dynamical precepts of classical physics, either the existence of, or any causal consequence of, the experientially described aspects of nature. Yet these experiential aspects of nature are all that we actually know.

This troublesome point was abundantly clear already at the outset:

Newton: "...to determine by what modes or actions light produceth in our minds the phantasm of colour is not so easie."

Leibniz: "Moreover, it must be confessed that perception and that which depends upon it are inexplicable on mechanical grounds, that is to say, by means of figures and motions."

Classical physics, by omitting all reference to the mental realities, produces a logical disconnect between the physically described properties represented in that theory and the mental realities by which we come to know them. The theory allows the mental realities to know about the physical aspects of nature, yet be unable to affect them in any way. Our mental aspects are thereby reduced to "Detached Observers", and Descartes' duality collapses, insofar as the causally closed physical universe is concerned, to a physics-based nonduality; to a physical monism, or physicalism. Each of us rejects in actual practice the classical-physics claim that our conscious thoughts and efforts can have no affects on our physical actions. We build our lives, and our political, judicial, economic, social, and religious institutions, upon the apparently incessantly reconfirmed belief that, under normal wakeful conditions, a person's intentional mental effort can influence his physical actions.

William James, writing in 1892, challenged, on rational grounds, this classical-physics-based claim of the impotence of our minds. At the end of his book Psychology: The Briefer Course he reminded his readers that "the natural science assumptions with which we started are provisional and revisable things". That was a prescient observation! Eight years later Max Planck discovered a new constant of nature that signaled a failure of the precepts of classical physics, and by 1926 the precepts of its successor, quantum mechanics, were firmly in place.

The most radical shift wrought by quantum mechanics was the explicit introduction of mind into the basic conceptual structure. Human experience was elevated from the role of 'a detached observer' to that of 'the fundamental element of interest':

Bohr: "In our description of nature the purpose is not to disclose the real essence of phenomena but only to track down as far as possible relations between the multifold aspects of our experience." (Bohr, 1934, p.18).

Bohr: "The sole aim [of quantum mechanics] is the comprehension of observations...(Bohr, 1958, p.90).

Bohr: The task of science is both to extend the range of our experience and reduce it to order (Bohr, 1934, p.1)

Heisenberg: "The conception of the objective reality of the elementary particles has evaporated not into the cloud of some new reality concept, but into the transparent clarity of a mathematics that represents no longer the behaviour of the particles but our knowledge of this behavior" (Heisenberg, 1958a, p. 95).

This general shift in perspective was associated with a recasting of physics from a set of mathematical connections between physically described aspects of nature, into set of practical rules that, eschewing ontological commitments, predicted correlations between various experiential realities on the basis of their postulated dynamical links to certain physically describable aspects of our theoretical understanding of nature.

In view of this fundamental re-entry of mind into basic physics, it is nigh on incomprehensible that so few philosophers and non-physicist scientists entertain today, more than eight decades after the downfall of classical physics, the idea that the physicalist conception of nature, based on the invalidated classical physical theory, might be profoundly wrong in ways highly relevant to the mind-matter problem.

Philosophers are often called upon to defend highly counter-intuitive and apparently absurd positions. But to brand as an illusion, and accordingly discount, the supremely successful conceptual foundation of our lives---the idea that our conscious efforts can influence our physical actions---on the basis of its conflict with a known-to-be-false theory of nature that leaves out all that we really know, is a travesty against reason, particularly in view of the fact that the empirically valid replacement of that empirically invalid classical theory is specifically about the details of the connection between our consciously chosen intentional actions and the experiential feedbacks that such actions engender.

1b. Von Neumann's Dualistic Quantum Mechanics. The logician and mathematician John von Neumann (1955/1932) formalized quantum mechanics in a way that allowed it to be interpreted as a dualistic theory of reality in which mental realities interact in specified causal ways with physically described human brains. This orthodox quantum ontology is in essential accord with the dualistic ideas of Descartes.

An objection often raised against Cartesian dualism is couched as the query: How can ontologically distinct aspects of nature ever interact? Must not nature consist ultimately of one fundamental kind of stuff in order for its varied components to be able to cohere.

This objection leads to a key question: What is the ontological character of the physical aspect of quantum mechanics?

2. The Ontological Character of the Physical Aspect of the Orthodox (von Neumann-Heisenberg) Quantum Mechanics.

The physical aspect of the quantum mechanical conception of nature is represented by the quantum state. This state is physical, in the defined sense that we can describe it by assigning mathematical properties to space-time points. But this physical aspect is does not have the ontological character of a material substance, in the sense in which the physical world of Newtonian (or classical) physics is made of material substance: it does not always evolve in a continuous manner, but is subject to abrupt "quantum jumps", sometimes called "collapses of the wave function".

Heisenberg (1958b) couched his understanding of the ontological character of the reality lying behind the successful quantum rules in terms of the Aristotelian concepts of "potentia" and "actual" . The quantum state does not have the ontological character of an "actual" thing. It has, rather, the ontological character of "potentia": of a set of "objective tendencies for actual events to happen". An actual event, in the von Neumann-Heisenberg orthodox ontology, is "The discontinuous change in the probability function [that] takes place with the act of registration…in the mind of the observer". (Heisenberg, 1958b, p. 55)

The point here is that in orthodox (von Neumann-Heisenberg) quantum mechanics the physical aspect is represented by the quantum state, and this state has the ontological character of potentia---of objective tendencies for actual events to happen. As such, it is more mind-like than matter-like in character. It involves not only stored information about the past, but also objective tendencies pertaining to events that have not yet happened. It involves projections into the future, elements akin to imagined ideas of what might come to pass. The physical aspects of quantum mechanics are, in these ways, more like mental things than like material things.

Furthermore, a quantum state represents probabilities. Probabilities are not matter-like. They are mathematical connections that exist outside the actual realities to which they pertain. They involve mind-like computations and evaluations: weights assigned by a mental or mind-like process.

Quantum mechanics is therefore dualistic in one sense, namely the pragmatic sense. It involves, operationally, on the one hand, aspects of nature that are described in physical terms, and, on the other hand, also aspects of nature that are described in psychological terms. And these two parts interact in human brains in accordance with laws specified by the theory. In these ways orthodox quantum mechanics is completely concordant with the defining characteristics of Cartesian dualism.

Yet, in stark contrast to classical mechanics, in which the physically described aspect is matter-like, the physically described aspect of quantum mechanics is mind-like! Thus both parts of the quantum Cartesian duality are ontologically mind-like.

In short, orthodox quantum mechanics is Cartesian dualistic at the pragmatic/ operational level, but mentalistic on the ontological level.

This conclusion that nature is fundamentally mind-like is hardly new. But it arises here not from some deep philosophical analysis, or religious insight, but directly from an examination of the causal structure of our basic scientific theory.

3. Natural Process, Sufficient Reason, and Human Freedom.

There are two fundamentally different ways to cope with the demands of the theory of relativity.

The first is the classical-physics-based Einsteinian idea of a Block Universe: a universe in which the entire future is laid out beforehand, with our experiences being mere perspectives on this preordained reality, viewed from particular vantage points in spacetime.

A second way to accommodate, rationally, the demands of special relativity is the quantum-physics-based Unfolding Universe, in which facts and truths become fixed and definite in the orderly way allowed by relativistic quantum field theory (Tomonaga, 1946; Schwinger 1951; Stapp, 2007, p. 92) with our experiences occurring in step with the coming into being of definite facts and truths.

I subscribe to the latter idea: to the idea of an unfolding reality in which each experienced increment of knowledge is associated with an actual event in which certain facts or truths become fixed and definite.

I also subscribe to the idea that this unfolding conforms to the principle of sufficient reason, which asserts that no fact or truth can simply "pop out of the blue", with no sufficient reason to be what it turns out to be.

An important question, then, is whether such a concordance with the principle of sufficient reason precludes the possibility of meaningful human freedom. Is human freedom an illusion, in the sense that every action that a person makes was fixed with certainty already at the birth of the universe?

Laplace's classical argument for the "certainty of the future" states (in condensed form):

"For a sufficiently powerful computing intellect that at a certain moment knew all the laws and all the positions, nothing would be uncertain, and the future, just like the past, would be present before its eyes."

This view argues for "certainty about the future"; for a certainty existing at an earlier moment on the basis of information existing at that earlier moment. It contemplates:

1. A computing intellect existing outside or beyond nature itself, able to "go" in thought where the actual evolving universe has not yet gone.

2. Invariant causal laws.

But nothing really exists outside the whole of nature itself! Thus nature itself must make its own laws/habits. And these habits could themselves evolve. Even if there is a sufficient reason, within the evolving reality, for every change in the laws, and every generation of a fact, it is not evident that any intellect standing outside the evolving reality itself could compute, on the basis of what exists at a certain moment, all that is yet to come. For the evolution of reason-based reasons may be intrinsically less computable than the evolution of the mathematically formulated physically described properties of the classical-physics approximation to the actual laws of nature. Reason encompasses computable mathematics, but computable mathematics may not encompass reason. Reason is a category of explanation more encompassing than mathematical computation.

The laws of classical mechanics are cast in a particular kind of mathematical form that allows, in principle, a "mathematical computation" performed at an early time to predict with certainty the state of the universe at any later time. But this is very special feature of classical mechanics. It is far from obvious that the---definitely nonclassical---real world must exhibit this peculiar 'computability" feature.

The notion that a reason-based unfolding of the actual world is computable is an extrapolation from the classical-physics approximation that is far too dubious to provide the basis of a compelling argument that, in a mind-based quantum universe evolving in accordance with the principles of both quantum mechanics and sufficient reason, the outcomes of human choices are certain prior to their actual occurrence. It is far from being proved that, in a universe of that kind, the exact movement of the computer key that I am now pressing was certain already at the birth of the universe. "Reasons" could lack the fantastic computability properties that the physically described features of classical physics enjoy. But in that case our present reason-based human choices need not have been fixed with certainty at the birth of the universe. Within orthodox quantum mechanics meaningful human freedom need not be an illusion.

4. Reason-Based Dynamics Versus Physical-Description-Based Dynamics.

The arguments given above rest heavily upon the contrast between the reason-based dynamics of the unfolding universe described by quantum mechanics and the physical-description-based dynamics of the block universe described by classical mechanics. In this final section I shall pinpoint the technical features of orthodox quantum mechanics that underlie this fundamental difference between these two theories.

Von Neumann created a formulation of quantum mechanics in which all the physical aspects of nature are represented by the evolving quantum mechanical state (density matrix) of the universe. Each subsystem of this physically described universe is represented by a quantum state obtained by performing a certain averaging procedure on the state of the whole universe. Each experience of a person is associated with an "actual event". This event reduces, in a mathematically specified way, the prior quantum state of this person's brain---and consequently the quantum state of the entire universe---to a new "reduced" state. The reduction is achieved by the removal of all components of the state of this person's brain that are incompatible with the increment of knowledge associated with the experience. The needed mapping between "experiential increments in a person's knowledge" and "reductions of the quantum mechanical state of that person's brain" can be understood as being naturally created by trial and error learning of the experienced correlations between intentional efforts and the experiential feedbacks that these efforts tend to produce.

A key feature of von Neumann's dynamics is that it has two distinct kinds of mind-brain interaction. Von Neumann calls the first of these two processes "process 1". It corresponds to a choice of a probing action by the person, regarded as an agent or experimenter. The second kind of mind-brain interaction was called by Dirac "a choice on the part of nature". It specifies nature's response to the probing action selected by a logically preceding process 1 action. Von Neumann uses the name "process 2" to denote the physical evolution that occurs between the mind-brain (collapse) interactions. I therefore use the name "process 3" to denote the reduction/collapse process associated with nature's response to the process 1 probing action.

The mathematical form of process 1 differs from that of process 3. This mathematical difference causes these two processes to have different properties. In particular, process-1 actions have only local effects, in the sense that the dependence of the predictions of quantum mechanics upon a process-1 action itself, without a specification of the response, is confined (in the relativistic version) to the forward light-cone of the region in which the process-1 physical action occurs: the empirically observable effects of a process-1 action never propagate faster than the speed of light. On the other hand, nature's response (process 3) to a localized process-1 action can have observable statistical effects in a faraway contemporaneous region. The no-faster-than-light property of the empirically observable effects of any process-1 action is what justifies the word "relativistic" in relativistic quantum theory, even though the underlying mathematical description involves abrupt process-1-dependent faster-than-light transfers of information in connection with nature's response to the process-1 action.

Process 2 is a generalization of the causal process in classical mechanics, and, like it, is deterministic: the state of the universe at any earlier time completely determines what it will evolve into at any later time, insofar as no process 1 or process 3 event intervenes. But if no process 1 or process 3 event intervenes then the process 2 evolution would take the initial "big bang" state of the universe into a gigantic smear in which, for example, the moon would be smeared out over the night sky, and the mountains, and the cities, and we ourselves, would all be continuously spread out in space.

It is the process 1 and process 3 actions that, in the orthodox ontology, keep the universe in line with human experiences. On the other hand, the von Neumann ontology certainly does not exclude the possibility that non-human-based analogs of the human-based process 1 and follow-up process 3 actions also exist. Rather, it explains why the existence of reduction processes associated with other macroscopic agents would be almost impossible to detect empirically. These features of the von Neumann ontology justify focusing our attention here on the human involvement with nature.

Process 1, unlike process 2, is not constrained by any known law. In actual practice our choices of our probing actions appear to us to be based on reasons. We open the drawer in order to find the knife, in order to cut the steak, in order to eat the steak, in order to satisfy our hunger. Whilst all of this chain of reasons would, within the deterministic framework of classical physics, need to be, in principle, explainable in mathematical ways based upon the physical description of the universe, there is no such requirement in orthodox quantum mechanics: the sufficient reasons could be "reasons"; reasons involving the experiential dimension of reality, rather than being fully determined within the physical dimension. And these reasons could be, at each individual moment of experience, sufficient to determine the associated process 1 choice, without those choices having been mathematically computable from the state of the universe at earlier times.

The process 3 selection on the part of nature, unlike the process 1 choice, is not completely unconstrained: it is constrained by a statistical condition. According to the principle of sufficient reason, the process 3 choice must also be, in principle, determined by a sufficient reason. But, as emphasized above, nature's choice is nonlocal in character. Thus the reason for a process 3 choice need not be located at or near the place where the associated process 1 action occurs. Yet, as was clear already in classical statistical mechanics, there is an á priori statistical rule: equal volumes of phase space are equally likely. The (trace-based) statistical rule of quantum mechanics is essentially the quantum mechanical analog of this á priori statistical rule. The quantum statistical rule is therefore the natural statistical representation of the effect of a reason-based choice that is physically far removed from its empirical process 3 manifestation.

In closing, it is worth considering the argument of some physicalist philosophers that the replacement of classical mechanics---upon which physicalism is based---by quantum mechanics is not relevant to the resolution of the mind-matter problem for the following reason: that replacement has no bearing on the underlying problem of human freedom. The argument is that the essential difference between the two theories is (merely) that the determinism of classical mechanics is disrupted by the randomness of quantum mechanics, but that an introduction of randomness into the dynamics in no way rescues the notion of meaningful human freedom: a random choice is no better than a deterministic choice as an expression of meaningful human freedom.

This physicalist argument flounders on the fact that the element of quantum randomness enters quantum mechanics only via process 3, which delivers nature's choice. Man's choice enters via process 1, which is the logical predecessor to nature's process 3 "random" choice. In orthodox quantum mechanics, no elements of quantum randomness enter into man's choice. Nor is man's choice fixed by the deterministic aspect of quantum mechanics: that aspect enters only via process 2. Von Neumann's process 1 human choice is, in this very specific sense, "free": it is von Neumann's representation of Bohr's "free choice of experimental arrangement for which the quantum mechanical formalism offers the appropriate latitude" (Bohr 1958. p.51). Human choices enter orthodox quantum mechanics in a way not determined by a combination of the deterministic and random elements represented in the theory.

References

Bohr, N. (1934). Atomic Physics and the Description of Nature. Cambridge University Press, Cambridge, UK.

Bohr, N. (1958). Atomic Physics and Human Knowledge. Wiley, New York, US.

Heisenberg, W. (1958a). The representation of ature in contemporary physics. Daedalus, 87 (summer), 95-108.

Heisenberg, W. (1958b). Physics and Philosophy. Harper, New York, US.

James. W. (1892). Psychology: The Briefer Course. In: William James: Writings 1879-1899. Library of America (1992), New York, US.

Schwinger, J. (1951). Theory of Quantized Fields 1. Physical Review, 82, 914-927.

Stapp, H.P. (2007). Mindful Universe: Quantum Mechanics and the Participating Observer. Springer, Berlin.

Tomonaga, S. (1946). On a relativistically invariant formulation of the quantum theory of wave fields. Progress of Theoretical Physics, 1, 27-42.

Von Neumann, J. (1955/1932). Mathematical Foundations of Quantum Mechanics. Princeton University Press, Princeton New Jersey, US. (Translation of the German original: Mathematische Grundlagen der Quantenmechanik, Springer, Berlin, 1932.)

4. Space, Time and Consciousness

Chris King

Emeritus, University of Auckland

Abstract

This paper presents a potential mechanism for the conscious brain to anticipate impending opportunities and threats to survival through massively parallel weak quantum measurement (MPWQM) induced by the combined effects of edge of chaos sensitivity and phase coherence sampling of brain states. It concludes that the underpinnings of this process emerged in single-celled eucaryotes in association with (a) excitability-induced sensitivity to electro-chemical perturbations in the milieu as an anticipatory sense organ and (b) cell-to-cell signaling necessary for critical phases in the life cycle.

Keywords: space, time, consciousness, evolution, neurodynamics, chaos, quantum entanglement, weak quantum measurement

1: Introduction: Consciousness Entangled

Subjective consciousness poses the ultimate dilemma for the scientific description of reality. We still have no idea of how the brain generates it, or even how, or why, such an objectively elusive phenomenon can come about from the physiology of brain dynamics. The problem is fundamental because, from birth to death, the sum total of all our observations of the physical world, and all our notions about it, come exclusively through our subjective conscious experience. Although neuroscience has produced new techniques for visualizing brain function, from EEG and MEG to PET and fMRI scans, which show a parallel relationship between mental states and brain processing, these go no way in themselves to solving the so-called hard problem of consciousness research — how these objective physiological processes give rise to the subjective effects of conscious experience.

One key to the possible role of subjective consciousness is that it appears to be a product of coordinated brain activity involving diverse regions operating together in a coherent manner so as to anticipate environmental challenges (see section 3).

This leads to another critical question: "Why did nervous systems evolve subjective consciousness?" If nervous systems are able to fully provide adaptive solutions simply as heuristic computers, there is no role for extraneous brain functions that simply add a subjective shadow reality, with no adaptive function, and presumably a physiological cost. A digital computer is a purely functional entity, so has no role for a subjective aspect, no matter how complex it becomes.

Diverse higher animal nervous systems appear to work on a common basis of edge- of-chaos excitation (see section 5) that arose in excitable single cells before multi- celled organisms evolved (see section 2), which, in humans is accompanied by subjective consciousness (King 2008). This suggests that subjectivity is a critical survival attribute, which has been reinforced by natural selection, its key role being anticipating opportunities and threats to survival (see section 4). Strategic decision-making in the open environment is notorious for being computationally intractable because of super-exponential runaway as the number of contingencies increases (see section 4). By contrast, vertebrate brains have a common mechanism of massively parallel processing using wave phase coherence to distinguish ground noise from attended signal, accompanied by transitions at the edge of chaos (see section 5), which successfully resolves intractability in real time.

A non-computational form of space-time anticipation may aid this process (see section 6). Chaotic sensitivity and self-organized criticality combined with stochastic resonance may enable the ongoing brain state to become sensitive to quantum uncertainties through nested instabilities running from the molecular level, through cell organelles and neurons to global activations, when the global context is critically poised (see section 5). Quantum entangled phase coherence sampling accompanying the wave excitations of brain states could then provide a means for anticipation of future threats to survival through massively parallel weak quantum measurement (see section 6). We shall explore how this capacity might provide an explanation for subjective consciousness and the notion of free-will.

2: Underpinnings of Consciousness Emerged in Single Celled Eucaryotes

The neurodynamic processes underpinning subjective consciousness are evolutionarily ancient, are based on fundamental bifurcations evident in biogenesis, and originate in single-celled protista before the emergence of multi-celled animals and nervous systems (King 2002, 2011).

Excitable membranes are universal to eucaryote cells, as is the need to sense electrochemical and nutrient changes in their milieu. The sodium channel key to the axon potential, for example, arose in founding single-celled eucaryotes. Chay and Rinzells (1985) model of bursting and beating derived from the alga Nitella demonstrates the widespread nature of chaotic excitability arising before animals and plants diverged. Similar excitability has been observed through cAMP dynamics in the social amoeba Dictyostelium (Mestler 2011) and action potentials in Paramecium (Hinrichsen & Schultz 1988).

The elementary neurotransmitter types, many of which are fundamental amino acids (glutamate, glycine, GABA) or amines derived from amino acids (serotonin, dopamine, histamine, choline) have primordial relationships with the membrane, as soluble molecules with complementary charge relationships to the hydrophilic ends of the phospholipids, which later became encoded in protein receptors.

Tryptophan, the amino acid from which serotonin (5-hydroxytryptamine) is generated, plays a key role in the transfer of electric charge in the earliest forms of photosynthesis. To make serotonin from tryptophan, oxygen is needed. Thus, serotonin is made specifically in unicellular systems capable of photosynthesis and the cellular production of oxygen. Consequently serotonin is up to 100 times more plentiful in plants, and animals have ceased to synthesize tryptophan depending on plants for their supply. This relationship with light continues to this day in human use of melatonin to define the circadian cycle and serotonin in wakefulness and sleep, with light deprivation causing depression through serotonin (Azmitia 2010).

The 5-HT1a receptor is estimated to have evolved 750 million to 1 billion years ago, (Peroutka & Howell 2004, Peroutka 2005) long before the Cambrian radiation. This places the emergence of receptor proteins and their neurotransmitters as occurring before the multicellular nervous systems, as cell-to-cell signalling molecules essential for survival, reproduction and positive and negative responses to nutrition and danger. It also explains that neurotransmitters originated from direct signalling pathways between the cell membrane and gene expression in the nucleus of single cells. Key enzymes in neurotransmitter pathways may have become ubiquitous through horizontal gene transfer from bacteria placing their emergence even earlier (Iyer et al. 2004).

Receptor proteins, second signalling pathways and key neurotransmitters occur widely in single-celled protists. Both Crithidia and Tetrahymena contain norepinephrine, epinephrine, and serotonin (Blum 1969). Aggregation of slime molds such as Dictyostelium is mediated by cyclic-AMP and uses glutamate and GABA (Halloy et al. 1998, Goldbeter 2006, Taniura et al. 2006, Anjard & Loomis 2006, Brizzi & Blum 1970, Essman 1987, Takeda & Sugiyama 1993, Nomura et al. 1998). Tetrahymena pyriformis also has circadian light-related melatonin expression (Köhidai et al. 2003). Trypanosoma cruzi can be induced to differentiate by increased cAMP levels that resulted from addition of epinephrine (Gonzalez- Perdomo et al. 1988). Species of Entamoeba secrete serotonin and the neuropeptides neurotensin and substance P (McGowan et al. 1985) and release and respond to catecholamine compounds during differentiation from the trophozoite stage into the dormant or transmissible cyst stage (Eichinger et al. 2002, 2005). Plasmodium falciparum malaria replication can be blocked by 5HT1a agonists (Locher et. al 2003).

This leads to a picture where the essential physiological components of conscious brain activity arose in single-celled eucaryotes, both in intra and intercellular communication, and in the chaotic excitability of single cells in sensing and responding to their environment. These include ion channel based excitability and action potentials, neurotransmitter modulated activity based on specific receptor proteins, membrane-nucleus signalling and precursors of synaptic communication.

Edge of chaos dynamics is a natural consequence of excitability providing arbitrary sensitivity to disturbances caused by predators and prey in the active environment. It is a function critical for survival in both single-celled and multicellular organisms, providing a selective advantage for the evolution of chaotically excitable brains from chaotically excitable cells. Once in place, this form of active anticipation, if linked to the anticipatory quantum process we are going to investigate, would then lead to a continuing use of edge of chaos wave coherence processing, subsequently expanded to primitive nervous systems as multicellular organisms evolved. One can see such strategically purposive behaviour in both single celled protists such as paramecium and in active human cells such as neutrophils hunting and consuming bacteria (King 2008).

Consequently the major neuroreceptor classes have a very ancient origin, with the 5HT1 and 5HT2 families diverging before the molluscs, arthropods and vertebrates diverged, close to the level of the founding metazoa. Sponges, with only two cell types, express serotonin (Wayrer et al. 1999) and have been shown to have the critical gene networks to generate synapses, in a pre-coordinated form (Conaco et al. 2012). Coelenterates already have all the key components of serotonin pathways, involved in signalling by sensory cells and neurons, despite having only a primitive nerve network (McCauley et al. 1997, Umbriaco et al. 1990). Given its ancient origin serotonin is also found to play a key role in development and embryogenesis in Molluscs (Buznikov et al. 2001, 2003, sea urchins (Brown and Shaver) and mammals, where the expression of serotonin

$$\frac{e^2}{GmM} \cong \frac{T_0}{\Delta t} \cong 10^{39}$$

receptors occurs at the earliest stages, activated by circulating plasma serotonin from the mother.

The metabotropic (protein-activating) glutamate and GABA receptors likewise go back to the social amoeba Dictyostelium discoideum, where there is a family of 17 GABA receptors and a glutamate receptor involved in differentiation (Taniura et al 2006). The glutamate-binding ""fly trap"" section of both ionotropic and metabotropic glutamate receptors show homologies with the bacterial periplasmic amino-acid binding protein (Felder et al 1999, Oh et al 1994, Lampinen et al 1998). The membrane-spanning section of the iGluRs also show homology with the bacterial voltage-gated K+ channel (Chen et al 1999). These changes are already in place in the cyanobacterial ionotropic glutamate receptor. The fact that an iGluR has also been found in Arabidopsis (Turano et al 2001) shows this class entered the eucaryotes before the plants, animals and fungi diverged. Elements of the protein signalling pathways, such as protein kinase C, essential to neuronal synaptic contact originated close to the eucaryote origin (Emes et al. 2008, Ryan & Grant 2009). Likewise the Dlg family of postsynaptic scaffold proteins, which bind neurotransmitter receptors and enzymes into signaling complexes originated before the divergence of the vertebrates and arthropods (Nithianantharajah et al. 2012).

Thus we can see how the survival modalities of complex organisms have continued to be mediated by classes of neurotransmitters modulating key motivational, aversive and social dynamics, from single cells to multi-celled organisms, with ascending central nervous system complexity. There are thus strong parallels in how the key classes of neurotransmitters modulate affect in organisms as diverse as arthropods and vertebrates.

In higher animals, 5-HT continues in its role as a homeostatic regulator in adjusting the dynamic interactions of these many functions within the organism, and how the organism interacts with the outside world, elaborated in humans into a variety of functions including the sleep-wakefulness cycle, triggering the psychedelic state, depression and social delinquency (King 2012). Similarly, dopamine and nor- epinephrine pathways modulate reward and vigilance, forming a spectrum of fundamental strategic responses in humans, including motor coordination roles whose overstimulation or disruption can lead to Parkinsons, dependency and psychosis. Reports of increased social dominance in primates (Edwards and Kravitz, 1997) and improved mood and confidence in social interactions in humans after using drugs which increase serotonin levels are well documented (Kramer, 1993; Young and Leyton, 2002).

Functional studies in the honey bee and fruit fly have shown that serotonergic signaling participates in aggression, sleep, circadian rhythms, responses to visual stimuli, and associative learning (Blenau & Thamm 2011). Serotonin in lobsters regulates socially relevant behaviours such as dominance-type posture, offensive tail flicks, and escape responses (Kravitz, 2000, Sosa et al. 2004). In insects, dopamine acts instead as a punishment signal and is necessary to form aversive memories (Barron et al. 2007, Schwaerzel et al. 2003, Selcho et al. 2009). In flies dopamine modulates locomotor activity, sexual function and the response to cocaine, nicotine, and alcohol (Hearn et al. 2002). Octopamine, the arthropod analogue of norepinephrine, regulates desensitization of sensory inputs, arousal, initiation, and maintenance of various rhythmic behaviors and complex behaviors such as learning and memory, and endocrine gland activity (Farooqui 2007). Web building in spiders is likewise affected by stimulants and psychedelics (Dunn).

These neurotransmitters are thus playing a similar role in humans in modulating the excitable brain to attune it to survival objectives that these same signaling molecules had in single celled eucaryote social and reproductive behaviours.

Moreover, although most neurophysiological investigations of arthropod and mollusc neural ganglia tend to be recordings of single neuronal action potentials (e.g. Paulk & Gronenberg 2005), ""silent"" cells with graded electrical responses are also integral to the function of small neuronal circuits (Kandel 1979), and as we have already noted, chaotic excitability occurs in bursting and beating action potentials in amoebae, Paramecium and simple algae. Furthermore studies in both molluscs (Schütt & Basar 1992) and arthropods (Kirschfeld 1992) have demonstrated coherent gamma-type oscillations. These results lead us to the hypothesis that there is a common basis of attentive processing in the gamma band across wide branches of the metazoa, based on edge-of-chaos processing and wave phase coherence, despite their highly varied neuroanatomies (Basar et al. 2001).

3: Consciousness - Coordinated Activity Anticipating Future Challenges

The organization of the cerebral cortex and its underlying structures, consist of a series of microcolumns vertically spanning the three to six layers of the cortex, acting as parallel processing units for an envelope of characteristics, a hologram-like featural mathematical transform space. Typical features represented in particular cortical regions include sensory attributes such as the line orientation and binocular dominance of visual processing, tonotopic processing of sounds, somato-sensory bodily maps, and higher level features such as facial expressions and the faces of individuals, leading to the strategic executive modules of the prefrontal cortex and our life aims and thought processes.

The many-to-many nature of synaptic connections forms the basis of this abstract representation, which is also adaptive through neural plasticity. Space and time also become features in the transform mapping, so that certain e.g. parietal areas have major roles in spatial navigation while other areas, for example in the temporal lobes elicit experiences of a memory-episodic nature. The hippocampus pivotal in consolidating sequential memory also appears to function as a spatial GPS, emphasizing the mutual relation between space and time in transform space. A key role of wave-based brain processing is to harness this transform representation to predict, using experiential memory and contextual clues, the ongoing nature of opportunities and threats to survival.

Subjective consciousness involves coordinated whole-brain activity (Baars 1997, 2001), as opposed to local activations, which reach only the subconscious level, as evidenced in both experiments on conscious processing and the effects of dissociative anaesthetics (Alkire et al. 2008). Attempts to find the functional locus of subjective consciousness in brain regions have arrived at the conclusion that active conscious experiences are not generated in a specific cortical region but are a product of integrated coherent activity of global cortical dynamics (Ananthaswamy 2009, 2010). This distributed view of conscious brain activity is consistent with experimental studies in which the cortical modules we see activated in fMRI and PET scans correspond to salient features of subjective conscious experience.

This implies that the so-called Cartesian theatre of consciousness is a product of the entire active cortex and that the particular form of phase coherent, edge-of-chaos processing adopted by the mammalian brain is responsible for the manifestation of subjective experience. This allows for a theory of consciousness in which preconscious processing e.g. of sensory information can occur in specific brain areas, which then reaches the conscious level only when these enter into coherent global neuronal activity integrating the processing, as Baars global workspace theory (1997, 2001) proposes, rather than being a product of a specific region such as the supplementary motor cortex (Eccles 1982, Fried et al. 1991, Haggard 2005).

The approach is also consistent with there being broadly only one dominant stream of conscious thought and experience at a given time, as diverse forms of local processing give way to an integrated global response. A series of experiments involving perceptual masking of brief stimuli to inhibit their entry into conscious perception (Sergent et al. 2005, Sigman and Dehaene 2005, 2006, Dehaene and Changeux 2005, Del Cul et al. 2007, 2009, Gaillard et al. 2009), studies of pathological conditions such as multiple sclerosis (Reuter et al. 2009, Schnakers 2009), and brief episodes in which direct cortical electrodes are being used during operations for intractable epilepsy (Quiroga et al. 2008) have tended to confirm the overall features of Baars model (Ananthaswamy 2009, 2010). EEG studies also show that under diverse anesthetics, as consciousness fades, there is a loss of synchrony between different areas of the cortex (Alkire et al. 2008). The theory also tallies with Tononis idea of phi, a function of integrated complexity used as a measure of consciousness (Barras 2013, Pagel 2012).

The brain regions involved in our sense of self - the actor-agent behind conscious states - are specifically activated in idle periods, in the so-called default circuit, whose function appears to be adaptively envisaging future challenges. The default network (Fox 2008, Zimmer 2005) encompasses posterior-cingulate/precuneus, anterior cingulate/mesiofrontal cortex and temporo-parietal junctions, several of which have key integrating functions. The ventral medial prefrontal (Macrae et al. 2004) is implicated in processing risk and fear. It also plays a role in the inhibition of emotional responses, and decision-making. It has been shown to be active when experimental subjects are shown imagery they think apply to themselves. The precuneus (Cavanna & Trimble 2006) is involved with episodic memory, visuo- spatial processing, reflections upon self, and aspects of consciousness. The insulae are also believed to be involved in consciousness and play a role in diverse functions usually linked to emotion and the regulation of the body's homeostasis, including perception, motor control, self-awareness, cognitive functioning, and interpersonal experience. The anterior insula is activated in subjects who are shown pictures of their own faces, or who are identifying their own memories. The temporo- parietal junction is known to play a crucial role in self-other distinction and theory of mind. Studies indicate that the temporo-parietal junction has altered function during simulated out of body experiences (Ananthaswamy 2013).

Although subjective consciousness involves the entire cortex in coherent activation, brain scans highlight certain areas of pivotal importance, whose disruption can impede active consciousness. Three regions associated with global workspace have been identified as key participants in these higher integrative functions, the thalamus which is a critical set of relay centres underlying all cortical areas and possibly driving the EEG, lateral prefrontal executive function and posterior parietal spatial integration (Bor 2013). Another set of two regions, anterior cingulate and fronto- insular are highlighted in the saliency circuit (Williams 2012) in which von Economo (VEN) bipolar neurons provide fast connectivity between regions to maintain a sense of the conscious present providing a sense of immediate anticipation of the ongoing external and internal condition (saliency and interoception). These appear prominently in large brained animals, including humans, elephants and cetaceans where there is greater need to rapidly stitch together related processing areas critical to the ongoing conscious state.

Several researchers have highlighted specific aspects of consciousness in an attempt to understand how it evolved. Higher integrative processing associated with global workspace has been extended to other animals such as apes and dolphins (Wilson 2013). Another approach suggests that making integrative decisions socially would have aided better environmental decision-making concerning hard to discern situations involving the combined senses in which social discussion aids survival, such as two hunters trying to assess whether dust on the prairie suggests running from lions or hunting buffalo, or women discussing where to find hard to get herbs from the visual appearance, taste and smell of a sample (Bahrami et al. 2010).

4: Conscious Survival in the Wild

To discover what advantage subjective consciousness has over purely computational processing, we need to examine the survival situations that are pivotal to organisms in the open environment and the sorts of computational dilemmas involved in decision-making processes on which survival depends.

Many open environment problems of survival are computationally intractable and would leave a digital antelope stranded at the crossroads until pounced upon by a predator, because they involve a number n of factors, which increase super-exponentially with n. For example, in the traveling salesman problem - finding the shortest path around n cities - the calculation time grows super-exponentially with the factorial $(n-1)!/2$ - the number of possible routes which could be taken, each of which needs to me measured to find the shortest path (King 1991). There are probabilistic methods which can give a sub-optimal answer and artificial neural nets solve the problem in parallel by simulating a synaptic potential energy landscape, using thermodynamic annealing to find a local minimum not too far from the global one. Vertebrate brains appear to use edge of chaos dynamics to similar effect.

Open environment problems are intractable both because they fall into this broad class and also because they are prone to irresolvable structural instabilities, which defy a stable probabilistic outcome. Suppose a gazelle is trying to get to the waterhole along various paths. On a probability basis it is bound to choose the path, which, from its past experience, it perceives to be the least likely to have a predator, i.e. the safest. But the predator is likewise going to make a probabilistic calculation to choose the path that the prey is most likely to be on given these factors i.e. the same one. Ultimately this is an unstable problem that has no consistent computational solution.

There is a deeper issue in these types of situation. Probabilistic calculations, both in the real world and in quantum mechanics, require the context to be repeated to build up a statistical distribution. In an interference experiment we get the bands of light and dark color representing the wave amplitudes as probability distributions of photons on the photographic plate only when a significant number have passed through the apparatus in the same configuration. The same is true for estimating a probabilistically most viable route to the waterhole. But real life problems are plagued by the fact that both living organisms and evolution itself are processes in which the context is endlessly being changed by the decision-making processes. Repetition occurs only in the most abstract sense, which is one reason why massively parallel brains we have are so good at such problems.

Finally, in many real life situations, there is not one optimal outcome but a whole series of possible choices, any or all of which could lead either to death, or survival and reproduction. This is the super-abundance problem we shall investigate shortly. Despite having complex brains, even humans are very inferior computers with a digit span of only six or seven and a calculation capacity little better than a pocket calculator. We all know what we do and what conscious animals do in this situation. They look at the paths forward. If they have had a bad experience on one they will probably avoid it, but otherwise they will try to assess how risky each looks and make a decision on intuitive hunch to follow one or the other. In a sense, all their previous life experience is being summed up in their conscious awareness and their contextual memory. The critical point is that consciousness is providing something completely different from a computational algorithm, it is a form of real time anticipation of threats and survival that is sensitively dependent on environmental perturbation and attuned to be anticipatory in real time just sufficiently to jump out of the way and bolt for it and survive. Thus the key role of consciousness is to keep watch on the unfolding living environment, to be paranoid to hair-trigger sensitivity for any impending hint of a movement, or the signs, or sound of a pouncing predator — an integrated holographic form of space-time anticipation.

5: Edge of Chaos Sensitivity and Phase Coherence Processing

From the work of Walter Freeman (1991, Skarda & Freeman 1987) and others (Basar et al. 1989) it has been established that the electroencephalogram shows characteristics of chaos, including broad-spectrum frequency activity, strange attractors with low fractal dimension and transitions from high-energy chaos, to learned, or new attractors, during sensory and perceptual processing. A fundamental property of chaos is sensitivity to arbitrarily small perturbations - the butterfly effect.

Between the global, the cellular and the molecular level are a fractal cascade of central nervous processes, which, in combination, make it theoretically possible for a quantum fluctuation to become amplified into a change of global brain state. The neuron is itself a fractal with multiply branching dendrites and axonal terminals, which are essential to provide the many-to-many synaptic connections between neurons, which make adaptation and the transform representation of reality possible. Furthermore, like all tissues, biological organization is achieved through non-linear interactions which begin at the molecular level and have secondary perturbations upward in a series of fractal scale transformations through complex molecules such as enzymes, supra-molecular complexes such as ion channels and the membrane, organelles such as synaptic junctions, to neurons and then to neuronal complexes such as cortical mini-columns and finally to global brain processes.

Because neurons tend to tune to their threshold with a sigmoidal activation function, which has maximum limiting slope at threshold, they are capable of becoming critically poised at their activation threshold. It is thus possible in principle for a single ion channel, potentially triggered by only one or two neurotransmitter molecules, if suitably situated on the receptor neuron, e.g. at the cell body, where an action potential begins, to act as the trigger for activation (King 2008).

The lessons of the butterfly effect and evidence for transitions from chaos in perceptual recognition suggest that if a brain state is critically poised, the system may become sensitive to instability at the neuronal, synaptic, ion-channel, or quantum level.

A variety of lines of evidence have demonstrated that fluctuations in single cells can lead to a change of brain state. In addition to sensitive dependence in chaotic systems, stochastic resonance (Liljenström and Uno 2005), in which the presence of noise, somewhat paradoxically, leads to the capacity of ion channels to sensitively excite hippocampal cells and in turn to cause a change in global brain state. In this sense noise is equivalent to the properties of dynamical chaos, which distribute through the dynamic pseudo-randomly preventing the dynamic getting locked in a stable attractor. Such a dynamic is thus able to explore its dynamical space, just as thermodynamic annealing is used in artificial neural nets to avoid them becoming locked in sub-optimal local minima.

Chandelier cells, which are more common in humans than other mammals, such as the mouse, and were originally thought to be purely inhibitory, are axon-axonal cells, which can result in specific poly-synaptic activation of pyramidal cells. It has been discovered (Molnar 2008, Woodruff and Yuste 2008) that chandelier cells are capable of changing the patterns of excitation between pyramidal neurons that drive active output to other cortical regions and to the peripheral nervous system, in such a way that single action potentials are sufficient to recruit neuronal assemblies that are proposed to participate in cognitive processes.

6: Quantum Reality, Sentience and Intentional Will

Many scientists assume that all human activity must be a product of brain function and that any notion of conscious will acting on the physical is delusory. This flies in contradiction to our subjective assessment that we are autonomous beings with voluntary control over our fates. To claim free will is a delusion leads to a catatonic impotence of consciousness and contradicts the assumptions of legal accountability, where we assume a person of sound mind is physically responsible for the consequences of their consciously intentional actions.

Many physicists, from Arthur Eddingtons citation of the uncertainty of position of a synaptic vesicle in relation to the thickness of the membrane on, have drawn attention to the fact that the quantum universe is not deterministic in the manner of classical causality and that quantum uncertainty provides a causal loophole, which might make it possible for free will to coexist in the quantum universe.

Biology is full of phenomena at the quantum level, which are essential to biological function. Enzymes invoke quantum tunneling to enable transitions through their substrates activation energy. Protein folding is a manifestation of quantum computation intractable by classical computing. When a photosynthetic active centre absorbs a photon, the wave function of the excitation is able to perform a quantum computation, which enables the excitation to travel down the most efficient route to reach the chemical reaction site (McAlpine 2010, Hildne et al. 2013).

Quantum entanglement is believed to be behind the way some birds navigate in the magnetic field (Amit 2012, Courtland 2011). Light excites two electrons on one molecule and shunts one of them onto a second molecule. Their spins are linked through quantum entanglement. Before they relax into a decoherent state, the Earth's magnetic field can alter the relative alignment of the electrons' spins, which in turn alters the chemical properties of the molecules involved. Quantum coherence is an established technique in tissue imaging, demonstrating quantum entanglement in biological tissues at the molecular level (Samuel 2001, Warren 1998).

Although the brain needs to able to be resilient to noise in its stable functioning, in the event of a critically poised dynamic in which there is no stable determining outcome, several key processes, may make the brain state capable of being sensitive to fluctuations at the quantum level. These include chaotic sensitivity, self- organized criticality, the amplifying effects of chandelier cells and stochastic resonance (King 2008, 2012).

Karl Pribram (1991), in the notion of the holographic brain, has drawn attention to the similarity between phase coherence processing of brain waves in the gamma frequency range believed to be responsible for cognitive processes and the wave amplitude basis of quantum uncertainty in reduction of the wave packet and quantum measurements based on the uncertainty relation Et h , where the relation is determined by the number of phase fronts to be counted.

This raises an interesting implication, that the evolution of nervous systems may have arrived at a neurodynamic homologous with quantum processes at the foundation of physics, suggesting that quantum entanglement in brain states could in turn be a basis for active biological anticipation of immediate threats to survival through the forms of subjective consciousness the brain generates.

In quantum mechanics, not only are all probability paths traced in the wave function, but past and future are interconnected in a time-symmetric hand-shaking relationship, so that the final states of a wave-particle or entangled ensemble, on absorption, are boundary conditions for the interaction, just as the initial states that created them are. The transactional interpretation of quantum mechanics expresses this relationship neatly in terms of offer waves from the past emitter/s and confirmation waves from the future absorbers, whose wave interference becomes the single or entangled particles passing between. When an entangled pair are created, each knows instantaneously the state of the other and if one is found to be in a given state, e.g. of polarization or spin, the other is immediately in the complementary state, no matter how far away it is in space-time. This is the spooky action at a distance, which Einstein feared because it violates local Einsteinian causality — particles not communicating faster than the speed of light.

The brain explores ongoing situations which have no deductive solution, by evoking an edge-of-chaos state which, when it transitions out of chaos, results in the aha of insight learning. The same process remains sensitively tuned for anticipating any signs of danger in the wild. This is pretty much how we do experience waking consciousness. If this process involves sensitivity to quantum indeterminacy the coherent excitations would be quantum entangled, invoking new forms of quantum computation.

However quantum entanglement cannot be used to make classical causal predictions, which would formally anticipate a future event, so the past-future hand- shaking lasts only as long as a particle or entangled ensemble persist in their wave function.

Weak quantum measurement (WQM) is one way a form of quantum anticipation could arise. Weak quantum measurement (Aharonov et al. 1988) is a process where a quantum wave function is not irreversibly collapsed by absorbing the particle but a small deformation is made in the wave function whose effects become apparent later when the particle is eventually absorbed e.g. on a photographic plate in a strong quantum measurement. Weak quantum measurement changes the wave function slightly mid-flight between emission and absorption, and hence before the particle meets the future absorber involved in eventual detection. A small change is induced in the wave function, e.g. by slightly altering its polarization along a given axis (Kocsis et al. 2011). This cannot be used to deduce the state of a given wave-particle at the time of measurement because the wave function is only slightly perturbed, and is not collapsed or absorbed, as in strong measurement, but one can build up a prediction statistically over many repeated quanta of the conditions at the point of weak measurement, once post-selection data is assembled after absorption.

This suggests (Merali 2010, Cho 2011) that, in some sense, the future is determining the present, but in a way we can discover conclusively only by many repeats. Focus on any single instance and you are left with an effect with no apparent cause, which one has to put it down to a random experimental error. This has led some physicists to suggest that free-will exists only in the freedom to choose not to make the post- selection(s) revealing the futures pull on the present. Yakir Aharonov, the co- discoverer of weak quantum measurement (Aharonov et al. 1988) sees this occurring through an advanced wave travelling backwards in time from the future absorbing states to the time of weak measurement. What God gains by playing dice with the universe, in Einsteins words, in the quantum fuzziness of uncertainty, is just what is needed, so that the future can exert an effect on the present, without ever being caught in the act of doing it in any particular instance: ""The future can only affect the present if there is room to write its influence off as a mistake"", neatly explaining why no subjective account of prescience can do so either.

Weak quantum measurements have been used to elucidate the trajectories of the wave function during its passage through a two-slit interference apparatus (Kocsis et al. 2011), to determine all aspects of the complex waveform of the wave function (Hosten 2011, Lunden et al. 2011), to make ultra sensitive measurements of small deflections (Hosten & Kwiat 2008, Dixon et al. 2008) and to demonstrate counterfactual results involving both negative and positive post-selection probabilities, which still add up to certainty, when two interference pathways overlap in a way which could result in annihilation (Lundeen & Steinberg 2009).

WQM provides a potential way that the brain might use its brain waves and phase coherence to evoke entangled (coherent) states that carry quantum encrypted information about immediate future states of experience as well as immediately past states, in an expanded envelope - the quantum present. It is this coordinated state that corresponds to subjective experience of the present moment, encoded through the parallel feature envelope of the cerebral cortex, including the areas associated with consciousness.

Effectively the brain is a massively parallel ensemble of wave excitations reverberating with one another, through couplings of varying strength in which excitations are emitted, modulated and absorbed. Interpreted in terms of quantum excitations, the ongoing conscious brain state could be a reverberating system of massively parallel weak quantum measurements (MPWQMs) of its ongoing state. This could in principle give the conscious brain a capacity to anticipate immediate future threats through the intuitive avenues of prescience, paranoia and foreboding. This suggests that the reverberating ensemble of the quantum present could provide an intuitive form of anticipation complementing computational predictions.

This would require significant differences from the post-selection paradigm of weak quantum measurement experiments, which are designed to produce a classically confirmed result from an eventual statistical distribution in the future. In the brain, consciousness being identified with the coherent excitations and hence the entangled condition could reverse the implication of backwards causality of advanced waves, with the future effectively informing the present of itself in quantum encrypted form through the space-time expansion of the quantum present. Discovering a molecular-biological basis for such an effect would pose an ultimate challenge to experimental neuroscience.

An indication of how quantum chaos might lead to complex forms of quantum entanglement can be gleaned from an ingenious experiment forming a quantum analogue of a kicked top using an ultra-cold cesium atom kicked by a laser pulse in a magnetic field: the classical dynamical space of the kicked top, showing domains of order where there is periodic motion and complementary regions of chaos where there is sensitive dependence on initial conditions. In the quantum system (middle pair), in the ordered dynamic (left), the linear entropy of the system (bottom pair) is reduced and there is no quantum entanglement between the orbital and nuclear spin of the atom. However in the chaotic dynamic (right) there is no such dip, as the orbital and nuclear spins have become entangled as a result of the chaotic perturbations of the quantum tops motion (Chaudhury et al. 2009, Steck 2009). This shows that, rather than the suppression of classical chaos seen in closed quantum systems (King 2013), reverberating chaotic quantum systems can introduce new entanglements.

The prevailing theory for loss of phase coherence and entanglement is decoherence caused by the interaction of a wave-particle with other wave particles in the environmental milieu. The coherence of the original entanglement becomes perturbed by other successive forms of entanglement, which successively reduce the coherence exponentially over time in the manner of an open system chaotic billiards. However in a closed universe, such as the global excitations of a brain state, decoherence does not necessarily approach the classical limit, but may retain encoded entangled information, just as the above example of the quantum kicked top does in a simpler atomic system, which could be referenced by the brain in the same way multiple hippocampal representations over time can, as an organism explores a changing habitat. Intriguingly, continued weak quantum measurement, rather than provoking decoherence tends to preserve entanglement because the ordered nature of the weak quantum measurements reduces the disordered nature of the environment (Hosten 2011, Lundeen et al. 2011). Massively parallel weak quantum measurements in the brain might thus function to maintain the ongoing entanglement.

7: Unraveling the Readiness Potential

Many aspects of brain function display dynamic features, which show the brain is focused on attempting to anticipate ongoing events. When a cat is dropped into unfamiliar territory, the pyramidal cells in its hippocampus become desynchronized and hunt chaotically, in what is called the orienting reaction, until the animal discovers where it is, or gains familiarity with its environment, when phase synchronization ensues (Coleman & Lindsley 1975). In a similar manner, the EEG will show a desynchronized pattern when a subject is listening for a sound which is irregularly spaced, but will fall into a synchronized pattern if the subject can confidently anticipate when the next sound is going to occur. Greater capacity to shift synchronization rather than it remaining locked has been associated with higher IQ (Jung-Beeman 2008).

This kind of processing is consistent with a computational process involving transitions from chaos to order. The chaotic regime acts both to provide sensitive dependence on any changes in boundary conditions such as sensory or cognitive inputs, at the same time as preventing the dynamical system getting caught in a suboptimal attractor, by providing sufficient energy to cause the process to fully explore the space of dynamical solutions. Artificial neural net annealing and quantum annealing both follow similar paradigms using random fluctuations and uncertainty to achieve a similar global optimization. Such a dynamic also allows for ordered deductive computation, but enables the system to evolve chaotically when the ordered process fails to arrive at a computational solution. In combination with quantum entanglement and massively parallel weak quantum measurement, as we have seen, this process may enable the ongoing conscious state to be anticipative.

However, a historical experiment suggested that, far from anticipating reality in real time, conscious awareness of a decision might actually lag behind unconscious brain processing which is already leading to the decision, although being placed by subjective experience at the time the conscious decision was made. In 1983, neuroscientist Benjamin Libet and co-workers (1983, 1989) asked volunteers wearing scalp electrodes to flex a finger or wrist. When they did, the movements were preceded by a dip in the signals being recorded, called the "readiness potential". Libet interpreted this RP as the brain preparing for movement. Crucially, the RP came a few tenths of a second before the volunteers said they had decided to move. Libet concluded that unconscious neural processes determine our actions before we are ever aware of making a decision. Since then, others have quoted the experiment as evidence that free will is an illusion - a conclusion that was always controversial, particularly as there is no proof the RP represents a decision to move.

With contemporary brain scanning technology, Soon et al. (2008) were able to predict with 60% accuracy whether subjects would press a button with their left or right hand up to 10 seconds before the subject became aware of having made that choice. This doesn't of itself negate conscious willing because these prefrontal and parietal patterns of activation merely indicate a process is in play, which may become consciously invoked at the time of the decision, and clearly many subjects (40% of trials) were in fact making a contrary decision. Neuroscientist John-Dylan Haynes, who led the study, notes: "I wouldn't interpret these early signals as an 'unconscious decision', I would think of it more like an unconscious bias of a later decision" (Williams 2012).

The assumption that Libets RP is a subconscious decision has been undermined by subsequent studies. Instead of letting volunteers decide when to move, Trevena and Miller (2010) asked them to wait for an audio tone before deciding whether to tap a key. If Libet's interpretation were correct, the RP should be greater after the tone when a person chose to tap the key. While there was an RP before volunteers made their decision to move, the signal was the same whether or not they elected to tap. Miller concludes that the RP may merely be a sign that the brain is paying attention and does not indicate that a decision has been made. They also failed to find evidence of subconscious decision-making in a second experiment. This time they asked volunteers to press a key after the tone, but to decide on the spot whether to use their left or right hand. As movement in the right limb is related to the brain signals in the left hemisphere and vice versa, they reasoned that if an unconscious process is driving this decision, where it occurs in the brain should depend on which hand is chosen, but they found no such correlation.

Schurger and colleagues (2012) have elucidated an explanation. Previous studies have shown that, when we have to make a decision based on sensory input, assemblies of neurons start accumulating evidence in favor of the various possible outcomes. A decision is triggered when the evidence favoring one particular outcome becomes strong enough to tip its associated assembly of neurons across a threshold. The team hypothesized that a similar process happens in the brain during the Libet experiment. They reasoned that movement is triggered when this neural noise generated by random or chaotic activity accumulates and crosses a threshold. The team repeated Libet's experiment, but this time if, while waiting to act spontaneously, the volunteers heard a click they had to act immediately. The researchers predicted that the fastest response to the click would be seen in those in whom the accumulation of neural noise had neared the threshold -

something that would show up in their EEG as a readiness potential. In those with slower responses to the click, the readiness potential was indeed absent in the EEG recordings. "We argue that what looks like a pre-conscious decision process may not in fact reflect a decision at all. It only looks that way because of the nature of spontaneous brain activity." Both these newer studies thus cast serious doubt on Libets claim that a conscious decision is made after the brain has already put the decision in motion, leaving open the possibility that conscious decisions are actually made in real time.

Some aspects of our conscious experience of the world make it possible for the brain to sometimes construct a present that has never actually occurred. In the "flash-lag" illusion, a screen displays a rotating disc with an arrow on it, pointing outwards. Next to the disc is a spot of light that is programmed to flash at the exact moment the spinning arrow passes it. Instead, to our experience, the flash lags behind, apparently occurring after the arrow has passed (Westerhoff 2013). One explanation is that our brain extrapolates into the future, making up for visual processing time by predicting where the arrow will be, however, rather than extrapolating into the future, our brain is actually interpolating events in the past, assembling a story of what happened retrospectively, as was shown by a subtle variant of the illusion (Eagleman and Sejnowski 2000). If the brain were predicting the spinning arrow's trajectory, people would see the lag even if the arrow stopped at the exact moment it was pointing at the spot. But in this case the lag does not occur. If the arrow begins stationary and moves in either direction immediately after the flash, the movement is perceived before the flash. How can the brain predict the direction of movement if it doesn't start until after the flash? The perception of what is happening at the moment of the flash is determined by what happens to the disc after it. This seems paradoxical, but other tests have confirmed that what is perceived to have occurred at a certain time can be influenced by what happens later. This again does not show that the brain is unable to anticipate reality because it applies only to very short time interval spatial reconstructions by the brain, which would naturally be more accurate by retrospective interpolation.

8: Prescience - Three Personal Experiences

To fathom situations where real time anticipation may have occurred without any prevailing causal implication leading up to it, we need to turn to rare instances of prescience with no reasonable prior cause. These kinds of events tend to be rare, apocryphal and lack independent corroboration, like stories of telepathic connection or the sense of foreboding that a relative has died, which later receives confirmation. Paradoxically some of the most outstanding examples can come from alleged precognitive dreaming rather than the waking state, which tends to be more circumscribed by commonsense everyday affairs.

As a student, I picked up and read ""An Experiment with Time"" by J W

Dunne (1929), which outlined double blind experiments in which the dream diaries led to as many accounts linking to future events in the peoples lives as they did to past experiences. A few weeks later I had a horrific double nightmare that I was being agonizingly stung. In the dream it was a spider which I couldnt remove because it would leave poison fangs inside me (as a bee or wasp does) and in the second dream it had returned to sting me again when I was distracted, as one often is in dreams. At eight in the morning as my wife woke, I recounted the nightmares in detail to her, before falling asleep again. About an hour later I was stung wide-awake by a wasp that had flown in the window, which my wife had opened after getting up. Suddenly the dream I had reported to my wife had become a reality. A skeptic might try to interpret this as a coincidence - merely an application of Bayes theorem of conditional probabilities - but the complete absence of any such dream before, drove home to me that dreaming, and by implication waking experiences too, have properties violating classical causality. The fact that it closely followed on reading the book gave this prescience an added dimension, capped by the fact that the scientist providing an introduction to the work was none other than Arthur Eddington, who had suggested quantum uncertainty of the synaptic vesicle as a basis for free will.

This raises a series of questions about coincidence and Carl Jungs (1952) notion of synchronicity, the idea that seemingly unrelated events and experiences may be caught up in a deeper correspondence, as reminiscent of quantum entanglement as phase coherence in brain processing appears to be. Many peoples personal accounts attest to a currency of such prescience.

A month before the twin towers fell in New York I wrote a song and posted the lyrics online. They contained several prescient lines, one invoking jihad: ""When it comes to the final struggle, jihad of the biosphere, theres only one true rogue nation - the great American shaitan"". The lyrics continue with a lament for the dark canyons of lower Manhattan among the fallen towers: ""walking in the twilight, down in the valley of shadows"", and then the plane ""Well fly so high well pass right to the other side and never fall in flames again"". Then I watched live in prescient horror as one of the two planes struck the tower and passed right through, coming out in a burst of flames on the other side. The lyrics continue with the genocide - ""when will you comprehend the damage you have wrought in your indiscretion, can we undo the death trance you have set in motion?"" The last line closed with ""Can we bear it all again? It thus presciently echoed the Mayor of New Yorks own words on TV ""This ...... will be more than any of us can bear"". I was singing about a mass extinction of life, but why the Islamic jihad, meeting Icarus descending?

All shamanic practitioners have to answer a question of coincidence. When curing a sick person, it is not to explain why the person has contracted tuberculosis or leprosy i.e. that the respective bacteria were infectious, or their immune system was weakened, but why this person caught this sickness at this particular time.

In the process of writing this paper, I awoke from a dream in which I was gazing at a pregnant woman, touching her on the shoulders, absorbed in the glowing beauty and fecundity of her pregnant state. Then when I sat down to look at the news next morning, I found myself watching this time-lapse video clip taken of a womans 40 week pregnancy by photographer, Nicole Gourley.

9: Anticipating the Multiverse

The central enigma of quantum reality is the causality-violating reduction of the wave packet. We see this in Schrödingers cat paradox a cat set to be killed by a radioactive scintillation breaking a cyanide flask. In quantum reality the cat is both alive and dead with differing probabilities, but in our subjective experience, when we open the box the cat is either alive, or dead, with certainty. Reduction also occurs when a wave is absorbed as a particle in an interference experiment. Quantum mechanics appears to preserve all the conceivable outcomes in parallel superposition. Not only is Schrödingers cat both alive and dead, but Napoleon has both won and lost the battle of Waterloo. Many of these strategic outcomes, indeed all accidents of history, depend on uncertainties that go, in principle, right down to the quantum level.

There is continuing debate among physicists about how and where in the causal chain, reduction of the wave packet actually occurs. While decoherence theories suggest this may occur simply through interaction of single or entangled states with other particles, the wave function of the entire universe is in effect one single multi- particle entangled state and so the whole notion of a single line of history unfolding seems to be something only our conscious awareness is able to determine.

Several of the founding quantum physicists adhered to this view. John von Neumann suggested that quantum observation is the action of a conscious mind and that everything in the universe that is subject to the laws of quantum physics creates one vast quantum superposition. But the conscious mind is different, being able to select out one of the quantum possibilities on offer, making it real - to that mind. Max Planck, the founder of quantum theory, said in 1931, "I regard consciousness as fundamental. I regard matter as derivative from consciousness." Werner Heisenberg also maintained that wave function collapse - the destruction of quantum superposition - occurs when the result of a measurement is registered in the mind of an observer. In Henry Stapps words we are "participating observers" whose minds cause the collapse of superpositions. ""Before human consciousness appeared, there existed a multiverse of potential universes. The emergence of a conscious mind in one of these potential universes, ours, gives it a special status: reality"" (Brooks 2012). This is effectively a complement to the anthropic principle of physical cosmology in which conscious observers are selective boundary conditions on the laws of nature in the universe (Barrow and Tipler 1988).

Thus another idea of the role of subjective consciousness is that it is a way the universe can solve the super-abundance of multiverses to bring about a natural universe in which some things do happen and other things dont. One of the most central experiences of our transient mortal lives is historicity — that there is a line of actual history, in which each of us, however small and insignificant our lives, are participating in bringing the world into actual being, albeit sometimes rather diabolically in times of exploitation, but with some reflection on our own transience, perhaps reaching towards a more enlightened existence, in which the passage of the generations is able to reach towards a state where the universe comes to consciously understand itself ever more deeply and completely.

The idea that consciousness collapses the wave functions of the universe leads to some counter-intuitive conclusions, because it implies that the consciousness itself is inducing the historical collapse that is in turn causing my brain to have a memory of this process.

On the other hand, the notion of the brain using entanglement provides a paradigm for resolving many of the contradictory situations that arise when classical causality is applied to anticipatory processes. A premonition being either a cause of a future event or caused by it leads to contradiction, which is resolved in the space-time hand-shaking of the entanglement.

The process goes like this: Memory systems are used to form a model of the quantum collapsed history already experienced, which is sequentially stored in the hippocampus and then semantically re-encoded into the cortical feature envelope so that it can be interrogated from any contingent perspective. The conscious cerebral cortex contains a dynamical system of entangled states, which together envelop a space-time region extending a limited distance into both the past and future - the quantum-delocalized present. The cortical envelope thus maintains a state of context-modulated sensitively-dependent dynamic excitation which generates our conscious sense of the present moment by encoding the immediate past and future together in a wave function representation entangled in the global coherent dynamic.

The quantum present would extend over the entangled life-time of the coherent excitations, incorporating quantum-encrypted information about the immediate past and future of the organism into the current state of subjective experience. The quantum present provides the loophole in classical causality that permits intentional will, or free-will to alter brain states and hence physical states in the world through behavior, as an effect of the entanglement. An external observer will simply see a brain process sensitively dependent on quantum uncertainty.

It may also be possible for the brain to encode entangled states in a more permanent form. Highly active brain states have been shown in fMRI studies to elicit changes in cerebral activation lasting over 24 hours (Heaven 2013, Harmelech et al. 2013). Long-term potentiation and memory processes are in principle permanent and may involve epigenetic changes (Levenson & Sweatt

2005).

REFERENCES

Aharonov Y., Albert D.Z., Vaidman L. (1988) How the Result of a Measurement of a Component of the Spin of a Spin-2 Particle Can Turn Out to be 100 Physical review letters 60, 1351.

Alkire M, Hudetz A., Tononi G. (2008) Consciousness and Anesthesia Science 322/5903 876-880. Amit G. (2012) 'Eye bath' to thank for quantum vision in birds New Scientist http://www.newscientist.com/article/dn22199-eye-bath-to-thank-for-quantum-vision-in-birds.html

Ananthaswamy A. (2009) 'Consciousness signature' discovered spanning the brain New Scientist 17 March. http://www.newscientist.com/article/dn16775-consciousness-signature-discovered- spanning-the-brain.html

Ananthaswamy A. (2009) Whole brain is in the grip of consciousness New Scientist 18 March. http://www.newscientist.com/article/mg20127004.300-whole-brain-is-in-the-grip-of- consciousness.html

Ananthaswamy A. (2010) Firing on all neurons: Where consciousness comes from New Scientist 22 March. http://www.newscientist.com/article/mg20527520.400-firing-on-all-neurons-where- consciousness-comes- from.html

Ananthaswamy A. (2013) The self: Trick yourself into an out-of-body experience New Scientist 20 Feb.

Anjard C., Loomis W. (2006) GABA induces terminal differentiation of Dictyostelium through a GABAB receptor Development 133 2253-2261 doi:10.1242/dev.02399

Azmitia E. C. (2010) Evolution of Serotonin: Sunlight to Suicide Muller C & Jacobs B (Eds.) Handbook of Behavioral Neurobiology of Serotonin Elsevier ISBN 978-0-12-374634-4 DOI: 10.1016/B978-0-12-374634-4.00034-4

Baars, B. J. (1997) In the Theatre of Consciousness: Global Workspace Theory, A Rigorous Scientific Theory of Consciousness. Journal of Consciousness Studies, 4/4 292-309 8.

Baars, B. J. (2001) In the Theater of Consciousness Oxford University Press US.

Bahrami B., Olsen K., Latham P., Roepstorff A., Rees G., Frith C. (2010) Optimally Interacting Minds Science 329/5995 1081-5.

Barras C (2013) Mind maths: The sum of consciousness New Scientist 6 February. http://www.newscientist.com/article/mg21729032.400-mind-maths-the-sum-of-consciousness.html

Barron, A. B., Maleszka, R., Vander Meer, R. K., & Robinson, G. E. (2007). Octopamine modulates honey bee dance behavior. Proceedings of the National Academy of Sciences, 104(5), 1703- 1707. DOI:10.1073/pnas.0610506104. PMC 1779631.

Barrow J, Tipler F (1988) The Anthropic Cosmological Principle, Oxf. Univ. Pr., Oxford.

Basar E., Basar-Eroglu J., Röschke J., Schütt A., (1989) The EEG is a quasi-deterministic signal anticipating sensory-cognitive tasks, in Basar E., Bullock T.H. eds. Brain Dynamics Springer- Verlag, 43-71.

Basar E, Basar-Erogluc C, Karakas S, Schürmann M (2001) Gamma, alpha, delta, and theta oscillations govern cognitive processes International Journal of Psychophysiology 39 241-8. Blenau W & Thamm M (2011) Distribution of serotonin (5-HT) and its receptors in the insect brain with focus on the mushroom bodies. Lessons from Drosophila melanogaster and Apis mellifera Arthropod Structure & Development 40 381-394.

Bor D (2013) Consciousness: Watching your mind in action New Scientist 20 May.

Brooks M (2012) Reality: How does consciousness fit in? New Scientist 3 October.

Brizzi G & Blum J (1970) Effect of growth conditions on serotonin content of Tetrahymena pyriformis Journal of Eukaryotic Microbiology (J. Protozool.) 17/4 553-555.

Buznikov, G. A., Lambert, W. H., & Lauder, J. M. (2001). Serotonin and serotonin-like substances as regulators of early embryogenesis and morphogenesis. Cell and tissue research, 305(2), 177-186.

DOI10.1007/s004410100408

Buznikov, G. A., Lambert, W. H., & Lauder, J. M. (2001). Serotonin and serotonin-like substances as regulators of early embryogenesis and morphogenesis. Cell and tissue research, 305(2), 177-186. Cavanna A., Trimble M. (2006) The precuneus: a review of its functional anatomy and behavioural correlates Brain 129 564-583 doi:10.1093/brain/awl004.

Chaudhury S, Smith A, Anderson B, Ghose S, Jessen P (2009) Quantum signatures of chaos in a kicked top Nature 461 768-771.

Chay T.R., Rinzel J. (1985), Bursting, beating and chaos in an excitable membrane model, Biophys. J. 47, 357-366.

Chen, G. Q., Cui, C., Mayer, M. L., & Gouaux, E. (1999). Functional characterization of a potassium- selective prokaryotic glutamate receptor. Nature, 402(6763), 817-821

Cho A. (2011) Furtive Approach Rolls Back the Limits of Quantum Uncertainty Science 333 690-3. Coleman, J. R., Lindsley, D. B. (1975). Hippocampal electrical correlates of free behavior and behavior induced by stimulation of two hypothalamic-hippocampal systems in the cat. Experimental neurology, 49(2), 506-528.

Conaco, C., Bassett, D. S., Zhou, H., Arcila, M. L., Degnan, S. M., Degnan, B. M., & Kosik, K. S. (2012). Functionalization of a protosynaptic gene expression network. Proceedings of the National Academy of Sciences, 109(Supplement 1),

10612-10618. doi/10.1073/pnas.1201890109.

Courtland R. (2011) Quantum states last longer in birds' eyes New Scientist http://www.newscientist.com/article/mg20927963.000-quantum-states-last-longer-in-birds- eyes.html

Deacon T. (2012) Consciousness is a matter of constraint 30 November.

Del Cul A., Baillet S., Dehaene S. (2007) Brain dynamics underlying the nonlinear threshold for access to consciousness. PLoS Biol 5(10) e260. doi:10.1371/journal.pbio.0050260

Del Cul A., Dehaene S., Reyes P., Bravo E., Slachevsky A. (2009) Causal role of prefrontal cortex in the threshold for access to consciousness Brain 132 2531——2540.

Dehaene S., Changeux J.P. (2005) Ongoing spontaneous activity controls access to consciousness: A neuronal model for inattentional blindness. PLoS Biol 3(5) e141.

Dixon, P. B., Starling, D. J., Jordan, A. N., & Howell, J. C. (2009) Ultrasensitive beam deflection measurement via interferometric weak value amplification. Physical review letters, 102(17), 173601.

Dunn T. Spiders on drugs http://www.trinity.edu/jdunn/spiderdrugs.htm Dunne J. W. (1929) An Experiment with Time A & C Black, London.

Eagleman, D. M., Sejnowski, T. J. (2000) Motion integration and postdiction in visual awareness. Science. 287/5460 2036-8.

Eagleman, D.M., Sejnowski, T.J. (2000) Flash Lag Effect: Differential latency, not postdiction: Response. Science. 290/5494 1051a

Eccles J.C. (1982) The Initiation of Voluntary Movements by the Supplementary Motor Area Arch Psychiatr Nervenkr 231 423-441.

Eichinger, D., Coppi, A., Frederick, J., & Merali, S. (2002). Catecholamines in Entamoebae: Recent (re) discoveries. Journal of biosciences, 27(6), 589-593.

Eichinger, L., Pachebat, J. A., Glöckner, G., Rajandream, M. A., Sucgang, R., Berriman, M., ... & Hauser, H. (2005). The genome of the social amoeba Dictyostelium discoideum. Nature, 435(7038), 43-57.

Edwards, D.H., Kravitz, E.A. (1997) Serotonin, social status and aggression Curr. Opin. Neurobiol. 7 812-819.

Emes, R. D., Pocklington, A. J., Anderson, C. N., Bayes, A., Collins, M. O., Vickers, C. A., ... & Grant, S. G. (2008). Evolutionary expansion and anatomical specialization of synapse proteome complexity. Nature neuroscience, 11(7), 799-806.

Essman E (1987) The serotonergic system in Tetrahymena pyriformis International Journal of Clinical & Laboratory Research 17/1 77-82.

Farooqui T. (2007) Octopamine-Mediated Neuromodulation of Insect Senses Neurochem Res 32 1511-1529 DOI10.1007/s11064-007-9344-7

Felder C. et al. (1999) The venus flytrap of periplasmic binding proteins: an ancient protein module present in multiple drug receptors AAPS Pharm Sci. 1/2

E2.

Fox D. (2008) The secret life of the brain New Scientist 5 Nov.

Freeman W. (1991) The physiology of perception. Sci. Am. 264 Feb 35-41.

Fried I., Katz A., McCarthy G., Sass K., Williamson P., Spencer S. (1991) Functional Organization of Human Supplementary Motor Cortex Studied by Electrical Stimulation The Journal of Neuroscience, 1(11) 3656-3666.

Gaillard R., Dehaene S., Adam C., Clemenceau S., Hasboun D. (2009) Converging intracranial markers of conscious access. PLoS Biol 7(3) e1000061. doi:10.1371/journal.pbio.1000061

Goldbeter A (2006) Oscillations and waves of cyclic AMP in Dictyostelium: A prototype for spatio- temporal organization and pulsatile intercellular communication Bull Math Biol 68 1095-1109. Gonzales-Perdomo, M., Romero, P., & Goldenberg, S. (1988). Cyclic AMP and adenylate cyclase activators stimulate Trypanosoma cruzi differentiation. Experimental parasitology, 66(2), 205-212.

Haggard P. (2005) Conscious intention and motor cognition TRENDS in Cognitive Sciences 9/6 290- 295.

Halloy, J., Lauzeral, J., & Goldbeter, A. (1998). Modeling oscillations and waves of cAMP in Dictyostelium discoideum cells. Biophysical chemistry, 72(1), 9-19.

Harmelech, T., Preminger, S., Wertman, E., Malach, R. (2013). The Day-After Effect: Long Term, Hebbian-Like Restructuring of Resting-State fMRI Patterns Induced by a Single Epoch of Cortical Activation. The Journal of Neuroscience, 33(22), 9488-9497.

Hearn, M. G., Ren, Y., McBride, E. W., Reveillaud, I., Beinborn, M., & Kopin, A. S. (2002). A Drosophila dopamine 2-like receptor: Molecular characterization and identification of multiple alternatively spliced variants. Proceedings of the National Academy of Sciences, 99(22), 14554-9.

Heaven D. (2013) Echoes in the brain open a window on yesterday New Scientist 27 Jun.

Hildner, R., Brinks, D., Nieder, J. B., Cogdell, R. J., & van Hulst, N. F. (2013). Quantum Coherent Energy Transfer over Varying Pathways in Single Light-Harvesting Complexes. Science, 340(6139), 1448-1451. doi: 10.1126/science.1235820

Hinrichsen, R. D., Schultz, J. E. (1988) Paramecium: a model system for the study of excitable cells. Trends in neurosciences, 11(1), 27-32.

Hosten O. (2011) How to catch a wave Nature 474 170-1.

Hosten O., Kwiat P. (2008) Observation of the Spin Hall Effect of Light via Weak Measurements Science 319 787-790.

Iyer, L. M., Aravind, L., Coon, S. L., Klein, D. C., & Koonin, E. V. (2004). Evolution of cell—cell signaling in animals: did late horizontal gene transfer from bacteria have a role?. TRENDS in Genetics, 20(7), 292-299.

Jung, Carl G. (1993) [1952]. Synchronicity: An Acausal Connecting Principle. Bollingen, Switzerland: Bollingen Foundation. ISBN 978-0-691-01794-5.

Jung-Beeman, Mark (2008) The Eureka Hunt New Yorker July 28 84/22 40.

King C. C. (1991) Fractal and Chaotic Dynamics in Nervous Systems 1991 Progress in Neurobiology, 36 279-308.

King C. C. (2002) Biocosmology http://www.dhushara.com/book/bchtm/biocos.htm

King C. C. (2008) The Central Enigma of Consciousness Nature Precedings 5 November 2008 Journal of Consciousness Exploration and Research 2(1) 2011 http://www.dhushara.com/enigma/enigma.htm

King C. C. (2011) The Tree of Life: Tangled Roots and Sexy Shoots, DNA Decipher Journal 1(1) 73- 109.

King C. C. (2012) Entheogens, the Conscious Brain and Existential Reality http://www.dhushara.com/psyconcs/psychconsc8.htm

King C. C. (2013) Exploring Quantum, Classical and Semi-Classical Chaos in the Stadium Billiard Quanta 3/1 16-31 DOI: 10.12743/quanta.v3i1.23

Kirschfeld, K., (1992). Oscillations in the insect brain: do they correspond to the cortical gamma waves of vertebrates? Proc. Natl. Acad. Sci. USA 89, 4764-8.

Köhidai , L., Vakkuri, O., Keresztesi, M., Leppaluoto, J., & Csaba, G. (2003). Induction of melatonin synthesis in Tetrahymena pyriformis by hormonal imprinting-A unicellular" factory" of the indoleamine. Cellular And Molecular Biology-Paris-Wegmann-, 49(4), 521-524.

Kocsis, S., Braverman, B., Ravets, S., Stevens, M. J., Mirin, R. P., Shalm, L. K., & Steinberg, A. M. (2011). Observing the average trajectories of single photons in a two-slit interferometer. Science, 332(6034), 1170-1173.

Kramer, P. (1993) Listening to Prozac Penguin, New York.

Kravitz E.A. (2000) Serotonin and aggression: insights gained from a lobster model system and speculations on the role of amine neurons in a complex behavior J. Comp. Physiol. 186 221-238.

Lampinen, M., Pentikäinen, O., Johnson, M. S., & Keinänen, K. (1998). AMPA receptors and bacterial periplasmic amino acidbinding proteins share the ionic mechanism of ligand recognition. The EMBO journal, 17(16), 4704-4711.

Lampinen M. et al. (1998) AMPA receptors and bacterial periplasmic amino acid-binding proteins share the ionic mechanism of ligand recognition EMBO 17/16 4704—4711.

Levenson J., Sweatt D. (2005) Epigenetic Mechanisms In Memory Formation Nature Reviews Neuroscience 6 108.

Libet, B., Gleason, C. A., Wright, E. W., & Pearl, D. K. (1983). Time of conscious intention to act in relation to onset of cerebral activity (readiness-potential) the unconscious initiation of a freely voluntary act. Brain, 106(3), 623-642

Libet B. (1989) The timing of a subjective experience Behavioral Brain Sciences 12 183-5. (See also Libet, B. et al. (1985) Behav. Brain Sci. 8, 529-566.)

Liebeskind, B. J., Hillis, D. M., & Zakon, H. H. (2011). Evolution of sodium channels predates the origin of nervous systems in animals. Proceedings of the National Academy of Sciences, 108(22), 9154-9159. doi/10.1073/pnas.1106363108

Liljenström Hans, Svedin Uno (2005) Micro-Meso-Macro: Addressing Complex Systems Couplings Imperial College Press.

Locher, C. P., Ruben, P. C., Gut, J., & Rosenthal, P. J. (2003). 5HT1A serotonin receptor agonists inhibit Plasmodium falciparum by blocking a membrane channel. Antimicrobial agents and chemotherapy, 47(12), 3806-3809.

Lundeen J. S., Steinberg A. M. (2009) Experimental Joint Weak Measurement on a Photon Pair as a Probe of Hardys Paradox Physical review letters 102 020404.

Lundeen J.S., Sutherland B., Patel A., Stewart C, Bamber C. (2011) Direct measurement of the quantum wavefunction Nature 474 188-191.

Macrae C., Heatherton T., Kelley W. (2004) A Self Less Ordinary: The Medial Prefrontal Cortex and You.in Cognitive Neurosciences III. Ed Michael S. Gazzaniga. MIT Press. http://dartmouth.edu/~thlab/pubs/04_Macrae_etal_CogNeuroIII.pdf

McAlpine K. (2010) Nature's hot green quantum computers revealed New Scientist 3 February, http://www.newscientist.com/article/mg20527464.000-natures-hot-green-quantum-computers- revealed.html

McCauley, D.W. (1997) Serotonin plays an early role in the metamorphosis of the hydrozoan Phialidium gregarium Dev. Biol. 190 229-240.

McGowan , K., Guerina, V., Wicks, J., & Donowitz, M. (1985). Secretory hormones of Entamoeba histolytica. In Ciba Foundation Symposium 112-Microbial Toxins and Diarrhoeal Disease (pp. 139- 154). John Wiley & Sons, Ltd.

Merali Z. (2010) Back From the Future Discover Magazine August 26.

Mestler, T. (2011). Excitable Signal Relay and Emergent Behavior in the Social Amoeba Dictyostelium discoideum. Princeton University.

Murch, K. W., Weber, S. J., Macklin, C. & Siddiqi, I. (2013) Observing single quantum trajectories of a superconducting quantum bit Nature 502, 211—214.

Molnár, G., Oláh, S., Komlósi, G., Füle, M., Szabadics, J., Varga, C., ... & Tamás, G. (2008). Complex events initiated by individual spikes in the human cerebral cortex. PLoS biology, 6(9), e222.

Nithianantharajah, J., Komiyama, N. H., McKechanie, A., Johnstone, M., Blackwood, D. H., St Clair, D., ... & Grant, S. G. (2012). Synaptic scaffold evolution generated components of vertebrate cognitive complexity. Nature neuroscience. doi:10.1038/nn.3276.

Nomura, T., Tazawa, M., Ohtsuki, M., Sumi-Ichinose, C., Hagino, Y., Ota, A., & Nagatsu, T. (1998). Enzymes related to catecholamine biosynthesis in Tetrahymena pyriformis. Presence of GTP cyclohydrolase I. Comparative Biochemistry and Physiology Part B: Biochemistry and Molecular Biology, 120(4), 753-760.

Oh, B. H., Kang, C. H., De Bondt, H., Kim, S. H., Nikaido, K., Joshi, A. K., & Ames, G. F. (1994). The bacterial periplasmic histidine-binding protein. structure/function analysis of the ligand-binding site and comparison with related proteins. Journal of Biological Chemistry, 269(6), 4135-4143. Pagel M. (2012) How to measure consciousness New Scientist 1 August http://www.newscientist.com/article/mg21528762.000-how-to-measure-consciousness.html

Paulk, A. C., Gronenberg, W. (2008). Higher order visual input to the mushroom bodies in the bee, Bombus impatiens. Arthropod structure & development, 37(6), 443-458.

Peroutka S. (1995) Serotonin receptor subtypes: Their evolution and clinical significance CNS Drugs 4 suppl 18-28.

Peroutka, S., Howell, T. (1994) The molecular evolution of G-protein-coupled receptors: focus on 5- hydroxytryptamine receptors Neuropharmacology 33 319-324.

Pribram, K. H. (1991). Brain and perception: Holonomy and structure in figural processing. Psychology Press.

Quiroga R., Mukamel R., Isham E., Malach R., Fried I. (2008) Human single-neuron responses at the threshold of conscious recognition PNAS 105/9 3599-3604.

Reuter, F., Del Cul, A., Malikova, I., Naccache, L., Confort-Gouny, S., Cohen, L., ... & Audoin, B. (2009). White matter damage impairs access to consciousness in multiple sclerosis. Neuroimage, 44(2), 590-599.

Ryan T., Grant S. (2009) The origin and evolution of synapses Nature Reviews Neuroscience 10 701- 12.

Samuel E. (2001) Seeing the seeds of cancer New Scientist 24 Mar 42-45. 137

Schnakers C. (2009) Detecting consciousness in a total locked-in syndrome: An active event-related paradigm Neurocase 15/4 271-7.

Schurger A., Sitt J., Dehaene S. (2012) An accumulator model for spontaneous neural activity prior to self-initiated movement PNAS DOI: 10.1073. pnas.1210467109

Schütt, A., Basar, E., (1992). The effects of acetylcholine, dopamine and noradrenaline on the visceral ganglion of Helix Pomatia II: Stimulus evoked field potentials. Compar. Biochem. Physiol. 102C, 169-176.

Schwaerzel, M., Monastirioti, M., Scholz, H., Friggi-Grelin, F., Birman, S., & Heisenberg, M. (2003).

Dopamine and octopamine differentiate between aversive and appetitive olfactory memories in Drosophila. The Journal of neuroscience, 23(33), 10495-10502.

Selcho, M., Pauls, D., Han, K. A., Stocker, R. F., & Thum, A. S. (2009). The role of dopamine in Drosophila larval classical olfactory conditioning. PLoS One, 4(6), e5897.

Sergent C., Baillet S., Dehaene S. (2005) Timing of the brain events underlying access to consciousness during the attentional blink Nature Neuroscience 8/10 1391-1400.

Sheldrake R. (1981) A New Science of Life: the hypothesis of formative causation, Los Angeles, CA: J.P. Tarcher, 1981 ISBN 978-1-84831-042-1.

Sigman M., Dehaene S. (2005) Parsing a cognitive task: A characterization of the minds bottleneck. PLoS Biol 3(2) e37.

Sigman M., Dehaene S. (2006) Dynamics of the central bottleneck: Dual-task and task uncertainty. PLoS Biol 4(7) e220. DOI: 10.1371/journal.pbio.0040220

Skarda C., Freeman W., (1987) How brains make chaos in order to make sense of the world Behavioral and Brain Sciences 10 161-195.

Soon C., Brass M., Heinze H., Haynes J. (2008) Unconscious determinants of free decisions in the human brain. Nature Neuroscience 11(5): 543—545. doi:10.1038/nn.2112.

Sosa, M. A., Spitzer, N., Edwards, D. H., & Baro, D. J. (2004). A crustacean serotonin receptor: cloning and distribution in the thoracic ganglia of crayfish and freshwater prawn. Journal of Comparative Neurology, 473(4), 526-537.

Steck D. (2009) Passage through chaos Nature 461 736-7.

Takeda N., Sugiyama K. (1993) Metabolism of biogenic monoamines in the ciliated protozoan, Tetrahymena pyriformis Comparative biochemistry and physiology 106/1 63-70.

Taniura, H., Sanada, N., Kuramoto, N., & Yoneda, Y. (2006). A metabotropic glutamate receptor family gene in Dictyostelium discoideum. Journal of Biological Chemistry, 281(18), 12336-12343. Trevena J., Miller J. (2010) Brain preparation before a voluntary action: Evidence against unconscious movement initiation Consciousness and Cognition, 19/1, 447-456 DOI: 10.1016/j.concog.2009.08.006

Turano, F. J., Panta, G. R., Allard, M. W., & van Berkum, P. (2001). The putative glutamate receptors from plants are related to two superfamilies of animal neurotransmitter receptors via distinct evolutionary mechanisms. Molecular biology and evolution, 18(7), 1417-1420.

Umbriaco, D., Anctil, M., & Descarries, L. (1990). Serotoninimmunoreactive neurons in the cnidarian Renilla koellikeri. Journal of Comparative Neurology, 291(2), 167-178.

Warren W. (1998) MR Imaging contrast enhancement based on intermolecular zero quantum coherences Science 281 247.

Westerhoff J (2013) The self: You think you live in the present? New

Scientist 20 February. Weyrer, S., Rutzler, K., & Rieger, R. (1999). Serotonin in Porifera? Evidence from developing Tedania ignis, the Caribbean fire sponge (Demospongiae). Memoirs-Queensland Museum, 44, 659-666

Williams C. (2012) Are these the brain cells that give us consciousness? New Scientist 20 Jul. Wilson C. (2013) Consciousness: Why aren't we all zombies? New Scientist 15 May.

Woodruff A ., Yuste R. 2008 Of Mice and Men, and Chandeliers PLOS Biology 6/9 243.

Young, S.N., Leyton, M. (2002) The role of serotonin in human mood and social interaction. Insight from altered tryptophan levels Pharmacol. Biochem. Behav. 71 857-865.

Zimmer C. (2005) The Neurobiology of the Self Scientific American Nov 93.

5. Does the Universe have Cosmological Memory? Does This Imply Cosmic Consciousness?

Walter J. Christensen Jr.

Physics Department, Cal Poly Pomona University, 3801 W. Temple Ave, Pomona CA 91768

Abstract

Does the universe have cosmological memory? If so, does this imply cosmic consciousness? In this paper a cosmological model is proposed similar in structure to the famous thought experiment presented by James Clerk Maxwell, in which a "demon" tries to violate the Second Law of Thermodynamics. In such a proposed cosmological scenario, if the Second Law of Thermodynamics is to be preserved, it implies the existence of cosmological memory. Since consciousness and memory are intimately linked and a demon-like (intelligent) creature permits only fast moving particles to pass through a cosmic gate, it is argued the universe is necessarily conscious.

KEY WORDS: Consciousness, Cosmology, Quantum Physics, Cosmic Memory

I. Introduction

Cosmic consciousness is argued for in this paper. By consciousness we mean: any macroscopic or microscopic system that operates through the use of both memory and choice. Cosmic consciousness means, any cosmological system that requires both memory and choice to operate it. Of course the word 'choice' is a deeply philosophical concept and will be left for future discussions, such as those made by Robert Kane (1996) and his idea of 'ultimate responsibility'. For now, we will simply accept Maxwell's approach of an intelligent, or conscious, creature that attempts to violate the Second Law of Thermodynamics, as now discussed.

The validity of the assertion for the existence of cosmic consciousness (sometimes referred to as cosmic intelligence, intelligent creature, or cosmic creature, in this paper), begins with the seminal thought experiment made by the eminent mathematician and physicist James Clerk Maxwell, in a letter to Peter

Guthrie Tait (Maxwell 1867). Maxwell envisaged a tiny intelligent being who opens and closes a valve connecting separate chambers; each chamber filled with the same gas under the same conditions. This intelligent creature, referred to as 'Maxwell's demon' in literature (Leff and Rex 2002; Thomson 1897), functions to open a valve to allow the faster gas molecules to flow into one chamber, and slower gas molecules into the other chamber. In effect, the demon creates a temperature difference between the two compartments (It can be shown in classical thermodynamics that the temperature of the gas is strictly dependent on the speed of gas molecules). In this context, intelligent creature is used in the historical sense, as described by Maxwell (1871): "… if we conceive of a creature whose faculties are so sharpened that he can follow every molecule…"And subsequently nicknamed 'intelligent demon' by William Thomson (1874a; 1879): "This process of diffusion could be prevented by an army of Maxwell's 'intelligent demons'… separating the hot from the cold… "

If indeed, such an intelligent demon could perform such a separation task without expending energy (using a frictionless valve, which the creature opens slowly), the result would violate the Second Law of Thermodynamics (Serreli et al 2007). This is so, because such a self-contained system could perpetually perform work without the need for any external energy source.

The thought experiment proposed by Maxwell, has provoked a long-line of arguments in the scientific community as to whether or not the Second Law of Thermodynamics (SLT) can be violated or not. This ongoing battle has produced an extensive, and impressive list of authors who have introduced their own unique approach (as well as related discussions), and includes, in part: Thomson (1874b; 1879;), Poincare (1893), Planck (1922), Szilárd (1929a), Lewis (1930), von Neumann (1932); Gamow (1944); Born, M. (1948); Wiener (1950); Bohm (1951), Jacobson (1951), Brillouin (1951), Saha (1958), Feynman (1963), Asimov (1965), Bell (1968), Penrose, O. (1970; 1979), Beauregard and Tribus (1974), Popper (1982), Davies (1986), Bennett (1987), Hawking (1987), Landauer (1987), Rex (1987), Leff (1990), Christensen (1991), and more recently Penrose, R. (2002).

In this paper, we argue for the preservation of the Second Law of Thermodynamics by relating entropy with memory, as did Einstein's close friend, Leó Szilárd (1929b). Ever since his publication, his idea of relating entropy to memory has had a life of its own with many writers (information is often exchanged for memory in literature). For example Lewis, G. N. (1930) states: "Gain in entropy always means loss of information, and nothing more. ... if any essential data added, the entropy becomes less."Others view the entire universe as a dimensional information structure (Lloyd 2002; Davies 2004a).

The approach taken in this paper, rests on three assumptions:

1) SLT is the fundamental principle of space-time. That is, although different universes, or multiverses (soon to be discussed), may each have their own distinct physical parameters, constants and even dynamics, nevertheless they must obey some form of the Second Law of Thermodynamics both globally and locally, or the combination of the two; that any thought experiment, or actual system under consideration, must preserve the Second Law of Thermodynamics, otherwise such thought experiments are to be discounted, and any physical system that violates SLT is to be interpreted is not real, or at least that not all the variables are known.

2) Memory and entropy are deeply related aspects of each other, in much the same way that various forms of energy are related and can be converted into one form or the other without loss.

3) Any system converting entropy into memory, or memory into entropy, which also involves choice (such as opening or closing a gate), thus contributes to running the system, we characterizes as having intelligence or consciousness. If such a system is the universe itself, or multiverses, we say cosmic consciousness is involved the operation of the cosmology.

Since the goal in this article is to argue for the existence of cosmic consciousness, we take the prudent choice of developing a cosmological model following thought experiment to developed by James Clerk Maxwell.

2. Multiverses and Proposed Cosmological Model

Is our universe just one among an ensemble of many? Just an infinitesimal part of an elaborate structure, which consists of numerous universes, possibly an infinite number of universes, sometimes referred to as multiverses? Such questions were recently discussed by Rüdiger Vaas (2010). Vaas explains: "... there are many different multiverse accounts (see, e.g., Carr 2007; Davies 2004b; Deutsch 1997; Linde 2008; Mersini-Houghton 2010; Rees 2001; Smolin 1997a; Tegmark 2004, Vaas 2004b, 2005, 2008b, 2010; Vilenkin 2006), and even some attempts to classify them quantitatively (see, e.g., Deutsch 2001 for manyworlds in quantum physics, and Ellis, Kirchner & Stoeger 2004 for physical cosmology). They flourish especially in the context of cosmic inflation (Aguirre 2010; Linde 2005, 2008, Vaas 2008b), string theory (Chalmers 2007, Douglas 2010) and a combination of both, as well as, in different, quantum gravity scenarios, that seek to resolve the big bang singularity and, thus, explain the origin of our universe."

With so many possible types of multiverses to choose from, which one can we legitimately select to develop a cosmology that parallels the thought experiment of James Clerk Maxwell and his intelligent demon? The answer is, we must rely on various observations to guide us, and when those are not available, to be guided by sound theoretical models.

What is needed then, is, instead of using two chambers, we need a cosmology that incorporates a pair of universes separated by some kind of cosmic gate [for the sake of simplicity, (Occam's razor), a pair of universes is chosen, rather than numerous universes joined by a cosmic gate].

But what kind of gate could not only join two universes together, but be verified by empirical evidence? What is imagined is a black hole dynamically altering spacetime to create a multiverse, and which acts as a doorway between our universe and the newly formed universe There is much empirical evidence to support the existence of black holes and dynamics, in the context of this article: (Rees, 1989; Begleman et al, 1984; Casares, 1992; Remillard, 1992; Reynolds, 2008).

The cosmological model proposed thus far, is somewhat similar, yet distinct from, the model proposed by Lee Smolin (Smolin 1992a; Smolin 1997b): where locally, a collapsing black hole causes the emergence of a new universe, via the dynamical properties of the black hole. Our model allows for, as Smolin suggests, alternative universes to which fundamental constants or parameters such as the speed of light, gravitational constant, and so forth, can be different from our own universe. Multiverses are also referred to as Fecund Universes (Smolin 1992b ; Tegmark 2003). At the quantum level, Deutsch (Deutsch 2002) connected information to such multiverses, as we semi-classically do in this paper. Deutsch states: "The structure of the multiverse can be understood by analyzing the ways in which information can flow in it. We may distinguish between quantum and classical information processing. In any region where the latter occurs-which includes not only classical computation but also all measurements and decoherent processes (mechanism by which quantum systems interact with their environments to exhibit probabilistically additive behavior) the multiverse contains an ensemble of causally autonomous systems, each of which resembles a classical physical system."

The model also resembles string-theory (Susskind 2006) multiple-dimension arguments for why gravity is so weak, that is, it is leaking from one dimension into another (Horava and Witten 1996; Maartens and Koyama 2010); although CMS Collaboration is reporting results on microscopic black holes that makes this scenario less likely (CMS Collaboration 2010). However, the model proposed here has its distinctions; mainly that it places the Second Law of Thermodynamics as the 'prime mover,' by providing revitalized energy and matter back into our universe, as will be soon discussed.

To be clear, the cosmological model proposed in this article, has nothing to do with the "Big Crunch" scenario, in which the expansion of space eventually reverses and the universe collapses, eventually ending as a black hole singularity. Nor, do multiverses forming in various regions when space-time stops expanding, in so doing, form bubbles found in chaotic inflation theory proposed by Alan Guth (2007).

So just how does our universe work in tandem with the multiverse formed by a black hole? To begin with, it is assumed that massive particles trapped within the black hole are reduced to a common fundamental particle; each one being of equal size, spin and mass (Joseph 2010). When this occurs, identical particles pass through the black hole into the multiverse.

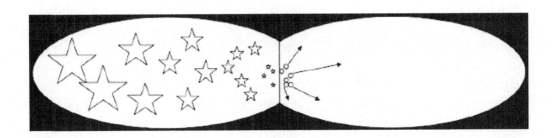

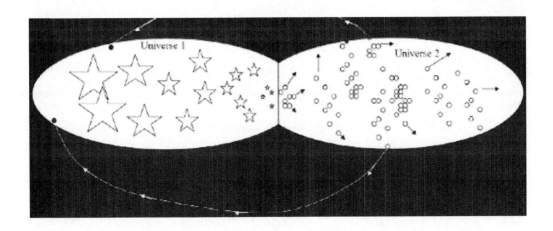

Because these particles are identical, with identical spins, gravity waves will cause the particles to repel each other (Penrose, R. 1960; Stacey, et al 1987; Economou, 1992; Gasperini 1998). What happens then? As they accelerate away from each other in all directions, they near the speed of light. When this occurs, it is assumed, following Maxwell's thought experiment, that a cosmic creature opens a gate leading to small pathways joining the two universes. Such gates are referred to as a string gates

As for massless particles (for example photons), they too pass into the multiverse via the black hole and continue moving at the speed of light c. Again the cosmic creature opens a string gate leading back into our universe. Overall, we have matter and energy leaving our universe, entering a multiverse via a black hole, then returning, via a string-gate (Stefano Ansoldi, Antonio Aurilia and Euro Spallucci, 2002), back into our universe. In effect, this process reseeds our universe with new energy and fast moving particles. Such a cosmology is reminiscent of a publication by Rhawn Joseph (2010). In his article he states: "The infinite, eternal universe continually recycles energy and mass at both the subatomic and macro-atomic level, thereby destroying and then reassembling atoms, molecules, stars, planets and galaxies. Mass, molecules, atoms, protons, electrons, and elementary particles are continually created and destroyed, and matter and energy, including hydrogen atoms, are continually recycled and recreated by super massive black holes and quasars at the center of galaxies, and via infinitely small gravity holes also known as "black holes", "Planck Particles", "Graviton Particles", and "Graviton-holes. ...Passageways may exist within these infinitely small spaces, which may lead to other dimensions (Appelquist and Chodos 1983; Aharony, et al., 2000; Greene 2003; Keeton and Petters 2005; Randall and Sundrum 1999) and thus to "other worlds" or another space-time (Hawking, 1988). A singularity may exist on both sides of a hole in space-time, simultaneously, thereby creating duality from singularity. An infinite number of holes would yield an infinite number of possibilities and would enable a singularity to have not just duality, but multiplicity via multiple dimensions existing on the other side of an infinity of holes." However, 'Joseph cosmology' violates SLT because it creates a perpetual machine, and should viewed as an incomplete model. Whereas the cosmology presented in this paper, which also is a perpetual machine, preserves SLT by having:

1) A cosmic creature (analogous to Maxwell's demon) make choices to open a string-gate to allow fast moving particles to pass back into our universe; or if these particles are not moving near the speed of light, to keep the string-gate closed.

2) Memory and entropy be different aspects of each other, suggested by Szilárd (1929c).

With these two points taken together (that an intelligent creature appears to create a perpetual machine-like-universe that violates SLT, but upon further consideration, the information gained by the creature restores SLT), the cosmology argued for in this article preserves SLT, and so meets the assumptive criteria to be considered a valid cosmology.

3. Cosmic Creature

By what mechanism does this cosmic creature observe massive and massless particles moving near or at the speed of light respectively? The mechanism is somewhat similar to what occurs when particles collide and scatter off of each other, as described by the Standard Model (Glashow 1961; Weinberg 1967). In particle physics, during a collision, virtual particles are emitted. These virtual particles can mediate force and transfer momentum to other particles (Eisberg and Resnick, 1985; O'Reilly, 2002), causing the colliding particles to alter their trajectory (Guralnik 1964). The mechanism is also similar to when a Goldstone boson (Goldstone 1961) is absorbed by bosons making them become massive.

Likewise, for the cosmological model presented here, we assume is that virtual particles are emitted by the accelerating massive particles traversing the multiverse. When a massive particle has a speed much less than that of light, its de Broglie wavelength will be longer, to that of a particle accelerating close to the speed of light, consequently the mediating virtual particle will also have a longer wavelength. This characterizes the massive particle and informs the cosmic creature to either choose to keep the string-gate open or closed. If the particle has a wavelength associated with moving at the speed of light, the cosmic creature opens the string gate --that is the creature absorbs the virtual particle and opens the string-gate so that the string absorbs the massive particle; in so doing the massive fundament particle passes from the multiverse, back into our universe (Joseph 2010; Gubser, 1997) (See Figure 3). As for any massless particles entering the multiverse via the black hole, they too return to our universe, via cosmic string-gate.

Thus our universes and the multiverse creates a kind of perpetual machine, but one that does not violate the Second Law of Thermodynamics because the decrease in entropy is balanced by the increase of memory, just as Leo Szilárd (1929d) did, in his thought experiment, where he considered particles having different chemical parameters inside a box with functioning pistons. Szilárd writes (1929e): "A perpetual motion machine therefore is possible if— according to the general method of physics— we view the experimenting man as a sort of deus ex machina, one who is continuously and exactly informed of the existing state of nature and who is able to start, or interrupt, the microscopic course of nature at any moment without expenditure of work."

Instead of an experimenting deus ex machina, we propose both memory and choice compensates for the decrease of entropy in the proposed cosmological model, hence cosmological consciousness allows for perpetual operating universes thereby preserving the Second Law of Thermodynamics. Leo Szilárd further writes: "We shall realize that the Second Law is not threatened as much by this entropy decrease as one would think, as soon as we see that the entropy decrease resulting from the intervention is compensated completely in any event, if the execution of such a measurement were, for instance, always accompanied by production of k ln2 units of entropy. In that case it will be possible to find a more general entropy law, which applies universally to all measurements." In regards to this paper, it is assumed since the task of opening the string gate involves selection, and that the reduction of entropy is compensated for by the intelligent creature gaining a equivalent amount of entropy (k ln2), no violation of the Second Law of Thermodynamics occurs. This the minimal condition necessary to claim, in such coupled universes, the existence of cosmological consciousness exists. In particular, we see the production of k ln2 units of entropy (equivalent to conscious memory and selection) are required to compensate for the perpetual workings, of the proposed cosmological universe, if and only if the Second Law of Thermodynamics is to be preserved.

Stated another way, over time, all matter in our gravitationally attractive universe must [according to various cosmological scenarios, such as the heat death of the universe first proposed by Lord Kelvin (Crosbie et al 1989)] eventually die out because of maximum entropy increase. However the view here is that of a cosmological consciousness that gains information so that our universe can be reseeded energetic matter and revitalized energy.

4. Other Considerations

Before going any further we must consider Brillouin's argument. Basically he argues that such an intelligent being opening the valve to let in fast gas molecules, needs light in order to see the fast gas molecules (Brillouin 1951). Brillouin states: "In an enclosure at constant temperature, the radiation is that of a "blackbody", and the demon cannot see the molecules. Hence, he cannot operate the trap door and is unable to violate the second principle (law). If we introduce a light source, the demon can see the molecules, but the over-all balance of entropy is positive." However, the thought experiment proposed in this paper, the system of coupled universes is not in thermal equilibrium and the intelligent creature cannot "see"via radiation. Instead the creature absorbs a virtual particle as previously discussed, which provides k ln2 information related to positive entropy, which is necessary to balance the decrease the entropy of the system when energetic particles are permitted to pass from the multiverse back into our universe. Thus no photons are required to detect fast moving elementary particles, only virtual particles.

Let us consider more closely the characteristics of the virtual particle under discussion. First of all, we realize that since all particulate matter is discrete, it is countable; that is there is a one-to-one correspondence between the natural numbers N, to the individual particles in the multiverse. Whether there are ten particles, ten billion, or even an arbitrarily large number of such particles residing in the multiverses, they are nevertheless countable. Secondly, if we assume the virtual particles are in one-to-one correspondence with the set of real numbers R, rather than the restricted set of natural numbers N, then the intelligent creature will never run out of information to keep the perpetual cosmic machine running.

To understand this, consider the closed interval between the numbers one and two [1, 2]. In this interval there exactly two natural counting numbers, i.e. number one and two. Whereas in the same interval there is uncountable real numbers such as the square root of two and $\pi/^2$. What this implies is that, even though the set of natural numbers {N} is infinite, the set of real numbers {R} is a larger infinite set that cannot be counted. Hence in set notation: {N} < {R}.

By assuming the virtual particles are associated with the set of real numbers R, they are uncountable. Consequently, even if the same particle cycles through our universe, into the multiverse and back to our universe an infinite amount of times, and each time the intelligent creature selects to absorb one of these virtual particles associated with the recycled countable particles, there will still be an uncountable many virtual particles left over to operate our universe with new energy; that is the cyclic process goes on forever, and the paired universes form a perpetual machine powered on memory and selection by a cosmic creature. Furthermore, if the cosmological model presented actually existed, then we are led to the conclusion that, either the Second Law of Thermodynamics is deeply flawed (or very limited domain), which contradicts all empirical observations, or indeed our universe powered by cosmological consciousness.

5. Conclusion

Though the cosmological model presented here was developed in part from a thought experiment argued by James Clerk Maxwell, and that the cosmology presented was purely hypothetical, should our current understanding of the universe prove to be incorrect, for example no big bang occurred, the question arises what powers a forever and infinite universe? Or put another way, if the universe has been here forever, why has not all the useable energy been consumed long ago? Such a scenario was first considered by William Thomson (Lord Kelvin), who argued mechanical energy loss in nature from the point of view of the 1st and 2nd Laws of thermodynamics. One solution might be the universe, coupled to a multiverse via a black hole, is powered by cosmological consciousness--an intelligent creature must make a choice to separate fast moving particles from slow moving particles. That is, these coupled universes form a perpetual machine. It is memory and choice that preserves the Second Law of Thermodynamics and make valid the proposed cosmological model. Both selection and memory imply cosmic awareness.

In conclusion, since it has been well established by empirical observation, that the Second Law of Thermodynamics is not observed to be violated, we argued, using a cosmological model relating memory, choice, entropy, that coupled universes are necessarily conscious.

Acknowledgement: I wish to thank Harvey Leff for his generous input into this paper. When I first entered University, he soon became one of my great professors and mentors; then a few years later my department chairperson, and finally a dear friend. I also wish to thank John Jewett who helped me with several early publications; I will always treasure our discussions about mathematics and quantum physics. John Fang, of course, is my very, very good friend. Over the years, with many side conversations, John taught me far more than a particle approach to gravity; he allowed a genuine friendship to develop while visiting both him and his gracious wife Stephanie, at their home, sometimes listening to such great composers as Brahms and Debussy. Also Kai Lam's wonderful conversations will always be remembered and cherished. Through the years I realize Kai is one of the most honest and sincere persons I have ever met. I would also like to commend with deep gratitude and friendship, Steven McCauley, who stood strong and noble on my behalf during a brief period of difficult times I had. Finally I wish to thank Kip Thorne for taking the time to converse with me at the 22nd Gravitational meeting in Santa Barbara, and then to subsequently correspond with kind intelligent honesty. And to Edward Witten who answered my questions by leaving the answers up to me.

References

Aguirre, A. (2010). Eternal Inflation: Past and Future. In: Vaas, R. (ed.). Beyond the Big Bang. Springer, Heidelberg.

Aharony, et al., (2000) Large N Field Theories, String Theory and Gravity. Phys.Rept.323, pp.183-386.

Ansoldi, Aurilia and Spallucci. (2002) Fuzzy Dimensions and Planck's Uncertainty Principle from p-brane Theory. Classical and Quantum Gravity 19, 3207.

Appelquist and Chodos (1983) Quantum effects in Kaluza-Klein theories. Phys. Rev. Lett. 50, pp. 141–145.

Asimov, I. (1965). Life and Energy. Bantam Books, New York, pp. 65-76.

Beauregard, O. and Tribus, M. (1974). Information theory and thermodynamics. Helv. Phys. Acta 47, pp. 238-247.

Begelman, M. C., Blandford, R. D. & Rees, M. (1984) Theory of extragalactic radio sources. J. Rev. mod. Phys. 56, pp. 255–351.

Bell, D. A. (1968). Information Theory. Sir Isaac Pitman & Sons, pp. 20-21; 212-219.

Bennett, C. H. (1987) Demons, engines and the second law. Sci. Am. 257, pp. 108-116.

Bohm, D. (1951); Quantum Theory. Prentice-Hall, Inc., Englewood Cliffs, New Jersey, pp. 608-609.

Born, M. (1948) Die Quantenmchanik und der Zweite Hauptsatz der Thermodynamik. Annalen der Physik 3, 107.

Brillouin, L. (1951). Maxwell's Demon Cannot Operate: Information and Entropy I. J. Appl. Phys. 22, pp. 334-337.

Carr, B. (2007). The Anthropic Principle Revisited. In: Carr, B. (ed.). The Universe or Multiverse? Cambridge University Press, Cambridge, pp. 77–89.

Casares, J., Charles, P. A., Naylor, T. (1992) Nature 355, 614–617.

Christensen, W. J. (1991) A Gedanken-experiment for the Plausible Existence of Cosmological Intelligence. JOPIPA Cal Poly Pomona University. Vol. 8 Number 1 Editor John Jewett.

CMS Collaboration (Dec 2010). Search for Microscopic Black Hole Signatures at the Large Hadron Collider, CERN-PH-EP/2010-073 CMS-EXO- 10-017; arXiv:1012.3375.

Davies, P. C. W. (1986). The ghost in the atom. Cambridge University Press pp. 20-22.

Davies, P. C. W. (2004). Multiverse cosmological models. Mod. Phys. Lett. A19, 727–744; arXiv:astro-ph/0403047.

Deutsch, D. (1997). The Fabric of Reality. Allen Lane, London, New York.

Deutsch, D. (2001). The Structure of the Multiverse; arXiv:quant-ph/0104033.

Deutsch D. (2002). The Structure of the Multiverse. Proc. R. Soc. Lond. A 458 pp. 2911-2923.

Douglas, M. (2010). The String Landscape: Exploring the Multiverse. In: Vaas, R. (ed.). Beyond the Big Bang. Springer, Heidelberg.

Economou, A. (1992). Gravitational effects of traveling waves along global cosmic strings, Phys. Rev. D 45, pp. 433–440.

Eisberg, R., and Resnick. R. (1985). Quantum Physics of Atoms, Molecules, Solids, Nuclei, and Particles. Wily, Fouqué, P.; Solanes, J. M.; Sanchis, T.; Balkowski, C. (2001). Structure, mass and distance of the Virgo cluster from a Tolman-Bondi model . Astronomy and Astrophysics 375: 770–780.

Ellis, G.F.R., Kirchner, U., Stoeger, W.R. (2004). Multiverses and physical cosmology. M.N.R.A.S. 347, 921–936; arXiv:astro-ph/0305292.

Feynman, R. P. Leighton, R. B. And Sands, M., (1963); Feynman Lectures on Physics. Addison-Wesley, Reading, Massachusetts. Vol 1, pp 46.1-46.9.

Gamow, G. (1944). Mr. Tompkins in Paperback. Cambridge University Press, (1971), pp. 95-111. Originally published in Mr. Tompkins Explores the Atom, 1944.

Gasperini, M. (1998) Repulsive Gravity in the very early Universe. General Relativity and Gravitation, Volume 30, Number 12, 1703-1709, DOI: 10.1023/A:1026606925857.

Glashow, S. L (1961) Partial-symmetries of weak interactions Nuclear Physics Volume 22, Issue 4, February 1961, pp. 579-588. doi:10.1016/0029-

5582(61)90469-2.

Goldstone, J (1961). Field Theories with Superconductor Solutions, Nuovo Cimento 19: pp. 154-164, doi:10.1007/BF02812722

Greene, B. (2003) The Elegant Universe: Superstrings, Hidden Dimensions, and the Quest for the Ultimate Theory. W.W. Norton & Co.

Gubser, S. et al, (1997). String theory and classical absorption by three-branes, Nuclear Physics B Volume 499, Issues 1-2, pp. 217-240.

Guralnik, G. S. et al (1964) Global Conservation Laws and Massless Particles, Physical Review Letters 13: pp. 585–587. doi:10.1103/PhysRevLett.13.585

Guth, A. (2007) Eternal inflation and its implications. J. Phys. A 40 pp. 6811- 6826, arXiv:hep-th/0702178v1.

Hawking, S. W., (1987). The direction of time. New Sci. 115, No. 1568, pp. 46-49.

Hawking, S. W., (1988) Wormholes in spacetime. Phys. Rev. D 37, 904–910.

Horava, P. and Witten, E. (1996). Nucl. Phys. B 460 506 [arXiv:hepth/9510209]; Nucl. Phys. B 475 94 [arXiv:hep-th/9603142].

Jacobson, H. (1951). The role of information theory in the inactivation of Maxwell's demon. Trans. N. Y. Acad. Sci. 14, pp. 6-10.

Joseph, K. (2010). The Quantum Cosmos and Micro-Universe: Black Holes, Gravity, Elementary Particles, and the Destruction and Creation of Matter Journal of Cosmology, Vol 6.

Kane, R. (1996) The Significance of Free Will. Oxford University Press, ISBN 0-19-512656-4.

Keeton, C. R. and Petters, A. O (2005) Formalism for testing theories of gravity using lensing by compact objects. III. Braneworld gravity. Physical Review D 73:104032.

Landauer, R. (1987). Computation: A fundamental physical view. Phys. Scr. 35, pp. 88-95.

Leff H. (1990). Maxwell's demon, power, and time. Am. J. Phys. 58, pp. 135- 142.

Leff H. & Rex, A. F. (2002) Maxwell's Demon 2: Entropy, Classical and Quantum Information, Computing, (Taylor & Francis).

Lewis, G. N. (1930). The symmetry of time in physics. Science 71, pp. 569- 577.

Linde, A. (2005). Particle Physics and Inflationary Cosmology. Contemp. Concepts Phys. 5 1–362; arXiv:hep-th/0503203.

Linde, A. (2008). Inflationary Cosmology. Lect. Notes Phys. 738, 1–54; arXiv:0705.0164.

Lloyd, S. (2002) Computational Capacity of the Universe . Physics Review Letters; American Physical Society 88 (23): 237901.

Maartens, R. and Koyama, K. (2010). Brane-World Gravity. Living Rev.

Relativity 13, (2010), 5 Living Rev. Relativity 13, (2010), 5 arXiv.org:hepth/ 1004.3962. p 26.

Maxwell J. C. (1871) Theory of Heat. Longmans, Green, and Co;, London. Ch 12.

Maxwell J. C. Letter to P. G. Tait, (1867). Quoted in C. G. Knott, Life and Scientific Work of Peter Guthrie Tait, Cambridge University Press, London, 1911, pp. 213-214; and reproduced in The Scientific Letters and Papers of James Clerk Maxwell Vol. II 1862-1873 (Ed.: P. M. Harman, 1871), Cambridge University Press, Cambridge University Press, Cambridge, 1995, pp. 331-332. Also J. C. Maxwell, Theory of Heat, Longmans, Green and Co., London, Chapter

Mersini-Houghton, L. (2010). Selection of Initial Conditions: The Origin of Our Universe from the Multiverse. In: Vaas, R. (ed.). Beyond the Big Bang. Springer, Heidelberg.

Neumann, J. von (1955). Mathematical Foundations of Quantum Mechanics. Princeton University Press, Princeton. (published originally in German 1932) Ch V.

Penrose, O. (1970). Foundations of statistical mechanics. Pergamon Press, Oxford, pp 221-238.

Penrose, O. (1979). Foundations of statistical mechanics. Rep. Prog. Phys. 42, pp. 1937-2006.

Penrose, R. (1960). A spinor approach to gravity, Ann. Phys. 10, p. 171.

Penrose, R. (2002) The emperor's new mind: concerning computers, minds, and the laws of physics, Oxford university press, [ISBN 0-19-286198-0]

Planck, M. (1922). Treatise on Thermodynamics. Dover Publications, Inc., New York, (translated from the 7th German Edition)) pp. 203-207.

Poincare, J. (1893). Mechanism and experience. Revue de Metaphysique et de Morale 1, pp 534-537. Reprinted in S. G. Brush (1966). Kinetic Theory . Vol. 2. –Irreversible Processes, pp. 203-207.

Popper, K. R. (1982). Quantum Theory and the Schism in Physics. Roman & Littlefield, p. 114.

Randall, L., and Sundrum, R. (1999). Large Mass Hierarchy from a Small Extra Dimension. Phys. Rev. Lett. 83, 3370–3373.

Rees, M. J. A. (1989) Rev. Astr. Astrophys. 22, pp. 471–506.

Rees, M. (2001). Our Cosmic Habitat. Princeton University Press, Princeton.

Remillard, R. A., McClintock, J. E., Bailyn, C. D. (1992). Astrophys. J. 399, L145–L149.

Reynolds, C. S. (2008). Bringing Black Holes into Focus. Nature 455, 39-40 (4 September 2008).

Saha, M. N. and Srivastava, B. N. (1958). A Treatise on Heat. The Indian Press, Calcutta, p 320.

Serreli V. et al (2007), Exercising Demons: A molecular information ratchet. Nature 445, 523-527.

Smith, C. and Wise, N. M. (1989). Energy and Empire: A Biographical Study of Lord Kelvin. (pg. 500). Cambridge University Press.

Smolin, L. (1992). Did the universe evolve? Class. Quant. Grav. 9, pp. 173–191.

Smolin, L. (1997ab). The Life of the Cosmos. Oxford University Press, Oxford. Stacey, F. D. Tuck, G. J. and Moore, G. I. (1987). Quantum gravity: Observational constraints on a pair of Yukawa terms, Phys. Rev. D 36, pp. 2374–2380.

Stefano Ansoldi, Antonio Aurilia and Euro Spallucci, (2002). Fuzzy dimensions and Planck's Uncertainty, Principle for p-branes, Classical and Quantum Gravity 19, 3207.

Susskind, L. (2006) The Cosmic Landscape, Back Bay Books; Little Brown (253 –292).

Szilárd, L. (1929a). On the extension of entropy in a thermodynamic system by the intervention of intelligent beings. Z. F. Physik 53, pp. 840-856. English Translations: Behavioral Science 9, pp. 301-310 (1964); B. T. Feld and G. Weiss Szilárd, The Collected Works of Leo Szilárd: Scientific Papers, (MIT Press, Cambridge, (1972), pp. 103-129; and J. A. Wheeler and W. H. Zurek, Quantum Theory and Measurement (Princeton University Press) pp. 539-548.

Szilárd, L. (1929a-f). On the Decrease of Entropy in a Thermodynamic System By the intervention of Intelligent Beings, pp. 124 - 131 In H. Leff and A. Rex (1990 Book Maxwell's Demon . Princeton University Press. Princeton, New Jersey.

Tegmark, M. (2003) Parallel Universes. Scientific American.

Tegmark, M. (2004). Parallel Universes. In: Barrow, J., Davies, P.C.W., Harper jr., C.L. (eds.). Science and Ultimate Reality. Cambridge University Press, Cambridge, pp. 459–491; arXiv:astro-ph/0302131

Thomson, W. (1874). The Kinetic Theory of the Dissipation of Energy. Nature 9, pp. 441-444.

Thomson, W. (1879). The Sorting Demon of Maxwell. R. Inst. Proc. IX, 113. Reprinted in Lord Kelvin's, Mathematical and Physical Papers. Vol 5 (Cambridge, U. P. London 1911) pp. 21-23.

Vaas, R. (2004a). Time before Time. Classifications of universes in contemporary cosmology, and how to avoid the antinomy of the beginning and eternity of the world. arXiv:physics/0408111.

Vaas, R. (2004b). Ein Universum nach Maß? Kritische Überlegungen zum Anthropischen Prinzip in der Kosmologie, Naturphilosophie und Theologie. In: Hübner, J., Stamatescu, I.- O., Weber, D. (eds.) (2004). Theologie und Kosmologie. Mohr Siebeck, Tübingen, pp. 375–498.

Vaas, R. (2005). Tunnel durch Raum und Zeit. Kosmos, Stuttgart.

Vaas, R. (2008a). Phantastische Physik: Sind Wurmlöcher und Paralleluniversen ein Gegenstand der Wissenschaft? In: Mamczak, S., Jeschke, W. (eds.).

Das Science Fiction Jahr 2008. Heyne, München, pp. 661–743.

Vaas, R. (2008b). Hawkings neues Universum. Kosmos, Stuttgart.

Vaas, R. (2010). Beyond the Big Bang, Springer, Heidelberg.

Vaas R. (2010). Multiverse Scenarios in Cosmology: Classification, Cause, Challenge, Controversy, and Criticism. Journal of Cosmology, Vol 4, pp. 664-673.

Vilenkin, A. 2006. ManyWorlds in One. Hill and Wang, New York.

Weinberg, S. (1967). A model for the Leptons. Phys. Rev. Lett. 19, 1264–1266.

Wiener, N. (1950). Entropy and information. Proc. Symp. Appl. Math. Amer. Math. Soc. 2 89.

6. Cosmological Foundations of Consciousness

Chris King

Emeritus, Mathematics Department, University of Auckland, New Zealand

Abstract

This chapter explores the cosmological foundations of subjective consciousness in the biological brain, from cosmic-symmetry-breaking, through biogenesis, evolutionary diversification and the emergence of metazoa, to humans, presenting a new evolutionary perspective on the potentialities of quantum interactions in consciousness, and the ultimate relationship of consciousness with cosmology.

1: Introduction: Scope and Design

This overview explores the cosmological foundations of consciousness as evidenced in current research and uses this evidence to present a radical view of what subjective consciousness is, how it evolved, and how it might be supported through quantum processes in the biological brain.

To do full justice to this very broad topic within the confines of the special issue and its planned book edition, I have prepared this paper as a short review article, referring to the full research monograph (King 2011b), as supporting online material, containing all the detailed references, a more complete explanation of the ideas and the ongoing state of the research in the diverse areas covered.

2: Non-linear Quantum and Cosmological Foundations of Biogenesis

While it is well understood that the fundamental forces of nature appear to have differentiated from a super-force in a founding phase of cosmic inflation, the interactive implications of cosmic symmetry-breaking for the chemical basis of life and its evolution into complex sentient organisms are equally as striking, and central to our existence. Cosmic symmetry-breaking and the ensuing preponderance of matter over anti-matter results in the hierarchi cal arrangement of quarks into neutrons and positively charged protons and then the 100 or so stable atomic nuclei, through the interaction of the strong and weak nuclear forces with electromagnetic charge, providing a rich array of stable, electromagnetically polarized, atoms with graduated energetics.

The non-linear molecular orbital charge energetics that results in strong covalent and ionic bonds also leads to a cascade of successively weaker bonding effects from H-bonds, to van-der-Waal's interactions, whose globally cooperative nature is responsible for the primary, secondary, and tertiary structures of proteins and nucl eic acids, and in a fractal manner to quaternary supra-molecul ar assemblies, cell organelles, cells, tissues and organisms. Thus, although genetic coding is a necessary condition for the development of cell organelles and organismic tissues, this is possible only because the symmetry-broken laws of nature can give rise to such dynamical structures. In this sense, tissue, culminating in the sentient brain, is the natural interactive full-complexity product of cosmic symmetry-breaking. Despite the periodi c quantum properties of the s, p, d and f-orbitals, which form the basis of the table of the elements, successive rows have non-periodic trends because of non-linear charge interactions, which result in a symmetrybreaking determining the bioelements pivotal to biogenesis. Life as we know it is based on the strong covalent bonding of first row elements C, N and O in relation to H, stemming from the optimally strong multiple -CN, -CC-, and >CO bonds, which are cosmically abundant in forming star systems and readily undergo polymerization to heterocyclic molecules, including the nucleic acid bases A, U, G, C and a variety of amino acids, as well as optically active cofactors such as porphyrins.

This interactive symmetry-breaking continues in a cascade. As we trend from C > N > O the electronegativity increases from non-polar C-H, to highly electronegative O, resulting in H_2O having extreme optimal properties as a polar hydride, bifurcating molecular dynamics into polar and non-polar phases, in addition to pH, and H-bonding effects, which define the aqueous structures and dynamics of proteins, nucleic acids, lipid membranes, ion and electron transport. Following on are secondary properties of S in lower energy -SH and -SS- bonds and the role of P as oligomeric phosphates in the energetics of biogenesis, cellular metabolism, dehydration polymerization and the nucleic acid backbone. We then have bifurcations of ionic properties K+/Na+ and Ca++/Mg++ and finally the catalytic roles of transition elements as trace ingredients.

This does not imply that this is the only elemental arrangement possible for life, as organisms claimed to be adapted to use arsenic in the place of phosphorus (Wolfe-Simon et. al. 2010) suggest, but it does confirm that life as we know it has optimal symmetry-breaking properties cosmologically. Many of the fundamental molecules associ ated with membrane excitation, including lipids such as phosphatidyl choline and amine-based neurotransmitters, also have potentially primordial status (King 1996). Effects of symmetry-breaking may also extend to the genetic code (King 1982). Recent research has begun to elucidate a plausible 'one-pot' rout e (Powner et. al. 2010) from simple cosmically abundant molecules such as HCN and HCHO to the nucleotide units making up RNA, giving our genetic origin a potentially cosmological status. There have also been advances with inducing selected RNAs to self-assemble from precursors and assume catalytic functions (see King 2011b).

3: Emergence of the Excitable Cell: From Universal Common Ancestor to Eucaryotes

Looking back at the universal common ancestor of life, likewise indicates a transition through an era in which RNA functioned as both catalyst and replicator, through the establishment of the genetic code, whose ribosomal protein translation units are still RNA-based, to the eventual emergence of DNA-based life, probably through viral genes (King 2011a). However the genetic picture of cell wall proteins is consistent with independent cellular origins of bacteria and archaea, implying more than one evolution of cellular life from a protected environment conducive to naked nucleotide replication (Russell 2011).

Nevertheless, once the branches of cellular life evolved, excitability based on ion channels and pumps rapidly became universal. It has been reported that as early as 3.3 billion years ago there was a massive genetic expansion, which may have contributed to the genes common to all forms of life facilitated by high levels of horizontal gene transfer, promoted by viruses (Joseph 2011).

Estimates of the adaptive computational power of the collective bacterial and archaean genome (King 2011a) give a presentation rate of new combinations of up to 10^{30} bits per second, compared with the current fastest computer at about 10^{17} bit ops per second. Corresponding rates for complex life forms are much lower, around 10^{17} per second, because they are fewer in total number and have lower reproduction rates and longer generation times. This picture of bit rates coincides closely with the Archaean expansion scenario and suggests that evolution has been a two-phase process of genetic algorithm super-computation, which arrived at a global solution to the notoriously intractable protein-folding problems of the central metabolic and electro-chemical pathways, which are later capitalized on by eukaryotes and metazoa.

Horizontal gene transfer, endosymbiosis and gene fusion may have led to a situation where sexuality and excitability, along with all the critical components for neural dynamics including ion-channels specific for Ca++, K+ and Na+, G-protein linked receptors, microtubules, and fast action potential became common among eukaryotes (Joseph 2011). Ion channel structure appears to have been established during the soup of lateral gene transfers that drove the evolution of eukaryotes. This means we should find neurotransmitter receptors from GABA a, b, and glutamate, through opioid, to dopamine, epinephrine, serotonin and melatonin in all multi-cellular eukaryotes. This universality would have continued up the evolutionary tree, implying that the very different nervous system designs of arthropods and vertebrates mask a deeper common neurodynamic and genetic basis.

The evolutionary key to sentient consciousness may lie in the survival advantage it could provide in anticipating threats and strategic opportunities. Since key genes for the brain evolved even before the Cambrian radiation (Joseph 2011), the key to the emergence of conscious sentience may be sourced in the evolution of excitable single cells. Chaotic excitation provides a eukaryote cell with a generalized quantum sense organ. Sensitive dependence would give a cell feedback about its external environment, perturbed by a variety of quantum modes - chemically through molecular orbital interaction, electromagnetically through photon emission and absorption, electrochemically through the perturbations of the fluctuating fields generated by the excitations, and through acoustic, mechanical and osmotic interaction.

As we move to founding metazoa, we find Hydra, which supports only a primitive diffuse neural net, in continuous transformation and reconstruction, has a rich repertoire of up to 12 forms of 'intuitive' locomotion from snail-like sliding to somersaulting (King 2008), as well as coordinated tentacle movements. This is consistent with much of the adaptive capacity of nervous systems arising from cellular complexity, rather than neural net design alone. Pyramidal neurons for example engage up to 104 synaptic junctions, having a diversity of excitatory and inhibitory synaptic inputs involving up to five types of neurotransmitter, with differing effects depending on receptor types, and their location on dendrites, cell body, or axons.

In the complex central nervous systems of vertebrates, we see the same dynamical features, now expressed in whole system excitations, such as the EEG, in which interacting excitatory and inhibitory neurons provide a basis for broadspectrum oscillation, phase coherence and chaos in the global dynamics, with the synaptic organization enabling the dynamics to resolve complex context-sensitive decision-making problems. Nevertheless the immediate decisionmaking situations around which life or death results, in the theatre of conscious attention are similar to those made by single celled organisms, based strongly on sensory input, and short term anticipation of immediate existential threats and opportunities, in a context of remembered situations that bear upon the current experience.

4: A Dynamical View of the Conscious Brain

Although long distance axons involve pulse coded action potentials, the brain appears to utilize dynamic processing involving broad-spectrum oscillations, rather than discrete signals. Unlike the digital computer, the human brain is a massively parallel organ with perhaps the order of 10 synapses between input and output, despite having an estimated 10^{10} neurons and 10^{14} synapses. Such design is essential to enable quick reactions to complex stimuli in real time and avoid the intractability problem of serial computers, which neural nets and genetic algorithms do solve effectively.

The cerebral cortex consists of six layers of cells organized in a sheet of functional columns about 1mm square. These have a fractal modular architecture, with each column representing one aspect of experi ence, from primary processing of lines at given angles, color, motion and auditory tones, through to cells recognizing individual faces. Major areas of the cortex also follow a modular pattern centered on the primary senses and our coordinated motor responses to our ongoing situation. Frontal areas are involved in abstractions of motor events, strategic planning and execution, parietal areas between touch and visual cortices are involved in spatial abstractions, with the temporal lobes extending laterally beyond visual and auditory areas representing attributes with specific meaning, such as specific faces and complex melodies, semantic and symbolic process, such as language, and the temporal relationships between experi ences. This is consistent with a 'holographic' model each experience being represented collectively, like a Fourier transform, in terms of its attributes consistently with the many-to-many connections neurons provide.

No single cortical area has been identified as the seat of consciousness (Joseph 2009). One proposal (Ananthaswamy 2009, 2010) is that conscious processes correspond to the coordinated activity of the whole brain engaging active communication in 'working memory' between the frontal cortex and major sensory and association areas, while activity confined to regional processing is subconscious. This tallies with Bernard Baars' (1997) model of the Cartesian theatre of consciousness as 'global workspace'.

While major input and output pathways pass through thalamic nuclei underlying the cortex, two other systems modulate the dynamics of brain activity. The cortex is energized by ascending pathways from the brain stem, involving the reticular activating system, and dopamine, nor-adrenalin and serotonin pathways, fanning out across wide areas of the cortex, modulating active wakefulness, dreaming and sleep. Our emotional experiences are modulated through the limbic system, a lateral circuit, passing through the hypothalamus regulating internal and hormonal processes, the cingulate cortex dealing with emotional representations, and the hippocampus and amygdala, setting down sequential memories and dealing with flight and fight survival.

There is also evidence active conscious processing corresponds to (30-80 Hz) EEG oscillations in the gamma band, driven by mutual feedback between excitatory and inhibitory neurons in the cortex, and that phase coherence distinguishes 'in-synch' neuronal assemblies forming conscious thought process from peripheral pre-processing (Basar et. al. 1989, Crick & Koch 1992).

While the brain may be 'holographic' spatially, it appears to use phases of dynamical chaos in the time domain. Modulated transitions at the edge of chaos can explain phenomena from perception to insight in a 'eureka' brain wave. In olfactory perception, the brain appears to enter high energy chaos, which frees the dynamic from getting inappropriately locked-in, as annealing does in formal networks, fully-exploring dynamical space, followed by a reduction of energy, causing the dynamic to fall, either into a recognized state, represented by a strange attractor, or to form a new attractor through an adaptive change in the potential energy landscape, through learning (Skarda & Freeman 1987). The same idea fits with the 'eureka' of insight, where an unstable dynamic generated by the problem is resolved in a single bifurcation from chaotic instability into lucidity.

Non-linear mode-locking, common to oscillating chaotic systems, has the potential to facilitate the coherent excitations that characterize coupled neurosystems, going a good way towards resolving the 'binding' problem how the brain 'brings it all back together'. By modulating the coupling between oscillating neurosystems, mode-locking could selectively bring related systems into phase coherence, just as the heartbeat is mode-locked to its local and brain pacemakers.

Chaos also makes the brain state arbitrarily sensitive to small perturbations, which is essential for a dynamical brain to be sensitive to small changes in its environment, and to its local instabilities. If the global state is critically poised at a tipping point, an unstable chaotic dynamic could become sensitive to perturbations at the level of the cell, synapse, or ion channel. There are several additional ways in which such sensitivity could come about. Stochastic resonance has been demonstrated to facilitate sensitivity, from ion channel, to cell, to global dynamic (Liljenstrm and Uno 2005). Fractal self-organized criticality has been found in cortical slices (Beggs and Plenz 2004). Chandelier cells have been shown to facilitate lateral spreading of local excitations to multiple pyramidal cells (Molnar et. al. 2008, Woodruff and Yuste 2008).

5: Quantum Dynamics and Conscious Anticipation

The two key questions confounding science about the brain are (1) how and why brain function generates subjective experience, and (2) whether there is any basis for our subjective conscious intentions having physical consequences in 'free-will' (Joseph 2009, 2011).

We thus explore how central to neurodynamic processes might exploit quantum effects to enhance survival prospects of the organism. To develop a realistic quantum theory of consciousness, we have to consider how whole brain states might become capable of quantum interaction (Joseph 2009) and how this could arise from neurophysiological processes common to excitable cells.

We have seen that various forms of global instability, from chaos, through tipping points to self-organized criticality could make the global brain state ultimately sensitive to change at the cellular, molecular or quantum level. Ion channels, such as for acetyl-choline display non-linear (quadratic) concentration dynamics, being excited by two molecules. Many aspects of synaptic release are also highly non-linear, due to biochemical feedback loops. A single vesicle excites up to 2000 ion channels, providing extreme amplification of a potentially quantum event. In addition to being candidates for quantum coherence, voltage gated ion channels display fract al kinetics (Liebovitch 1987).

How interacting systems respond to the quantum suppression of chaos, in processes such as scarring of the wave function (Gutzwiller 1992), received clarification (Chaudhury et. al. 2009, Steck 2009), when it was discovered that an electron in an orbit around a Cs atom in a classically chaotic regime enters into entanglement with nuclear spin. This illustrates how the chaotic 'billiards' of molecular kinetics, and chaotic membrane excitation, might become entangled with other states at the quantum level. One characteristic of time-dependent quantum 'chaos' is transient chaotic behavior ending up in a periodic orbital scar as wave spreading occurs. This would suggest that chaotic sensitivity, with an increasing dominance by quantum uncertainty over time, would contribute to which entanglements ultimately occur in a given kinetic encounter.

The evolutionary argument is a potent discriminator of models of consciousness. Quantum attributes making subjective consciousness possible need to evolve in confluence with essential physiological processes, thus potentially dating back to the epoch when the central components of modulated excitability evolved. Many theories of consciousness have been devised invoking quantum processes which emphasize unusual interpretations of physics, esoteric forms of quantum computation invoking properties extraneous to the known physiological functions of biological organelles, or hypothetical fields in addition to known physiology, raising questions as to whether they pass the evolutionary test. One of the most famous is Hameroff and Penrose's (2003) OOR theory combining objective reduction of the wave function with hypothetical forms of quantum computing on microtubules, which might be extended between cells through gap junctions. These are extensively discussed in the supporting online material, (King 2011b).

One idea fitting closely with neurophysiology is Bernroider's (2003, 2005) proposal that quantum coherence may be sustained in ion channels long enough to be relevant for neural processes and that the channels could be entangl ed with surrounding lipids and proteins and with other channels in the same membrane. He suggests that the ion channel functions through quantum coherence. MacKinnon's group (Zhou et. al. 2001) have shown that the K+-specific ion channel filter works by holding two K+ ions bound to water structures induced by protein side chains. These have similarities to models of quantum computing using ion traps. The solitonic nature of action potentials could provide such entangled connectivity between channels.

While decoherence theories and objective reduction do not provide an active role for will, several physicists have suggested consciousness could play a part in the way the wave function representing a superposition of states, collapses to one real instance of the particle. Quantum theory predicts Schrodinger's cat subjected to cyanide if a radioactive scintillation occurs, is in a shadowy superposition - both alive and dead. In our conscious experience of the real world, we find the cat is either alive or dead. This suggests subjective consciousness could play an intervening role within quantum reality, reducing the superabundance of quantum probability multiverses to the historical process we experience. If so, consciousness may have a direct window on the entangled sub-quantum realm

(Joseph 2009). We thus explore a model of quantum anticipation, which could extend back to single celled evolution.

Feynman diagrams of quantum interactions show that the quantum interaction is time-reversible. The diagram for electron scattering, when the scattered electron path is time-reversed, becomes positron creation and annihilation. Moreover in real quantum experiments, such as quantum erasure and the Wheeler delayed-choice experiment, it is possible to change how an intervening wave-particle behaves by making different measurements after the wave-particle has passed through the 'apparatus'. All forms of quantum entanglement possess this time-symmetric property. John Cramer (1983) incorporat ed time-symmetry into the 'transactional interpret ation' of quantum mechanics, in which space-time handshaking between the future and past becomes the basis of each real quantum interaction. The emitter of a particle sends out an offer wave forwards and backwards in time, whose energies cancel. The prospective absorbers respond with confirmation waves, and the real quantum exchange arises from constructive interference between the retarded component of the chosen emitter's offer wave and the advanced, time-reversing component of the chosen absorber's confirmation wave. The boundary conditions defining the exchange thus involve both past and future states of the universe. Upon wave function collapse, the exchanged real particle traveling from the emitter to the absorber is identical with its negative energy anti-particle traveling backwards in time.

The transactional interpretation is a heuristic device, which is not essential to the argument, since its predictions coincide, largely, or exclusively with conventional quantum mechanics, but it does highlight future boundary conditions, which could play a part in conscious anticipation. Regardless of the interpretation of quantum mechanics we use, an exchanged particl e has a wave function existing throughout the space-time interval in which it exists, so any process involving collapse of a wave function has boundary conditions extending in principle throughout space-time, involving future prospective absorbers. Advanced entanglement becomes clear in experiments creating two entangled particles (Aspect 1981), where subsequent measurement of the polarization of one photon immediately results in the other having complementary polarization, although neither had a defined polarization beforehand. The only way this correlation can be maintained within quantum reality is through a wave function extending back to the creation event of the pair and forward again in time to the other particle.

If subjective consciousness has a complementary role to brain function, correlated with entangled, quanta emitted and absorbed by the biological brain, it is then correlated with a superposition of possible states in the brain's future, as well as having access to memories of the past. In pair-splitting experiments, the boundary conditions do not permit a classically-causal exploitation. This does not result in a contradiction here, because the brain state is quantum indeterminate and the conscious experience corresponding to the entangled collapse provides an intuitive 'hunch', not a causal deduction.

A possible basis for the emergence of subjective consciousness, which could also be pivotal in explaining the source of free-will, is thus that the excitable cell gained a fundamental form of anticipation of threats to survival. These cells also evolved the ability to perceive strategic opportunities, through anticipatory quantum non-locality induced by chaotic excitation of the cell membrane, in which the cell becomes both an emitter and absorber of its own excitations. Non-locality in space-time is a fundamental quantum property shared by all physical systems, including macroscopic systems with coherent resonance.

The coherent global excitations in the gamma range associated with conscious states, could thus be the 'excitons' in such a quantum model. Unlike quantum computing, which depends on not being disturbed by decoherence caused by interaction with other quanta. Stringent requirements, avoiding decoherence, may not apply to transactions, where real particle exchange occurs even under scattering.

Quantum phenomena abound in biological tissues. Entanglement has been observed in healthy tissues in quantum coherence MRI imaging and bird navigation has been suggested to use entangled electrons. Excitations in photosynthetic antennae have also been shown to perform spatial quantum computing. Enzyme activation energy transition states and synaptic transmission also use quantum tunneling.

By making the organism sensitive to a short envelope of time, extending into the immediate future, as well as the past, subjective consciousness could thus gain an evolutionary advantage, making the organism sensitive to anticipated threats to survival as well as hunting and foraging opportunities. It is these primary needs, guided by the nuances of hunch and familiarity, rather than formal calculations, that the central nervous systems of vertebrates have evolved to successfully handle. Such temporal anticipation need not be of causal efficacy but just provide a small statistical advantage, complemented by computational brain processes associated with learning, which edge-of-chaos wave processing is ideally positioned to do.

These objectives are shared in precisely the same way by single-celled organisms and complex nervous systems. Because of the vastly longer evolutionary time since the Archaean expansion, than the Cambrian metazoan radiation, and the fact that all the components of neuronal excitability were already present when the metazoa emerged, quantum anticipation could have become an evolutionary feature of single celled eukaryot es, before metazoa evolved.

6: Quantum Sensitivity, Sensory Transduction and Subjective Experience

One of the mysteries that distinguish the richness of subjective conscious experience from the colorless logic of electrodynamics is that sensory experiences of vision, sound, smell and touch are richly and qualitatively so different that it is difficult to see how mere variations in neuronal firing organization can give rise to such qualitatively different subjective affects. How is it when dreaming, or in a psychedelic reverie, we can experience ornate visions, hear entrancing music, or smell fragrances as rich, real, intense and qualitatively diverse as those of waking life? Since the senses are actually fundamental quantum modes by which biological organisms can interact with the physical world, this raises the question whether subjective sensory experience is in some way related to the quantum modes by which the physical senses communicate with the world (Joseph 2009). Clearly our senses are sensitive to the quantum level.

Individual frog rod cells have been shown to respond to individual photons, the quietest sound involves movements in the inner ear of only the radius of a hydrogen atom and single molecules are sufficient to excite pheromonal receptors. Many genes we associate with peripheral sensory transduction in several senses are also expressed in the mouse brain (King 2007) at least in the form of RNA transcripts, including stomatin-like protein 3 associated with touch, epsin, otocadherin and otoferlin associated with hearing, and several types of opsin, including rhodopsin and encephalopsin. This suggests the brain could harbour an 'internal sensory system' which might play a role in generating the 'internal model of reality', although these ideas are speculative and it is a major challenge to see how such processes could be activated reversibly in the CNS.

Several researchers (Pocket 2000, McFadden 2002) have proposed that neural excitation is associated with electromagnetic fields, which might play a formative role in brain dynamics. Attention has recently been focused on biophotons as a possible basis of processing in the visual cortex based on quantum releases in mitochondrial redox reactions (Rahnama et. al. 2010, Bkkon et. al. 2010). Microtubules have also been implicated (Cifra et. al. 2010).

All excitable cells have ion channels, which undergo conformation changes associated with voltage, and orbital or 'ligand'-binding, both of internal effectors such as G-proteins and externally via neurotransmitters, such as acetylcholine. They also have osmotic and mechano-receptive activation, as in hearing, and in some species can be also activated directly and reversibly by photoreception. Conformation changes of ion channels are capable of exchanging photons, phonons, mechano-osmotic effects and orbital perturbations, representing a form of quantum synesthesia. Since the brain uses up to 40% of our metabolic energy for functions with little or no direct energy output, it is plausible that some of the 'dissipated' energy could be generating novel forms of interaction.

7: Complementarity, Symmetry-breaking, Subjective Consciousness, and Cosmology

This leads to the most perplexing chasm facing the scientific description of reality. What is the existential nature of subjective consciousness, from waking life, through dreaming to psychedelic and mystical experi ence, and does it have cosmological status in relation to the physical universe?

The key entities forming the physical universe manifest as symmetry-broken complementarities. Quanta are waveparticles, with complementary discrete particle and continuous wave aspects. The fundamental forces are symmetry broken in a manner that results in complementary force-radiation bearing bosons and matter forming fermions. In the standard model these have symmetry broken properties, with differing collections of particles. Supersymmetry proposes each boson has a fermion partner to balance their positive and negative energy contributions, but E8's 112 'bosonic' and 128 'fermionic' root vectors, suggest symmetry-breaking could be fundamental (Fielder and King 2010).

Further symmetry-broken complementarities apply to the biological world, where the dyadic sexes of complex organisms and many eukaryot es are both complementary and symmetry broken, with themes of discreteness and continuity even more obviously expressed at the level of sperm and ovum than in our highly symmetry-broken human bodily forms, involving pregnancy, live birth and lactation.

The relationship between subjective consciousness and the physical universe displays a similar complementarity, with profound symmetry breaking. The 'hard problem of consciousness research' (Chalmers 1995) underlines the fundamental di fferences between subjective 'qualia' and the participatory continuity of the Cartesian theatre on the one hand, and the objective, analyzable properties of the physical world around us.

Although we depend on a pragmatic accept ance of the real world, knowing we will pass out if concussed and could die if we cut our veins, from birth to death, the only veridical reality we experience is the envelope of subjective conscious experience. It is only through the consensual regularities of subjective consciousness that we come to know the real world and discover its natural and scientific properties. As pointed out by Indian philosophy, this suggests that mind is more fundamental than matter. The existential status of subjective consciousness thus also has a claim to cosmological status.

A further cosmological interpret ation of consciousness we have noted in association with the cat paradox is that it may function to solve the problem of super-abundance, by reducing probability multiverses to the unique course of history we know and witness. This view of consciousness in shaping the universe is consistent with several of the conclusions of biocentrism (Lanza 2009).

The lessons of quantum and fundamental particle complement arity and symmetry-breaking, sexuality and the Yin-Yang complementarity of the Tao and of Shakti-Shiva in Tantric mind-world cosmologies, lead to a cosmology of consciousness, as symmetry-broken complement to the physical universe.

References

Ananthaswamy, A. (2009) Whole brain is in the grip of consciousness New Scientist 18 March.

Ananthaswamy, A. (2010), Firing on all neurons: Where consciousness comes from, New Scientist, 22 March.

Aspect, A., Grangier P., Roger G. (1981), Phys. Rev. Lett. 47, 460; (1982) Phys. Rev. Lett. 49, 1804; 49, 91.

Baars, B. (1997) In the Theatre of Consciousness: Global Workspace Theory, A Rigorous Scientific Theory of Consciousness. Journal of Consciousness Studies, 4/4 292-309.

Basar E., Basar-Eroglu J., Rschke J., Schtt A., (1989) The EEG is a quasi-deterministic signal anticipating sensory-cognitive tasks, in Basar E., Bullock T.H. eds. Brain Dynamics Springer-Verlag, 43-71.

Beggs J, Plenz D. (2004) Neuronal Avalanches Are Diverse and Precise Activity Patterns That Are Stable for Many Hours in Cortical Slice Cultures Journal of Neuroscience, 24, 5216-9.

Bernroider, G. (2003) Quantum neurodynamics and the relation to conscious experience Neuroquantology, 2, 1638.

Bernroider, G., Roy, S. (2005) Quantum entanglement of K ions, multiple channel states and the role of noise in the brain SPIE 5841/29 205214.

Bkkon I, Salari V, Tuszynski J, Antal I (2010) Estimation of the number of biophotons involved in the visual perception of a singleobject image: Biophoton intensity can be considerably higher inside cells than outside http://arxiv.org/abs/1012.3371

Chalmers D. (1995) The Puzzle of Conscious Experiencee, Scientific American Dec. 62-69.

Chaudhury S, Smith A, Anderson B, Ghose S, Jessen P (2009) Quantum signatures of chaos in a kicked top, Nature 461 768-771.

Cifra M, Fields J, Farhadi A (2010) Electromagnetic cellular interactions Progress in Biophysics and Molecular Biology doi:10.1016/j.pbiomolbio.2010.07.003

Cramer J.G. (1983) The Transactional Interpretation of Quantum Mechanics, Found. Phys. 13, 887.

Crick F, Koch C. (1992) The Problem of Consciousness, Sci. Am. Sep. 110-117.

Dagan T, Artzy-Randrup Y, Martin W (2006) Modular networks and cumulative impact of lateral transfer in prokaryote genome evolution, PNAS 105/29, 10039-10044.

Darwin C. (1871) The Descent of Man and Selection in Relation to Sex, John Murray, London.

David L, Alm E (2010) Rapid evolutionary innovation during an Archaean genetic expansion Nature doi:10.1038/nature09649

Fielder Christine and King Chris (2004) Sexual Paradox: Complementarity,

Reproductive Conflict and Human Emergence Lulu Press.

Gutzwiller, M.C. (1992) Quantum Chaos, Scientific American 266, 78 - 84.

Hameroff, Stuart, Penrose, Roger (2003) Conscious Events as Orchestrated Space-Time Selections, NeuroQuantology; 1, 10-35. Hauser M. (2009) Origin of the Mind, Scientific American, Sept, 44-51.

Joseph, R. (2009). Quantum Physics and the Multiplicity of Mind: Split-Brains, Fragmented Minds, Dissociation, Quantum Consciousness, Journal of Cosmology, 3, 600-640.

Joseph, R. (2011). The neuroanatomy of free will. Loss of will, against the will, "alien hand". Journal of Cosmology, 14, 6000-6045.

King C.C. (1982) A Model for the Development of Genetic Translation, Origins of Life, 12 405-417.

King C.C, (1996) Fractal Neurodynamics and Quantum Chaos : Resolving the Mind-Brain Paradox through Novel Biophysics, in Advances in Consciousness Research, The Secret Symmetry : Fractals of Brain Mind and Consciousness (eds.) E. Mac Cormack and M. Stamenov, John Benjamin.

King C.C. (2007) Sensory Transduction and Subjective Experience Nature Preceedings hdl:10101/npre.2007.1473.1 2009 edition: Activitas Nervosa Superior, 51/1, 45-50. http://www.dhushara.com/lightf/light.htm

King C.C. (2008) The Central Enigma of Consciousness Nature Preceedings hdl:10101/npre.2008.2465.1 2010 edition: http://www.dhushara.com/enigma/enigma.htm

King C. C. (2011a) The Tree of Life: Tangled Roots and Sexy Shoots: Tracing the genetic pathway from the Universal Common Ancestor to Homo sapiens, DNA Decipher J., 1. http://www.dhushara.com/book/unraveltree/unravel.htm

King C. C., (2011b) Cosmological Foundations of Consciousness http://www.dhushara.com/cosfcos/cosfcos2.html

Lanza, Robert and Berman, Bob (2009) Biocentrism: How Life and Consciousness are the Keys to Understanding the True Nature of the Universe, BenBella, ISBN 978-1933771694

Liebovitch L.S., Sullivan J.M., (1987) Fractal analysis of a voltage-dependent potassium channel from cultured mouse hippocampal neurons, Biophys. J., 52, 979-988.

Liljenstrm Hans, Svedin Uno (2005) Micro-Meso-Macro: Addressing Complex Systems Couplings, Imperial College Press.

Martin, W. and Russell, M. J. (2003) On the origins of cells: a hypothesis for the evolutionary chemoautotrophic transitions from abiotic geochemistry to prokaryotes, and from prokaryotes to nucleated cells, Phil. Trans. R. Soc. Lond. B 358, 59-85.

McFadden J (2002) The Conscious Electromagnetic Information (Cemi) Field Theory: The Hard Problem Made Easy? Journal of Consciousness Studies, 9/8, 45-60. http://www.surrey.ac.uk/qe/pdfs/mcfadden_JCS2002b.pdf

Molnar, G et. al. (2008) Complex Events Initiated by Individual Spikes in the Human Cerebral Cortex, PLOS Biology, 6/9 222. Pockett, Susan (2000) The Nature of Consciousness, ISBN 0595122159.

Powner M., Sutherland J., Szostak J. (2010) Chemoselective Multicomponent One-Pot Assembly of Purine Precursors in Water, J. Am. Chem. Soc., 132, 16677-16688.

Rahnama M, Bkkon I, Tuszynski J, Cifra M, Sardar P, Salari V (2010) Emission of Biophotons and Neural Activity of the Brain, http://arxiv.org/abs/1012.3371

Russell, M. (2011). Origins, abiogenesis, and the search for life. Cosmology Science Publishers, Cambridge.

Skarda C.J., Freeman W.J., (1987) How brains make chaos in order to make sense of the world, Behavioral and Brain Sciences, 10, 161-195.

Steck D (2009) Passage through chaos, Nature, 461, 736-7.

Woodruff, A and Yuste R (2008) Of Mice and Men, and Chandeliers, PLOS Biology, 6/9, 243.

Zhou, Y., Morais-Cabral, A., Kaufman, A. & MacKinnon, R. (2001) Chemistry of ion coordination and hydration revealed in K+ channel-Fab complex at 2.0 A resolution, Nature, 414, 43-48.

7. What Consciousness Does: A Quantum Cosmology of Mind

Chris J. S. Clarke
School of Mathematics, University of Southampton, University Road,
Southampton SO17 1BJ, UK

Abstract

This article presents a particular theoretical development related to the conceptualisation of the role of consciousness by Hameroff and Penrose. The first three sections review, respectively: the different senses of "consciousness" and the sense to be used in this article; philosophical conceptions of how consciousness in this sense can be said to do anything; and the historical development of understanding of the role of consciousness in quantum theory. This background is then drawn upon in the last two sections, which present a cosmological perspective in which consciousness and quantum theory are complementary processes governed by different logics.

1. Consciousness: What Are We Talking About?

"Consciousness" is notoriously difficult to define because it is so fundamental; it is the precondition for our being able to do or know anything. Surveying the voluminous controversies over the meaning of the word suggests, however, that "consciousness" tends to be used in two fairly distinct ways. Broadly considered, just as the word "spirit" has two quite different referential meanings, viz., alcoholic beverage vs religion/parapsychology, so "consciousness" has two meanings: One meaning refers essentially to subjective experience: our moment- by-moment qualitative awareness of what is happening both internally (thoughts, feelings) and externally. It is the "what it is like" of Nagel's seminal paper (Nagel, 1974). The other meaning is that used by Dennett (1991). Taking to heart Wittgenstein's dictum that "whereof one cannot speak, thereof one must be silent", he restricts the topic of consciousness to those aspects of experience that we can report on, verbally, to other people. From this he is led to restrict the concept to that part of our internal experience that is contained in our inner dialogue, the almost constant talking to ourselves whereby we make sense of the world to ourselves in verbal terms. Thus consciousness in Dennett's sense of the word is the process of our forming "drafts" of parts of our internal dialogue. I shall call these senses of "consciousness" as used by Nagel and Dennett qualis-consciousness and quid-consciousness, respectively, from the Latin words for "how" and "what". Qualis is related to quale, quality, and with the idea that qualis-consciousness is comprised of qualities (qualia) associated with perception and thinking.

This difference between these two senses is crucial when we consider what we know about the consciousness of other people or other beings. Whereas we can, and by its definition can only, explore the quid-consciousness of another person by talking to them, we can only know the non-verbal part of another's qualis-consciousness through empathy; that is, through our evolved capacity for mirroring the sensations of others in response to a range of bodily cues and contextual information (Berger, 1987). This means that, as cogently argued by Nagel (1974), in the case of an organism like a bat with which it is difficult to have much empathy, we cannot know explicitly that they have qualis-consciousness, even though we might postulate that this is the case because they are mammals like ourselves. On the other hand when it comes to the verbally based quid-consciousness we know that bats, lacking language, cannot have it. The distinction between the two concepts is thus vital when discussing non-human consciousness. Without deeper analysis, we cannot rule out the occurrence of a "hidden" qualis-consciousness from any organism, or even from physical systems that we may not consider organisms at all - a vital point that will be revisited in section 5.

2. What Does Consciousness Do?

A major strand in the philosophy of consciousness concerns the notion of epiphenomenalism - the idea that consciousness is an add-on that appears upon ("epi") information processing without having any functional role. This is not relevant to quid-consciousness, which is actually a part of information processing rather than something added to it. In the case of qualis-consciousness, on the other hand, "epiphenomenalism" seems meaningful while at the same time seeming odd, because the whole notion of causation, in the physical sense, seems problematic in connection with qualis-consciousness. This consciousness does not do things like digesting food or moving limbs in a purely mechanical sense, but it comprises the whole of our experienced world (McGilchrist, 2009) and thereby establishes the context and preconditions as a result of which doing-events like moving limbs take place. The distinction between the two senses of "consciousness" lies not in whether they either do things or not; it lies in the distinct categories of "doing" and "being" that are involved. Quid-consciousness does things in a causal sense as part of a whole control structure of information processing. Qualis-consciousness constitutes a meaningful world within which doing is possible.

Here it becomes a matter of one's philosophical position, whether or not qualis-consciousness is anything other than a sort of emotional fog generated by processing in the brain. If one adopts a scientific-realist position on which the world is entirely reducible to mechanical processes, then qualis-consciousness is indeed such a fog. The alternative to this is to recognise that there is a whole area of discourse concerning existence, value, meaning and so on which is related to the mechanical properties of the world, but which is not equivalent to the mechanical aspect of the world.

Since it is qualis-consciousness that raises the most significant problems in consciousness studies, I shall from now on restrict attention to this sense of the word and, with this understood, I shall usually drop the "qualis" and just call it "consciousness".

3. The Changing View of the Role of Consciousness in Quantum Mechanics.

The earlier history of this topic falls into four phases:

(a) The "quantum theory" of Planck and Einstein, based on a conventionally mechanical concept of "quanta".

(b) The "quantum mechanics" of Bohr and Heisenberg from about 1925. This was based on complementarity and the uncertainty principle, which increasingly involved the idea of the collapse of the quantum state (also known as the wave function). It culminated in von Neumann's picture (von Neumann, 1932) of two quite distinct processes: a smooth deterministic evolution of the state under a dynamics, and a discontinuous transition from one state to another related to observation. He did not, however, suppose that consciousness was peculiarly concerned in this, arguing that it was sufficient to consider the human being as an assemblage of rather sensitive physical detectors.

(c) The views of Wigner and London and Bauer (London & Bauer, 1939, 1983) that consciousness was essential for collapse. According to this, the quantum state of the human brain was, through the process of experimental observation, coupled to the quantum state of a microscopic system; then the consciousness of the human being collapsed the joint state of human, apparatus and microsystem. This role for consciousness was strictly limited. Consciousness was not responsible for determining what particular quantity was being measured, because this was determined by the apparatus (a point that will be revisited in section 5). It could not bias the probabilities for different outcomes, because this would undermine the very laws of physics. All that consciousness could do was, somehow, to demand that some definite outcome did emerge, rather than a mixture or superposition of possibilities.

(d) A focus on the quantum-classical distinction. This began with Daneri, Loinger and Prosperi (1962) suggesting that "collapse" was the transition from a quantum state to a classical state, and that this was located not in the brain of the observer, but in the experimental apparatus. They showed that it was the large size of the apparatus, with a large number of possible quantum states all linked to the state of the microsystem being observed, which averaged out the peculiarly quantum mechanical nature of the microsystem, resulting in an essentially classical, non-quantum state for the apparatus. Subsequently Zeh (1970) included in this averaging-out of quantum states the highly effective role of interaction with the wider universe through the phenomenon of "decoherence". By this time the idea that consciousness had a role in quantum theory came to be regarded as superfluous.

In consequence of this history, it has become clear that we are here dealing with two distinct (though interrelated) physical representations. One is the superposition of states, a peculiarly quantum effect resulting in, for instance, the interference patterns produced in the experiment where particles are fired towards two parallel slits. The other is the statistical mixture of states used to represent mathematically a situation such as the result of a rolling a dice, where there is a range of possible outcomes with different probabilities for each. Considered purely mathematically, decoherence turns a superposition into a mixture. This does not, however, explain why we are actually aware, at the end of the process, of one particular outcome as opposed to a fuzzy blur of possibilities. We may recall that this, and only this, was what consciousness was supposed to achieve on London and Bauer's earlier way of looking at things. Despite much clarification between 1939 and 1970, the possible role for consciousness has remained little changed, and its operational details have until recently remained obscure.

4. The Perspective of Cosmology on the Role of Consciousness

More recent arguments from the surprising direction of cosmology now clarify things a great deal. In particular, quantum cosmology starkly underlines the need for something like consciousness. To take a particular example: the WMAP satellite observations of the universe at an age of some 380,000 years confirm a picture in which the universe has evolved as if it started in a perfectly smooth homogenous state (though strictly speaking there can be no "initial state" since the very earliest stages merge into the as yet unknown timeless conditions of quantum gravity). By the epoch observed by WMAP we see minute fluctuations superimposed on this uniform background, of the same character as the quantum fluctuations that can be detected when a uniform beam of radiation is observed in the laboratory. On conventional theory, these cosmological fluctuations grew under the influence of gravity to produce stars, galaxies and ourselves. Note, however, that in quantum theory it is the act of observation that precipitates quantum fluctuations: without observation (in whatever generalised form we may conceive it) a homogeneous initial state evolving under homogeneous laws must remain homogeneous. So the early fluctuations that eventually give rise to the existence of planets, people and WMAP are caused by observations such as those made by people and WMAP! The problem of quantum observation lies at the heart of modern cosmology.

This cosmological perspective makes it clear that the bare mathematical formalism of quantum theory in insufficient on its own. Without some additional ingredient, the universe would remain homogeneous and sterile. Two ideas from quantum cosmology are needed in order to make sense of this. They will also provide the key to the role of consciousness.

The first was introduced by James Hartle (1991), building on the "histories" interpretation of Griffiths (1984). Instead of considering probabilities for different outcomes to a single quantum observation, Hartle examined the probabilities of sets of outcomes for any collection of observations scattered throughout the universe in space and time. The mathematics was almost the same as it would have been if one had assumed a collapse of the wave function simultaneously across the universe with each observation; but strictly speaking the latter concept cannot be used in cosmology because it is not consistent with the fact that in relativity theory "simultaneous" is an observer-dependent concept. By considering this "super- observation" extended over the whole of space-time there is no need to consider either collapse or issues of causality between future and past events.

Hartle gave no indication as to what was actually meant by an "observation" or "observer". This issue was made explicit through the second key idea, first raised by Matthew Donald. He considered quid-consciousness - i.e. information processing - but this cannot help because it is in no way essentially different from any other purely mechanical process. Then, however, the idea was explored by Don Page who focussed on "sensation", which is close to the qualis-consciousness of this paper. The aim of a cosmological theory, he argued, was to explain the universe as we see it, and this is equivalent to requiring that the quantum state of the universe is compatible with an instance of conscious sensation like ours. This in turn is equivalent to the quantum state assigning a non-zero probability to such an instance. This then gives a new way of thinking about the role of consciousness: consciousness does not alter the quantum state of the universe, but it imposes a filter on the state, selecting a component (if there is one) compatible with our capacity for sensation.

The combined work of Hartle and Page gives a picture of a universe arising from the interplay of a background homogeneous quantum cosmology with possible networks in space and time of instances of consciousness. Self-contradictory networks of awareness are ruled out because quantum mechanics assigns to them a zero probability (Everett, 1957; Clarke, 1974) . But in addition the networks of awareness are shaped by their own internal logic, manifested by qualis- consciousness and different from the Aristotelian logic of quid-consciousness (Clarke, 2007). This logic brings in elements such as agency and meaning. Consciousness, on this view, "does something", but by selection rather than modification, and in a way which is compatible with and dependent on the known laws of physics.

5. A Theoretical Understanding of Consciousness and Quantum Theory

One final building block still seems required: a non-arbitrary criterion is needed for what physical systems have the capacity for (qualis-)consciousness. Many recent authors (de Quincey, 2002; Skrbina, 2005) have, however, come to the conclusion that no such criterion exists. In other words, everything might be conscious, a position known as "panpsychism". A problem remains, however: if "everything" is conscious, what is a "thing"? The answer of Heidegger (1967) concerned only a pejorative cultural aspect of the word; the answer of Döring and Isham (2011) invokes an ad hoc external mechanism; instead we need to explore naturally occurring physical criteria for what is a thing. A consciousness-carrying "thing" must have some internal unity rather than being an arbitrary aggregate of objects, which suggests that it has an internal coherence. The simplest definition of this is that its parts are in quantum entanglement (Clarke, 2007) . In addition, it must not be merely an arbitrary subset of a larger "thing", so that it must be maximal with respect to this coherence. In other words, it must be on the boundary between the quantum and the classical, a boundary set by the onset of decoherence. The structures considered by Hameroff and Penrose (1996) are of this sort.

It now becomes clearer what consciousness does. At this quantum-classical boundary the question of what "observation" (or, more formally, what algebra of propositions) is to be expressed is not yet determined by decoherence, and so is open to determination by consciousness (Clarke, 2007). Following Hartle, this happens not in isolation, but within the whole network of "things" throughout the universe. Physical causation operates through quantum state of the universe, while consciousness independently filters this into awareness through its own sort of logic (in the sense of the structure of an algebra of propositions). The large scope this gives for future experimental and theoretical research has been outlined in (Clarke, 2007,8). Several candidates for the logic of consciousness are available, allowing us to understand how consciousness brings creativity alongside rational deduction. This model raises for the first time the possibility of a rigorous theoretical framework for parapsychology (Clarke, 2008) without which that subject remains only a semi-science. It turns out that consciousness can itself, through the "Zeno effect", enlarge the length scale for the onset of decoherence, which then offers hope for understanding how small-scale elements can be "orchestrated", in Hameroff's sense (Hammeroff & Penrose, 1996), into the ego-consciousness known to us. In addition, there will be other candidates for what a "thing" is, opening up alternative theories that can be tested against the theory just outlined.

References

Berger, D. M. (1987). Clinical empathy. Northvale: Jason Aronson, Inc.

Clarke, C. J. S. (1974) Quantum Theory and Cosmology. Philosophy of Science, 41, 317-332.

Clarke, C. J. S. (2007). The role of quantum physics in the theory of subjective consciousness. Mind and Matter 5(1), 45-81.

Clarke C. J. S. (2008). A new quantum theoretical framework for parapsychology. European Journal of Parapsychology, 23(1), 3-30.

Daneli, A., Loinger, A., Prosperi, G. M. (1962). Quantum Theory of Measurement and Ergodicity Conditions., Nuclear Physics 33, 297-319.

de Quincey, C. (2002). Radical Nature: Rediscovering the Soul of Matter. Montpelier VT : Invisible Cities Press.

Dennett, D. C., (1991). Consciousness Explained, Allen Lane.

Donald, M. (1990). Quantum Theory and the Brain, Proceedings of the Royal Society (London) Series A, 427, 43-93.

Döring, A., Isham, C. (2011). "What is a Thing?": Topos Theory in the Foundations of Physics. In B. Coecke (Ed.), New Structures for Physics, Lecture Notes in Physics, Vol. 813 (pp 753-941). Berlin: Springer.

Everett, H., (1957). Relative State Formulation of Quantum Mechanics, Reviews of Modern Physics 29, pp 454-462.

Griffiths, R..B. (1984). Consistent histories and the interpretation of quantum mechanics. J. Stat. Phys. 36, 219-272.

Hameroff, S., Penrose, R. (1996). Conscious events as orchestrated space-time selections. Journal of Consciousness Studies, 3(1), 36-53.

Hartle, J. (1991). The quantum mechanics of cosmology. In Coleman, S., Hartle, P., Piran, T., Weinberg, S., (Eds) Quantum cosmology and baby universes. Singapore: World Scientific.

Heidegger M. (1967). What Is a Thing? (Trans. W. B. Barton Jr., V. Deutsch). Chicago: Henry Regnery Company.

London, F., Bauer, E. (1939). La théorie de l'observation en mécanique quantique. Hermann, Paris.

London, F., Bauer, E. (1983). The theory of observation in quantum mechanics (translation of the above). In J. A. Wheeler, W. H. Zurek (Eds), Quantum Theory and Measurement (pp. 217- 259). Princeton: Princeton University Press.

McGilchrist, I. (2009). The Master and his Emissary: the divided brain and the making of the Western world. New Haven and London: Yale University Press.

Nagel, T. (1974). What Is it Like to Be a Bat? Philosophical Review 83(4), 435-450.

Skrbina, D. (2005). Panpsychism in the West. Cambridg: Bradford Books.

von Neumann, J. (1932). Mathematical Foundations of Quantum Mechanics, (Beyer, R. T., trans.), Princeton Univ. Press.

Zeh, H. D., (1970). On the Interpretation of Measurement in Quantum Theory, Foundation of Physics, 1, pp. 69-76.

8. Detecting Mass Consciousness: Effects of Globally Shared Attention and Emotion

Roger Nelson, Ph.D.

Princeton University,

Director, Global Consciousness Project, Princeton NJ 08540

Abstract

A long term research program called the Global Consciousness Project is designed to identify and study effects of mass consciousness engendered by shared attention and emotion. An operationally defined "global consciousness" appears to result from interactions of human beings around the world. We find statistical evidence for small effects from this source in the output of a network of devices which use quantum tunneling to generate random numbers. Detectable changes occur during great events of importance to humans, in which synchronized data collected at independent network nodes separated by thousands of kilometers become correlated. The correlations show that when the attention and emotions of large numbers of people are driven toward coherence by great tragedies or great celebrations, a slight but detectable structure is imposed on our random data. The bottom line formal statistic shows a 6-sigma departure from expectation over the full 12-year database. This is evidence that human consciousness and emotion are part of the physical world, and the design of the experiment suggests a particular interpretation: we interact to produce a mass consciousness even though we are generally unaware that this is possible.

Key Words: Consciousness, Global Consciousness, Mass Consciousness, Attention, Emotion, Noosphere, Random Number Generator, Network, Random Sequence, Synchronized Random Data

1. Introduction

The Global Consciousness Project (GCP) is designed to study hypothesized unconscious interactions among human beings over global distances. It extends laboratory research showing effects of human intention on the behavior of physical random systems (Radin & Nelson, 1989; Jahn, et al., 1997), and field research showing effects of group consciousness (Nelson, et al., 1996; 1998).

The data we will consider show that we come together in an effective interaction, though we are not conscious of this, in response to great events on the world stage. Driven by tragedies or celebrations, we share emotions deeply and this appears to be coincident with slight changes in the GCP data. The effects are very small correlations where there should be none, in a world-spanning network of physical random sources. Human beings evidently interconnect unconsciously to create a singular mass consciousness that has detectable effects in the world. A full interpretation is speculative at this point, but the data are rich with potential for insight at the margins of what we know about human consciousness. This article is a basic description of the work, and is an invitation to questions and comment.

The GCP extends research on mind-matter interactions conducted over several decades in laboratories around the world. In the Princeton Engineering Anomalies Research (PEAR) lab at Princeton University, the primary experiment used a custom designed Random Event Generator (REG or RNG) incorporating a refined commercial source of electronic white noise. This benchtop experiment provided control over parameters such as the speed and size of the samples drawn from the random sequence of bits. For example, it might be set to collect a 200 bit sample at a rate of 1000 bits per second, and to register a trial each second consisting of the sum of the 200 bits. The equipment displayed the current output trial value and a running mean as feedback to the participant. The experiment used a tri-polar protocol, with instructions to maintain an intention to achieve either a high or a low mean, or to let the machine generate baseline data. Over more than a decade, this rigorously controlled experiment yielded an enormous database, with a bottom line indicating a small but highly significant effect of human intention on random data sequences (Jahn, et al., 1997).

A system to record a continuously running random data stream was developed in the early 1990's, and when truly portable RNG devices became available we were able to take equipment out of the laboratory to ask new kinds of questions. By recording data continuously at concerts, ceremonies, rituals, meetings - group gatherings - we could ask whether group consciousness would affect the RNG. The FieldREG experiment (Nelson, et al., 1996) was not based on intentions, and indeed could be used to gather data in situations where people typically had no knowledge of the experiment. We looked for occasions that might produce a "group consciousness" because everyone would be engaged in a common focus, resulting in a kind of coherence or resonance of thoughts and emotions. For contrast, we identified other, mundane situations (shopping centers, busy street corners) which we predicted would not produce coherence resulting in changes in the data. A long series of FieldREG experiments (Nelson, et al., 1998) produced statistically significant results.

Other investigators, including Dean Radin (Radin, et al., 1996) and Dick Bierman (1996), began doing similar field experiments in a broad array of situations, and we set up collaborations. Radin asked colleagues to collect RNG data during the O. J. Simpson trial, which was expected to garner synchronized attention from huge numbers of people. The combined data from five RNGs showed an impressive departure from expectation at the time the verdict was announced. Other tests looked at data taken during the Oscars, with segregation of the data into periods of strong and weak interest. Again the difference was significant (Radin, 1997).

A chance meeting with people who were organizing a global "Gaiamind Meditation" coincided with the developing idea that we could register some indication of a global consciousness by creating a FieldREG-style group consciousness experiment on a large scale. I arranged a collaboration with colleagues who could record RNG data that might show evidence of a "consciousness field" during the Gaiamind event. The composite of data from 14 independent RNG systems showed a significant effect (Nelson, 1997).

This was a prelude for an attempt to register effects of the world-wide expression of compassion at Princess Diana's funeral in September of 1997, which, coincidentally, was followed exactly a week later by the memorial ceremonies for Mother Teresa (Nelson, et al., 1998). These were prototypical "global events" for the GCP, in that they were the focus of attention from literally millions of people around the world, and, especially in the case of Princess Diana, occasions for widespread emotional sharing. Shortly thereafter, at a meeting of professional researchers in parapsychology and psychophysiology, the various component ideas for what ultimately became the Global Consciousness Project coalesced into a practical form. The technology was becoming available to create an Internet-based array or network of continuously recording RNG devices placed around the world. After some months of design and implementation, the network began recording data in August, 1998 (Nelson, 2001).

2. Method

This is a new type of experiment, and at the outset no direct precedents were available for certain aspects of the methodology. In particular, while we intended to study the effects of "great events" we had no experience to guide their definition and selection. We knew little or nothing about what factors might be important, precluding the use of "objective" but arbitrary selection criteria. In addition, acquisition of random data from a world-spanning network was new, and required the development of appropriate analytical tools. To address the unique conditions, we adopted a multi-layer research design which would allow exploration of parameters while ensuring robust analysis. During the course of the project, we have gained useful experience allowing refinement, but the basic methodology has remained in place.

2.1. The GCP Instrument The global network of RNGs may be thought of as an instrument designed to look for an effect of special shared states of human consciousness and emotion. The system uses shielded random number generators developed for professional research in laboratory settings. These devices are based on a quantum level source of random fluctuation called electron tunneling. Diodes or field effect transistors are placed in a circuit arranged to force electrons against the barrier in a solid state junction. Some electrons penetrate the barrier via quantum tunneling, and this results in a tiny, completely unpredictable fluctuating voltage which can be sampled. High and low samples are converted to become 1 and 0 bits. In the GCP, we take 200 samples each second and record the sum of the bits, yielding trial values which are approximately normally distributed with mean 100 and variance 50, and typically range between 70 and 130.

The network has 65 or 70 operational nodes distributed broadly around the world as shown in Fig. 1, each hosting an RNG connected to a computer running custom software that collects data every second of every day, year after year, synchronized to the second.

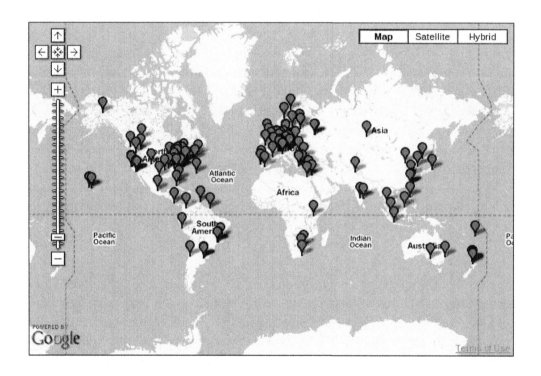

Figure1. Google map showing locations of all RNGs that have been in the network and contributed data. The distribution depends on Internet infrastructure.

The software sends the data to a server in Princeton, NJ, where they are added to a continuously growing archive. The result is a database of continuous parallel sequences of numbers – a history of random data – which we can compare with a history of events that are meaningful to humans. At this time, early 2011, the project has been collecting data for more than 12 years, and we have examined more than 345 events meeting the criteria for our formal experiment.

2.2. Hypothesis Testing. Events are selected for analysis from categories including natural disasters and accidents, acts of war and terrorist attacks, and positive events such as celebrations like New Years, religious holidays, and globally organized meditations. We identify engaging events of various kinds about 2 or 3 times per month on average for inclusion in the database. The experiment asks whether the network is affected when powerful events cause large numbers of people to pay attention to the same thing. The question is formally defined in a general hypothesis that frames the experiment: Periods of collective attention or emotion in widely distributed populations will correlate with deviations from expectation in a global network of physical random number generators.

This hypothesis is very broad, providing the flexibility required at the beginning of an experiment without precedents. It is a composite hypothesis intended to be tested using fully specified simple hypotheses in a series of replications. A registry for the specific hypotheses identifies a priori for each event a period of time and an analysis procedure to examine the data for changes in standardized statistical measures. The events and their timing are specified uniquely case by case, and a statistical recipe is set, thus defining a simple hypothesis test for each event in the formal series. This two-level approach – a broad general hypothesis evaluated via specific hypothesis tests – provides flexibility while also ensuring valid, interpretable statistics. The individual event results, when combined, yield a rigorously established confidence level for the composite of all formal trials. This constitutes a general test of the broadly defined formal hypothesis, and characterizes the database for further analysis.

2.3. Data Archive. We collect and archive data from the network continuously, in such a way that it can be used both for the event-based original experiment and for other analyses such as correlation with independent measures (for example, geomagnetic or cosmic or sociological variables) as well as for non-event control comparisons. The archival database at the heart of the research program is the raw trial data stored in a binary format with information to identify the source (RNG device and location) and the precise timing for every trial. In early 2011, the database is about 25 billion trials accumulated over 12 years, representing locations all over the world.

For precise, sophisticated analyses, we normalize the trial values using empirical parameters for each RNG to produce a working database of standardized Z scores. Since these are hardware devices which can break or suffer from electrical instability, we filter out an occasional bad trial using simple, standardized criteria. We use the empirical mean and variance of each device for normalization because each RNG is unique and may exhibit real, albeit barely detectable variations from theoretical performance.

An important aspect of the GCP research design is complete public access to the data archive and software; anyone can download the data for inspection or analysis. This has resulted in valuable independent analyses.

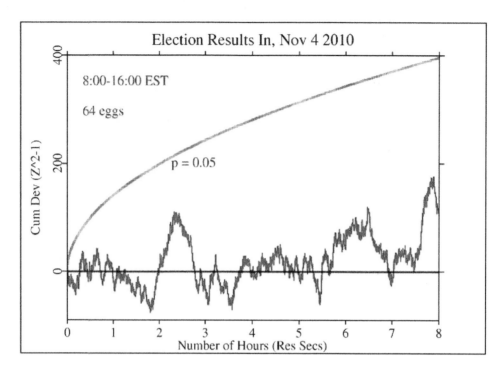

Figure 2. An example of a "null" result. Cumulative deviation during the final hours of the US congressional election in November, 2010.

2.4. Analysis Most analyses are based on a measure we call "network variance." This is calculated as the squared Stouffer's Z (normalized average Z) for each second across all RNGs in the network. The result is a Chisquare distributed quantity with one degree of freedom. This is summed across all the seconds in the time period specified for the event, and compared with the expected value or degrees of freedom, which is just the number of seconds. For a few events we specify a measure called "device variance," which is the inter-RNG variance (the sum of Z2). The network variance is closely related to and may be expressed as the pairwise inter-RNG correlation. For analyses at the fundamental trial level, we use this version of the network variance measure, which can be symbolized as Z_i*Z_j. Because the trial level data have more complete information, including the location and identity of the data source as well as the precise time of each data point, this correlation measure allows deeper analysis leading toward understanding the mechanisms by which the anomalous results may be generated (Bancel and Nelson, 2008).

The trial statistics are combined across the total time of the event to yield the formal result, and for presentation we typically use a "cumulative deviation" graph tracing the history of the second-by-second deviations during the event, leading to a terminal value which is the test statistic. If there is no anomalous effect, positive and negative chance deviations will tend to cancel, resulting in a trace that wanders randomly with little movement away from the flat null expectation. Such a result is shown in Fig. 2, which presents data generated during the US congressional "midterm" elections, November 3 2010. Political events are a category we have regularly sampled, and unless charismatic figures are involved they typically don't show effects, even though huge numbers of people pay attention.

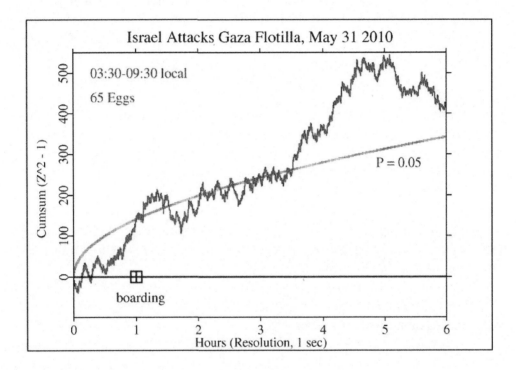

Figure 3. An example of a "positive" result. Cumulative deviation during a 6 hour period representing the Israeli attack on the Gaza flotilla, beginning 1 hour before the ill-fated boarding.

In contrast, if there is a persistent excess in the network variance (or, equivalently, the inter-node correlation) the cumulative deviation will show a trend which may culminate in a statistically significant departure from expectation. We see such a case in Fig. 3, which shows 6 hours beginning just before the Israeli navy dropped commandos from helicopters to stop the humanitarian flotilla heading for Gaza in May 2010. Several of the volunteers on the ship were killed in the action, leading to an international outcry and probable long-term consequences.

In either case, it is important to recognize that on average the effect size is too small for single events to be interpreted reliably. An effect may be masked by noise, or statistical noise may masquerade as an effect. The signal to noise ratio is very low in these data, resulting in an average effect size of half a standard deviation or less depending on the event type. This means we need dozens of replications to achieve robust statistics.

2.5. Controls It is possible to test the data against various kinds of controls, including matched analysis with a time offset in the actual database, or comparisons with an automatically generated pseudorandom clone database. An instructive control background can be created by simulation using random samples from the null hypothesis distribution or, similarly, by resampling to obtain the empirical distribution of the test statistic. Since the event data comprise less than 2% of the whole database, the non-event data can be resampled to produce a distribution of "control" events with the same parameters as the formal events, but random start times.

3. Results

Over the 12 years since the inception of the project, hundreds of replications of the basic hypothesis test have been accumulated. The composite result is a statistically highly significant departure from expectation, but it is a small effect, as can be seen in the scatterplot of individual scores shown in Fig. 4. The mean of the distribution is shifted in the direction specified by the hypothesis, but compared with the range of scores, the shift does not look impressive. However, the replication design is powerful: The combined result across 345 formal events as of January 2011 departs from expectation by 6.174 sigma, which translates as odds against chance of about a billion (109) to one.

The cumulative deviation display of the results shown in Fig. 5 makes this extreme statistic much easier to recognize and comprehend, especially in contrast with a background of control data.

The bottom line result for the GCP formal experiment is based on a concatenation of all events specified in the hypothesis registry. Of course we include both the hits and the misses – every event that is identified and registered is analyzed and reported. About 70% are positive in the sense they show deviations in the predicted direction, and roughly 15% are statistically significant at the 5% level.

It is important to note that reliable differentiation of an anomalous effect requires many events, perhaps 50 on average (refer again to Fig. 5). Even in categories that consistently show strong effects we need a dozen or more events for signal to rise convincingly out of the noise. This is a consequence of a small effect size. Only the patient accumulation of many tests of our general hypothesis can give us confidence that there is an anomalous effect. Nevertheless, based on our long series of formal replications, the GCP hypothesis is well supported in comparisons of the real data against theoretical expectation or against appropriate control data which have no linkage with events in the world. This result also provides a sound basis for deeper analysis using refined methods to re-examine the original findings and extend them using other methods (Nelson and Bancel, 2006; Nelson, 2008; Bancel and Nelson, 2008).

3.1. Other Structure Several kinds of exploratory

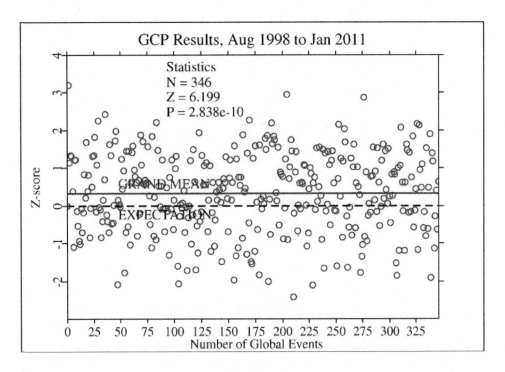

Figure 4: Scatterplot of 345 independent results. The dashed horizontal line shows expectation. The solid line shows mean deviation for all formal trials.

analysis have given useful perspectives on the database (Nelson, et al., 2002; Nelson & Bancel, 2006). Beyond the primary formal hypothesis testing we have a program of secondary analyses, managed by Peter Bancel, intended to characterize the data fully and facilitate the identification of other non-random structure. For this we use trial level data, the finest scale available, which includes not only the fundamental trial outcomes, but complete spatial and temporal information.

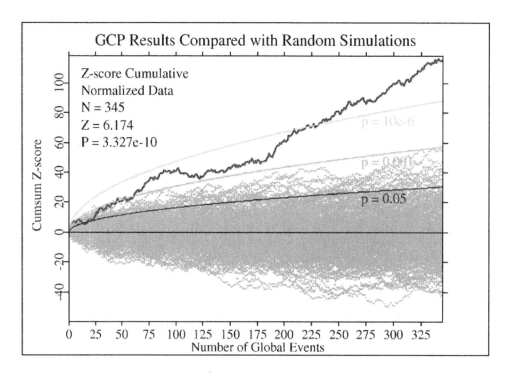

Figure 5: The bold jagged line shows the cumulative sum of deviations from expectation in the formal data. The grey cloud shows 250 simulated datasets drawn from the (0, 1) normal distribution. The horizontal line is null expectation and smooth parabolas show confidence levels.

For example, the original measure represents a correlation of meanshifts, and a natural question is whether there may be other correlations or structure in the higher moments of the analytical distributions. An independent measure assessing the variance of correlations (symbolized as $Zi\ 2*Zj2$) does show effects of a similar magnitude to the $Zi*Zj$ correlation described earlier. The general hypothesis also contains implicit questions about spatial and temporal aspects of the anomalous effects. Structure in these dimensions will help us understand the nature of what we are calling global consciousness. A series of as yet unpublished analyses addresses these questions, and the results are promising (Bancel, personal communication).

For practical and theoretical reasons, the question whether distance matters is useful. Most psi researchers consider the phenomena to be non-local, implying connection or entanglement over distance and possibly across time. The GCP database provides a rich opportunity to assess the empirical basis for a general non-local model. This is not a simple task, however. For example, the question requires careful consideration of what "distance" means in this context. It turns out that the events we examine frequently do not have well-defined locations, because our hypothesis actually addresses effects of an attentional and emotional response of people all around the planet. Thus, the most important distance metric may be psychological – the meaning of an event may be the operative source of its effect.

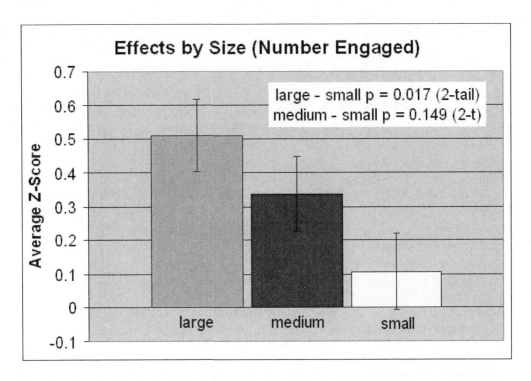

Figure 6. The formal data are categorized by estimating the number of people engaged. Larger, presumably more important events correspond to larger deviations.

As for time, we want to know how well our guesses about the length of the event match the duration of detectable effects. More generally, we need to learn about the time course of any anomalous effects we find. For some events there is a sharply defined moment – an explosion, an earthquake, a speech – and we can ask how the data correlations relate to that moment. Is there any indication of a precursor response? (Nelson & Bancel, 2006) Are there typical lags or durations of effects? What is the minimum time for an effect to develop, and what factors affect the rise time and the persistence of the anomalous correlations?

3.2. Categories. When we look at psychological and sociological variables, we find other indications of structure. By categorizing the events, we can identify modulating factors that influence the correlations in the data. For example, we find clear evidence that larger, more important events (indicated by number of people engaged) produce larger effects, as shown in Fig. 6. This is consonant with normal psychological expectation. On the other hand, while many people expect a difference for positive and negative events, the data show virtually equal effects.

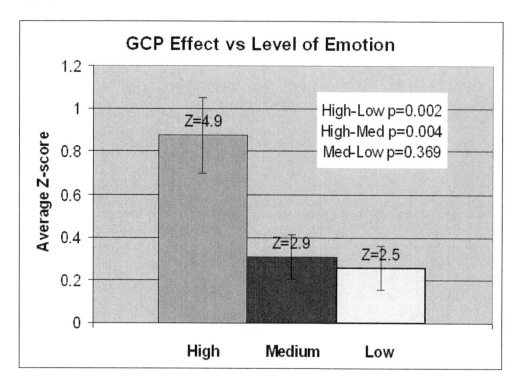

Figure 7. The formal data are categorized according to the level of compassion evoked by the event. Those characterized by greater compassion produce larger deviations.

The GCP's general hypothesis explicitly proposes an impact of shared emotions, and this can be assessed using subjective ratings. Analysis confirms that deviations during events are modulated by this factor. Figure 7 shows the substantial difference between high and low levels of emotion.

Other results using subjective categorization similarly show differentiations that parallel what is found in individual psychology (Nelson, 2008). For example, if we ask raters to decide how strongly fear is evoked, the data follow the ratings. Similarly, if we ask how much compassion is embodied in the events, we find a clear differentiation, with events characterized by deep and widespread compassion yielding relatively strong effects. This makes sense if we understand that compassion is a model for interconnection: compassion means that we feel and share the emotional states of others. It is by definition a condition that brings us together and makes us psychologically coherent. Differentiations like these provide some insight into the conditions underlying the anomalous correlations, and may contribute to sensible models for the effects.

4. Discussion

The GCP is a long-term experiment that asks fundamental questions about the presence of human consciousness in the world. It provides evidence for effects of synchronized collective attention – operationally defined mass consciousness – on a world-spanning network of physical devices. Indicators of anomalous data structure are correlated specifically with moments of importance to humans. The convergence of independent analytical findings provides strong evidence for the anomalies, and integrating these into scientific models will enrich our understanding of consciousness. The findings suggest that some aspect of consciousness may directly create effects in the material world. This is a provocative notion, but it is the most viable of several alternative explanations.

This is the only research program of its kind, but there is good reason to study the questions it raises. Replication is desirable but difficult because of the size and complexity of the project. However, the data are available for independent replications re-testing the hypothesis we propose with a new, independent selection of events. Perhaps equally important, the data are available to pose many good questions we have not been able to address.

The GCP findings are not explained by conventional sources or spurious influences, and we provisionally conclude that the effects are correlated with qualities or states of collective consciousness. Social and psychological variables are important to the extent they reflect mental and emotional coherence among the people engaged by the events. The evidence suggests an interdependence of consciousness and the environment, though we cannot yet describe the mechanisms in a formal way. The GCP findings do not fit into our current scientific models of the world, but facts at the edges of our understanding can be expected to direct us toward fundamental questions. As Richard Feynman remarked (1981), "The thing that doesn't fit is the thing that is most interesting."

4.1. Models We have demonstrated the existence of unexpected correlations and structure in the event data, and these results can serve as input for theoretical models of the deviations. Successful models will not only describe the empirical findings, but also refine our understanding of the structure, and they should lead to testable predictions and better models. Ultimately we seek a theory that provides a bridge from the empirical findings to a deeper understanding of the role mind or consciousness plays in the material world.

Three classes of models to consider are: 1) conventional physical and electromagnetic fields, or conventional methodological errors or biases, 2) unconventional fortuitous selection of events via experimenter intuition, or determination by retroactive information flow from future results, and 3) consciousness or information fields sourced in individual human minds, or a non-linear field representing a dynamical interaction among minds.

We can show that the first class is excluded by the experimental design and by empirical tests (Bancel and Nelson, 2008). Intuitive selection and retroactive information approaches are variants of a parapsychological theory which has been advanced to explain psi functioning (May, et al., 1995; Shoup, 2002). The idea is that expectations about the experiment play a role, and that deviations may result from a fortuitous choice of timing rather than an actual change in the data. Anomalies are attributed in some models of this type to the selection of unlikely data excursions in a naturally varying sequence, mediated by the experimenter's intuition, or, more forcefully put, by precognition of the eventual results, which informs the choice of events, their timing, and the test procedures. An explicit version of this model (Schmidt, 2009) has been tested against the GCP data and nominally rejected, with the rejection further supported by the model's failure to accommodate the second-order correlations and the spatial and temporal structure found in the data (Nelson & Bancel, 2009).

The picture is more promising when we look at field-type models associated with human consciousness. A simple version is similar to ordinary physical models of fields generated by a distribution of sources. In this case the field sources are associated with individual conscious humans, while the field dynamics that might explain the RNG correlations derive from the coherence of human activity during events. This proposal can accommodate all the inter-node correlations and structure seen in the data, but it remains phenomenological since it does not explain how the field arises in terms of underlying principles. A more complex non-linear dynamic field model would propose that individual minds are mutually interactive, and that the interactions are responsible for an emergent field which depends on individual consciousness but is not reducible to it. The model implies that the dynamic and interactive qualities of consciousness also involve subtle interactions with the physical world and that these are responsible for certain anomalous phenomena such as are found in the GCP experiment.

4.2. Implications What should we take away from this scientific evidence of interconnection? If we are persuaded that the subtle structuring of random data does indicate an effect of human attention and emotion in the physical world, it broadens our view of what consciousness means. One implication is that our attention matters in a way we have not imagined possible, and that cooperative intent can have real consequences. On a philosophical/scientific level, the evidence is consonant with V. I. Vernadsky's and Teilhard de Chardin's vision of the noosphere – a sheath of intelligence they believed would envelop the earth when humans advanced to the next stage of evolution (Teilhard, 1961; Vernadsky, 1926).

The GCP results inspire deeper questions about our relationship to the world and each other. The questions reach beyond the supply lines of our scientific position, but the experimental results are consistent with the idea that subtle linkages exist between widely separated people, and that consciousness is an essential and creative element in the physical world. If we conceive a noosphere, even one that is too subtle to perceive, we will be motivated to be more conscious of the interconnection it implies. It means we are part of a great being, as Eddington observed, (1928) and this confers responsibility but also confidence in the potentials we share.

Acknowledgments: Greg Nelson and John Walker created the architecture and the software for data collection and archiving. Paul Bethke ported the software to Windows. Peter Bancel developed the secondary analysis program. Rick Berger designed the original website. Dean Radin, Dick Bierman, and others provided ideas and experience. All their contributions are deeply appreciated. We also are grateful for the time, resources, and good will volunteered by the Egghosts. Financial support is from individuals including Charles Overby, Tony Cohen, Reinhilde Nelson, Marjorie Bancel, Richard and Connie Adams, Richard Wallace, Michael Breland, Joseph Giove, J. Z. Knight, Hans Wendt, Jim Warren, John Walker, Alex Tsakiris, and the Lifebridge Foundation. We also gratefully acknowledge online donations from many individuals. The GCP is affiliated with the Institute of Noetic Sciences, which provides a non-profit home.

References

Bancel, P. A., Nelson, R. D. (2008) The GCP Event Experiment: Design, Analytical Methods, Results. Journal of Scientific Exploration, 22, 309-333.

Bierman, D. J. (1996) Exploring correlations between local emotional and global emotional events and the behavior of a random number generator. Journal of Scientific Exploration, 10, 363-374.

Eddington, A. S. (1928) The Nature of the Physical World. MacMillan (1926–27 Gifford lectures.)

Feynman R. (1981) The Pleasure of Finding Things Out. Interview: BBC television program Horizon, accessed Jan 28 2010 http://www.scribd.com/doc/23587979/.

Jahn, R. G., Dunne, B. J., Nelson, R. D., Dobyns, Y. H., Bradish, G. J. (1997) Correlations of random binary sequences with pre-stated operator intention: A review of a 12-year program. Journal of Scientific Exploration, 11, 345-368.

May, E. C., Utts, J. M., Spottiswoode, S. J. P. (1995) Decision Augmentation Theory: Toward a Model of Anomalous Mental Phenomena. Journal of Parapsychology, 59, 195-220.

Nelson, R. D., Bradish, G. J., Dobyns, Y. H., Dunne, B. J., Jahn, R. G. (1996) FieldREG Anomalies in Group Situations. J. Scientific Exploration, 10, 111-141.

Nelson, R. D. (1997) Multiple Field REG/RNG Recordings during a Global Event. Electronic Journal Anomalous Phenomena (eJAP), accessed July 31 2010. http://noosphere.princeton.edu/ejap/gaiamind/abstract.html.

Nelson, R. D., Boesch, H., Boller, E., et al. (1998) Global Resonance of Consciousness: Princess Nelson, Detecting Mass Consciousness 21 01/01/11 Diana and Mother Teresa. Electronic Journal Anomalous Phenomena (eJAP) , accessed July 31 2010 http://noosphere.princeton.edu/ejap/diana/1998_1.html.

Nelson, R. D., Jahn, R. G., Dunne, B. J., Dobyns, Y. H., Bradish, G. J. (1998) FieldREG II: Consciousness Field Effects: Replications and Explorations, Journal of Scientific Exploration, 12, 425-454.

Nelson, R. D. (2001) Correlation of Global Events with REG Data: An Internet-Based, Nonlocal Anomalies Experiment. J of Parapsychology, 65, 247-271.

Nelson, R. D., Radin, D.I., Shoup, R., Bancel, P.A. (2002) Correlations of Continuous Random Data with Major World Events. Foundations of Physics Letters,15, 537-550.

Nelson, R. D. and Bancel, P. A. (2006) Anomalous Anticipatory Responses in Networked Random Data. Frontiers of Time: Retrocausation -- Experiment and Theory, Ed. Daniel P. Sheehan, AIP Conference Proceedings, 2006, Vol. 863.

Nelson, R. D. & Bancel, P. A. (2009) Response to Schmidt's commentary on the Global Consciousness Project, Letter to the Editor. Journal of Scientific Exploration, 23, 510-516.

Nelson, R. D. (2008) The Emotional Nature of Global Consciousness. Behind and Beyond the Brain. 7th Symposium of the Bial Foundation 2008. Emotions, Proceedings. Porto: Fundaçao Bial.

Radin, D. I., and Nelson, R. D. (1989). Evidence for consciousness-related anomalies in random physical systems. Foundations of Physics, 19, 1499-1514.

Radin, D. I., Rebman, J.M., Cross, M. P. (1996) Anomalous organization of random events by group consciousness: Two exploratory experiments. Journal of Scientific Exploration, 10, 143-168.

Radin, D. I. (1997) The Conscious Universe: The Scientific Truth of Psychic Phenomena. New York: Harper Collins.

Schmidt, H. (2009) A Puzzling Aspect of the "Global Consciousness Project", Letter to the Editor. Journal of Scientific Exploration, 23, 507-509.

Shoup, R. (2002) Anomalies and Constraints - Can clairvoyance, precognition and psychokinesis be accommodated within known physics? Journal of Scientific Exploration, 16, 3-18.

Teilhard de Chardin, P. (1961) The Phenomenon of Man, written 1938–40, French publication 1955, New York: Harper & Row.

Vernadsky, V. I. (1926) Biosphera, Nauchnoe khimiko-technicheskoye izdatel'stvo (Scientific Chemico-Technical Publishing): Leningrad.

II: Neuroscience, Cosmology and the Evolution of Consciousness of the Universe

****
****
****

9. Paleolithic Cosmic Consciousness of the Cosmos

R. Joseph, Ph.D.

Cosmology.com

Abstract

The emergence of cosmological consciousness and its symbolism, is directly linked to the evolution of the Cro-Magnon peoples who may have developed the first cosmologies, 20,000 to 30,000 years ago. These ancient peoples of the Upper and Middle Paleolithic believed in spirits and ghosts which dwelled in a heavenly land of dreams, and interned their dead in sleeping positions and with tools, ornaments and flowers. By 30,000 years ago, and because they believed souls ascended to the heavens, the people of the Paleolithic searched the heavens for signs, and between 30,000 to 20,000 years ago, they observed and symbolically depicted the association between woman's menstrual cycle and the moon, patterns formed by stars, and the relationship between Earth, the sun, and the four seasons. These include depictions of 1) the "cross" which is an ancient symbol of the fours seasons and the Winter/Summer solstice and Spring/Fall equinox; 2) the constellations of Virgo, Taurus, Orion/Osiris, the Pleiades, and the star Sirius; 3) and the 13 new moons in a solar year. Although it is impossible to date these discoveries with precision, it can be concluded that cosmological consciousness first began to evolve over 30,000 years ago, and this gave birth to the first heavenly cosmologies over 20,000 years ago.

1. Cro-Magnon Cosmology and the Frontal Lobes

When humans first turned their eyes to the sun, moon, and stars to ponder the nature of existence and the cosmos, is unknown. The Cro-Magnon people were keen observers of the world around them, which they depicted with artistic majesty. The heavens were part of their world and they searched the skies for signs and observed the moon, the patterns formed by clusters of stars, and perhaps the relationship between the Earth, the sun, and the changing seasons. Although it is impossible to date cave paintings with precision, the first evidence of this awareness of the cosmic connection between Sun, Moon, Woman, Earth and the changing seasons are from the Paleolithic; symbolized in the creations of the Cro-Magnon of the Paleolithic.

As based on cranial comparisons and endocasts of the inside of the skull, and using the temporal and frontal poles as reference points, it has been demonstrated that the brain has tripled in size over the course of human evolution, and that the frontal lobes significantly expanded in length and height during the Middle to Upper Paleolithic transition (Blinkov and Glezer 1968; Joseph 1993; MacLean 1990; Tilney 1928; Weil 1929; Wolpoff 1980).

It is obvious that the height of the frontal portion of the skull is greater in the six foot tall, anatomically modern Upper Paleolithic H. sapiens (Cro-Magnon) versus Neanderthal and archaic H. sapiens (Joseph 1996, 2000b; Tilney, 1928;

Wolpoff 1980). The evolution and expansion of the frontal lobe is also evident when comparing the skills and creative and technological ingenuity of the Cro-Magnons, vs the Neanderthals (Joseph 1993, 1996, 2000b).

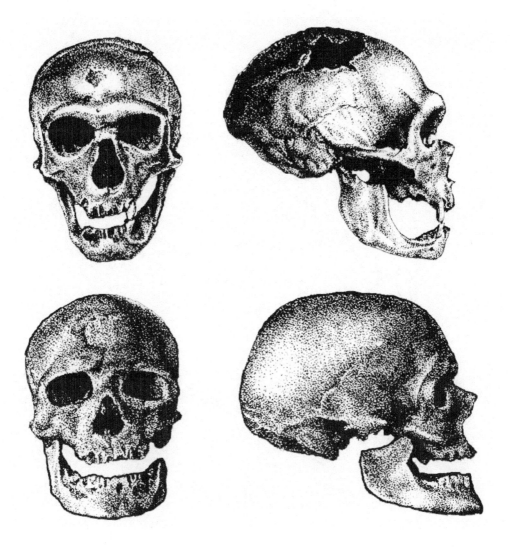

Figure: Neanderthal (top), Cro-Magnon (bottom)

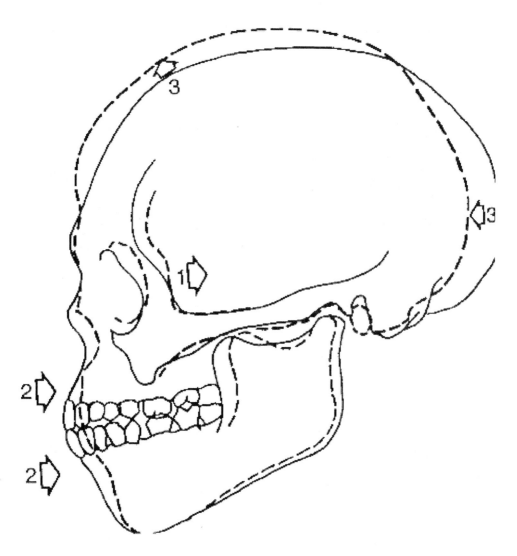

FIGURE A modern (dotted line) mesolithic cranium compared with a more ancient cranium (solid line). Arrows indicate the main average changes in skull structure including a reduction in the length of the occiput and an increase and upward expansion in the frontal cranial vault. Reproduced from M. H. Wolpoff (1980), Paleo- Anthropology. New York, Knopf.

Therefore, whereas the temporal, occipital and parietal lobes were well developed in archaic and Neanderthals, the frontal lobes would increase in size by almost a third in the transition from archaic humans to Cro-Magnon (Joseph 1996, 2000a,b, 2001). It is the evolution of the frontal lobes which ushered in a cognitive and creative big bang which gave birth to a technological revolution and complex spiritual rituals and beliefs in shamans and goddesses and their relationship to the heavens, and thus the moon and the stars.

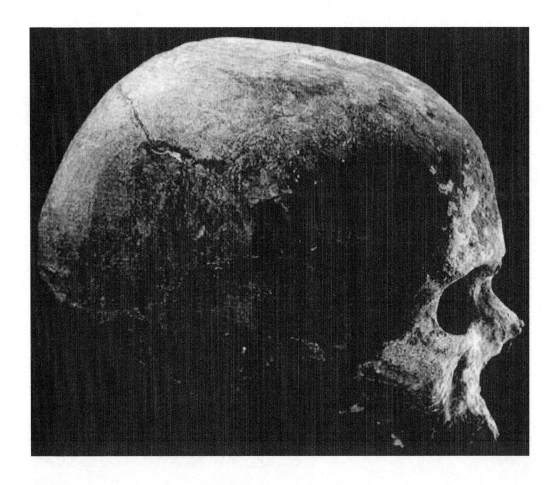

FIGURE: Cro-Magnon

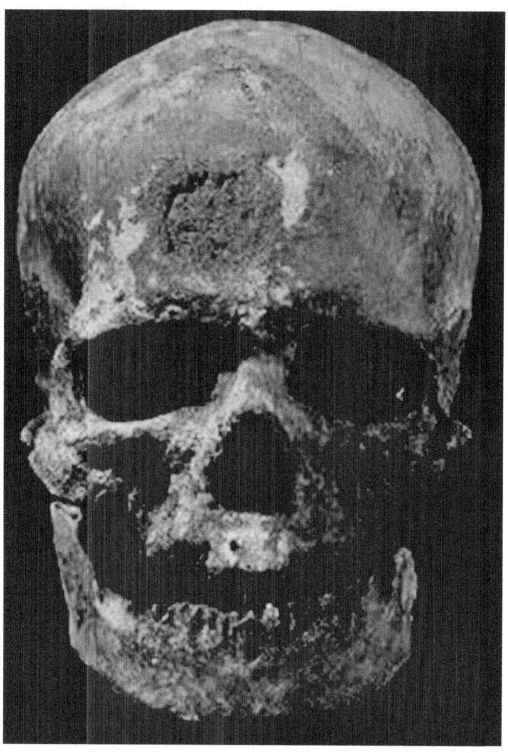

It is well established that the frontal lobes enable humans to think symbolically, creatively, imaginatively, to plan for the future, to consider the consequences of certain acts, to formulate secondary goals, and to keep one goal in mind even while engaging in other tasks, so that one may remember and act on those goals at a later time (Joseph 1986, 1990b, 1996, 1999c). Selective attention, planning skills, and the ability to marshal one's intellectual resources so as to to anticipate the future rather than living in the past, are capacities clearly associated with the frontal lobes.

FIGURE: Paleolithic Goddess

 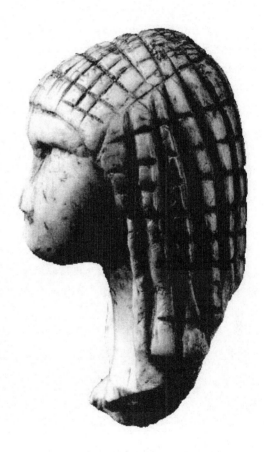

The frontal lobes are associated with the evolution of "free will" (Joseph 1986, 1996, 1999c, 2011b) and the Cro-Magnon were the first species on this planet to exercise that free will, shattering the bonds of environmental/genetic determinism by doing what had never been done before: After they emerged upon the scene over 35,000 years ago, they created and fashioned tools, weapons, clothing, jewelry, pottery, and musical instruments that had never before been seen. They created underground Cathedrals of artistry and light, adorned with magnificent multi-colored paintings ranging from abstract impressionism to the surreal and equal to that of any modern master (Breuil, 1952; Leroi-Gourhan

1964, 1982). And they used their skills to carve the likeness of their female gods.

Thirty five thousand years ago, Cro-Magnon were painting animals not only on walls but on ceilings, utilizing rich yellows, reds, and browns in their paintings and employing the actual shape of the cave walls so as to conform with and give life-like dimensions, including the illusion of movement to the creature they were depicting (Breuil, 1952; Leroi-Gourhan 1964, 1982). Many of their engraving on bones and stones also show a complete mastery of geometric awareness and they often used the natural contours of the cave walls, including protuberances, to create a 3-dimensional effect (Breuil, 1952; Leroi-Gourhan 1964, 1982).

With the evolution of the Cro-Magnon people, the frontal lobes mushroomed in size and there followed an explosion in creative thought and technological innovation. The Cro-Magnon were intellectual giants. They were accomplished artists, musicians, craftsmen, sorcerers, and extremely talented hunters, fishermen, and highly efficient gatherers and herbalists. And they were the first to contemplate the heavens and the cosmos which they symbolized in art.

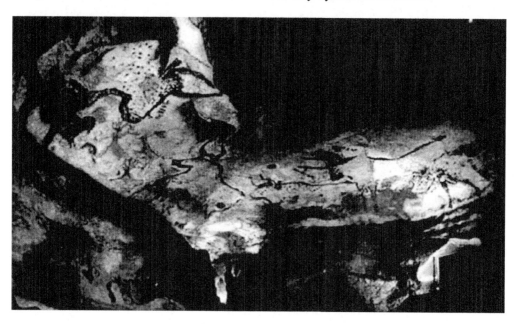

FIGURE: The cosmic clock and some of the constellation symbolized by bulls in the Lascaux Cave in Dordogne? There is a group of dots on the back of the bull to the far right (Taurus) which may represent the Pleiades (the seven sisters).

2. GODDESS OF THE MOON

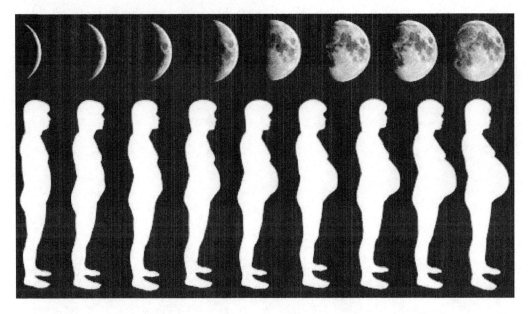

Among the ancients, the Sun and the Moon were of particular importance and the Cro-Magnon observed the relationship between woman and the lunar cycle. Consider, the pregnant goddess, the Venus of Laussel, who holds the crescent moon in her hand (though others say it is a bison's horn). Although the length of a Cro-Magnon woman's menstrual cycle is unknown, it can be assumed that like modern woman she menstruated once every 28 to 29 days, which corresponds to a lunar month 29 days long, and which averages out to 13 menstrual cycles in a solar year. And not just menstruation, but pregnancy is linked to the phases of the moon.

3. THE FOUR CORNERS OF THE SOLAR CLOCK.

When the Cro-Magnon turned their eyes to the heavens, seeking to peer beyond the mystery that separated this world from the next, they observed the sun. With a brain one third larger than modern humans, and given their tremendous power of observation, it can be predicted these ancient people would have associated the movement of the sun with the changing seasons which effected the behavior of animals, the growth of plants, and the climate and weather; all of which are directly associated with cyclic alterations in the position of the sun and the length of a single day over the course of a solar year which is equal to 13 moons.

FIGURE: The entrance to the underground Upper Paleolithic cathedral. The Chauvet cave. Note the sign of the cross. Reprinted from Chauvet et al., (1996). Dawn of Art: The Chauvet Cave. Henry H. Adams. New York.

The four seasons, marked by two solstices and the two equinoxes have been symbolized by most ancient cultures with the sign of the cross, e.g. the "four corners" of the world and the heavens. The "sign of the cross" generally signifies religious or cosmic significance. The Cro-Magnon also venerated the sign of the cross, the first evidence of which, an engraved cross, is at least 60,000 years old (Mellars, 1989). Yet another cross, was painted in bold red ochre upon the entry-way to the Chauvet Cave, dated to over 30,000 years ago (Chauvet et al., 1996).

The illusion of movement of the Sun, from north to south, and then back again, in synchrony with the waxing and waning of the four seasons, is due to the changing tilt and inclination of the Earth's axis, as it spins and orbits the sun. Thus over a span of 13 moons, it appears to an observer that the days become shorter and then longer and then shorter again as the sun moves from north to south, crosses the equator, and then stops, and heads back north again, only to stop, and then to again head south, crossing the equator only to again stop and head north again. The two crossings each year, over the equator (in March and September) are referred to as equinoxes and refers to the days and nights being of equal length. The two time periods in which the sun appears to stop its move-ment, before reversing course (June and December), are referred to as solstices—the "sun standing still."

The sun was recognized by ancient astronomer priests, as a source of light and life-giving heat, and as a keeper of time, like the hands ticking across the face of a cosmic clock. Because of the scientific, religious, and cosmological sig-nificance of the sun, ancient peoples, in consequence, often erected and oriented their religious temples to face and point either to the rising sun on the day of the solstice (that is, in a southwest—northeast axis), or to face the rising sun on the day of the equinox (an east-west axis). For example, the ancient temples and pyramids in Egypt were oriented to the solstices, whereas the Temple of Solomon faced the rising sun on the day of the equinox.

Thus the sign of the cross is linked to the heavens and to the sun. Under-standing the heavens and the sun, has been been a common astronomical method of divining the the will of the gods, and for navigation, localization, and calcula-tion: these celestial symbols have heavenly significance.

Regardless of time and culture, from the Aztecs, Mayans, American Indi-ans, Romans, Greeks, Africans, Christians, Cro-Magnons, Egyptians (the key of life), and so on, the cross consistently appears in a mystical context, and/or is attributed tremendous cosmic significance (Budge,1994; Campbell, 1988; Jo-seph, 2000a; Jung, 1964). The sign of the cross was the ideogram of the goddess "An", the Sumerian giver of all life from which rained down the seeds of life on all worlds including the worlds of the gods. An of the cross gave life to the gods, and to woman and man.

FIGURE: The God Seb supporting the Goddess Nut who represents heaven and possibly the Milky Way galaxy. Note the repeated depictions of the key of life; i.e. a ring with a cross at the end.

The symbol of the cross is in fact associated with innumerable gods and goddesses, including Anu of the ancient Egyptians, the Egyptian God Seb, the Goddess Nut, the God Horus (the hawk), as well as Christ and the Mayan and Aztec God, Quetzocoatl. For example, like the Catholics, the Mayas and Aztecs adorned their temples with the sign of the cross. Quetzocoatl, like Jesus, was a god of the cross.

In China the equilateral cross is represented as within a square which represents the Earth, the meaning of which is: "God made the Earth in the form of a cross." It is noteworthy that the Chinese cross-in-a-box can also be likened to the swastika—also referred to as the "gammadion" which is one of the names of the Lord God: "Tetragammadion." The cross, in fact forms a series of boxes when aligned from top to bottom or side by side, and cross-hatchings such as these were carved on stone over 60,000 years ago.

FIGURE: Quetzocoatl the Mayan and Aztec god of the cross. The round shield encircling the cross represents the sun.

FIGURE: Ochre etched with crosses, forming a series of cross-hatchings, dating to 77,000 years ago.

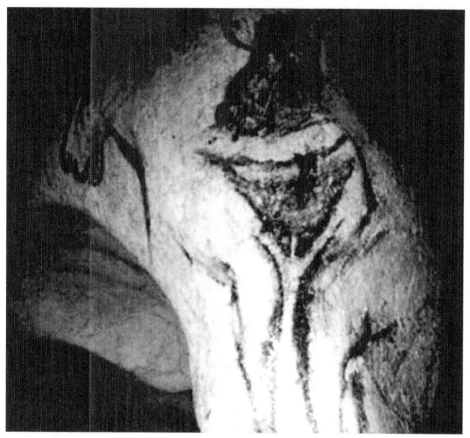

FIGURE: Sign of the cross (far left)

Among the ancient, the sign of the cross, represented the journey of the sun across the four corners of the heavens. The Cro-Magon adorned the entrance and the walls of their underground cathedrals with the sign of the cross, which indicates this symbol was of profound cosmic significance. However, that some of the Cro-Magnon depictions of animal-headed men have also been found facing the cross, may also pertain to the heavens: the patterns formed by stars, which today are refereed to as "constellations."

4.. THE CONSTELLATION OF VIRGO

FIGURES (above and below) Cro-Magnon / Paleolithic goddess, depicting the constellation of Virgo. La Magdelain cave.

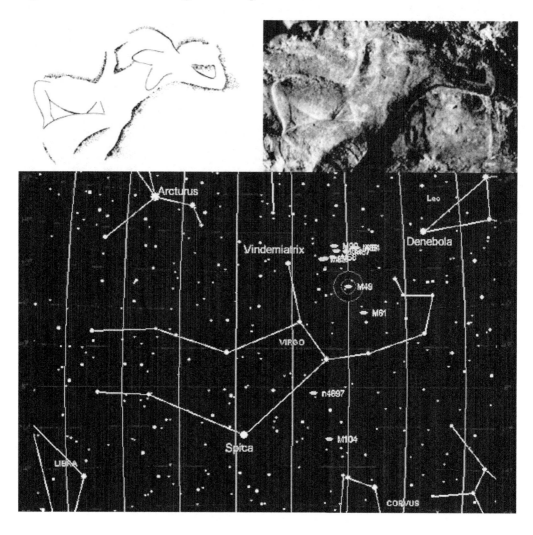

There is nothing "virginal" about the constellation of Virgo. The pattern can be likened to a woman in lying on her back with an arm behind her head, and this may have been the visage which stirred the imagination of the Cro-Magnon.

5. THE CONSTELLATIONS OF OSIRIS

It would be unreasonable to assume that the Cro-Magnon would not have observed the heavens or the illusory patterns formed by the alignment of various stars. Depictions of the various constellations, such as Taurus and Orion, and "mythologies" surrounding them, are of great antiquity, and it appears that similar patterns were observed by the Cro-Magnon people.

Consider, for example the "Sorcerers" or "Shamans" wearing the horns of a bull, and possibly representing the constellation of Taurus; a symbol which appears repeatedly in Lascaux, the "Hall of the Bulls" and in the deep recesses of other underground cathedrals dated from 18,000 to 30,000 B.P. And above the back of one of these charging bulls, appears a grouping of dots, or stars, which many authors believe may represent the Pleiades which is associated with Taurus. These Paleolithic paintings of the bull appear to be the earliest representation of the Taurus constellation.

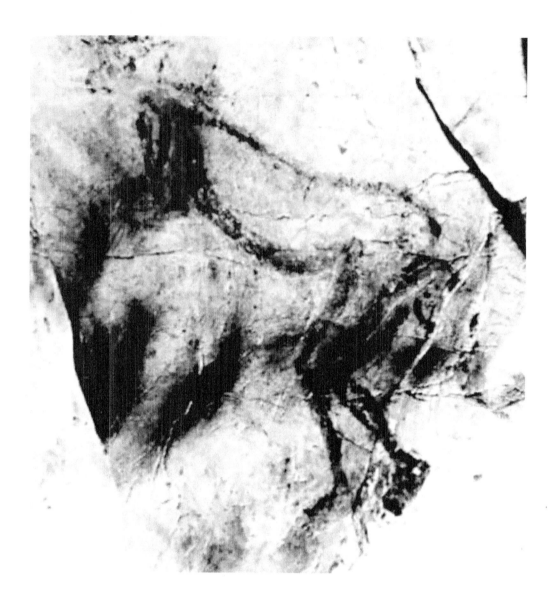

FIGURE: Ancient shaman attired in animal skins and stag antlers, graces the upper wall directly above the entrance to the 20,000-25,000 year-old grand gallery at Les Trois-Freres in southern France. Possibly representing the constellation of Orion.

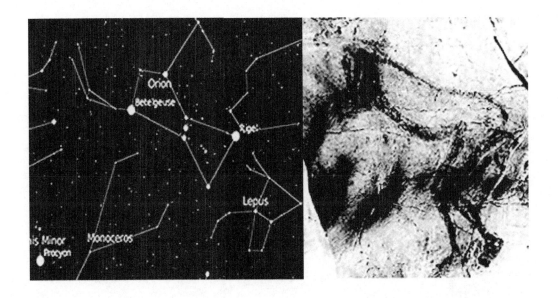

FIGURE. (Upper Right / Lower Left) The "Sorcerer" Trois-Frères cave. (Upper Left / Lower Right) Constellation of Orion/Osiris.

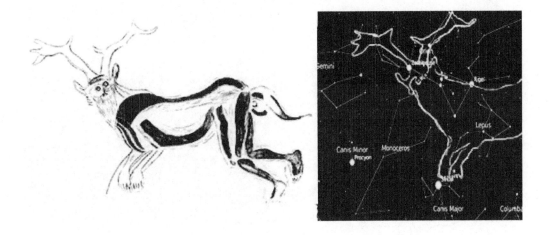

6. THE PLEIADES AND THE CONSTELLATIONS OF TAURUS AND ORION

In the "modern" sky, the constellation of Orisis/Orion the hunter, faces Taurus, the bull; and these starry patterns would not have been profoundly different 20,000 to 30,000 years ago. In ancient Egypt, dating back to the earliest dynasties (Griffiths 1980), Osiris was the god of death and of fertility and rebirth, who wore a a distinctive crown with two horns (later symbolized as ostrich feathers at either side). He was the brother and husband of Isis. According to myth, Orisis was killed by Set (the destroyer) and dismembered. Isis recovered all of his body, except his penis. After his death she becomes pregnant by Orisis. The Kings of Egypt were believed to ascend to heaven to join with Osiris in death and thereby inherit eternal life and rebirth, symbolized by the star Sirius (Redford 2003). The Egyptian "King list" (The Turin King List) goes backward in time, 30,000 years ago to an age referred to as the "dynasty of gods" which was followed by a "dynasty of demi-gods" and then dynasties of humans (Smith 1872/2005).

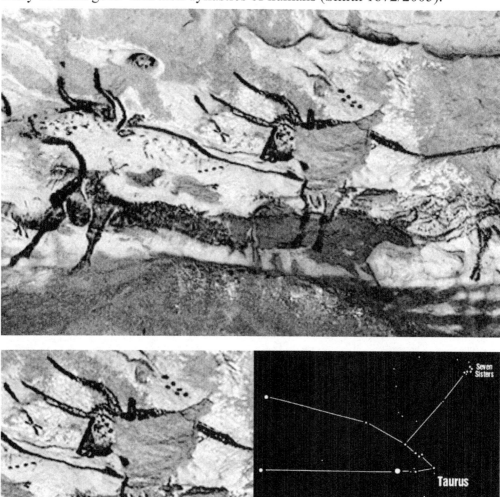

FIGURE: (Top) The main freeze of the bulls in the Lascaux Cave in Dordogne. There is a group of dots on the back of the great bull (Taurus) which may represent six of the seven stars of the Pleiades (the seven sisters). As stars are also in motion, not all would be aligned or as bright or dim today, as was the case 20,000 to 30,000 years ago.

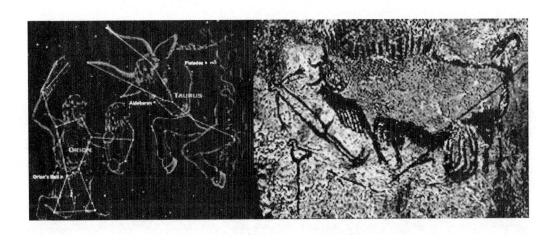

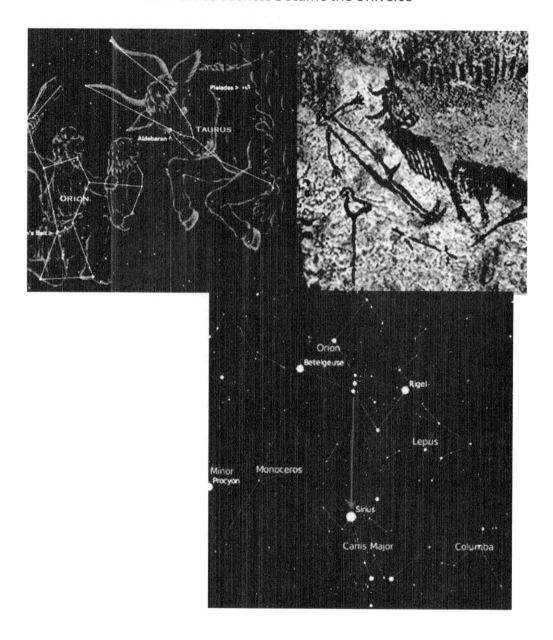

Over 20,000 years ago, the 6ft tall Cro-Magnon, with their massive brain one third larger than modern humans, painted a hunter with two horns who had been killed. And just as the constellation of Orion the hunter faces Taurus, so too does the dead Cro-Magnon hunter who has dismembered/disembowled the raging bull. And below and beneath the dead Cro-Magnon hunter, another bird, symbol of rebirth, and perhaps symbolizing the star Sirius.

The constellation of Osiris (Orion the hunter) in Egyptian mythology is the god of the dead who was dismembered; but also represents resurrection and eternal life as signified by the star Sirius. (Upper Right) Constellation of Osiris/Orion and Taurus. (Upper Left) Cave painting. Lascaux. The dead (bird-headed or two horned) hunter killed by a bull whom he disemboweled. (Bottom) Constellation of Orion/Osiris in relation to Sirius.

7. THE PALEOLITHIC AND NEOLITHIC MILKY WAY GALAXY

These peoples of the Paleolithic were capable of experiencing love, fear, and mystical awe, and they believed in spirits and ghosts which dwelled in a heavenly land of dreams. Because they believed souls ascended to the heavens, the people of the Paleolithic searched the heavens for signs. By 30,000 years ago, and with the expansion of the frontal lobes, they created symbolic rituals to help them understand and gain control over the spiritual realms, and created signs and symbols which could generate feelings of awe regardless of time or culture. They observed and symoblically depicted the association between woman and the moon, patterns formed by stars, and the relationship between Earth, the sun, and the four seasons.

The Milky Way galaxy can be viewed in the darkness of night, edge-on, snaking in a curving arc, forming part of a circle. If the peoples of the Paleolithic, through careful observation, deduced the existence of a spiraling galaxy, of which Earth, and the constellations circled round, or which circled round forming a cosmic clock, is unknown.

FIGURE: Quetzalcoatl Maya Galaxy

FIGURE: Petroglyph, date unknown

FIGURE: Colliding Galaxies (above). Figure (Below) 12,000 B.C>

FIGURE (below): Sagittarius dwarf galaxy orbiting the Milky

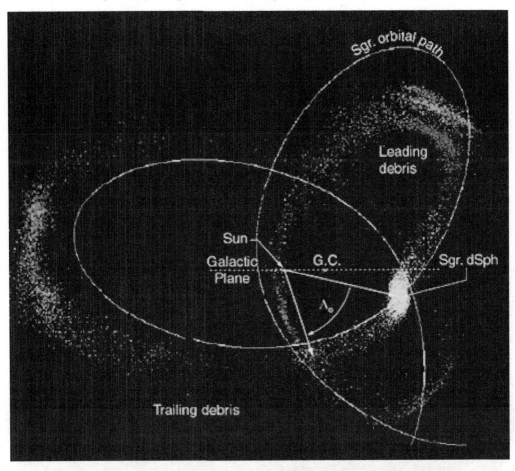

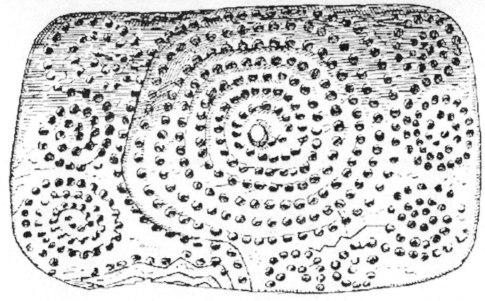

FIGURE (above): Mal'ta, Irkutskaya Oblast, Russia, 12000-15,000 B.C.

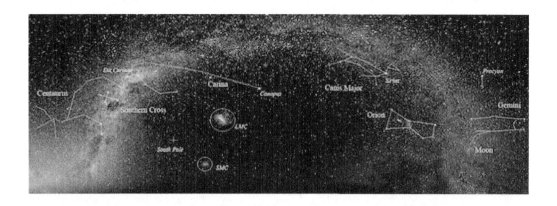

FIGURE: Milky Way Galaxy, viewed from Earth, with some of the constellations depicited.

FIGURE: Ancient Eguypt: Osiris atended by the Gemini twins, and above: the Milky Way galaxy, and 12 constellations of the zodiac represented by snakes.

FIGURE: Milky Way Galaxy

FIGURE: Quetzalcoatl (above). Milky Way Galaxy (below)

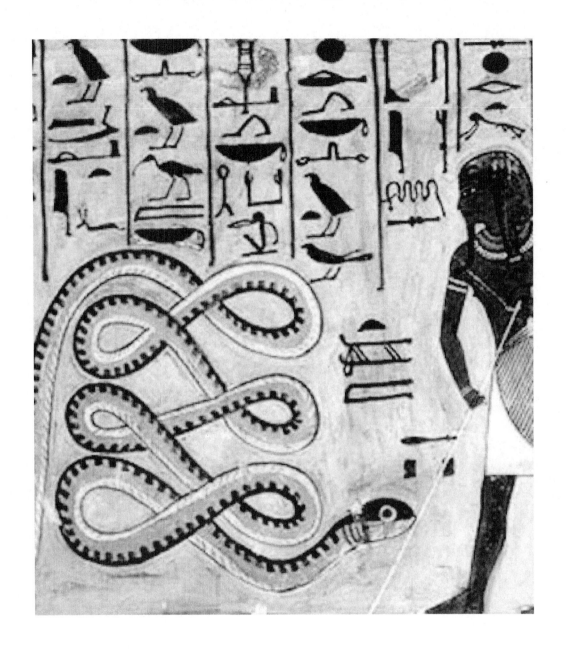

FIGURE: Apep - Egyptian - Milky Way Galaxy

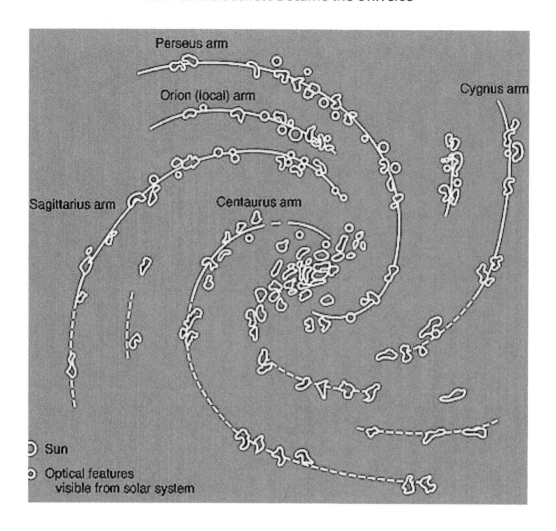

FIGURE: Milky Way Galaxy

FFIGURE: Aztec, Quetzalcoatl / Galaxy

FIGURE: Three belt stars of Osiris (above) Three Pyramids of Giza (below)

References

Akazawa , T & Muhesen, S. (2002). Neanderthal Burials. KW Publications Ltd.

Amaral, D. G., Price, J. L., Pitkanen, A., & Thomas, S. (1992). Anatomical organization of the primate amygdaloid complex. In J. P. Aggleton (Ed.). The Amygdala. (Wiley. New York.

Bandi, H. G. (1961). Art of the Stone Age. New York, Crown PUblishers, New York.

Bear, D. M. (1979). Temporal lobe epilepsy: A sydnrome of sensory-limbic hyperconnexion. Cortex, 15, 357-384.

Belfer-ohen, A., & E.Hovers, (1992). In the eye of the beholder: Mousterian and Natufian burials in the levant. Current Anthropology 33: 463-471.

Breuil. H. (1952). Four hundred centuries of cave art. Montignac.

Budge, W. (1994). The Book of the Dead. New Jersey, Carol.

Butzer, K. (1982). Geomorphology and sediment stratiagraphy, in The Middle Stone Age at Klasies River Mouth in South Africa. Edited by R. Singer and J. Wymer. Chicago: University of Chicago Press.

Binford, L. (1981). Bones: Ancient Men & Modern Myths. Academic Press, NY

Binford, S. R. (1973). Interassemblage variability--the Mousterian and the 'functional' argument. In The explanation of culture change. Models in prehistory. edited by C. Renfrew. Pittsburgh: Pittsburgh U. Press.

Binford S. R. (1982). Rethinking the Middle/Upper Paleolithic transition. Current Anthropology 23: 177-181.

Blikkov, S. M., & Glezer, I. I. (1968). The human brain in figures and tables. New York: Plenum.

Campbell, J. (1988) Historical Atlas of World Mythology. New York, Harper & Row.

Cartwright , R. (2010) The Twenty-four Hour Mind: The Role of Sleep and Dreaming in Our Emotional Lives. Oxford University Press.

Chauvet, J-M., Deschamps, E. B. & Hillaire, C. (1996) Dawn of Art: The Chauvet Cave. H.N. Abrams.

Clark, G. (1967) The stone age hunters. Thames & Hudson.

Clark, J. D., & Harris, J. W. K. (1985). Fire and its role in early hominid lifeways. African Archaeology Review, 3, 3-27.

Conrad, N. J., & Richter, J. (2011). Neanderthal Lifeways, Subsistence and Technology. Springer.

Dennell, R. (1985). European prehistory. London, Academic Press.

Eadie, B. J. (1992). Embraced by the light. California, Gold Leaf Press.

Frazier, J. G. (1950). The golden bough. Macmillan, New York.

Gowlett, J. (1984). Ascent to civlization. New York: Knopf.

Gowlett, J.A. (1981). Early archaeological sites, hominid remains and traces of fire from Chesowanja, Kenya. Nature, 294, 125-129.

Griffiths, J. G. (1980). The Origins of Osiris and His Cult. Brill.

Harold, F. B. (1980). A comparative analysis of Eurasian Palaeolithic burials. World Archaeology 12: 195-211.

Harold, F. B. (1989). Mousterian, Chatelperronian, and Early Aurignacian in Western Europe: Continuity or disconuity?" In P. Mellars & C. B. Stringer (eds). The human revolution: Behavioral and biological perspectives on the origins of modern humans, vol 1.. Edinburgh: Edinburgh University Press.

Harris, M. (1993) Why we became religious and the evolution of the spirit world. In Lehmann, A. C. & Myers, J. E. (Eds) Magic, Witchcraft, and Religion. Mountain View: Mayfield.

Harvati, K., & Harrison, T. (2010). Neanderthals Revisited. Springer.

Hayden, B. (1993). The cultural capacities of Neandertals: A review and re-evaluation. Journal of Human Evolution 24: 113-146.

Holloway, R. L. (1988) Brain. In: Tattersall, I., Delson, E., Van Couvering, J. (Eds.) Encyclopedia of human evolution and prehistory. New York: Garland.

Joseph, R. (1990b) The frontal lobes. In A. E. Puente and C. R. Reynolds (series editors). Critical Issues in Neuropsychology. Neuropsychology, Neuropsychiatry, Behavioral Neurology. Plenum, New York.

Joseph, R. (1992) The Limbic System: Emotion, Laterality, and Unconscious Mind. The Psychoanalytic Review, 79, 405-456.

Joseph, R. (1993) The Naked Neuron. Evolution and the languages of the body and the brain. Plenum. New York.

Joseph, R. (1994) The limbic system and the foundations of emotional experience. In V. S. Ramachandran (Ed). Encyclopedia of Human Behavior. San Diego, Academic Press.

Joseph, R. (1996). Neuropsychiatry, Neuropsychology, Clinical Neuroscience, 2nd Edition. 21 chapters, 864 pages. Williams & Wilkins, Baltimore.

Joseph, R. (1998a). The limbic system. In H.S. Friedman (ed.), Encyclopedia of Human health, Academic Press. San Diego.

Joseph, R. (2001). The Limbic System and the Soul: Evolution and the Neuroanatomy of Religious Experience. Zygon, the Journal of Religion & Science, 36, 105-136.

Joseph, R. (2002). NeuroTheology: Brain, Science, Spirituality, Religious Experience. University Press.

Joseph, R. (2011a). Dreams and Hallucinations: Lifting the Veil to Multiple Perceptual Realities, Cosmology, 14, In press.

Joseph, R. (2011). The neuroanatomy of free will: Loss of will, against the will "alien hand", Journal of Cosmology, 14, In press.

Jung, C. G. (1945). On the nature of dreams. (Translated by R.F.C. Hull.), The collected works of C. G. Jung, (pp.473-507). Princeton: Princeton University Press.

Jung, C. G. (1964). Man and his symbols. New York: Dell.

Kawashima, R., Sugiura, M., Kato, T., et al., (1999). The human amygdala plays an important role in gaze monitoring. Brain, 122, 779-783.

Kling. A. S. & Brothers, L. A. (1992). The amygdala and social behavior. In J. P. Aggleton (Ed.). The Amygdala. New York, Wiley-Liss.

Kurten, B. (1976). The cave bear story. New York: Columbia University Press.

Leroi-Gourhan, A. (1964.) Treasure of prehistoric art. New York: H. N. Abrams.

Leroi-Gourhan, A. (1982). The archaeology of Lascauz Cave. Scientific American 24: 104-112.

MacLean, P. (1990). The Evolution of the Triune Brain. New York, Plenum.

Malinowski, B. (1954) Magic, Science and Religion. New York. Doubleday.

McCown, T. (1937). Mugharet es-Skhul: Description and excavation, in The stone age of Mount Carmel. Edited by D. A. E. Garrod and D. Bate. Oxford: Clarendon Press.

Mellars, P. (1989). Major issues in the emergence of modern humans. Current Anthropology 30: 349-385.

Mellars, P. (1996) The Neanderthal legacy. Princeton University Press.

Mellars, P. (1998). The fate of the Neanderthals. Nature 395, 539-540.

Morris, J. S., Frith, C. D., Perett, D. I., Rowland, D., Young, A. W., Calder, A. J., & Colan, R. J. (1996). A differential neural response in the human amygdala to fearful and happy facial expression. Nature, 383, 812-815.

Petrides, M., & Pandya, D. N. (1999). Dorsolateral prefrontal cortex: comparative cytoarchitectonic analysis in the human and the macaque brain and corticocortical connection patterns. European Journal of Neuroscience 11.1011–1036.

Petrides, M., & Pandya, D. N. (2001). Comparative cytoarchitectonic analysis of the human and the macaque ventrolateral prefrontal cortex and corticocortical connection patterns in the monkey. European Journal of Neuroscience 16.291–310.

Prideaux, T. (1973). Cro-Magnon. New York: Time-Life.

Redford, D. B. (2003). The Oxford Guide: Essential Guide to Egyptian Mythology, Berkley.

Rightmire, G. P. (1984). Homo sapiens in Sub-Saharan Africa, In F. H. Smith and F. Spencer (eds). The origins of modern humans: A world survey of the fossil evidence. New York: Alan R. Liss.

Roginskii Y. Y., & Lewin S. S. (1955). Fundamentals of Anthropology. Moscow: Moscow University Press.

Schwarcz, A. et al. (1988). ESR dates for the hominid burial site of Qafzeh. Journal of Human Evolution 17: 733-737.

Smirnov, Y. A. (1989). On the evidence for Neandertal burial. Current Anthropology 30: 324.

Smith, G. A. (1872/2005). Chaldean Account of Genesis (Whittingham & Wilkins, London, 1872). Adamant Media Corporation (2005).

Solecki, R. (1971). Shanidar: The first flower people. New York: Knopf.

Subirana, A., & Oller-Daurelia, L. (1953). The seizures with a feeling of paradisiacal happiness as the onset of certain temporal symptomatic epilepsies. Congres Neurologique International. Lisbonne, 4, 246-250.

Tilney, F. (1928). The brain from ape to man. New York: P. B. Hoeber.

Tobias, P. V. (1971). The Brain in Hominid Evolution. Columbia University Press, New York.

Trinkaus, E. (1986). The Neanderthals and modern human origins. Annual Review of Anthropology 15: 193-211.

Weingarten, S. M., Cherlow, D. G. & Holmgren. E. (1977). The relationship of hallucinations to depth structures of the temporal lobe. Acta Neurochirugica 24: 199-216.

Williams, D. (1956). The structure of emotions reflected in epileptic experiences. Brain, 79, 29-67.

Wilson, J. A. (1951) The culture of ancient Egypt. Chicago, U. Chicago Press.

Wolpoff, M. H. (1980), Paleo-Anthropology. New York, Knopf.

10. The Brain and Consciousness: Dynamics and Evolution

Hans Liljenström

Biometry and Systems Analysis Group, Energy & Technology, SLU, Box 7013, S-750 07 Uppsala, Sweden, Agora for Biosystems, Box 57, S-193 22 Sigtuna, Sweden

Abstract

All through the history of the universe there is an apparent tendency for increasing complexity, with the organization of matter in evermore elaborate and interactive systems. The living world in general, and the human brain in particular, provides the highest complexity known. Presumably, the neural system with its complex dynamics has evolved to cope with the complex dynamics of the environment, where it is embedded. The evolution of a nervous system constitutes a major transition in biological evolution and allows for an increasing capacity for information storage and processing. Neural knowledge processing, cognition, shows the same principal features as non-neural adaptive processes. Similarly, consciousness might appear, to different degrees, at different stages in evolution. Both cognition and consciousness seem to depend critically on the organization and complexity of the organism. Different states of consciousness can apparently be associated with different levels of neural activity, in particular with different oscillatory modes at the mesoscopic level of cortical networks. Transitions between such modes could also be related to transitions between different states of consciousness. For example, a transition from an awake to an anaesthetized state, or sleep, is accompanied by a transition from high frequency oscillations to low frequency oscillations in the cortical neurodynamics. In this article, I will briefly discuss some general aspects on the evolution of the nervous system and its complex neurodynamics, which provides organisms with ever increasing capacity for complex behaviour, cognition and consciousness. Consciousness and cognition apparently evolve through interaction with the environment, where the organism is embedded. Such exploration of the environment requires both attention and intention. I will discuss these dual and complementary aspects of consciousness, and their effects as perception and action. Finally, I will speculate on consciousness related to life, and how it may be regarded as a driving force in the exploration of our world.

KEY WORDS: Attention, intention, free will, neurodynamics, cortical networks, EEG, evolution

1. Introduction

When we open our eyes after a good night's sleep, we again become conscious of the world around us. A few moments before, we had closed our senses to the external world, resting in an inner world, which only in the dreaming state had some degree of consciousness. We were unable to attend to our physical environment, or move voluntarily in it. When we wake up, we make a transition into a state, where we suddenly can perceive and act intentionally. If we wake up in a familiar environment, we can act almost automatically in it, but otherwise, we may start to explore our environment, by attending to it and interact with it intentionally. However, in our wake conscious state, we may shift between several sub-states, corresponding to different levels of alertness or wakefulness.

During sleep, our cognitive activity is mostly unconscious. We may wake up from this state spontaneously (by some internal "clock" or other internal event), or as a result of a sounding alarm clock, or the whispering of our name, or a weak smell of smoke, or any other significant signal, that is below threshold for any insignificant sensory input. Obviously, there is a certain level of "awareness" also in the so-called unconscious state.

Even in our wake state, most of our cognitive activity may be unconscious. While it is important to distinguish between cognition and consciousness, (which is often mixed up in the literature), both seem to linked to system and process complexity. In fact, the cognitive and conscious capacity seems to increase with an increasing level of complexity, or interconnectedness (Århem & Liljenström, 2007).

The brain, like other biological systems, has presumably evolved to efficiently increase the probability of survival in a constantly changing environment. This would imply, among other things, a rapid and appropriate response to external (and internal) events. We may assume that the neural system with its complex dynamics has evolved to cope with the complex dynamics of the environment, by constantly interacting with it.

In the following, I attempt to relate the neurodynamics of the brain with our cognitive and conscious activity, and also set it in an evolutionary context. Specifically, I will consider the dual aspects of consciousness, intention and attention, and its effective counterparts of the neural system as perception and action. Finally, I will speculate on these aspects as universal to all life, and on consciousness as a driving force in nature.

2. Neural Dynamics

Brain structures are characterized by their complexity in terms of organization and dynamics. This complexity appears at many different spatial and temporal scales, which in relative terms can be considered as micro, meso, and macro scales. The corresponding dynamics may range from ion channel kinetics, to spike trains of single neurons, to the neurodynamics of cortical networks and areas. The high complexity of this neurodynamics is partly a result of the web of non-linear interrelations between levels and parts, including positive and negative feedback loops. (Freeman, 2000; Århem & Liljenström, 2001; Århem et al, 2005).

Very little is still known about the functional significance of the neural dynamics at the various organizational levels, and even less about the relation between activities at these levels. However, it is reasonable to assume that different dynamical states correlate with different functional or conscious states. Transitions within the brain dynamics at some level would correlate with transitions in the "consciousness dynamics", involving various cognitive levels and conscious states, e.g. when going from sleep to awake states, or from drowsiness to alertness, etc. In general, there is a spectrum of states, each one with its own characteristic neurodynamical (oscillatory) mode.

Presumably, phase transitions at the mesoscopic level of neural systems, i.e. at levels between neurons and the entire brain, are of special relevance to mental state transitions. The mesoscopic neurodynamics of cortical neural networks typically occurs at the spatial order of a few millimetres to centimetres, and temporally on the order of milliseconds to seconds. This type of dynamics can be measured by methods, such as electrocorticography (ECoG), electroencephalography (EEG), or magnetoencephalography (MEG).

Mesoscopic brain dynamics with its transitions is partly depending on thresholds and the summed activity of a large number of microscopic elements (molecules and cells) interconnected with positive and negative feedback. Some of this activity is spontaneous and can be considered as noise (which may have a functional significance, see e.g. Århem et al., 2005).

In addition, the mesoscopic dynamics is influenced and regulated by various hormones and neuromodulators, such as acetylcholine and serotonin, as well as by the state of arousal or motivation, relating to more macroscopic processes of the brain. Hence, mesoscopic neurodynamics can be seen as resulting from the dynamic balance between opposing processes at several scales, from the influx and efflux of ions, inhibition and excitation etc. Such interplay between opposing processes often results in (transient or continuous) oscillatory and chaoticlike behaviour (Skarda & Freeman, 1987; Freeman, 2000; Liljenström, 2010). Clearly, the brain activity is constantly changing, due to neuronal information processing, internal fluctuations, neuromodulation, and sensory input.

An essential feature of the mesoscopic brain dynamics is spatio-temporal patterns of activity, appearing at the collective level of a very large number of neurons. Waves of activity move across the surface of sensory cortices, with oscillations at various frequency bands (Freeman, 1975, 2000). In general, low frequencies correspond to low mental activity, drowsiness or sleep, whereas higher frequencies are associated with alertness and higher conscious activity. Fig. 1 shows the simulated effect of certain anaesthetics, which are presumed to cause a transition from high frequency (gamma) to low frequency (theta) oscillations, mimicking a transition from an awake to an anaesthetized state (Halnes et al., 2007).

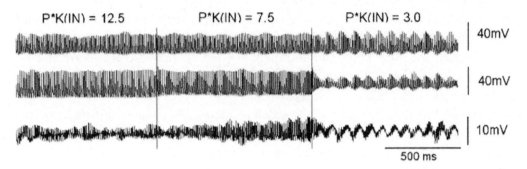

Fig. 1. Simulated effect of anaesthetics, which may shift the mesoscopic neurodynamics from high frequency (gamma) oscillations to low frequency (theta) oscillations for three different concentration levels of potassium ion channel blocking, increasing from left to right. These shifts in neurodynamics would presumably correspond to shifts in conscious states, going from alert (left) to anaestetized/ sleep (right). The two upper time series show the activity of a single excitatory and inhibitory neuron, respectively, while the lower time series is the network mean. (Adopted from Halnes et al, 2007).

In particular, oscillations in the gamma frequency band, around 40 Hz, has been associated with (visual) attention, based on experiments on cats about two decades ago (Eckhorn et al., 1988; Gray & Singer, 1989). It was this phenomenon that triggered a lot of studies on neural correlates of consciousness, as e.g. suggested by Crick and Koch (1990; Koch, 2004) and contributed to opening the field of neuroscience to consciousness studies. This experimental and theoretical research on neural oscillations has been complemented by computational models, which attempt to relate structure to dynamics and function. (I have dealt with these issues in more detail elsewhere, e.g. in Liljenström 1991, 1995, 1997, 2010).

3. Consciousness Dynamics

The complex neurodynamics at a mesoscopic level of the brain seem significant for cognitive functions and conscious activity. It has been related to perception, attention and associative memory, but also to volition and activity in the sensory motor areas of the brain. Even though many details are still unknown, there is an interplay between the neurodynamics of the sensory and motor pathways, which seem essential for the interaction with our environment.

We explore our world in a perception-action cycle (Freeman, 2000). The development of our cognitive and conscious abilities depend on an appropriate interaction with the complex and changing environment, in which we are embedded. Our perceptions and actions develop and are refined to effectively deal with our external (and internal) world.

However, prior to perception is attention, and prior to action is intention. Some believe that attention and intention are at the core of our experience of existence (Popper et al., 1993). While attention has been shown to correlate with certain neural oscillations, intention has not been demonstrated to the same extent. Attention is primarily related to the sensory/perceptual pathways and brain areas, whereas intention would be more related to the motor areas and pathways. In particular, the supplementary motor area (SMA), but also the parietal cortex, show early signs of intentional motor activity (Eccles, 1982; Libet 1985; Desmurget et al., 2009).

Attention could be extended, but also be focused to some specific part of our internal or external worlds. We can turn our attention to some specific memory, thought, or sensory experience, while neglecting or inhibiting the rest. Naturally, and perhaps more commonly, our attention is drawn to some object or event in our environment, something that is of special relevance or interest to us, for our survival or for our curiosity.

We may also intentionally turn our attention to some area of interest. Intention can be viewed as a precursor to volition and will, as an "urge" or "desire" to act in a certain direction, to attain a certain goal. Voluntary movement, or more generally, behavior, is based on perception and past experience (memory), which are required for prediction of internal and external interactions. Attention may provide information about the internal and external worlds, but intention guides our actions. We can attend to our intentions, but we can also intentionally guide our attention.

While attention and intention would be most effective in the wake conscious state, they could also be present, to lesser degree, in "unconscious" states (e.g. visual attention in the original 40 Hz experiments were made on anesthetized cats (Eckhorn et al., 1988; Gray & Singer, 1989)). They could be present at different levels of intensity; where we become conscious awake above a certain threshold.

Attention and intention could be seen as complementary aspects of consciousness, with their effective neural counterparts of perception and action, respectively, when implemented through the interactions within sensory and motor hierarchies of the nervous system. They correspond to an "inward" and an "outward" going activity of consciousness (see Fig. 2). Both of these aspects seem essential for exploring our external (and internal) world. In other words, we play the dual role of actor and observer in the drama of existence (Joseph, 1982, 2011).

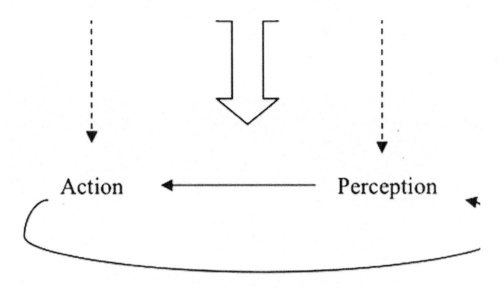

EXPLORATION

Fig. 2. The relation between the "implicate" order of consciousness, as in the dual aspect of attention and intention, and the "explicate order" of exploration, as in the perception-action cycle.

4. Consciousness and Life

Attention and intention, as complementary aspects of consciousness are presumably not only part of the human experience, but could be much more universal. For example, (visual) attention has been studied in insects, such as fruit-flies (van Swinderen, 2008) and honey bees (Srinavasan 2009), and can be expected to be found also in other invertebrates. Likewise, intentional behaviour can be attributed to many types of (in particular social) animals, including crustaceans (Hauser & Nelson, 1991; Mather 2011; Nani et al., 2011).

Indeed, these aspects of consciousness might be intimately linked to life at all levels, albeit not in the same sense as we use the terms for humans (or other mammals). Naturally, in organisms without a nervous system, attention and intention could never be implemented through any sensory or motor hierarchy of such a system, but would rather have to be implemented through other molecular or cellular structures.

This view is akin to that of Delbrück (1986), who considers consciousness to include all types of "awareness" of external and internal events, from a crude form of perception in the simplest organisms to self-consciousness in Man. The more complex the cellular organization of an organism is the more this organism can be aware, or conscious, of the external and internal world. In this sense, consciousness has evolved together with other properties of life. In his book,

"Mind from Matter?" (1986), Delbrück regards perception as the basic form of consciousness and he states (p. 43) that,

"The unity and continuity of life is equally manifest in its psychic aspects. Perception in plants and animals is a familiar phenomenon, but the beginnings of perception are also clearly present in microorganisms, in which adaptive behavior demonstrates that they can detect and evaluate signals from the environment and respond appropriately".

This is not a dominating view today, but it is appealing in the sense that it relates processes in simple organisms with those in higher. It avoids the difficult task of finding a possible origin of consciousness in evolution, and points to a continuity in the living world. A similar view is shared by Margulis and Sagan (1995), who suggest that also intentionality may be attributed to simple organisms, including bacteria.

The electro-chemical (or other) processes that take place in the intricate neural networks of the brain can be assumed to be associated to various internal states and "mental" processes of an animal. In lower animals the nervous system may allow only for "primitive mental" processes, such as perception, learning, recalling, drives, and emotions (Mather 2011; Nani et al., 2011). To a large extent the animal is presumably unconscious of these internal processes, and it is only aware (conscious, in the Delbrück sense) of the external environment. As the nervous system evolves and attains a higher degree of complexity and organization, its processes become more advanced and sophisticated, including cognition, as an act of knowing, thinking, reasoning, believing, and willing. Eventually, (symbolic) language becomes an important and integrated part of the cognitive functions (Joseph 2000).

In birds and mammals, and most articulate in man, there is an advanced ability to "internalize" the world through the formation of spatial and temporal patterns. In particular, temporal binding allows us to understand the relation between cause and effect and to experience "the arrow of time". For humans, the internal model of the world also includes other individuals and their minds. Models of other individuals are important for determining the significance of their behavior, and for predicting the "next step" in that behavior.

Self-consciousness, a sense of an "I", may develop when experienced events are given a sequential context in the internal model of the world. It is obvious that many cognitive functions (but not consciousness in general) depend upon memory, but the "I" needs memories well structured in time, in order to be perceived. Obviously, also planning for the future, involving attention as well as intention, is an essential component in the making of an "I" (Ingvar 1994). Our subjective experience of a decision to act, as well as of a sensory stimulation, seems to require a time span of a few to several hundred milliseconds (Libet 1985, Crick 1994, Soon et al., 2008).

Thus, the capabilities to predict future events have been extended to the anticipation and expectation of a continuous individual life. Also, if one has a (good) model of oneself one can infer ones own thinking, feelings and behaviors also to others, thus allowing for a more efficient interaction with other individuals, and better prediction of their behavior. The ultimate pattern in our understanding of the world results in an experience of meaning, where our interrelationships can be set in a context (attention), and be seen as purposeful (intention). Fig. 3 shows an attempt to link the evolution of cognitive and conscious interaction with the external environment to an increasing complexity of living organisms.

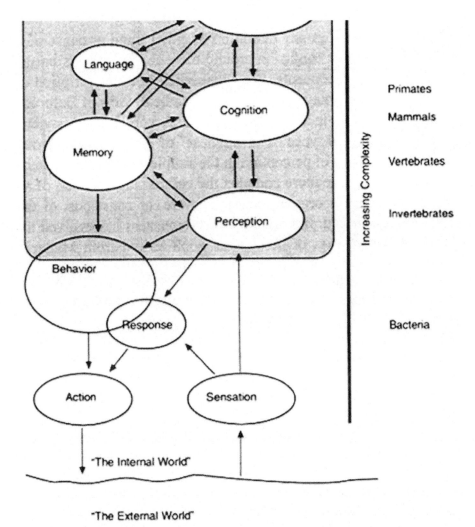

Fig. 3. A crude attempt to map various cognitive functions and relate them to each other on an "evolutionary scale" that is at the same time a measure of the degree of complexity. Intention would correspond to the downward direction,

and attention to the upward direction in this figure. (Adopted from Liljenström, 1997).

Consciousness and cognition apparently evolve through interaction with the environment, where the organism is embedded. Such exploration of the environment requires both attention and intention. The evolution of consciousness presumably occurs through larger leaps when new species appear, and through smaller steps within a species and even smaller steps within an organism. A great leap of consciousness must have happened when we became aware of ourselves and our own cognitive activity. That leap should also include an awareness of our intentions, a sense of a free will. This more advanced consciousness is presumably experienced, or at least reflected on, by humans alone.

5. Discussion

In previous sections, I have given an outline of a view on consciousness that is based on its complementary aspects of intention and attention, and more universal than commonly considered. It implies that both of these aspects of consciousness are essential for exploring our internal and external world. As suggested by William James (1890), consciousness could be viewed as a constantly changing process, interacting with a constantly changing environment in which it is embedded. Another view is that consciousness can be seen as a "force field", similar to an electromagnetic field (Popper et al., 1993; Lindahl & Århem, 1994). These views imply that we cannot reduce consciousness to neural or electrochemical processes. Indeed, that would have little meaning to us, even if we claimed we had succeeded. Concepts at one level are in many cases not transferable in a meaningful way to another level. New qualities and properties emerge at each new level in the hierarchical organization of matter, qualities which are irrelevant at lower levels. Such a "holistic" view was also given by Delbrück, who compared mind with quantum reality:

"The mind is not a part of the man-machine but an aspect of its entirety extending through space and time, just as, from the point of view of quantum mechanics, the motion of the electron is an aspect of its entirety that cannot be unambiguously dissected into the complementary properties of position and momentum."

Penrose (1989, 1994) brings this analogy further, believing that mind indeed may need some quantum mechanical description. He argues that there are some aspects of mind, or mental phenomena, like e.g. understanding and insight, that are non-computable in nature, and thus, for example, can never be simulated on a computer. Such phenomena may even require a new physics, new laws and principles that are not mechanistically derivable from lower levels. With this perspective, consciousness seems to fundamentally transcend physics, chemistry and any mechanistic principle of biology.

If intentionality is a fundamental aspect of consciousness, and if intentionality corresponds to our sense of free will, it is difficult to fit it within the framework of current science, which is based on deterministic laws and chance. In my view, consciousness provides a freedom beyond the indeterminism of quantum physics or the determinism of classical physics. Indeed, consciousness should perhaps not at all be viewed as a phenomenon, that is observable within the framework of current scientific approaches (even though science entails observation and experiment, as an advanced form of attention and intention). Instead, consciousness could be considered a meta-phenomenon (or noumenon, in a Kantian sense), which can only be "observed" indirectly (by a conscious observer) through its effects on the material world.

The effects of consciousness is most clearly linked to intention, as its more active aspect, which has to be considered if we are to understand its role in evolution and in the universe. Exploration, through attention-perception and intention-action, is fundamental to all levels of existence. In this sense, consciousness is inseparable from life, expanding and evolving together. It is expressed and evolving through inter-relations (attention) and inter-actions (intention). Hence, consciousness can be regarded as a driving force in nature.

References

Århem, P., Liljenström, H. (2001) Fluctuations in neural systems: From subcellular to network levels. In: Moss, F. & Gielen, S. (Eds.) Handbook of Biological Physics, Vol. 4: Neuro-informatics, Neural Modelling, Elsevier, Amsterdam, pp. 83-125.

Århem, P., Liljenström, H. (2007). Beyond cognition - on consciousness transitions. In: Liljenström, H. and Århem, P., (Eds.), Consciousness Transitions - Phylogenetic, Ontogenetic and Physiological Aspects. Elsevier, Amsterdam, pp. 1-25.

Århem, P., Braun, H., Huber, M. and Liljenström, H. (2005). Non-Linear state transitions in neural systems: From ion channels to networks. In: Liljenström, H. & Svedin, U. (Eds.) Micro - Meso - Macro: Addressing Complex Systems Couplings, World Scientific Publ. Co., Singapore, pp. 37-72.

Crick, F. (1994). The Astonishing Hypothesis - the Scientific Search for the Soul. Simon & Schuster, London.

Crick, F., Koch, C. (1990). Towards a neurobiological theory of consciousness, Seminars Neurosci. 2, 263-275.

Delbrück, M. (1986). Mind from Matter? Blackwell Scientific Publ., Palo Alto, CA.

Desmurget, M., Reilly, K. T., Richard, N., Szathmari, A., Mottolese, C., Sirigu, A. (2009). Movement intention after parietal stimulation in humans. Science 324, 811-813.

Eccles, J. C. (1982). The initiation of voluntary movements by the supplementary motor area. Arch. Psychiatr. Nervenkr. 231, 423-441.

Eckhorn, R., Bauer, R., Jordon, W., Brosch, M., Kruse, W., Monk, M., Reitboeck, H.J. (1988). Coherent oscillations: A mechanism of feature linking in the in the visual cortex? Biol. Cybern. 60, 121-130.

Freeman, W. J. (1975) Mass Action in the Nervous System. Academic Press, New York.

Freeman, W. J. (2000). Neurodynamics: An Exploration in Mesoscopic Brain Dynamics. Springer, London.

Gray, C. M., Singer, W.(1989). Stimulus-specific neuronal oscillations in orientation columns of cat visual cortex. Proc. Natl. Acad. Sci. USA 86, 1698-1702.

Halnes, G., Liljenström, H., Århem, P. (2007). Density dependent neurodynamics. Biosystems 89,126-134.

Hauser, M. D., Nelson, D. A. (1991). 'Intentional' signaling in animal communication. TREE 6, 186-189.

Ingvar, D. H. (1994). The will of the brain: Cerebral correlates of willful acts, J. theor. Biol. 171, 7-12.

James, W. (1890). The Principles of Psychology. Harvard Univ. Press, Cambridge, MA.

Joseph, R. (1982). The neuropsychology of development. Hemispheric laterality, limbic language, the origin of thought. Journal of Clinical Psychology, 44 4-33.

Joseph, R. (2000). The evolution of sex differences in language, sexuality, and visual spatial skills. Archives of Sexual Behavior, 29, 35-66.

Joseph, R. (2011). Consciousness, language, and the development and origins of thought, Journal of Cosmology, 14, In press.

Koch, C. (2004). The Quest for Consciousness - A Neurobiological Approach. Roberts & Co. Publ., Greenwood Village, CO.

Libet, B. (1985). Unconscious cerebral initiative and the role of conscious will in voluntary action. Behav. Brain Sc. 8, 529-566.

Liljenström, H. (1991). Modeling the dynamics of olfactory cortex using simplified network units and realistic architecture, Int. J. Neural Syst. 2:1-15

Liljenström, H. (1995). Autonomous learning with complex dynamics. Int. J. Intell. Syst. 10, 119-153

Liljenström, H. (1997). Cognition and the efficiency of neural processes. In: Århem, P., Liljenström, H., Svedin, U. (Eds.), Matter Matters? On the Material Basis of the Cognitive Activity of Mind, Springer, Heidelberg, pp. 177-213.

Liljenström, H. (2010). Inducing transitions in mesoscopic brain dynamics. In: Steyn-Ross, D. A., Steyn-Ross, M. (Eds.) Modeling Phase Transitions in the Brain, 149, Springer Series in Computational Neuroscience 4, pp. 149-179.

Lindahl, B. I. B., Århem, P. (1994). Mind as a force field: Comments on a new interactionistic hypothesis. J. theor. Biol. 171, 111-122.

Margulis, L., Sagan, D. (1995). What is Life? Widenfeld & Nicolson, London.

Mather, J. (2011). Consciousness in Cephalopods? Journal of Cosmology, 14, In press.

Nani, A., Clare M. Eddy, C. M., Cavanna, A. E. (2011). The quest for animal consciousness. Journal of Cosmology, 14, In press.

Penrose, R. (1989). The Emperor's New Mind. Oxford University Press, GB.

Penrose, R. (1994). Shadows of the Mind. Oxford University Press, GB.

Popper, K., Lindahl, B. I. B., Århem, P. (1993). A discussion of the mind-brain problem. Theor. Medicine 14, 167-180.

Skarda, C.A., Freeman, W.J.(1987). How brains make chaos in order to make sense of the world. Behav. Brain Sci. 10, 161-195.

Soon, C. S., Brass, M., Heinze, H-J., Haynes, J-D. (2008). Unconscious determinants of free decisions in the human brain. Nature Neuroscience 11, 543-545.

Srinavasan, M. V. (2009). Honey bees ans a model for vision, perception, and cognition. Annu. Rev. Entomol. 55, 267-284.

van Swinderen, B. (2008). The remote roots of consciousness in fruit-fly selective attention? In: Liljenström, H. & Århem, P. (Eds.), Consciousness Transitions. Phylogenetic, Ontogenetic and Physiological Aspects. Elsevier, Amsterdam, pp. 27-44.

11. Quantum Physics and the Multiplicity of Mind: Split-Brains, Fragmente Minds, Dissociation, Quantum Consciousness

R. Joseph, Ph.D.
Cosmology.com
Emeritus, Brain Research Laboratory, Northern California

Abstract

Quantum physics and Einstein's theory of relativity make assumptions about the nature of the mind which is assumed to be a singularity. In the Copenhagen model of physics, the process of observing is believed to effect reality by the act of perception and knowing which creates abstractions and a collapse function thereby inducing discontinuity into the continuum of the quantum state. This gives rise to the uncertainty principle. Yet neither the mind or the brain is a singularity, but a multiplicity which include two dominant streams of consciousness and awareness associated with the left and right hemisphere, as demonstrated by patients whose brains have been split, and which are superimposed on yet other mental realms maintained by the brainstem, thalamus, limbic system, and the occipital, temporal, parietal, and frontal lobes. Like the quantum state, each of these minds may also become discontinuous from each other and each mental realm may perceive their own reality. Illustrative examples are detailed, including denial of blindness, blind sight, fragmentation of the body image, phantom limbs, the splitting of the mind following split-brain surgery, and dissociative states where the mind leaves the body and achieves a state of quantum consciousness and singularity such that the universe and mind become one.

1. Introduction

In 1905 Albert Einstein published his theories of relativity, which promoted the thesis that reality and its properties, such as time and motion had no objective "true values", but were "relative" to the observer's point of view (Einstein, 1905a,b,c). However, what if the observer is not a singularity and has more than one point of view and more than one stream of observing consciousness? And what if these streams of consciousness were also relative?

Quantum physics, as exemplified by the Copenhagen school (Bohr, 1934,

1958, 1963; Heisenberg, 1930, 1955, 1958), also makes assumptions about the nature of reality as related to an observer, the "knower" who is conceptualized as a singularity. Because the physical world is relative to being known by a "knower" (the observing consciousness), then the "knower" can influence the nature of the reality which is being observed. In consequence, what is known vs what is not known becomes relatively imprecise (Heisenberg, 1958).

For example, as expressed by the Heisenberg uncertainty principle (Heisenberg, 1955, 1958), the more precisely one physical property is known the more unknowable become other properties, whose measurements become correspondingly imprecise. The more precisely one property is known, the less precisely the other can be known and this is true at the molecular and atomic levels of reality. Therefore it is impossible to precisely determine, simultaneously, for example, both the position and velocity of an electron.

However, we must ask: if knowing A, makes B unknowable, and if knowing B makes A unknowable, wouldn't this imply that both A and B, are in fact unknowable? If both A and B are manifestations of the processing of "knowing," and if observing and measuring can change the properties of A or B, then perhaps both A and B are in fact properties of knowing, properties of the observing consciousness, and not properties of A or B.

In quantum physics, nature and reality are represented by the quantum state. The electromagnetic field of the quantum state is the fundamental entity, the continuum that constitutes the basic oneness and unity of all things.

The physical nature of this state can be "known" by assigning it mathematical properties (Bohr, 1958, 1963). Therefore, abstractions, i.e., numbers, become representational of a hypothetical physical state. Because these are abstractions, the physical state is also an abstraction and does not possess the material consistency, continuity, and hard, tangible, physical substance as is assumed by Classical (Newtonian) physics. Instead, reality, the physical world, is created by the process of observing, measuring, and knowing (Heisenberg, 1955).

Consider an elementary particle, once this positional value is assigned, knowledge of momentum, trajectory, speed, and so on, is lost and becomes "uncertain." The particle's momentum is left uncertain by an amount inversely proportional to the accuracy of the position measurement which is determined by values assigned by the observing consciousness. Therefore, the nature of reality, and the uncertainty principle is directly affected by the observer and the process of observing and knowing (Heisenberg, 1955, 1958).

The act of knowing creates a knot in the quantum state; described as a "collapse of the wave function;" a knot of energy that is a kind of blemish in the continuum of the quantum field. This quantum knot bunches up at the point of observation, at the assigned value of measurement.

The process of knowing, makes reality, and the quantum state, discontinuous. "The discontinuous change in the probability function takes place with the act of registration...in the mind of the observer" (Heisenberg, 1958).

Reality, therefore, is a manifestation of alterations in the patterns of activity within the electromagnetic field which are perceived as discontinuous. The perception of a structural unit of information is not just perceived, but is inserted into the quantum state which causes the reduction of the wave-packet and the collapse of the wave function.

Knowing and not knowing, are the result of interactions between the mind and concentrations of energy that emerge and disappear back into the electromagnetic quantum field.

However, if reality is created by the observing consciousness, and can be made discontinuous, does this leave open the possibility of a reality behind the reality? Might there be multiple realities? And if consciousness and the observer and the quantum state is not a singularity, could each of these multiple realities also be manifestations of a multiplicity of minds?

Heinserberg (1958) recognized this possibility of hidden realities, and therefore proposed that the reality that exists beyond or outside the quantum state could be better understood when considered in terms of "potential" reality and "actual" realities. Therefore, although the quantum state does not have the ontological character of an "actual" thing, it has a "potential" reality; an objective tendency to become actual at some point in the future, or to have become actual at some point in the past.

Therefore, it could be said that the subatomic particles which make up reality, or the quantum state, do not really exist, except as probabilities. These "subatomic" particles have probable existences and display tendencies to assume certain patterns of activity that we perceive as shape and form. Yet, they may also begin to display a different pattern of activity such that being can become nonbeing and thus something else altogether.

The conception of a deterministic reality is therefore subjugated to mathematical probabilities and potentiality which is relative to the mind of a knower which effects that reality as it unfolds, evolves, and is observed (Bohr 1958, 1963; Heisenberg 1955, 1958). That is, the mental act of perceiving a non-localized unit of structural information, injects that mental event into the quantum state of the universe, causing "the collapse of the wave function" and creating a bunching up, a tangle and discontinuous knot in the continuity of the quantum state.

Einstein ridiculed these ideas (Pais, 1979): "Do you really think the moon isn't there if you aren't looking at it?"

Heisenberg (1958), cautioned, however, that the observer is not the creator of reality: "The introduction of the observer must not be misunderstood to imply that some kind of subjective features are to be brought into the description of nature. The observer has, rather, only the function of registering decisions, i.e., processes in space and time, and it does not matter whether the observer is an apparatus or a human being; but the registration, i.e., the transition from the "possible" to the "actual," is absolutely necessary here and cannot be omitted from the interpretation of quantum theory."

Shape and form are a function of our perception of dynamic interactions within the continuum which is the quantum state. What we perceive as mass (shape, form, length, weight) are dynamic patterns of energy which we selectively attend to and then perceive as stable and static, creating discontinuity within the continuity of the quantum state. Therefore, what we are perceiving and knowing, are only fragments of the continuum.

However, we can only perceive what our senses can detect, and what we detect as form and shape is really a mass of frenzied subatomic electromagnetic activity that is amenable to detection by our senses and which may be known by a knowing mind. It is the perception of certain aspects of these oscillating patterns of continuous evolving activity, which give rise to the impressions of shape and form, and thus discontinuity, as experienced within the mind.

This energy that makes up the object of our perceptions, is therefore but an aspect of the electromagnetic continuum which has assumed a specific pattern during the process of being sensed and processed by those regions of the brain and mind best equipped to process this information.

Perceived reality, therefore, becomes a manifestation of mind.

However, if the mind is not a singularity, and if we possessed additional senses or an increased sensory channel capacity, we would perceive yet other patterns and other realities which would be known by those features of the mind best attuned to them. If the mind is not a singularity but a multiplicity, this means that both A and B, may be known simultaneously.

2. Duality vs Multiplicity

In the Copenhagen model, the observer is external to the quantum state the observer is observing, and they are not part of the collapse function but a witness of it (Bohr, 1958, 1963; Heisenberg 1958). However, if the Copenhagen model is correct, and as the cosmos contains observers, then the standard collapse formulation can not be used to describe the entire universe as the universe contains observers (von Neumann, 1932, 1937).

Further, reality becomes, at a minimum, a duality (observer and observed) with the potential to become a multiplicity.

As described by DeWitt and Graham (1973; Dewitt, 1971), "This reality, which is described jointly by the dynamical variables and the state vector, is not the reality we customarily think of, but is a reality composed of many worlds. By virtue of the temporal development of the dynamical variables the state vector decomposes naturally into orthogonal vectors, reflecting a continual splitting of the universe into a multitude of mutually unobservable but equally real worlds, in each of which every good measurement has yielded a definite result and in most of which the familiar statistical quantum laws hold."

The minimal duality is that aspect of reality which is observed, measured, and known, and that which is unknown.

However, this minimal duality is an illusion as indicated not only by the potential to become multiplicity, but by the nature of mind which is not a singularity (Joseph, 1982, 1986a; 1988a,b).

Even if we disregard the concept of "mind" and substitute the word "brain", the fact remains that the brain is not a singularity. The human brain is functionally specialized with specific functions and different mental states localized to specific areas, each of which is capable of maintaining independent and semi-independent aspects of conscious-awareness (Joseph 1986a,b, 1988a,b, 1992, 1999a). Different aspects of the same experience and identical aspects of that experience may be perceived and processed by different brain areas in different ways (Gallagher and Joseph, 1982; Joseph 1982; Joseph and Gallagher 1985; Joseph et al., 1984).

Therefore, although it has been said that orthodox quantum mechanics is completely concordant with the defining characteristics of Cartesian dualism, this is an illusion. Cartesian duality assumes singularity of mind, when in fact, the overarching organization of the mind- and the brain- is both dualistic and multiplistic.

If quantum physics is "mind-like" (actual/operational at the quantum level, but mentalistic on the ontological level) then quantum physics, or rather, the quantum state (reality, the universe) is not a duality, but a multiciplicity. Indeed, the entire concept of duality is imposed on reality by the dominant dualistic nature of the brain and mind which subordinates not just reality, but the multiplicity of minds maintained within the human brain (Joseph, 1982).

Like the Copenhagen school, Von Neumann's formulation of quantum mechanics (1932, 1937), fails to recognize or understand the multiple nature of mind and reality. Von Neumann postulated that the physical aspects of nature are represented by a density matrix. The matrix, therefore, could be conceptualized as a subset of potential realities, and that by averaging the values of these evolving matrices, the state of the universe and thus of reality, can be ascertained as a unified whole. However, in contrast to the Copenhagen interpretation, Von Neumann shifted the observer (his brain) into the quantum universe and thus made it subject to the rules of quantum physics.

Ostensibly and explicitly, Von Neumann's conceptions are based on a conception of mind as a singularity acting on the quantum state which contains the brain. Von Neumann's mental singularity, therefore, imposes itself on reality, such that each "event" that occurs within reality, is associated with one specific experience of the singularity-mind. Thus, Von Neumann assumes the brain and mind has only "one experience" which corresponds with "one event;" and this grossly erroneous misconception of the nature of the brain and mind, unfortunately, is erroneously accepted as fact by most cosmologists and physicists. Further, he argues that in the process of knowing, the quantum state of this singularity brain/

mind also collapses, or rather, is reduced in a mathematically quantifiable manner, just as the quantum universe is collapsed and reduced by being known (Von Neumann, 1932, 1937).

However, the brain and mind are not a singularity, but a multiplicity (Joseph, 1982, 1988a,b, 1999a). Nevertheless, Von Neumann's conceptions can be applied to the multiplicity of mind/brain when each mental realm is considered individually as an interactional subset of the multiplicity.

3. The Multiplicity of Mind and Perception

According to Von Neumann (1932), the "experiential increments in a person's knowledge" and "reductions of the quantum mechanical state of that person's brain" corresponds to the elimination of all those perceptual functions that are not necessary or irrelevant to the knowing of the event and the increase in the knowledge associated with the experience.

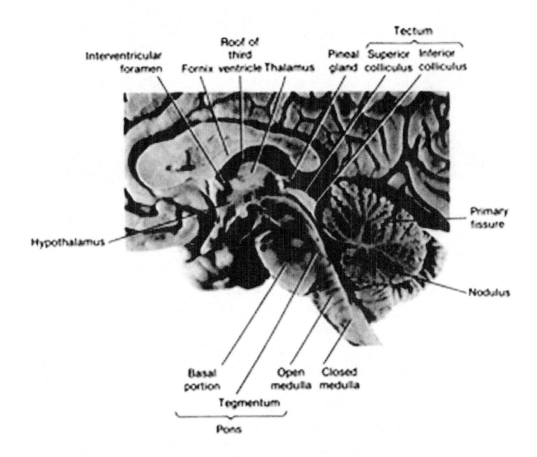

If considered from the perspective of an isolated aspect of the mind and the dominating stream of consciousness, Von Neuman's conceptions are essentially correct. However, neither the brain nor the mind function in isolation but in interaction with other neural tissues and mental/perceptual/sensory realms (Joseph 1982, 1992, 1999a). Perceptual functions are not "eliminated" and removed from the brain. Instead, they are prevented from interfering with the attentional processes of one aspect of the multiplicity of mind which dominates during the knowing event (Joseph, 1986b, 1999a).

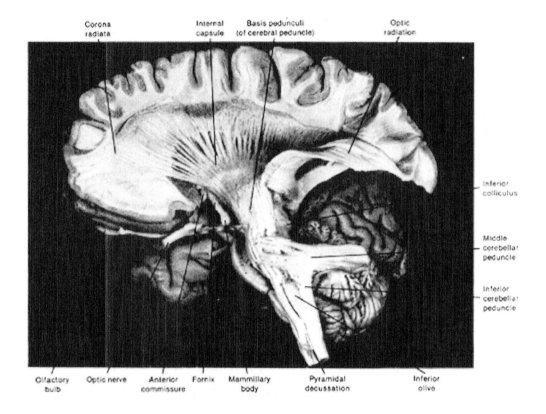

Consider, by way of example, you are sitting in your office reading this text. The pressure of the chair, the physical sensations of your shoes and clothes, the musculature of your body as it holds one then another position, the temperature of the room, various odors and fragrances, a multitude of sounds, visual sensations from outside your area of concentration and focus, and so on, are all being transmitted to the brainstem, midbrain, and olfactory limbic system. These signals are then relayed to various subnuclei within the thalamus.

The neural tissues of the brainstem, midbrain, limbic system and thalamus are associated with the "old brain." However, those aspects of consciousness we most closely associated with humans are associated with the "new brain" the neocortex (Joseph, 1982, 1992). Therefore, although you may be "aware" of these sensations while they are maintained within the old brain, you are not "conscious" of them, unless a decision is made to become conscious or they increase sufficiently in intensity that they are transferred to the neocortex and forced into the focus of consciousness (Joseph, 1982, 1986b, 1992, 1999a).

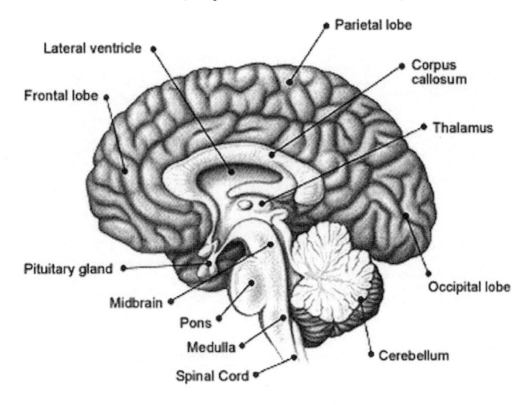

The different parts of the brain

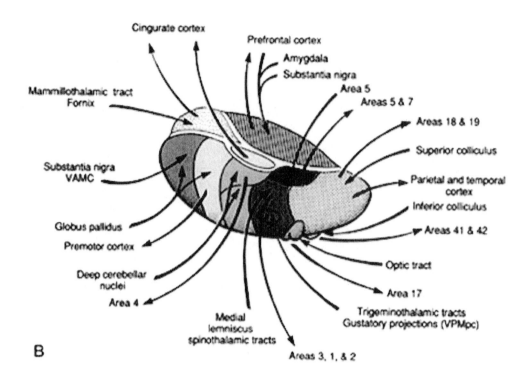

B

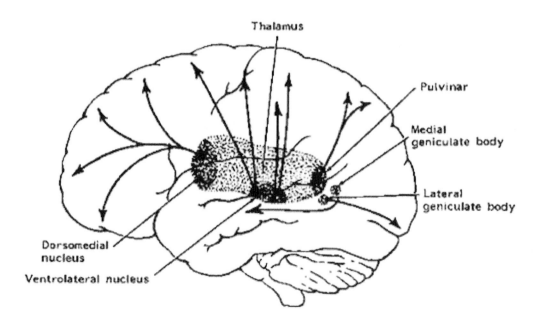

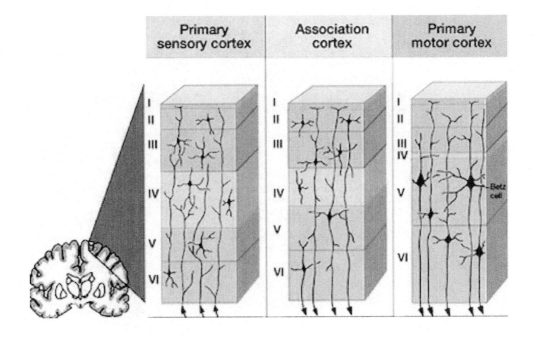

The old brain is covered by a gray mantle of new cortex, neocortex. The sensations alluded to are transferred from the old brain to the thalamus which relays these signals to the neocortex. Human consciousness and the "higher" level of the multiplicity of mind, are associated with the "new brain."

For example, visual input is transmitted from the eyes to the midbrain and thalamus and is transferred to the primary visual receiving area maintained in the neocortex of the occipital lobe (Casagrande & Joseph 1978, 1980; Joseph and Casagrande, 1978). Auditory input is transmitted from the inner ears to the brainstem, midbrain, and thalamus, and is transferred to the primary auditory receiving area within the neocortex of the temporal lobe. Tactual-physical stimuli are also transmitted from the thalamus to the primary somatosensory areas maintained in the neocortex of the parietal lobe. From the primary areas these signals are transferred to the adjoining "association" areas, and simple percepts become more complex by association (Joseph, 1996).

The Corona Radiata.

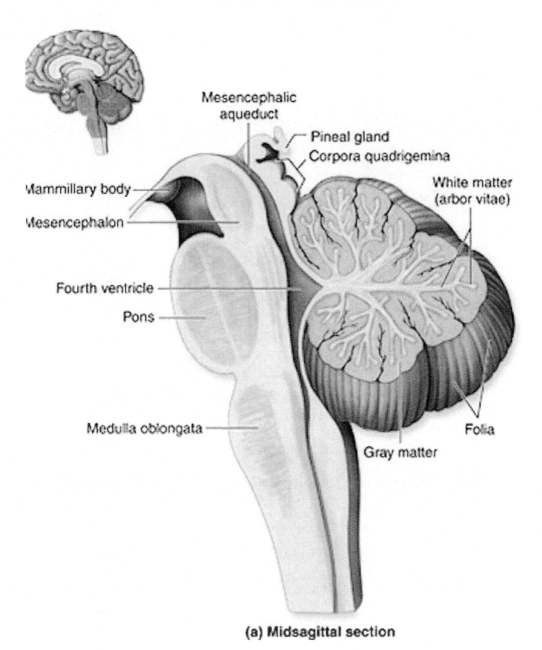

(a) Midsagittal section

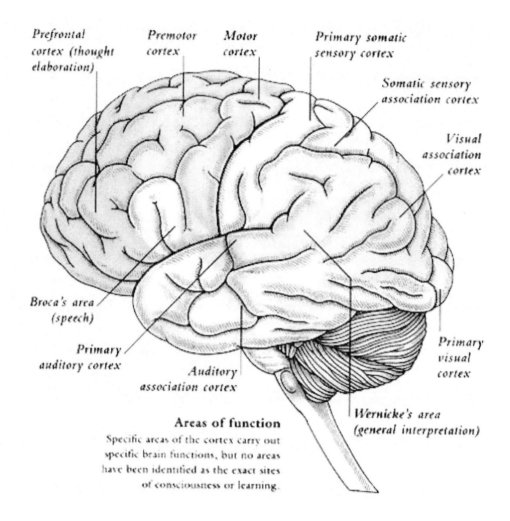

Prefrontal cortex (thought elaboration)

Premotor cortex

Motor cortex

Primary somatic sensory cortex

Somatic sensory association cortex

Visual association cortex

Broca's area (speech)

Primary auditory cortex

Auditory association cortex

Primary visual cortex

Wernicke's area (general interpretation)

Areas of function
Specific areas of the cortex carry out specific brain functions, but no areas have been identified as the exact sites of consciousness or learning.

Monitoring all this perceptual and sensory activity within the thalamus and neocortex is the frontal lobes of the brain, also known as the senior executive of the brain and personality (Joseph 1986b, 1999a; Joseph et al., 1981). It is the frontal lobes which maintain the focus of attention and which can selectively inhibit any additional processing of signals received in the primary areas.

There are two frontal lobes, a right and left frontal lobe which communicate via a bridge of nerve fibers. Each frontal lobe, and subdivisions within each are concerned with different types of mental activity (Joseph, 1999a).

The left frontal lobe, among its many functions, makes possible the ability to speak. It is associated with the verbally expressive, speaking aspects of consciousness. However, there are different aspects of consciousness associated not only with the frontal lobe, but with each lobe of the brain and its subdivisions (Joseph, 1986b; 1996, 12012).

4. Knowing Yet Not Knowing: Disconnected Consciousness

Consider the well known phenomenon of "word finding difficulty" also known as "tip of the tongue." You know the word you want (the "thingamajig") but at the same time, you can't gain access to it. That is, one aspect of consciousness knows the missing word, but another aspect of consciousness associated with talking and speech can't gain access to the word. The mind is disconnected from itself. One aspect of mind knows, the other aspect of mind does not.

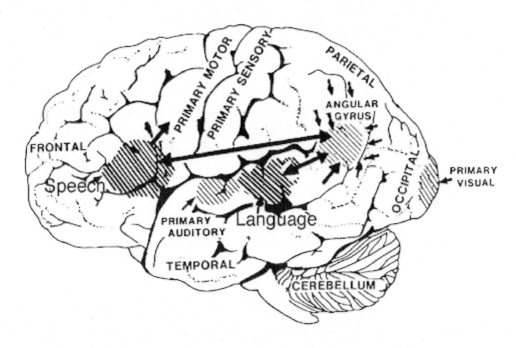

This same phenomenon, but much more severe and disabling, can occur if the nerve fiber pathway linking the language areas of the left hemisphere are damaged. For example, Broca's area in the frontal lobe expresses humans speech. Wernicke's area in the temporal lobe comprehends speech. The inferior parietal lobe associates and assimilates associations so that, for example, we can say the word "dog" and come up with the names of dozens of different breeds and then describe them (Joseph, 1982; Joseph and Gallagher 1985; Joseph et al., 1984). Therefore, if Broca's area is disconnected from the posterior language areas, one aspect of consciousness may know what it wants to say, but the speaking aspect of consciousness will be unable to gain access to it and will have nothing to say. This condition is called "conduction aphasia."

Or consider damage which disconnects the parietal lobe from Broca's area. If you place an object, e.g., a comb, out-of-sight, in the person's right hand, and ask them to name the object, the speaking aspect of consciousness may know something is in the hand, but will be unable to name it. However, although they can't name it, and can't guess if shown pictures, if the patient is asked to point to the correct object, they will correctly pick out the comb (Joseph, 1996).

Therefore, part of the brain and mind may act purposefully (e.g. picking out the comb), whereas another aspect of the brain and mind is denied access to the information that the disconnected part of the mind is acting on.

Thus, the part of the brain and mind which is perceiving and knowing, is not the same as the part of the brain and mind which is speaking. This phenomenon occurs even in undamaged brains, when the multiplicity of minds which make up one of the dominant streams of consciousness, become disconnected and/or are unable to communicate.

5. The Visual Mind: Denial of Blindness

All visual sensations first travel from the eyes to the thalamus and midbrain. At this level, these visual impressions are outside of consciousness, though we may be aware of them. These visual sensations are then transferred to the primary visual receiving areas and to the adjacent association areas in the neocortex of the occipital lobe. Once these visual impressions reach the neocortex, consciousness of the visual word is achieved. Visual consciousness is made possible by the occipital lobe.

Destruction of the occipital lobe and its neocortical visual areas results in cortical blindness (Joseph, 1996, 2012). The consciousness mind is blinded and can not see or sense anything except vague sensations of lightness and darkness. However, because visual consciousness is normally maintained within the occipital lobe, with destruction of this tissue, the other mental systems will not know that they can't see. The remaining mental system do not know they are blind.

Wernicke's area in the left temporal lobe in association with the inferior parietal lobe comprehends and can generate complex language. Normally, visual input is transferred from the occipital to the inferior parietal lobe (IPL) which is adjacent to Wernicke's area and the visual areas of the occipital lobe. Once these signals arrive in the IPL a person can name what they see; the visual input is matched with auditory-verbal signals and the conscious mind can label and talk about what is viewed (Joseph, 1982, 1986b; Joseph et al., 1984). Talking and verbally describing what is seen is made possible when this stream of information is transferred to Broca's area in the left frontal lobe (Joseph, 1982, 1999a). It is Broca's area which speaks and talks.

Therefore, with complete destruction of the occipital lobe, visual consciousness is abolished whereas the other mental system remain intact but are unable to receive information about the visual world. In consequence, the verbal aspects of consciousness and the verbal-language mind does not know it can't see because the brain area responsible for informing these mental system about seeing, no longer exists. . In fact the language-dependent conscious mind will deny that it is blind; and this is called: Denial of blindness.

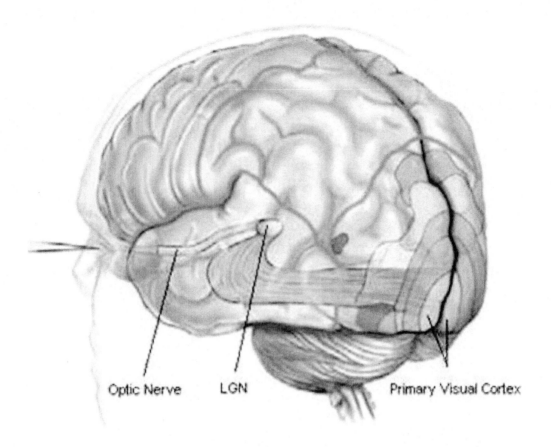

Optic Nerve   LGN   Primary Visual Cortex

Normally, if it gets dark, or you close your eyes, the visual mind becomes conscious of this change in light perception and will alert the other mental realms. These other mental realms do not process visual signals and therefore they must be informed about what the visual mind is seeing. If the occipital lobe is destroyed, visual consciousness is destroyed, and the rest of the brain cannot be told that visual consciousness can't see. Therefore, the rest of the brain does not know it is blind, and when asked, will deny blindness and will make up reasons for why they bump into furniture or can't recognize objects held before their eyes (Joseph, 1986b, 1988a).

For example, when unable to name objects, they might confabulate an explanation: "I see better at home." Or, "I tripped because someone moved the furniture."

Even if you tell them they are blind, they will deny blindness; that is, the verbal aspects of consciousness will claim it can see, when it can't. The Language-dependent aspects of consciousness does not know that it is blind because information concerning blindness is not being received from the mental realms which support visual consciousness.

The same phenomenon occurs with small strokes destroying just part of the occipital lobe. Although a patient may lose a quarter or even half of their visual field, they may be unaware of it. This is because that aspect of visual consciousness no longer exists and can't inform the other mental realms of its condition.

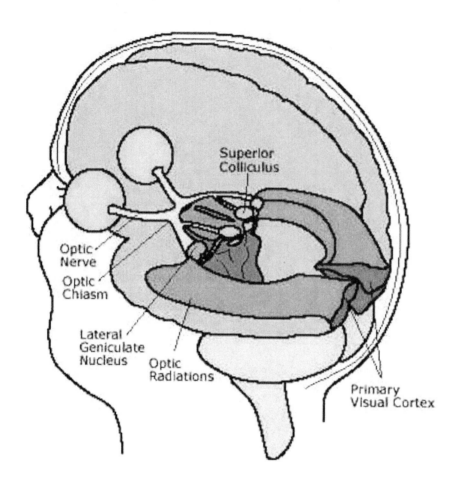

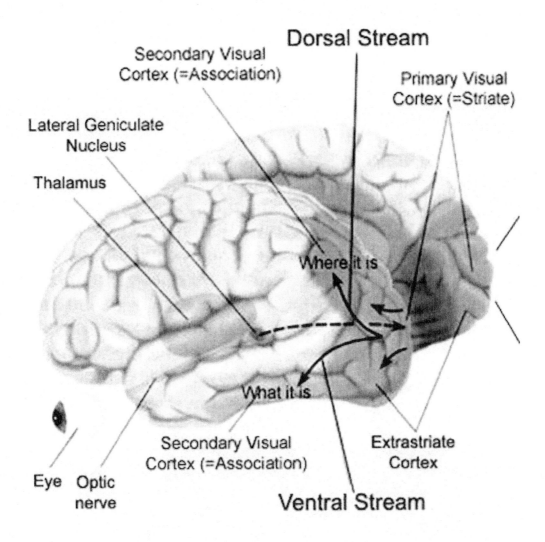

Dorsal Stream

Secondary Visual
Cortex (=Association)

Primary Visual
Cortex (=Striate)

Lateral Geniculate
Nucleus

Thalamus

Where it is

What it is

Secondary Visual
Cortex (=Association)

Extrastriate
Cortex

Eye Optic
nerve

Ventral Stream

6. "Blind Sight"

The brains of reptiles, amphibians, and fish do not have neocortex. Visual input is processed in the midbrain and thalamus and other old-brain areas as these creatures do not possess neocortex or lobes of the brain. In humans, this information is also received in the brainstem and thalamus and is then transferred to the newly evolved neocortex. As is evident in non-mammalian species, these creatures can see, and they are aware of their environment. They possess an older-cortical (brainstem-thalamus) visual awareness which in humans is dominated by neocortical visual consciousness.

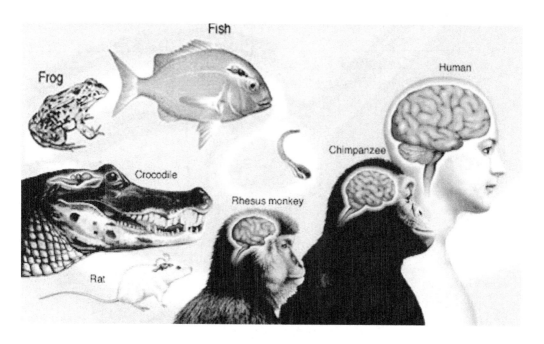

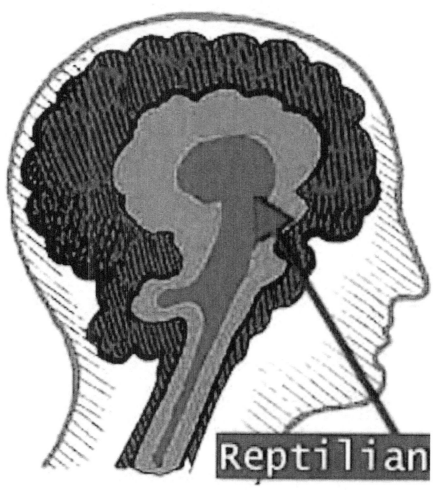

FIGURE: Human Reptile Brain

Therefore, even with complete destruction of the visual neocortex, and after the patient has had time to recover, some patients will demonstrate a non-conscious awareness of their visual environment. Although they are cortically blind and can't name objects and stumble over furniture and bump into walls, they may correctly indicate if an object is moving in front of their face, and they may turn their head or even reach out their arms to touch it--just as a frog can see a fly buzzing by and lap it up with its tongue. Although the patient can't name or see what has moved in front of his face, he may report that he has a "feeling" that something has moved.

Frogs do not have neocortex and they do not have language, and can't describe what they see. However, humans and frogs have old cortex that process visual impressions and which can control and coordinate body movements. Therefore, although the neocortical realms of human consciousness are blind, the mental realms of the old brain can continue to see and can act on what it sees; and this is called: Blind sight (Joseph, 1996).

7. Body Consciousness: Denial of the Body, and Phantom Limbs

All tactile and physical-sensory impressions are relayed from the body to the brainstem and the thalamus, and are then transferred to the primary receiving and then the association area for somatosensory information located in the neocortex of the parietal lobe (Joseph, 1986b, 1996). The entire image of the body is represented in the parietal lobes (the right and left half of the body in the left and right parietal lobe respectively), albeit in correspondence with the sensory importance of each body part. Therefore, more neocortical space is devoted to the hands and fingers than to the elbow.

It is because the body image and body consciousness is maintained in the parietal area of the brain, that victims of traumatic amputation and who lose an arm or a leg, continue to feel as if their arm or their leg is still attached to the body. This is called: phantom limbs. They can see the leg is missing, but they feel as if it is still there; body-consciousness remains intact even though part of the body is missing (Joseph, 1986b, 1996). They may also continue to periodically experience the pain of the physical trauma which led to the amputation, and this is called "phantom limb pain."

Thus, via the mental system of the parietal lobe, consciousness of what is not there, may appear to consciousness as if it is still there. This is not a hallucination. The image of the body is preserved in the brain and so to is consciousness of the body; and this is yet another example of experienced reality being a manifestation of the brain and mind. In this regard, reality is literally mapped into the brain and is represented within the brain, such that even when aspects of this "reality" are destroyed and no longer exists external to the brain, it nevertheless continues to be perceived and experienced by the brain and the associated realms of body-consciousness.

Conversely, if the parietal lobe is destroyed, particularly the right parietal lobe (which maintains an image of the left half of the body), half of the body image may be erased from consciousness (Joseph, 1986b, 1988a). The remaining realms of mind will lose all consciousness of the left half of the body, which, in their minds, never existed.

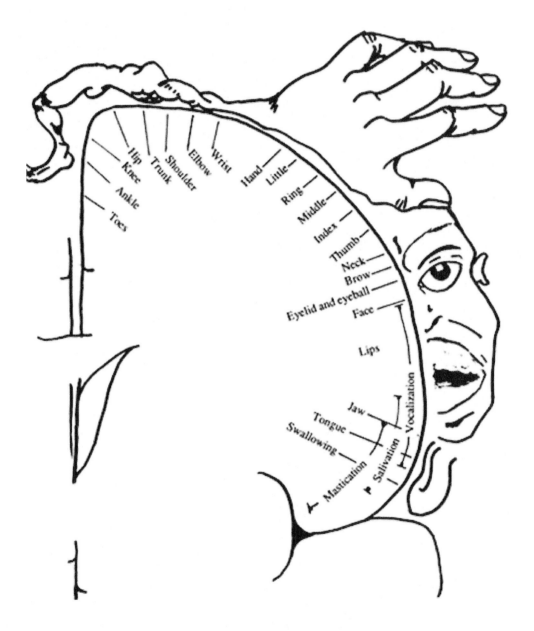

Doctor: "Give me your right hand!" (Patient offers right hand). "Now give me your left!" (The patient presents the right hand again. The right hand is held.)

"Give me your left!" (The patient looks puzzled and does not move.) "Is there anything wrong with your left hand?"

Patient: "No, doctor."

Doctor: "Why don't you move it, then?"

Patient: "I don't know."

Doctor: "Is this your hand?" (The left hand is held before her eyes.)

Patient: "Not mine, doctor."

Doctor: "Whose hand is it, then?"

Patient: "I suppose it's yours, doctor."

Doctor: "No, it's not; I've already got two hands. look at it carefully." (The left hand is again held before her eyes.)

Patient: "It is not mine, doctor."

Doctor: "Yes it is, look at that ring; whose is it?" (Patient's finger with marriage ring is held before her eyes)

Patient: "That's my ring; you've got my ring, doctor. You're wearing my ring!"

Doctor: "Look at it—it is your hand."

Patient: "Oh, no doctor."

Doctor: "Where is your left hand then?"

Patient: "Somewhere here, I think." (Making groping movements near her left shoulder).

Because the body image has been destroyed, consciousness of that half of the body is also destroyed. The remaining mental systems and the language-dependent conscious mind will completely ignore and fail to recognize their left arm or leg because the mental system responsible for consciousness of the body image no longer exists. If the left arm or leg is shown to them, they will claim it belongs to someone else, such as the nurse or the doctor. They may dress or groom only the right half of their body, eat only off the right half of their plates, and even ignore painful stimuli applied to the left half of their bodies (Joseph, 1986b, 1988a).

However, if you show them their arm and leg (whose ownership they deny), they will admit these extremities exists, but will insist the leg or arm does not belong to them, even though the arm or the leg is wearing the same clothes covering the rest of their body. Instead, the language dependent aspects of consciousness will confabulate and make up explanations and thus create their own reality. One patient said the arm belonged to a little girl, whose arm had slipped into the patient's sleeve. Another declared (speaking of his left arm and leg), "That's an old man. He stays in bed all the time."

One such patient engaged in peculiar erotic behavior with his left arm and leg which he believed belonged to a woman. Some patients may develop a dislike for their left arms, try to throw them away, become agitated when they are referred to, entertain persecutory delusions regarding them, and even complain of strange people sleeping in their beds due to their experience of bumping into their left limbs during the night (Joseph, 1986b, 1988a). One patient complained that the person sharing her bed, tried to push her out of the bed and then insisted that if it happened again she would sue the hospital. Another complained about "a hospital that makes people sleep together." A female patient expressed not only anger but concern least her husband should find out; she was convinced it was a man in her bed.

The right and left parietal lobes maintain a map and image of the left and right half of the body, respectively. Therefore, when the right parietal lobe is destroyed, the language-dependent mental systems of the left half of the brain, having access only to the body image for the right half of the body, is unable to become conscious of the left half of their body, except as body parts that they then deduce must belong to someone else.

However, when the language dominant mental system of the left hemisphere denies ownerhip of the left extremity these mental system are in fact telling the truth. That is, the left arm and leg belongs to the right not the left hemisphere; the mental system that is capable of becoming conscious of the left half of their body no longer exist.

When the language axis (Joseph, 1982, 2000), i.e. the inferior parietal lobe, Broca's and Wernicke's areas, are functionally isolated from a particular source of information, the language dependent aspect of mind begins to make up a response based on the information available. To be informed about the left leg or left arm, it must be able to communicate with the cortical area (i.e. the parietal lobe) which is responsible for perceiving and analyzing information regarding the extremities. When no message is received and when the language axis is not informed that no messages are being transmitted, the language zones instead relie on some other source even when that source provides erroneous input (Joseph, 1982, 1986b; Joseph et al., 1984); substitute material is assimilated and expressed and corrections cannot be made (due to loss of input from the relevant knowledge source). The patient begins to confabulate. This is because the patient who speaks to you is not the 'patient' who is perceiving- they are in fact, separate; multiple minds exist in the same head.

8. Split-Brains and Split-Minds.

The multiplicity of mind is not limited to visual consciousness, body consciousness, or the language-dependent consciousness. Rather the multiplicity of mind include social consciousness, emotional consciousness, and numerous other mental realms linked with specific areas of the brain such as the limbic system (emotion), frontal lobes (rational thought), the inferior temporal lobes (memory) and the two halves of the brain where multiple streams of mental activity become subordinated and dominated by two distinct realms of mind; consciousness and awareness (Joseph, 1982, 1986a,b, 1988a,b, 2012).

The brain is not a singularity. This is most apparent when viewing the right and left half of the brain which are divided by the interhemispheric fissure and almost completely split into two cerebral hemispheres. These two brain halves are connected by a rope of nerve fibers, the corpus callosum, which enables them to share and exchange some information, but not all information as these two mental realms maintain a conscious awareness of different realities.

For example, it is well established that the right cerebral hemisphere is dominant over the left in regard to the perception, expression and mediation of almost all aspects of social and emotional functioning and related aspects of social/emotional language and memory. Further, the right hemisphere is dominant for most aspects of visual-spatial perceptual functioning, the comprehension of body language, the recognition of faces including friend's loved ones, and one's own face in the mirror (Joseph, 1988a, 1996).

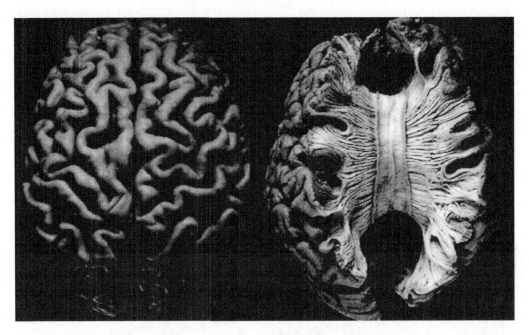

Recognition of one's own body and the maintenance of the personal body image is also the dominant realm of the right half of the brain (Joseph, 1986b, 1988a). The body image, for many, is tied to personal identity; and the same is true of the recognition of faces including one's own face.

The right is also dominant for perceiving and analyzing visual-spatial relationships, including the movement of the body in space (Joseph, 1982, 1988a). Therefore, one can throw or catch a ball with accuracy, dance across a stage, or leap across a babbling brook without breaking a leg.

The perception of environmental sounds (water, wind, a meowing cat) and the social, emotional, musical, and melodic aspects of language, including the ability to sing, curse, or pray, are also the domain of the right hemisphere mental system (Joseph, 1982, 1988a). Hence, it is the right hemisphere which imparts the sounds of sarcasm, pride, humor, love, and so on, into the stream of speech, and which conversely can determine if others are speaking with sincerity, irony, or evil intentions.

By contrast, expressive and receptive speech, linguistic knowledge and thought, mathematical and analytical reasoning, reading, writing, and arithmetic, as well as the temporal-sequential and rhythmical aspects of consciousness, are associated with the functional integrity of the left half of the brain in the majority of the population (Joseph, 1982, 1996). The language-dependent mind is linked to the left hemisphere.

Certainly, there is considerable overlap in functional representation. Moreover, these two mental system interact and assist the other, just as the left and right hands cooperate and assist the other in performing various tasks. For example, if you were standing at the bar in a nightclub, and someone were to tap you on the shoulder and say, "Do you want to step outside," it is the mental system of the left hemisphere which understands that a question about "outside" has been asked, but it is the mental system of the right which determines the underlying meaning, and if you are being threatened with a punch in the nose, or if a private conversation is being sought.

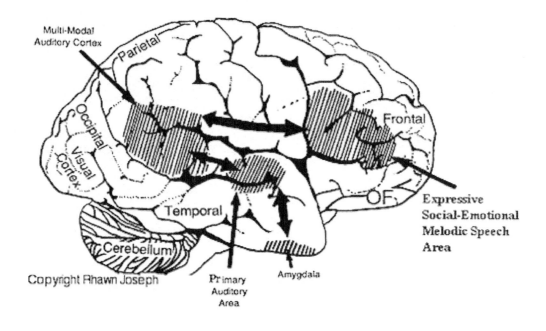

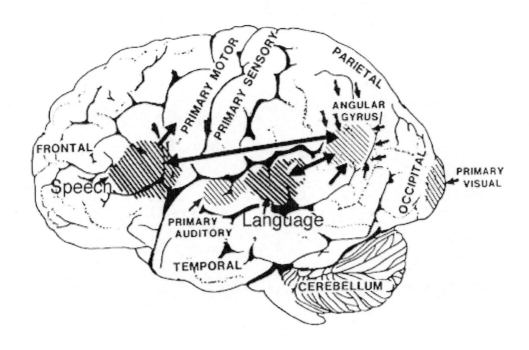

However, not all information can be transferred from the right to the left, and vice versa (Gallagher and Joseph, 1982; Joseph, 1982, 1988a; Joseph and Gallagher, 1985; Joseph et al., 1984). Because each mental system is unique, each "speaks a different language" and they cannot always communicate. Not all mental events can be accurately translated, understood, or even recognized by the other half of the brain. These two major mental systems, which could be likened to "consciousness" vs "awareness" exist in parallel, simultaneously, and both can act independently of the other, have different goals and desires, and come to completely different conclusions. Each mental system has its own reality.

The existence of these two independent mental realms is best exemplified and demonstrated following "split-brain" surgery; i.e. the cutting of the corpus callosum fiber pathway which normally allows the two hemisphere's to communicate.

As described by Nobel Lauriate Roger Sperry (1966, p. 299), "Everything we have seen indicates that the surgery has left these people with two separate minds, that is, two separate spheres of consciousness. What is experienced in the right hemisphere seems to lie entirely outside the realm of awareness of the left hemisphere. This mental division has been demonstrated in regard to perception, cognition, volition, learning and memory."

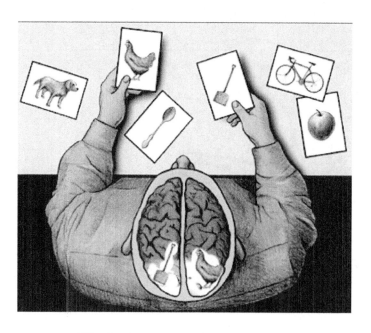

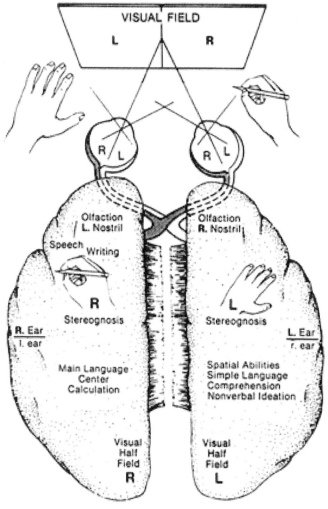

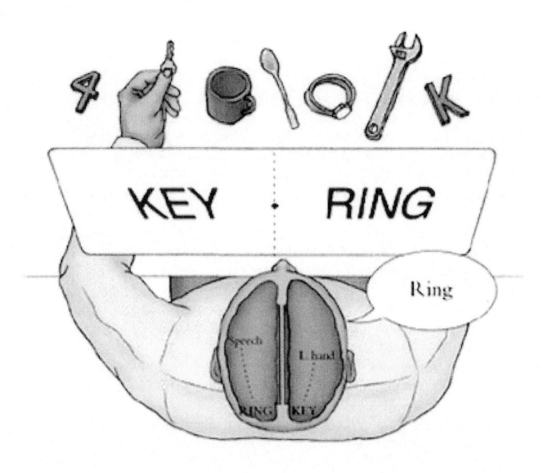

The right half of the brain controls and perceives the left half of the body and visual space, whereas the right half of the body and visual space is the domain of the left hemisphere. Therefore, following split-brain surgery, if a comb, spoon, or some other hidden object is placed in the left hand (out of sight), the left hemisphere, and the language-dependent conscious mind, will not even know the left hand is holding something and will be unable to name it, describe it, or if given multiple choices point to the correct item with the right hand (Joseph 1988a,b; Sperry, 1966). However, the right hemisphere can raise the left hand and not only point to the correct object, but can pantomime its use.

If the split-brain patient is asked to stare at the center of a white screen and words like "Key Ring" are quickly presented, such that the word "Key" falls in the left visual field (and thus, is transmitted to the right cerebrum) and the word "Rings" falls in the right field (and goes to the left hemisphere), the language dependent conscious mind will not see the word "Key." If asked, the language-dependent conscious mind will say "Ring" and will deny seeing the word "Key." However, if asked to point with the left hand, the mental system of the right hemisphere will correctly point to the word "Key."

Therefore, given events "A" and "B" one half of the brain may know A, but know nothing about B which is known only by the other half of the brain. In consequence, what is known vs what is not known becomes relatively imprecise depending on what aspects of reality are perceived and "known" by which mental system (Joseph 1986a; Joseph et al., 1984). There is no such thing as singularity of mind. Since the brain and mind is a multiplicity, "A" and "B" can be known simultaneously, even when one mind is knows nothing about the existence of A or B.

In that the brain of the normal as well as the "split-brain" patient maintains the neuroanatomy to support a multiplicity of mind, and the presence of two dominant psychic realms, it is therefore not surprising that "normal" humans often have difficulty "making up their minds," suffer internal conflicts over love/hate relationships, and are plagued with indecision even when staring into an open refrigerator and trying to decide what to eat. "Making up one's mind" can be an ordeal involving a multiplicity of minds.

However, this conflict becomes even more apparent following split-brain surgery and the cutting of the corpus callosum fiber pathway which links these two parallel streams of conscious-awareness.

Akelaitis (1945, p. 597) describes two patients with complete corpus callosotomies who experienced extreme difficulties making the two halves of their bodies cooperate. "In tasks requiring bimanual activity the left hand would frequently perform oppositely to what she desired to do with the right hand. For example, she would be putting on clothes with her right and pulling them off with her left, opening a door or drawer with her right hand and simultaneously pushing it shut with the left. These uncontrollable acts made her increasingly irritated and depressed."

Another patient experienced difficulty while shopping, the right hand would place something in the cart and the left hand would put it right back again and grab a different item.

A recently divorced male patient complained that on several occasions while walking about town he found himself forced to go some distance in another direction by his left leg. Later (although his left hemisphere was not conscious of it at the time) it was discovered that this diverted course, if continued, would have led him to his former wife's new home.

Geschwind (1981) reports a callosal patient who complained that his left hand on several occasions suddenly struck his wife--much to the embarrassment of his left (speaking) hemisphere. In another case, a patient's left hand attempted to choke the patient himself and had to be wrestled away.

Bogen (1979, p. 333) indicates that almost all of his "complete commissurotomy patients manifested some degree of intermanual conflict." One patient, Rocky, experienced situations in which his hands were uncooperative; the right would button up a shirt and the left would follow right behind and undo the buttons. For years, he complained of difficulty getting his left leg to go in the direction he (or rather his left hemisphere) desired. Another patient often referred to the left half of her body as "my little sister" when she was complaining of its peculiar and independent actions.

Another split-brain patient reported that once when she had overslept her left hand began slapping her face until she (i.e. her left hemisphere) woke up. This same patient, in fact, complained of several instances where her left hand had acted violently toward herself and other people (Joseph, 1988a).

Split brain patient, 2-C, complained of instances in which his left hand would perform socially inappropriate actions, such as striking his mother across the face (Joseph, 1988b). Apparently his left and right hemisphere also liked different TV programs. He complained of numerous instances where he (his left hemisphere) was enjoying a program, when, to his astonishment, the left half of his body pulled him to the TV, and changed the channel.

The right and left hemisphere also liked different foods and had different attitudes about exercise. Once, after 2-C had retrieved something from the refrigerator with his right hand, his left took the food, put it back on the shelf and retrieved a completely different item "Even though that's not what I wanted to eat!" On at least one occasion, his left leg refused to continue "going for a walk" and would only allow him to return home.

In the laboratory, 2-C's left hemisphere often became quite angry with his left hand, and he struck it and expressed hate for it. Several times, his left and right hands were observed to engage in actual physical struggles, beating upon each other. For example, on one task both hands were stimulated simultaneously (while out of view) with either the same or two different textured materials (e.g., sandpaper to the right, velvet to the left), and he was required to point (with the left and right hands simultaneously) to an array of fabrics that were hanging in view on the left and right of the testing apparatus. However, at no time was he informed that two different fabrics were being applied.

After stimulation he would pull his hands out from inside the apparatus and point with the left to the fabric felt by the left and with the right to the fabric felt by the right.

Surprisingly, although his left hand (right hemisphere) responded correctly, his left hemisphere vocalized: "Thats wrong!" Repeatedly he reached over with his right hand and tried to force his left extremity to point to the fabric experienced by the right (although the left hand responded correctly! His left hemisphere didn't know this, however). His left hand refused to be moved and physically resisted being forced to point at anything different. In one instance a physical struggle ensued, the right grappling with the left with the two halves of the body hitting and scratching at each other!

Moreover, while 2-C was performing this (and other tasks), his left hemisphere made statements such as: "I hate this hand" or "This is so frustrating" and would strike his left hand with his right or punch his left arm. In these instances there could be little doubt that his right hemisphere mental system was behaving with purposeful intent and understanding, whereas his left hemisphere mental system had absolutely no comprehension of why his left hand (right hemisphere) was behaving in this manner (Joseph, 1988b).

These conflicts are not limited to behavior, TV programs, choice of clothing, or food, but to actual feelings, including love and romance. For example, the right and left hemisphere of a male split-brain patient had completely different feelings about an ex-girlfriend. When he was asked if he wanted to see her again, he said "Yes." But at the same time, his left hand turned thumbs down!

Another split-brain patient suffered conflicts about his desire to smoke. Although is left hemisphere mental system enjoyed cigarettes, his left hand would not allow him to smoke, and would pluck lit cigarettes from his mouth or right hand and put them out. He had been trying to quit for years.

Because each head contains multiple minds, similar conflicts also plague those who have not undergone split-brain surgery. Each half of the brain and thus each mental system may have different attitudes, goals and interests. As noted above, 2-C experienced conflicts when attempting to eat, watch TV, or go for walks, his right and left hemisphere mental systems apparently enjoying different TV programs or types of food (Joseph 1988b). Conflicts of a similar nature plague us all. Split-brain patients are not the first to choke on self-hate or to harm or hate those they profess to love.

Each half of the brain is concerned with different types of information, and may react, interpret and process the same external experience differently and even reach different conclusions (Joseph 1988a,b; Sperry, 1966). Moreover, even when the goals are the same, the two halves of the brain may produce and attempt to act on different strategies.

Each mental system has its own reality. Singularity of mind, is an illusion.

9. Dissociation and Self-Consciousness

The multiplicity of mind is not limited to the neocortex but includes old cortical structures, such as the limbic system (Joseph 1992). Moreover, limbic nuclei such as the amygdala and hippocampus interact with neocortical tissues creating yet additional mental systems, such as those which rely on memory and which contribute to self-reflection, personal identity, and even self-consciousness (Joseph, 1992, 1998, 1999b, 2001).

For example, both the amygdala and the hippocampus are implicated in the storage of long term memories, and both nuclei enable individuals to visualize and remember themselves engaged in various acts, as if viewing their behavior and actions from afar. Thus, you might see yourself and remember yourself engage in some activity, from a perspective outside yourself, as if you are an external witness; and this is a common feature of self-reflection and self-memory and is made possible by the hippocampus and overlying temporal lobe (Joseph, 1996, 2011).

The hippocampus in fact contains "place neurons" which cognitive map one's position and the location of various objects within the environment (Nadel, 1991; O'Keefe, 1976; Wilson & McNaughton, 1993). Further, if the subject moves about in that environment, entire populations of these place cells will fire. Moreover, some cells are responsive to the movements of other people in that environment and will fire as that person is observed to move around to different locations or corners of the room (Nadel, 1991; O'Keefe, 1976; Wilson and McNaughton, 1993).

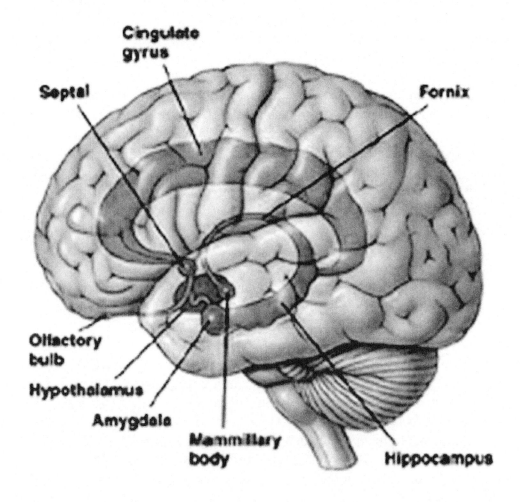

Electrode stimulation, or other forms of heightened activity within the hippocampus and overlying temporal lobe can also cause a person to see themselves, in real time, as if their conscious mind is floating on the ceiling staring down at their body (Joseph, 1998, 1999b, 2001). During the course of electrode stimulation and seizure activity originating in the temporal lobe or hippocampus, patients may report that they have left their bodies and are hovering upon the ceiling staring down at themselves (Daly, 1958; Penfield, 1952; Penfield & Perot 1963; Williams, 1956). That is, their consciousness and sense of personal identity appears to split off from their body, such that they experience themselves as as a consciousness that is conscious of itself as a conscious that is detached from the body which is being observed.

One female patient claimed that she not only would float above her body, but would sometimes drift outside and even enter into the homes of her neighbors. Penfield and Perot (1963) describe several patients who during a temporal lobe seizure, or neurosurgical temporal lobe stimulation, claimed they split-off from their body and could see themselves down below. One woman stated: "it was though I were two persons, one watching, and the other having this happen to me." According to Penfield (1952), "it was as though the patient were attending a familiar play and was both the actor and audience."

Under conditions of extreme trauma, stress and fear, the amygdala, hippocampus and temporal lobe become exceedingly active (Joseph, 1998, 1999b). Under these conditions many will experience a "splitting of consciousness" and have the sensation they have left their body and are hovering beside or above themselves, or even that they floated away (Courtois, 2009; Grinker & Spiegel, 1945; Noyes & Kletti, 1977; van der Kolk 1987). That is, out-of-body dissociative experiences appear to be due to fear induced hippocampus (and amygdala) hyperactivation.

Likewise, during episodes of severe traumatic stress personal consciousness may be fragmented and patients may dissociate and experience themselves as splitting off and floating away from their body, passively observing all that is occurring (Courtois, 1995; Grinker & Spiegel, 1945; Joseph, 1999d; Noyes & Kletti, 1977; Southard, 1919; Summit, 1983; van der Kolk 1987).

Noyes and Kletti (1977) described several individuals who experienced terror, believed they were about to die, and then suffered an out-of body dissociative experience: "I had a clear image of myself... as though watching it on a television screen." "The next thing I knew I wasn't in the truck anymore; I was looking down from 50 to 100 feet in the air." "I had a sensation of floating. It was almost like stepping out of reality. I seemed to step out of this world."

One individual, after losing control of his Mustang convertible while during over 100 miles per hour on a rain soaked freeway, reported that "time seemed to slow down and then... part of my mind was a few feet outside the car zooming above it and then beside it and behind it and in front of it, looking at and analyzing the respective positions of my spinning Mustang and the cars surrounding me. Simultaneously I was inside trying to steer and control it in accordance with the multiple perspectives I was given by that part of my mind that was outside. It was like my mind split and one consciousness was inside the car, while the other was zooming all around outside and giving me visual feedback that enabled me to avoid hitting anyone or destroying my Mustang."

Numerous individuals from adults to children, from those born blind and deaf, have also reported experiencing a dissociative consciousness after profound injury causing near death (Eadie 1992; Rawling 1978; Ring 1980). Consider for example, the case of Army Specialist J. C. Bayne of the 196th Light Infantry Brigade. Bayne was "killed" in Chu Lai, Vietnam, in 1966, after being simultaneously machine gunned and struck by a mortar. According to Bayne, when he opened his eyes he was floating in the air, looking down on his burnt and bloody body: "I could see me... it was like looking at a manikin laying there... I was burnt up and there was blood all over the place... I could see the Vietcong. I could see the guy pull my boots off. I could see the rest of them picking up various things... I was like a spectator... It was about four or five in the afternoon when our own troops came. I could hear and see them approaching... I looked dead... they put me in a bag... transferred me to a truck and then to the morgue. And from that point, it was the embalming process. I was on that table and a guy was telling jokes about those USO girls... all I had on was bloody undershorts... he placed my leg out and made a slight incision and stopped... he checked my pulse and heartbeat again and I could see that too... It was about that point I just lost track of what was taking place.... [until much later] when the chaplain was in there saying everything was going to be all right.... I was no longer outside. I was part of it at this point" (reported in Wilson, 1987, pp 113-114; and Sabom, 1982, pp 81-82).

Therefore, be it secondary to the fear of dying, or depth electrode stimulation, these experiences all appear to be due to a mental system which enables a the conscious mind to detach completely from the body in order to make the body an object of consciousness (Joseph, 1998, 1999b, 2001).

10. Quantum Consciousness

It could be said that consciousness is consciousness of something other than consciousness. Consciousness and knowledge of an object, such as a chair, are also distinct. Consciousness is not the chair. The chair is not consciousness. The chair is an object of consciousness, and thus become discontinuous from the quantum state.

Consciousness is consciousness of something and is conscious of not being that object that is is conscious of. By knowing what it isn't, consciousness may know what it is not, which helps define what it is. This consciousness of not being the object can be considered the "collapse function" which results in discontinuity within the continuuum.

Further, it could be said that consciousness of consciousness, that is, self-consciousness, also imparts a duality, a separation, into the fabric of the quantum continuum. Therefore this consciousness that is the object of consciousness, becomes an abstraction, and may create a collapse function in the continuun.

However, in instances of dissociation, this consciousness is conscious of itself as a consciousness that is floating above its body; a body which contains the brain. The dissociative consciousness is not dissociated from itself as a consciousness, but only from its body. That is, there is an awareness of itself as a consciousness that is floating above the body, and this awareness is simultaneously one with that consciousness, as there is no separation, no abstractions, and no objectification. It is a singularity that is without form, without dimension, without shape.

Moreover, because this dissociated consciousness appears to be continuous with itself, there is no "collapse function" except in regard to the body which is viewed as an object of perception.

Therefore, in these instances we can not say that consciousness has split into a duality of observer and observed or knower and known, except in regard to the body. Dissociated consciousness is conscious of itself as consciousness; it is self-aware without separation and without reflecting. It is knowing and known, simultaneously.

In fact, many patients report that in the dissociated state they achieve or nearly achieved a state of pure knowing (Joseph, 1996, 2001).

A patient described by Williams (1956) claimed she was lifted up out of her body, and experienced a very pleasant sensation of elation and the feeling that she was "just about to find out knowledge no one else shares, something to do with the link between life and death." Another patient reported that upon leaving her body she not only saw herself down below, but was taken to a special place "of vast proportions, and I felt as if I was in another world" (Williams, 1956).

Other patients suffering from temporal lobe seizures or upon direct electrical activation have noted that things suddenly became "crystal clear" or that they had a feeling of clairvoyance, of having the ultimate truth revealed to them, of having achieved a sense of greater awareness and cosmic clarity such that sounds, smells and visual objects seemed to have a greater meaning and sensibility, and that they were achieving a cosmic awareness of the hidden knowledge of all things (Joseph, 1996, 2001).

Although consciousness and the object of consciousness, that which is known, are not traditionally thought of as being one and the same, in dissociative states, consciousness and knowing, may become one and the same. The suggestion is of some type of cosmic unity, particularly as these patients also often report a progressive loss of the sense of individuality, as if they are merging into something greater than themselves, including a becoming one with all the knowledge of the universe; a singularity with god.

Commonly those who experience traumatic dissociative conscious states, not only float above the body, but report that they gradually felt they were losing all sense of individuality as they became embraced by a brilliant magnificent whiteness that extended out in all directions into eternity.

Therefore, rather than the dissociated consciousness acting outside the quantum state, it appears this mental state may represent an increasing submersion back into the continuity that is the quantum state, disappearing back into the continuum of singularity and oneness that is the quantum universe.

Dissociated consciousness may be but the last preamble before achieving the unity that is quantum consciousness, the unity of all things.

11. Conclusion: Quantum Consciousness and the Multiplicity of Mind

What is "Objective Reality" when the mind is a multiplicity which is capable of splitting up, observing itself, becoming blind to itself, and becoming blind to the features of the world which then cease to exist for the remaining mental realms?

Each mental system has its own "reality." Each observer is a multiplicity that engages in numerous simultaneous acts of observation. Therefore, non-local properties which do not have an objective existence independent of the "act of observation" by one mental system, may achieve existence when observed by another mental system. The "known" and the "unknown" can exist simultaneously and interchangeably and this may explain why we don't experience any macroscopic non-local quantum weirdness in our daily lives.

This means that quantum laws may apply to everything, from atoms to monkeys and woman and man and the multiplicity of mind. However, because of this multiplicity, this could lead to seemingly contradictory predictions and uncertainty when measuring macroscopically objective systems which are superimposed on microscopic quantum systems. Indeed, this same principle applies to the multiplicity of mind, where dominant parallel streams of conscious awareness may be superimposed on other mental systems, and which may be beset by uncertainty.

Because of the multiplicity of mind, as exemplified by dissociative states, the observer can also be observed, and thus, the observer is not really external to the quantum state as is required by the standard collapse formulation of quantum mechanics. This raises the possibility that the collapse formulation can be used to describe the universe as a whole which includes observers observing themselves being observed.

The multiplicity of mind also explains why an object being measured by one mental system therefore becomes bundled up into a state where it either determinately has or determinately does not have the property being measured. Measurements performed by one mental system are not being performed by others, such that the same object can have an initial state and a post-measurement state and a final state simultaneously as represented in multiple minds in parallel, or separate states as represented by each mental realm individually.

The collapse dynamics of observation supposedly guarantees that a system will either determinately have or determinately not have a particular property. However, because the observer is observing with multiple mental systems the object can both have and not have specific properties when it is being measure and not measured, simply because it is being measured and not measured, or rather, observed and not observed or its different features observed simultaneously by multiple mental systems. Therefore, it can be continuous and discontinuous in parallel, and different properties can be known and not known in parallel simultaneously.

And the same rules apply to the mental systems which exist in multiplicity within the head of a single observer. Mental systems can become continuous or discontinuous, and can be known and not known simultaneously, in parallel. Thus, the standard collapse formulation can be used to describe systems that contain observers, as the mind/observer can be simultaneously internal and external to the described system.

The mind is a multiplicity and there is no such thing as a "single observer state." Therefore, each element may be observed by multiple observer states which perceive multiple object systems thereby giving the illusion that the object has been transformed during the collapse function. What this also implies is that contrary to the standard or Copenhagen interpretations, states may have both definite position and definite momentum at the same time.

Each mental system perceives a different physical world giving rise to multiple worlds and multiple realities which may be subordinated by one or another more dominant stream of conscious awareness.

Moreover, as the multiplicity of mind can also detach and become discontinuous with the body, whereas dissociative consciousness is continuous with itself, this indicates that the mind is also capable of becoming one with the continuum, and can achieve singularity so that universe and mind become one.

References

Akelaitis, A. J. (1945). Studies on the corpus callosum. American Journal of Psychiatry, 101, 594-599.

Bogen, J. (1979). The other side of the brain. Bulletin of the Los Angeles Neurological Society. 34, 135-162.

Bohr, N. (1934/1987), Atomic Theory and the Description of Nature, reprinted as The Philosophical Writings of Niels Bohr, Vol. I, Woodbridge: Ox Bow Press.

Bohr, N. (1958/1987), Essays 1932-1957 on Atomic Physics and Human Knowledge, reprinted as The Philosophical Writings of Niels Bohr, Vol. II, Woodbridge: Ox Bow Press.

Bohr, N. (1963/1987), Essays 1958-1962 on Atomic Physics and Human Knowledge, reprinted as The Philosophical Writings of Niels Bohr, Vol. III,

Woodbridge: Ox Bow Press.

Casagrande, V. A. & Joseph, R. (1978). Effects of monocular deprivation on geniculostriate connections in prosimian primates. Anatomical Record, 190, 359.

Casagrande, V. A. & Joseph, R. (1980). Morphological effects of monocular deprivation and recovery on the dorsal lateral geniculate nucleus in prosimian primates. Journal of Comparative Neurology, 194, 413-426.

Courtois, C. A. (2009). Treating Complex Traumatic Stress Disorders: An Evidence-Based Guide Daly, D. (1958). Ictal affect. American Journal of Psychiatry, 115, 97-108.

DeWitt, B. S., (1971). The Many-Universes Interpretation of Quantum Mechanics, in B. D.'Espagnat (ed.), Foundations of Quantum Mechanics, New York: Academic Press. pp. 167–218.

DeWitt, B. S. and Graham, N., editors (1973). The Many-Worlds Interpretation of Quantum Mechanics. Princeton University Press, Princeton, New-Jersey.

Eadie, B. J. (1993) Embraced by the light. New York, Bantam

Einstein, A. (1905a). Does the Inertia of a Body Depend upon its Energy Content? Annalen der Physik 18, 639-641.

Einstein, A. (1905b). Concerning an Heuristic Point of View Toward the Emission and Transformation of Light. Annalen der Physik 17, 132-148.

Einstein, A. (1905c). On the Electrodynamics of Moving Bodies. Annalen der Physik 17, 891-921.

Einstein, A. (1926). Letter to Max Born. The Born-Einstein Letters (translated by Irene Born) Walker and Company, New York.

Gallagher, R. E., & Joseph, R. (1982). Non-linguistic knowledge, hemispheric laterality, and the conservation of inequivalance. Journal of General Psychology, 107, 31-40.

Geschwind. N. (1981). The perverseness of the right hemisphere. Behavioral Brain Research, 4, 106-107.

Grinker, R. R., & Spiegel, J. P. (1945). Men Under Stress. McGraw-Hill.

Heisenberg. W. (1930), Physikalische Prinzipien der Quantentheorie (Leipzig: Hirzel). English translation The Physical Principles of Quantum Theory, University of Chicago Press.

Heisenberg, W. (1955). The Development of the Interpretation of the Quantum Theory, in W. Pauli (ed), Niels Bohr and the Development of Physics, 35, London: Pergamon pp. 12-29.

Heisenberg, W. (1958), Physics and Philosophy: The Revolution in Modern Science, London: Goerge Allen & Unwin.

Joseph, R. (1982). The Neuropsychology of Development. Hemispheric Laterality, Limbic Language, the Origin of Thought. Journal of Clinical Psychology, 44 4-33.

Joseph, R. (1986). Reversal of language and emotion in a corpus callosotomy patient. Journal of Neurology, Neurosurgery, & Psychiatry, 49, 628-634.

Joseph, R. (1986). Confabulation and delusional denial: Frontal lobe and later-alized influences. Journal of Clinical Psychology, 42, 845-860.

Joseph, R. (1988) The Right Cerebral Hemisphere: Emotion, Music, Visual-Spatial Skills, Body Image, Dreams, and Awareness. Journal of Clinical Psychology, 44, 630-673.

Joseph, R. (1988). Dual mental functioning in a split-brain patient. Journal of Clinical Psychology, 44, 770-779.

Joseph, R. (1992) The Limbic System: Emotion, Laterality, and Unconscious Mind. The Psychoanalytic Review, 79, 405-455.

Joseph, R. (1996). Neuropsychiatry, Neuropsychology, Clinical Neuroscience, 2nd Edition. Williams & Wilkins, Baltimore.

Joseph, R. (1998). Traumatic amnesia, repression, and hippocampal injury due to corticosteroid and enkephalin secretion. Child Psychiatry and Human Development. 29, 169-186.

Joseph, R. (1999a). Frontal lobe psychopathology: Mania, depression, aphasia, confabulation, catatonia, perseveration, obsessive compulsions, schizophrenia. Psychiatry, 62, 138-172.

Joseph, R. (1999b). The neurology of traumatic "dissociative" amnesia. Commentary and literature review. Child Abuse & Neglect. 23, 71-80.

Joseph, R. (2000). Limbic language/language axis theory of speech. Behavioral and Brain Sciences. 23, 439-441.

Joseph, R. (2001). The Limbic System and the Soul: Evolution and the Neuroanatomy of Religious Experience. Zygon, the Journal of Religion & Science, 36, 105-136.

Joseph, R., & Casagrande, V. A. (1978). Visual field defects and morphological changes resulting from monocular deprivation in primates. Proceedings of the Society for Neuroscience, 4, 1978, 2021.

Joseph, R. & Casagrande, V. A. (1980). Visual field defects and recovery following lid closure in a prosimian primate. Behavioral Brain Research, 1, 150-178.

Joseph, R., Forrest, N., Fiducia, N., Como, P., & Siegel, J. (1981). Electrophysiological and behavioral correlates of arousal. Physiological Psychology, 1981, 9, 90-95.

Joseph, R., Gallagher, R., E., Holloway, J., & Kahn, J. (1984). Two brains, one child: Interhemispheric transfer and confabulation in children aged 4, 7, 10. Cortex, 20, 317-331.

Joseph, R., & Gallagher, R. E. (1985). Interhemispheric transfer and the completion of reversible operations in non-conserving children. Journal of Clinical Psychology, 41, 796-800.

Nadel, L. (1991). The hippocampus and space revisited. Hippocampus, 1,

221-229.

Neumann, J. von, (1937/2001), "Quantum Mechanics of Infinite Systems. Institute for Advanced Study; John von Neumann Archive, Library of Congress, Washington, D.C.

Neumann, J. von, (1938), On Infinite Direct Products, Compositio Mathematica 6: 1-77.

Neumann, J. von, (1955), Mathematical Foundations of Quantum Mechanics, Princeton, NJ: Princeton University Press.

Noyes, R., & Kletti, R. (1977). Depersonalization in response to life threatening danger. Comprehensive Psychiatry, 18, 375-384.

O'Keefe, J. (1976). Place units in the hippocampus. Experimental Neurology, 51-78-100. Pais, A. (1979). Einstein and the quantum theory, Reviews of Modern Physics, 51, 863-914.

Penfield, W. (1952) Memory Mechanisms. Archives of Neurology and Psychiatry, 67, 178-191.

Penfield, W., & Perot, P. (1963) The brains record of auditory and visual experience. Brain, 86, 595-695.

Rawlins, M. (1978). Beyond Death's Door. Sheldon Press.

Ring, K. (1980). Life at Death: A Scientific Investigation of the Near-Death Experience. New York: Quill.

Sabom, M. (1982). Recollections of Death. New York: Harper & Row.

Southard, E. E. (1919). Shell-shock and other Neuropsychiatric Problems. Boston.

Sperry, R. (1966). Brain bisection and the neurology of consciousness. In F. O. Schmitt and F. G. Worden (eds). The Neurosciences. MIT press.

van der Kolk, B. A. (1985). Psychological Trauma. American Psychiatric Press.

Williams, D. (1956). The structure of emotions reflected in epileptic experiences. Brain, 79, 29-67.

Wilson, I. (1987). The After Death Experience. Morrow.

Wilson, M. A., & McNaughton, B. L. (1993). Dynamics of the hippocampus ensemble for space. Science, 261, 1055-1058.

12. Many Mansions: Special Relativity, Higher-Dimensional Space, Neuroscience, Consciousness and Time

John Smythies

Director, Integrative Neuroscience Program, Center for Brain and Cognition, University of California, San Diego

Abstract:

This paper first reviews what is known about the neural correlates of consciousness (NCCs), both at the nerve network and cellular levels, that lays stress the importance of small differences in the dynamic microanatomy of wiring patterns orchestrated by an epigenetic code. However, information about NCCs themselves does not throw light on the logically different problem of how NCCs are related to the phenomenal experiences they induce. To tackle that problem I suggest it is necessary to reformulate our basic concepts of space, time and matter, as well as replacing the psychoneural Identity Theory (IT), whose defects I outline. In particular neuroscience needs to be based on special relativity (SR) in place of the Newtonian cosmology that forms its present framework. This replaces the concept of neurons as 3D entities, that generate physicochemical events in a separate time, with the concept that neurons are 4D structures, whose world lines are extended in the 4D block universe of SR. This requires, as Broad noted, an ontologically independent conscious observer located in a space of its own (phenomenal space). The hypothesis of material dualism suggests that physical space-time (4D) and phenomenal space (3 spatial dimensions) plus 1 dimension of real time—t2, are cross-sections of a common higher dimensional space that are in relative motion in t2 along the time axis of the block universe. This movement generates the 'now' and the passage of the time that we experience. The contents of phenomenal space are our sensations, images and thoughts all causally related to (but not identical with) particular brain events. This hypothesis has implications for what has been called "the idea of another world".

Keywords: Neural correlates of consciousness, epigenetic code, identity theory, special relativity, time, material dualism, Plato's cave, out-of-the-body experiences, near-death experiences, body-image, Hindu psychology, astral body

Introduction

Whereas our knowledge of the neural correlates of consciousness (NCCs) is steadily increasing under the impetus provided by advanced scanning and other neuroscientific techniques (Fingelkurts et al. 2013), the same cannot be said about what this correlation amounts to. A review of the current literature reveals a sorry state of entangled confusion in the very basic concepts with which this attempt is framed, relating in particular to our ideas about space, time, matter and phenomenal consciousness. The dominant hypothesis today is the Identity Theory (IT) which states that consciousness, however defined, must be identical with certain events in particular regions in the brain: but concrete details of how this is done have singularly failed to materialize. The purpose of this essay is to argue that, to order to clarify and solve this problem, it will be necessary to reformulate our basic concepts of space, time and matter. As a preliminary I will present a short account of what is currently known about NCCs.

Neural Correlates Of Consciousness

This information can be presented at two scales—at the macroscopic level and the cellular level. In the former case the leading hypothesis is the Global Workspace theory (Bartolomei and Naccache 2011). This proposes that conscious processing results from coherent neuronal activity between widely distributed brain regions, with fronto-parietal associative cortices as key elements. The main activity involved is the synchronization of neuronal oscillations, in particular in two synchronized networks—the retrolandic (cognitive network) and the frontal (executive control network) (Leon-Carrion et al. 2012). These authors suggest that the executive control network could facilitate the synchronization and coherence of large populations of distant cortical neurons using high frequency oscillations on a precise temporal scale. They suggest that the synchrony between anterior and retrolandic regions is essential to awareness. Other aspects of the role of integrated networks in NCCs are presented by Achard et al. (2012), Demertzi et al. 2013, Orpwood et al. 2013, Lewis et al. (2012) and Smythies et al. (2014).

At the neuronal level some interesting information has been obtained. Evidence from de- and re-afferentation and sensory pathway rerouting experiments show that the modality of a sensory neuron (i.e. whether it is an auditory or a visual neuron) is determined, not by where it is located, but by where it's afferent inflow comes from (Smythies and Edelstein 2013). For example, in blind patients skilled in Braille, axons from the hand region of the somatosensory cortex grow and take over adjacent, and now inactive, neurons in the visual cortex. If these ex-visual neurons are now activated by transcranial magnetic stimulation, the patient feels a touch on the finger. This change is orchestrated by the epigenetic code, whereby the afferent axon transfers instructional epigenetic material (transcription factor proteins and a variety of RNAs including microRNAs) to the post-synaptic neuron, which is thereby restructured (Smythies and Edelstein 2013). The differences between the different sensory cortices (visual, auditory and somatosensory) consist of subtle differences in the microanatomical wiring patterns (brought about in part by the epigenetic code) between these brain areas (Linden and Schriener 2003). Yet the results of their activation results in the enormously qualitatively different type of sensation experienced.

This raises another question. What is it about a neuron's activity that determines what kind of conscious sensation results—is it the pattern of action potentials? Or are sub-threshold dendritic potentials involved? Or it the total electrical field? There is some experimental evidence that throws some light upon this question. If we stimulate the retina with a flashing (stroboscopic) light at a frequency of between 6-18 Herz with both eyes open, the subject will see a series of simple, regular geometrical flickering patterns with such forms as parallel lines, grids, checkerboards, spirals, concentric circles and mazes (Smythies 1959a,b; 1960). However if we stimulate only one retina, the results is quite different. In this case the same geometrical patterns (called the bright phase) appear but these are soon replaced with another quite different series of pattern (called the dark phase). These are non-flickering oily swirls like oil on water or boiling lava, usually in two colors with green and red predominant. These two types of pattern then alternate in retinal rivalry. There is evidence that the dark phase patterns arise in the cortical neurons belonging to the closed eye (Brown and Gebhart 1948). The stimulation may come from the adjacent active neurons belonging to the open eye via direct current carried by the dense interneuronal network provided by the interlinked dendrites of GABAergic interneurons (Fukada et al. 2006). Thus the digital code carried by the open-eye cortical neurons appears to result in the perception of digital flickering geometrical patterns— whereas the analog code carried by the GABAergic network appears to result in the perception of analog oily swirls. However, none of this evidence is directly relevant to the question of what is the relation between these brain events and the events that take place on the stage of consciousness. To answer this we will have to take a look at our fundamental ideas about space, time and matter—starting with space and time.

Special Relativity

One foundational problem here is that, whereas Special Relatively (SR) is accepted in physics, the disciplines of biology and psychology are mired in Newtonian cosmology. Biology still deals with a Newtonian cosmos in which 3D spatially extended organisms move, evolve and behave in a separate time. In contrast, in the Minkowskian block universe of SR, an organism is a stationary 4D material object extended in a 4D space- time. The Earth, for instance is not a globular 3D object rotating in a spiral pathway around another 3D globular object—the sun: rather it is a stationary 4D hyperhelix that is wound around the stationary 4D sun. In Newtonian cosmology matter exists only at the 'now' of time, whereas in SR cosmology matter exists from the beginning to the end of time. Furthermore in SR cosmology the 'now' and the 'passage' of time are not supplied by the physical universe but are subjective 'illusions'. Newtonian cosmology and SR cosmology involve quite different accounts of Darwinian evolution. In the former organisms are born, grow and die over time. In the SR cosmology the evolution of organisms expresses the fact that the stationary world lines of the atoms that constitute them possess a more complicated structure if we examine them 'later' as compared with 'earlier' locations in the block universe. Darwinian evolution is a dynamic process in Newtonian cosmology, but it is a matter of 4D structure in SR cosmology. The appearance of dynamic changes in the physical world experienced by conscious observers is an illusion generated by the movement of the observing consciousness along the time-like dimension of the 4D block universe from the place labeled 'past' towards the place labeled 'future'. Current biology and neuroscience have not accommodated this fact and it is time to do so.

As I am not a physicist it will be fitting to list a series of statements presenting this case from a number of leading physicists and cosmologists Louis de Broglie was one of the founders of quantum theory. He put it thus: "Each observer, as his time passes, discovers, so to speak, new slices of space-time which appear to him as successive aspects of the material world, though in reality the ensemble of events constituting space-time exist prior to his knowledge of them... the aggregate of past, present and future phenomena are in some sense given a priori." (De Broglie, 1959)."

Russell Stannard, Emeritus Professor of Physics, at the Open University makes the static sculpture of the SR universe plain:

"Physics itself recognizes no special moment called 'now' — the moment that acts as the focus of 'becoming' and divides the 'past' from the 'future'. In four-dimensional space-time nothing changes, there is no flow of time, everything simply is...It is only in consciousness that we come across the particular time known as 'now'... It is only in the context of mental time that it makes sense to say that all of physical space-time is. One might even go so far as to say that it is unfortunate that such dissimilar entities as physical time and mental time should carry the same name!" (Stannard, 1987).

Penrose himself (1994) says that in the universe described by special relativity *"...particles do not even move, being represented by "static" curves drawn in space-time". Thus what we perceive as moving 3D objects are really successive cross sections of immobile 4D objects past which our field of observation is sweeping."*

The list continues:

—Quine (1982): *"A drastic departure from English is required in the matter of time. The view to adopt is the Minkowskian one, which sees time as a fourth dimension on a par with the three dimensions of space."*

—Lloyd (1978): *"For the Quinean, what differences we see between past, present and future pertain to our limited mode of access to reality."*

—Heller (1984): "*...a physical object is not an enduring hunk of matter but an enduring spatio-temporal hunk of matter.*"

—Eddington (1920): "*Events do not happen: they are just there, and we come across them ... [as] the observer on his voyage of exploration.*"

—Weyl (1922): "*The objective world simply is, it does not happen. Only to the gaze of my consciousness crawling upward along the life-line [world line] of my body does a section of this world come to life as a fleeting image.*"

—Werth (1978) makes the important point that this new formulation applies to somatic sensation as well as to vision: "*Our apparent body ['body image' is the neurological name for this] at each instant is simply a 'slice' of our four-dimensional body. That is the experiencing subject sequentially 'intersects' his four-dimensional body and 'projects' the sequence of three-dimensional intersections upon the 'screen' of his consciousness: his body appears to him as being ever changing though in physical reality it is a static and immutable four-dimensional object.*"

—Lastly Broad (1953): "*...if we assume one additional spatial dimension beside the three we can observe, and if we suppose that our field of observation at any one moment is confined to the content of a {3,4}-fold which moves uniformly at right angles to itself along a straight line in the {3,4}-fold, then there is no need to assume any other motion in the universe. This one uniform rectilinear motion of the observer's field of observation, together with the purely geometrical properties of the stationary material threads in the four-fold, will account for all the various observed motions (various in both magnitude and direction) of the material particles which are the appearances of these threads in the successive fields of observation.*"

Broad also points out that his assumption requires two 'times'. Time 1 has become fused with space into space-time. But a real time — t2 — is still required in which the 'observer's field of observation' moves through space-time. However, these statements raise a problem. De Broglie speaks of 'each observer', Lloyd of 'our limited mode of access to reality', Eddington of 'the observer on his voyage of exploration', Broad of 'the observer's field of observation'. In these instances the terms 'observer' and 'our' cannot refer, as is usual, to the physical body of the scientist, for this is composed of the world lines of the atoms that make up the physical body and that belongs to the immobile block universe. So what is the "observer", "field of observation", and "gaze of my consciousness" that travels from the past into the future marking the fleeting 'now' of time as it does so? Before we can tackle this question we will need to look at another source of confusion underlying this whole subject. This is the almost universal confusion between physical space and phenomenal space that has its roots in the attempt to believe in two mutually incompatible theories of perception—namely Naïve Realism (NR) and the Representative Theory (RT).

Scientific theories emerge from a background of "common sense" ideas about the world. Early cosmological theories reflected the "obvious" fact that the earth is flat and that the heavens arch above it as a great crystal dome. It took centuries of observation and challenging of dogmas to realize that this model is mistaken. Likewise, most people today, including many philosophers, believe that NR gives an accurate account of how we perceive the world. That is that the colored objects that fill our visual field really are physical objects, or at least the surfaces of physical objects. In contrast the current scientific theory of (visual) perception holds that these colored objects, that we experience, are the products of a long and complex mechanical process which involves light rays landing on the retina and setting off neuronal reactions that spread to the visual cortex where the percepts that we experience are manufactured. Thus our visual system works like television and not like the simple telescope proposed by NR. The contents of our visual fields that we experience are constructs of the visual nervous system and are not direct views of external objects. However, unfortunately most scientists who may adhere to RT in their laboratories, slip back unwittingly into NR as soon as they get home. A similar state of affairs holds in the other spatially organized senses such as somatic sensation. Neurologists have known for more than a century that the body we experience is not the physical body itself but is an image of the body (the "body image") constructed by representative mechanisms of perception. As the neurologist Paul Schilder (1942, 1950) said "...the empirical method leads immediately to a deep insight that even our own body is beyond our immediate reach, that even our own body justifies Prospero's words "We are such stuff as dreams are made on and our little life is rounded by a sleep."

If we reject NR, and accept RT fully, then we can recognize how the problem of the relationship between phenomenal space and physical space arises. Physical space is that in which physical objects are located and extended. Phenomenal space is that in which our spatially organized sensations are located and extended. Under NR these two spaces can be topologically and geometrically the same. Phenomenal objects and events and physical objects and events can be located in the same location in space where they appear to be to the naïve observer. Whereas, under RT one of either of two other systems is necessary. The first is that phenomenal objects and physical objects can be in the same space but must be in different parts of it. Objects and events in phenomenal space can be located in the physical brain that is located in the physical world (as in the Identity Theory IT)—but they cannot be located in the external physical world where they appear to the naïve observer to be. The second possibility is that phenomenal space and physical space are different spaces as expressed in the cosmological theory known as material dualism, which will be the subject of the next section.

Material Dualism

Material dualism is based on the premise that phenomenal space is a real space, with which we have direct experience, and which possesses topological and geometrical properties in which the events we experience are located (French 1987). Wright (1983) proposes that there is a primary 'phenomenal field' that actually exists in which sensations and after-images are located. Fitzgerald (1978) says "None [visual sensations] are located out in physical space: all are in a visual phenomenal space with causal relations with the observer's brain in that the brain's doings produce the sense-data in this space, and indeed the space itself." The neurologist Jason Brown (1991) gets it right I think: "Space itself is an object: volumetric, egocentric, and part of the mind of the observer...Mind is positioned in a space of its own making...We wonder about the limits of the universe but never ask what is beyond the space of a dream."

Phenomenal space may be defined in the following manner. If you obtain a spatially extended visual after-image (e.g. by looking at a square green illuminated surface and then closing your eyes) you can observe that the boundary of that after-image forms a closed Jordan curve that uniquely divides phenomenal space into one inside and one outside. This is an undeniable ontological and topological property of the after-image located in your own phenomenal space (visual field). The image is constructed by causal relations with specific NCCs in your visual cortex.

The fact that the after-image cannot be identical with these NCCs, and so that IT is false, can be shown by the following argument. Leibniz's Law of the Identity of Indiscernibles states that, for any entity A to be identical with an entity B, they must have all properties in common. For example the entities Monte Cervino and the Matterhorn have all their properties in common. 'Monte Cervinio' and 'Matterhorn' are just different names for the same entity. Whereas the after-image described above is square, red and its boundary forms a Jordan curve—whereas their causal NCCs have the shape of a distributed net, the color grey (according to Poirot) and their boundary does not form a Jordan curve. The after-image can be read by the conscious observer to have the same information as the NCCs (i.e. that there is a square red entity out there) but only if that observer already knows that green lights produce red after-images. A similar situation holds for a TV set. The events portrayed have one format inside the set and quite a different format on the TV screen. The events inside the set are not identical with the events on the screen.

It might be argued that this argument fails to recognize the difference between an objective color (physical reflectance and adsorption spectra) and subjective color. In reply I would argue that the word 'color' here is being used to two different senses. The nature of a phenomenal color is simply experienced as a raw fact not amenable to further analysis, whereas the nature of an 'objective' color is discovered by scientific measurements. The 'inner nature' of an objective color—like the 'inner nature' of matter— is not something that we can discover.

With these considerations in mind, it is possible to ask what are the topological and geometrical relations between physical space (ignoring time for the moment) and phenomenal space. There are four, and only four, possible answers.

—PheS is topologically inside all of phyS within the range of vision (as expressed in NR).

—PheS is topologically inside only that portion of phyS that is inside the brain (as expressed in RT and IT).

—PheS and phyS are two different cross-sections of a common higher dimensional space (as suggested by C.D. Broad (1923), Bernard Carr (2008) and myself (Smythies 1994).

—PheS and phyS are wholly different spaces and bear no spatial relations with each other: only causal relations link their contents (physical and phenomenal events respectively (as suggested by Price 1953).

Since we know that NR is false, and the IT fails the Leibniz test, our choice is limited to the other two hypotheses. Of these the fourth can be treated as a minor variant of the third, so I will next discuss the Broad-Carr-Smythies hypothesis in some detail.

Dualistic concepts of mind reach far back into human history, but, in most, the autonomous mind was thought of in terms of non-material spirits in the manner later crystalized by Descartes. However, ideas that the mind might incorporate material elements were developed by the Hindu philosophers of the classical era. They suggested that the mind was material like the body, but of a form of matter so diaphanous as to be undetectable by ordinary instruments.

Joseph Priestly (1777) was the first in the West to take up this topic:

"But how anything could have extension, and yet be immaterial, without coinciding with our idea of mere empty space, I know not. I am therefore bound to conclude, that the sentient principle in man, containing ideas which certainly have parts [is] not the simple, indivisible, and immaterial substance that some have imagined it to be; but something that has real extension and therefore may have the other properties of matter."

The Cambridge philosopher C.D. Broad took the next, and very significant, step in 1923 when he wrote:

"For reasons already stated, it is impossible that sensa should literally occupy places in scientific space, though it may not, of course, be impossible to construct a space-like whole of more than three dimensions, in which sensa of all kinds, and scientific objects literally have places. If so, I suppose, that scientific space would be one kind of section of such a quasi-space, and e.g. a visual field would be another kind of section of the same quasi-space (pp. 392-393)."

Further details of this new theory were supplied by Smythies (1956) who provided links with both neurology and introspectionist psychology. The concept that phenomenal space and physical space are ontologically different spaces has also been expressed briefly by others: Ayer (1940) "...John Stuart Mill and Berkeley fail to distinguish properly between physical space and sensible space."
— Russell (1948) "...*the space in which the physical table is located must be*

different from the space we know by experience"—and Moore (1971) *""...it seems to me just possible that the two sensations in question [those belonging to two coins] though not circular in my private space may yet be circular in physical space".* Unfortunately this work was almost ignored in the 1950s and 1960s owing to the rise of linguistic philosophy. Bernard Carr (2008) was the first physicist to enter this field when he published his theory that phenomenal space and physical space are both cross-sections of a higher-dimensional space. He writes: *"My proposal is that mental and physical space can be integrated into a communal space which is higher dimensional, in the sense that it has more than the three dimensions perceived by our physical sensors. This involves what I call a "Universal Structure."* (see Smythies 1994 pp. 149-150 for details).

This hypothesis can be illustrated by the following introspective experiments.

Sit down in a comfortable chair in a dark room, close your eyes and observe what you experience. First direct your attention to the dark visual field in front of you. Ask yourself what this darkness consists of. Is it just nothing? However, that is not right as evidenced by the difference between retinal blindness and cortical blindness. In the former patients experience a black field whereas in the latter they experience nothing at all.

When you open your eyes your visual field becomes filled with colored mobile shapes i.e. your visual sensations. When you close your eyes again these vanish to be replaced by the black uniform field. So what lies behind this field? IT would say that other neurons lie behind it. This hypothesis entails that the black field itself consists of activity in NCCs and what lies behind them must be activity in pre-NCCs.

A similar situation holds in the case of somatic sensations. Sitting in your chair examine your bodily sensations. These will consist of a variety of feelings of touch, pressure, stretch, itch, proprioception, tingling and others that make up your body image. IT holds that these are composed of NCCs and what lies immediately outside them is activity in pre-NCCs—because your body image that you experience is identical, according to IT, not with your actual physical body but with Penfield's homunculus located in your somatosensory cortex. In contrast, the theory of material dualism holds that all the contents of your phenomenal consciousness, including your phenomenal visual field and your body-image, lie outside the brain altogether and are located in a space of their own.

We can illustrate this by considering how IT and this theory deal with the image of Plato's cave (Smythies 1994). In this model, prisoners have always been strapped to posts and cannot move their heads. Behind them a great fire burns. Statues of objects are carried behind them so that their shadows fall on the wall of the cave in front of the prisoners. Would not the prisoners, Plato asks, then consider that these shadows represent reality? In IT Plato's cave is the brain and the shadows represent NCCs in the visual cortex. In material dualism the cave is an extra part of the human organism (the 'consciousness module') located outside the brain in a (higher-dimensional) space of its own that has an inner screen on which the shadows (our actual visual sensations) are projected. For a modern version of Plato's cave we can use television. A mad scientist takes an infant and straps a TV set over its eyes with an external camera so that the developing child will see on its TV screen whatever the camera is pointing at. Would not this child grow up believing that the TV images, that are all she ever sees, were the objects televised themselves that she can feel by touch (Wright 1983).

To account for the 'now' and the passage of time in this new theory we must add a detail. As Broad (1953) noted in the earlier quotation, the theory needs two times. Time in the sense of past, present and future becomes the fourth dimension of space, as in SR. The 'now' and the passage of time requires a second real time t2 in which the time- traveling 'field of observation' described above travels from the past into the future. Geometrically this can be expressed in the following way. Any n-dimensional structure (say a cube) can be cut by two (n-1) D structures (in this case planes). The resulting planes can either be parallel or they can intersect. The 4D cross-section A of Carr's 5D Universal Structure that contains phenomenal space-time and the cross-section B that is physical space-time are different cross-sections of the Universal Structure. If these cross- sections are not parallel but intersect then they (and their contents) can be in relative motion to each other along the time axis of B in t2. This entails that the 'now' of time is wherever A (that carries phenomenal consciousness) has reached in its travel along B. The existence of this second time might find confirmation in some Near Death Experience reports which mention that during the experience the notions of time or of duration may disappear leading to notions of "no time" or "eternal present" along with the feeling of a 'second sort of time" (Jourdan 2011).

The proposed causal interactions between events in NCCs and events in phenomenal consciousness can be represented by higher-dimensional vectors. Causal interactions between events wholly inside A, or wholly inside B, can be represented by vectors (straight lines) that are geometrically wholly within A or wholly within B. Interactions between events in A and events in B can be represented by vectors that originate in one of these and terminate in the other, crossing the dimensional interface between these two spaces as they do so. A dimensional interface is any surface that an n- dimensional space presents to an n+1 dimensional space of which it is a cross section— for example the surface of a plane that is a cross-section of a cube.

Material dualism also has implications for "the idea of another world" (Price 1953). If phenomenal events are ontologically separate from physical events and exist in a space (or space-time) of their own, they could continue to exist in some form after the wreck of the brain. This hypothesis is congruent with the proposal that the physical world exists as a means of communication between Selves that lie outside it in a phenomenal world of their own. This supports the notion that the events reported by observers during out-of-the-body experiences (OBEs) and near-death experiences (NDEs) suggest what these post-mortem experiences may be like (Jourdan 2010). However, the theory suggests one basic change. Since it holds that the Self and its phenomenal consciousness were never geometrically in the physical body, the term out-of-the-body needs changing. During our present life the Self is located in the body-image, not the body, under any valid theory. To return to Plato's cave: the picture drawn by Plato refers to events during our present life. After the death of the brain the observers may be freed from their chains and can leave the cave (or sensorium) and are able to explore the beautiful countryside around it. Hindu psychology has long held that, in addition to our physical body, we also have an astral body that could survive the death of the physical body. Material dualism supports this idea but with an important difference. The Hindu theory is based on the idea that we experience the physical body: and the astral body only hovers in the wings as it were. However, the truth may be is that which we always experience—i.e. the body image— metamorphoses under different circumstances into the astral body during OBEs, NDEs and after death itself.

Conclusion

The theory of material dualism represents a paradigmic change in our basic concepts of space, time and matter.

—The real world, according to Newton, consists of 3D physical objects that exist in a separate time. Matter only exists at the 'now' of time.

—According to Special Relativity the real world consists a 4D block of matter in which t_1 time and physical space are fused into space-time. Matter exists throughout space-time. The 'now' of time and the passage of time are held to be 'subjective illusions'.

—In material dualism the real world consists of a 5D spatiotemporal system (involving t_1) of which the Einsteinian physical world and the phenomenal world are located in two different cross-sections. These both exist in real time t_2. Thus the world contains two different kinds of matter i.e. physical matter (atoms and fields: brains and planets) and phenomenal matter (sensations, images and thoughts). The two interact via causal relations between events in the NCCs in the brain and events in phenomenal consciousness.

REFERENCES

Achard S, Delon-Martin C, Vértes PE, Renard F, Schenck M, Schneider F, Heinrich C, Kremer S, Bullmore ET. (2012) Hubs of brain functional networks are radically reorganized in comatose patients. Proc Natl Acad Sci U S A. 2012 Dec 11;109(50):20608-13. doi: 10.1073/pnas.1208933109. Epub 2012 Nov 26.

Ayer, A.J. (1940) comments I P. Laslett (ed.) The Physical Basis of mind.. Blackwell., Oxford, UK.

Bartolomei F1, Naccache L. (2011) The global workspace (GW) theory of consciousness and epilepsy. Behav Neurol. 2011;24(1):67-74. doi: 10.3233/BEN-2011-0313.

Broad, C.D. (1923), Scientific Thought (London: Routledge & Kegan Paul).

Broad, C.D. (1953) Religion, Philosophy and Psychical Research .(London: Routledge & Kegan Paul).

Brown and Gebhardt JW. (1948) Visual field articulation in the absence of spatial stimulus gradients. J. Exp. Psychol. 38, 188-200.

Brown, J. W. The Life of the Mind. London, Erlbaum, 1988.

Carr, B. (2008) Worlds apart? Proceedings of the Society for Psychical Research, 59, 1- 96.

de Broglie, L. (1959), 'A general survey of the scientific work of Albert Einstein', in Albert EinsteinPhilosopher-Scientist, ed. P.A. Schlipp (New York: Harper & Row), pp. 107–28.

Demertzi A, Soddu A, Laureys S. (2013) Consciousness supporting networks. Curr Opin Neurobiol. 2013 Apr;23(2):239-44. doi: 10.1016/j.conb.2012.12.003. Epub 2012 Dec 27. Review.

Eddington, A.S. (1920), Space, Time and Gravitation (Cambridge: Cambridge University Press).

Fingelkurts, A.A., Fingelkurts, A.A., Bagnato, S., Boccagni, C., and Galardi, G. (2013) Dissociation of vegetative and minimally conscious patients based on brain operational architectonics: factor of etiology. Clinical Electroencephalography and Neuroscience, 2013 May 10. [Epub ahead of print].

Fitzgerald, P. (1978) Review of C.W.K. Mundle Perception, Facts and Theories, in Philosophy of Science, 45, 165-169.

French R.E. (1987) The Geometry of Vision and the Mind Body Problem. New York: Lang.

Fukada H, Kosaka T, Singer W, Gakuske RA. (2006) Gap junctions among dendrites of cortical GABAergic neurons establish a dense and widespread intercolumnar network. J.Neurosci. 26, 8589-8604. doi: 10.1523/JNEUROSCI.4076-05.2006.

Heller, M. (1984), 'Temporal parts of four dimensional objects', Philosophical Studies, 46, pp. 323–34.

Jourdan J-P. (2010) Deadline. Paris: Les Tres Orangers.

Jourdan J-P. (2011) Near Death Experiences and the 5th dimensional spatio-temporal perspective. J. Cosmol. 14, 4743-4762. http://journalofcosmology.com/Consciousness152.html

Leibniz G. W. (1981) New Essays on Human Understanding. (P. Remnant and J. Bennett Tr.). Cambridge University Press. 1981.

Leon-Carrion J, Leon-Dominguez U, Pollonini L, Wu MH, Frye RE, Dominguez- Morales MR, Zouridakis G. (2012) Synchronization between the anterior and posterior cortex determines consciousness level in patients with traumatic brain injury (TBI). Brain Res. 2012 Oct 2;1476:22-30. doi: 10.1016/j. brainres.2012.03.055. Epub 2012 Mar 29.

Lewis LD1, Weiner VS, Mukamel EA, Donoghue JA, Eskandar EN, Madsen JR, Anderson WS, Hochberg LR, Cash SS, Brown EN, Purdon PL. (2012) Rapid fragmentation of neuronal networks at the onset of propofol-induced unconsciousness. Proc Natl Acad Sci U S A. 2012 Dec 4;109(49):E3377-86. doi: 10.1073/pnas.1210907109. Epub 2012 Nov 5.

Lloyd, G. (1978), 'Time and existence', Philosophy, 53, pp. 215–28.

Moore, G.E. (1971) Philosophical Studies. Harcourt and Brace, New York, US.

Orpwood R. (2013) Qualia could arise from information processing in local cortical networks. Front Psychol. 2013 Mar 14;4:121. doi: 10.3389/ fpsyg.2013.00121. eCollection 2013.

Penrose, R. (1994), Shadows of the Mind: A Search for the Missing Science of Consciousness (Oxford: Oxford University Press).

Price, H.H. (1953) Survival and the idea of another world. Proc.Soc. Psychical Res. 50, 1-25.

Priestly, J. (1777) Disquisitions relating to Matter and Spirit. Johnson, London, UK.

Russell, B. (1948) Human Knowledge. Its Scope and Limits. Allen and Unwin, London, UK (pp. 45 & 582-593).

Schilder, P. Mind. Perception and Thought in their Constructive Aspects. New York. Columbia University Press. 1942.

Schilder, P. The Image and Appearance of the Human Body. New York. International Universities Press, 1950.

Smythies J. (1959a) The stroboscopic patterns. Part I. The dark phase. Brit.J.Psychol. 50, 106-116.

Smythies J. (1939b) The stroboscopic patterns. Part II. The phenomenology of the bright phase and after-images. Brit.J.Psychol. 50, 305-324. DOI: 1e.1111/j.2044- 8295.1959.tb00710.x

Smythies J. (1960) The stroboscopic patterns: part III. Further experiments and discussion, Brit.J.Psychol, 247-255. DOI: 10.1111/j.2044-8295.1960.tb00747.x

Smythies, J. The Walls of Plato's Cave. Aldershot, Averbury Press, 1994.

Smythies J, Edelstein L. (2013) Transsynaptic modality codes in the brain: possible involvement of synchronized spike timing, microRNAs, exosomes and epigenetic processes. Frontiers in Intregrative Neuroscience. 2012;6:126. doi: 10.3389/fnint.2012.00126. Epub 2013 Jan 4.

Stannard, R. (1987), 'Making sense of God's time', The Times, August 22nd.

Werth, L.F. (1978), 'Normalizing the paranormal', American Philosophical Quarterly, 15, pp. 47–56.

Weyl, H. (1922), Space-Time-Matter (London: Constable).

Wright (1983) Inspecting images. Philosophy. 58. 57-72.

13. Brain, Consciousness, and Free Will

Andrea Nani[1], Andrea E. Cavanna[2,3]

[1]School of Psychology, University of Turin, Italy.
[2]Dept. of Neuropsychiatry, BSMHFT, University of Birmingham, UK.
[3]Dept. of Neuropsychiatry, Institute of Neurology, University College London

Abstract

Consciousness seems to be a fundamental ingredient of human life: our common sense tells us that without it we would not behave in the same way. However since the end of the XIX century among some philosophers and scientists have become increasingly familiar with a counterintuitive position on the place of consciousness in nature, known as epiphenomenalism. Epiphenomenalism excludes from scientific accounts of human behavior any appeal to conscious processes occurring in the brain. Its main claim is that conscious experience is an epiphenomenon of brain activity, without causal powers in terms of volition and action. This paper examines the issue whether consciousness can be regarded as a mere epiphenomenon from both the theoretical and empirical perspective. The epiphenomenalist theory is analyzed with reference to the work of leading neuroscientist Gerald Edelman and neurological syndromes defined by key alterations in conscious domains. It is argued that conscious states are likely to play essential causal roles in the scientific account of how the brain brings about the voluntary actions that contribute to form our deepest personal identities.

Key Words: Causality, Consciousness, Edelman, Epiphenomenalism, Neurology

1. Introduction. The Temptation of Epiphenomenalism

One of the most enduring and intriguing questions for both philosophical and scientific researchers is whether we have conscious minds capable to control and produce the motivations for all our actions. In the light of our common experience, an affirmative answer to that question would be but a platitude. Indeed, brains seem to be capable to create a great variety of mental events. Love, hate, sadness, joy, sorrow, pleasure, shame, grief, delight, and resentment are only a few of the many different psychological states composing our rich mental lives. However, on more accurate reflection the solution to the problem of the nature of consciousness would not appear as evident as it may seem at first sight.

There are, in fact, philosophers and neuroscientists who firmly believe that mental properties, particularly the conscious ones, are wholly epiphenomenal with respect to brain processes (Edelman 2004, 2007; Fuster 2003). According to epiphenomenalism, mental properties are superfluous by-products of the function of our cerebral mechanism, just like the images which are reflected by mirrors are not made by glass, and the shadows which objects cast on the ground are not parts of those objects. This view is not new: in a famous conference held at the British Association for the Advancement of Science, Thomas Henry Huxley compared consciousness to the steam whistle of a locomotive (Huxley 1884). In contrast with Descartes, Huxley did not consider animals as unconscious machines, but was very perplexed with regard to the exact function of consciousness and hypothesized that conscious states played no role in behavioral mechanisms (Huxley 1874). Just as the steam whistle of a locomotive did not influence the work of the locomotive's motor, he thought, so animal consciousness could neither cause nor modify animal behavior. Being also a strenuous advocate of Darwin's theory of natural selection, Huxley assumed for reasons of biological continuity that there are no differences between animal and human consciousness (Huxley 1884).

We can affirm that the modern shape of the problem of epiphenomenalism was set with Huxley, even though he never used this word in his writings. In effect, the Modern Age (post-Cartesian) thinkers did not tend to contrast sharply the concepts of mind and body. Ancient Greeks had a much broader idea of mind, closely linked with bodily functions (Bremmer 1983). Mind (i.e. the soul) was considered the principle of life capable to animate the body in order for it to perform its basic biological processes, such as breathing, digestion, procreation, growth, motion, and, for humans, also other sophisticated processes of life, such as thinking, perceiving, imagining, and reasoning. Of course every school of ancient Greek philosophy had its own concept of "soul". For instance, Aristotle thought of the soul as the body's system of active abilities to accomplish the vital functions that organisms naturally perform, e.g. nutrition, movement or thought (Nussbaum and Rorty 1992). On the other hand, Stoic philosophy of mind conceived the soul itself as a corporeal entity (Inwood 2003). This position was similar to that of Epicurus, who taught the soul to be a kind of body composed of atomic particles (Kerferd 1971). Perhaps Plato and the Pythagoreans held the closest concept of soul to the Cartesian view. They maintained it to be as something incorporeal and able to exist independently of the body (Lorenz 2008; Huffman 2009). Nevertheless, it is only after Descartes' philosophy that the debate of mental causation was to be set down in its modern form. An important echo of this debate is to be found in the discussion upon the automatism of behavior raised by Huxley in the second half of the nineteenth century.

Positions similar to those embraced by Huxley are still held by some contemporary philosophers and neuroscientists. Epiphenomenalists would be willing to explain the origin of consciousness in the same way as we can physically explain how mirrors produce reflected images or bodies cast their shades on the ground. According to this explanatory model, all our psychological states should, in theory, be accounted for entirely in terms of scientific vocabularies which contain no mental concepts.

A similar approach, at least in relation to its practical consequences for psychological research, was maintained by Burrhus Skinner with his theory of "radical behaviorism". Skinner supported the view that mental terms could be completely paraphrased in behavioral terms, or eliminated from explanatory discourse altogether (Skinner 1974). Therefore, all accounts of human behavior would have to be given in neutral and objective terms, such as stimulus, response, conditioning, reinforcement, and so on. This position has some analogies with epiphenomenalism in that it considers consciousness a nonphysical entity which has nothing to do with behavior.

Such epiphenomenalist lines of reasoning imply that a rigorous discourse on human actions should deny the reality of consciousness, and thereby of all mental states correlated with this phenomenon. In fact, when human beings express propositions about conscious states, they actually intend to speak of other things, specifically of certain brain physical states which are to be the unique causes of all their bodily dispositions. In William James' words, "consciousness ... would appear to be related to the mechanism of [the] body simply as a collateral product of its working, and to be completely without any power of modifying that working" (James 1890). In a sense, arguing that conscious mental phenomena are causally real would be like arguing that the black spots which are on the tails of some fishes are real eyes capable of seeing and not just evolutionary tricks for misleading predators.

The solution offered by epiphenomenalism to the problem of the nature of consciousness can be roughly summarized in the assertion that such a problem does not exist because we have no consciousness, but only the illusion of having it. Although epiphenomenalism could be somehow attractive, it does not present a satisfactory solution to the problem of what consciousness really is. The present paper will show that the epiphenomenalist perspective does not offer a consistent account of certain neuropsychological phenomena which seem to be intrinsically subjective.

We will start by examining the arguments that drive some philosophers and neuroscientists to regard consciousness as an empty concept involving outdated thinking.

2. Causal Links

Epiphenomenalism upholds that the conscious mind is not part of the physical world. This implies that, given the physical causal closure of the universe, conscious mental events cannot interact with the physical reality in any way. If we think of ourselves as consciously acting agents, the epiphenomenalist claim sounds counterintuitive: is it plausible that our conscious will cannot influence the physical world?

In order to answer this question we first need a better understanding of exactly what it means to claim that conscious mental events cannot influence physical events in any way. This doctrine implies that the only possible type of causation we have to deal with is the so-called bottom-up causality, i.e. the causation that goes from the physical level to the conscious one. According to this concept of causality, the irresistible desire for an apple pie cannot actually cause the act of eating a slice of pie, since the account of our behavior is to be determined only at the physical level, where physical entities move other physical entities. However, if all causation processes belong to the physical level, how could our ontological catalogue list phenomena which are not included in causal accounts of behavioral expressions given in physical terms only? A reasonable philosophical precept (epitomized by Occam's razor) warns us that ontology should not be expanded without necessity. Moreover, there is the problem of defining the nature of those phenomena. If these entities were completely different from physical processes, then conscious mental events would necessarily belong to a distinct ontological domain, but it is easy to conclude that in such a case epiphenomenalism would be just like a spurious kind of dualism. On the other hand, if conscious mental events were physical phenomena of a very special nature, how could we distinguish the physical events capable to cause other physical events from the ones which have no causal power at all?

We cannot actually make a distinction of this kind by means of the third person vocabulary that scientists generally use to depict their objective vision of the world. Therefore, those who trust epiphenomenalism would have to include in their ontological catalogue states, events, and processes susceptible to be described exclusively in terms of the first person perspective, and to identify these states, events, and processes with non-causal physical phenomena. In addition, this sort of phenomena would have to be put together with all the other states, events, and processes liable both to be described in terms of the third person perspective and to be identified with causal physical phenomena. However, it is by no means clear why some processes – whose nature is basically physical – would have to be described exclusively in terms of the first person perspective rather than third person perspective.

In addition to these conceptual difficulties, a further grave quandary is whether we maintain the division between causal and non-causal physical events. In other words, taken for granted such a division, what in this case would the principle of the physical causal closure precisely mean? The principle of the physical causal closure states that if a physical event has a cause that occurs at t, it has a physical cause that occurs at t. Jaegwon Kim (2005) correctly observes that the "physical causal closure does not by itself exclude nonphysical causes, or causal explanations, of physical events." For instance, there could be a nonphysical causal explanation of a physical event being the first ring of a chain of other numerous physical events. According to Kim (2005), in order to rule out this kind of explanation, we need an exclusion principle such as the following: if an event e has a sufficient cause c at t, no event at t distinct from c can be a cause of e.

Following the principle of exclusion, the sufficient cause c of e at time t may be either physical or mental. However, this instance is ruled out if the principle of exclusion is linked to the principle of the physical causal closure and the event e is identified with an event whose nature is purely physical. As a result, the two principles joined together hold that only physical events can cause other physical events.

It is important to highlight that these two principles are not stricto sensu in contrast with the folk psychology view that there is a conscious mind in every human being. Moreover, these assumptions are consistent with the hypothesis of psycho-physical parallelism, according to which there could be a distinct domain of specific conscious mental events coming to occur whenever other particular physical events come to occur. Still it is unconditionally denied that conscious mental phenomena can causally interact with physical phenomena. In fact, in order to be closed, any causal explanation is to be expressed as a chain of purely physical events. This leads us back to our previous question: if we accept that both epiphenomenal events and non-causal physical entities can by no means be part of scientific accounts given in causal physical terms, then why should we expand our ontology without necessity by including allegedly redundant conscious phenomena?

3. An Argument from Quantum Physics?

An interesting argument against the plausibility of epiphenomenalism can be derived from a specific interpretation of the theory of quantum mechanics. It is well-known that the act of measurement is a crucial aspect from the perspective of quantum theory. The implications and the account of this process has been the subject of controversy for more than seven decades and the debate does not seem to be closed yet.

The fundamental point of the argument from quantum physics holds that the observer's consciousness plays a key role in the collapse of the wave function to a certain state, described by a second-order differential equation by Erwin Schrödinger. The root of this idea can be found in the so-called Copenhagen interpretation of quantum mechanics. Although the Copenhagen interpretation is not a homogenous view (Howard 2004), Heisenberg (1955) appears to be the one who first coined the term and developed the underlying philosophy as a unitary interpretation (Heisenberg 1958). On the other hand, Niels Bohr – the Danish physicist commonly regarded as the father of the Copenhagen interpretation – never seems to have emphasized or privileged the role of the observer in the wave packet collapse (Howard 1994). Bohr argued for an interpretation of complementarity with regard to the wave-particle duality which is incompatible with Heisenberg's interpretation of wave function collapse (Gomatam 2007). Bohr's view regarding the wave function was more moderate than Heisenberg's and based on epistemological concerns, rather than ontological commitments. When Bohr referred to the subjective character of quantum phenomena he was not referring to the conscious intervention of the observer in the process of measurement, but to the context-dependent status of all physical observations (Murdoch 1987; Faye 1991). However the drastic theoretical move – outlined in Heisenberg's writings – that quantum measurement is to be understood by involving the observer's act in addition to a physical process, has become the core of the so-called Copenhagen interpretation.

This idea was further developed by other physicists. Von Neumann (1932) postulated an ad hoc intervention of an observing system in order to account for the collapse or reduction of the wave function through measurement. Quite cautiously, he never claimed that the observing system had to be conscious (von Neumann 1932). In contrast to von Neumann's view, London and Bauer (1932) attributed to the oberver's consciousness only the key role in understanding the process of quantum measurement. Such a proposal was later expanded on by the physicist Eugene Wigner, according to whom "it was not possible to formulate the laws (of quantum theory) in a fully consistent way without reference to consciousness" (Wigner 1967).

The proposal to consider consciousness as causally involved in physical state reductions was further developed following Heisenberg, von Neumann, and Wigner (Stapp 1993, 1999, 2006; Schwartz et al. 2005). Undoubtedly, this approach challenges the epiphenomenal position. In fact, how is it possible for consciousness to be non-causal if it can bring about the collapse of the wave packet? If those who champion the Copenhagen interpretation are right, then epiphenomenalism should be completely refuted. On the one hand, this approach gives a fundamental causal power to consciousness in understanding the universe; on the other hand, it has the serious shortcoming of putting consciousness outside the physical world. In fact, if consciousness really causes the collapse of the wave function, then it must be a process that is not be describable by Schrödinger equation, because otherwise it would be caught in an infinite regress. Based on these arguments, consciousness should be a nonphysical entity. Therefore, if both the principle of the physical causal closure and the principle of exclusion discussed in the previous section are true, the so-called Copenhagen interpretation of quantum mechanics does not provide a strong argument for refuting epiphenomenalism.

4. Consciousness and Causality

In view of the foregoing reflections, we would have to be very reluctant to claim the distinction between causal and non-causal physical events or between causally efficacious physical and causally efficacious nonphysical events, although these distinction are of course logically possible. Accordingly, both philosophers and neuroscientists well-disposed to epiphenomenalism have to maintain that the nature of conscious mental processes cannot be physical, since, by definition, a state/event/process exists in physical terms only if it has the property of influencing and exerting causal effects over other physical entities.

An interesting type of neuroscientific approach is exemplified by the epiphenomenalist position held by Gerald Edelman, a leading neuroscientist who has given remarkable contributions to the study of mind and consciousness and their place in nature (Edelman 1989, 1993, 2007). According to Edelman's approach ("Neural Darwinism"), different configurations or patterns of neurons compete with each other to gain constancy and stability within the brain. The Neural Darwinism approach holds that groups of neurons and the neural patterns and configurations which nerve cells form ("neural networks") are subject to natural selection, just like biological species are evolutionarily selected by the environment. Specifically, Edelman's theory of "neuronal group selection" postulates that anatomical connectivity in the brain occurs via selective mechanochemical events that take place epigenetically during development. This process creates a structurally diverse primary repertoire by differential reproduction. A second selective process occurs during postnatal behavioral experience through epigenetic modifications in the strength of synaptic connections between neuronal groups, thus creating a diverse secondary repertoire by differential amplification.

In Edelman's view, human consciousness depends on and arises from the uniquely complex physiology of the human brain. He advanced a theory of how the brain generates different levels of consciousness through multiple parallel re-entrant connections between individual cells and between larger neuronal groups, in which he endorsed an epiphenomenalist position with regard to consciousness, which is central to the scope of this paper (Edelman 2004, 2007).

It has been argued that the question whether consciousness can have a causal role in determining behavior and other mental states should find an answer supported by both conceptual and empirical considerations. (Flanagan 1992; Heil and Mele 1993; Searle 2004). Contrary to this view, Edelman seems to give pre-eminence to theoretical arguments over empirical results. In fact his thesis – that consciousness is not causal – is almost exclusively based upon the following theoretical argument:

This account [which is that conscious processes arise from enormous numbers of re-entrant interactions between different areas of the brain] implies that the fundamental neural activity of the reentrant dynamic core converts the signals from the world and the brain into a "phenomenal transform" – into what it is like to be that conscious animal, to have its qualia. The existence of such a transform (our experience of qualia) reflects the ability to make high-order distinctions or discriminations that would not be possible without the neural activity of the core. Our thesis has been that the phenomenal transform, the set of discriminations, is entailed by that neural activity. It is not caused by that activity but it is, rather, a simultaneous property of that activity. (Edelman, 2004).

Edelman's idea is that some cerebral processes entail certain phenomenal transforms, which are the contents of our conscious mental states. Following him, we can call the cerebral processes C' and the phenomenal transforms C. We can put both C' and C in a row and index them to indicate their successive states in time: C'0–C0; C'1–C1; C'2–C2; C'3–C3; and so forth. It is crucially important to highlight how in that view only the underlying cerebral processes are endowed with causal powers, whereas the phenomenal processes entailed by those brain states are not. However the relationship between the cerebral processes and the phenomenal transforms is considered by Edelman as necessary. This necessary correlation appears to be of a metaphysical kind, i.e. a correlation that holds in every possible world. Therefore, Edelman's position does not appear to be consistent with the philosophical "zombie argument", which assumes the existence of an individual capable to behave just in the same way as conscious human beings do, but in the absence of any subjective conscious experience (in Edelman's words, an individual having C' but not C). In fact, Edelman claims that "The argument we are making here implies, however, that if C' did not entail C, it could not have identical effects" (Edelman 2004; the emphasis is not ours). Consequently, an individual lacking C (phenomenal consciousness) cannot show the same behavior of an individual who has C. Indeed, specific activities of the nervous system necessarily give rise to particular conscious sensations, which in turn cannot exist without a specific underlying activity of the brain. As a result, the zombie hypothesis should be utterly inconsistent (Jackson 1982).

Edelman's theory is central to the discourse on epiphenomenalism advanced so far. In fact, the phenomenal properties which he refers to are necessarily implied by the underlying neural activity of the brain. Strictly speaking, those phenomenal properties are not redundant but absolutely non-causal, even though they have a sort of physical nature. In addition, those properties have to be seen as by-products, since they cannot play any specific role in our scientific account of natural phenomena. Therefore, neither the principle of physical causal closure nor the principle of physical exclusion seem to be violated by Edelman's perspective.

In our view, the arguments put forward by Edelman in order to demonstrate the epiphenomenalist nature of consciousness raise a number of issues. What is most unclear is the very nature of the necessary relationship between the causal physical events (i.e., the cerebral processes or C') and the non-causal physical events (i.e., the mental processes or C). If we accept that this relationship is necessary, there is no reason to assume an ontology in which conscious mental processes and physical processes within the nervous system are distinct. If a certain property is necessarily implied by certain physical processes (in such a way that the latter could not bring about the same effect without the former, as Edelman claims), then either that very property and those physical processes are different aspects of the same entity, or that very property is part of the co-occurring physical processes. From the logical point of view, an effect cannot find its cause in one event which is the result of the sum of a causal physical state and a non-causal physical state, since the non-causal physical process cannot play any causal role at all (Heil and Mele 1993). In fact, what Edelman believes to be non-causal, "the phenomenal transform", must be provided with causal powers.

In this sense, Edelman's theory with regard to the epiphenomenalist nature of consciousness appears to be anomalous. A "true" epiphenomenalist would, in fact, plausibly think of the causal relationship between physical and conscious states as contingent rather than necessary. Thus, epiphenomenalists should be willing to accept the zombie argument, since it is logically possible to accept that, if conscious mental processes are contingent, there could be possible worlds in which they do not bring about any behavioral effect.

In addition to these theoretical considerations, empirical data can raise other reservations with regard to epiphenomenalism. For example, if we agree on depriving mental entities of their causal role, we would encounter difficulties accounting for a host of well described neurological conditions. These include, but are not limited to, blindsight (cortical blindness with preserved ability to locate objects), unilateral neglect syndrome (loss of ability to detect information coming from the left side of the body), allochiria (experience of a sensory stimulation at the contralateral side to the applied stimulus), anosognosia (denial of gross neurological deficit), prosopognosia (inability to recognize familiar faces), and somatoparaphrenia (a condition in which patients deny ownership of a limb or an entire side of their body). Arguably, these neurological disorders can be explained at least to some extent in terms of a dysfunction in the causal role played by consciousness in dealing with perceptive or proprioceptive information.

The understanding of somatoparaphrenia is an exemplar case, based on the concept of verbal manifestations commonly referred to as propositional attitudes in the tradition of analytic philosophy (Bisiach and Geminiani 1991). Propositional attitudes are all the expressions whose contents consist of subjective beliefs, desires, intentions, fears, etc. In case of a patient showing somatoparaphrenic symptoms, it is plausible to suppose that a dysfunction in the conscious processing of proprioceptive information about the patient's limb (for instance, the left leg), results in the patient holding the belief that the leg does not belong to his body. Patients with somatoparaphrenia will therefore verbally deny that they own that leg, and some of them have in fact been reported trying to reject the limb that they perceive as alien (Critchley 1974).

Somatoparaphrenia has been described, with a few exceptions, in patients suffered from right parietal (or parieto-occipital) lobe injury – and almost invariably concerns the left side of the body. This condition is usually associated with motor and somatosensory deficits, and with the syndrome of unilateral spatial neglect. In a study on 79 acute stroke right-brain-damaged patients (Baier and Karnath 2008), 12 patients showed anosognosia for hemiplegia. Eleven out of these 12 patients exhibited somatoparaphrenic symptoms, and 6 among them displayed the strong belief that their limbs belonged to another person. In other cases, body parts can be just felt by the patient as separated from the body (Starkstein et al. 1990). More complex symptoms have been described: for instance, a patient can refer to the affected limb as "a make-believe leg" (Levine et al. 1991), or as "a baby in bed" (Richardson 1992).

The spectrum of somatoparaphrenic symptoms is wide, however a distinction can be drawn between misidentifications that can be corrected by patients when the error is pointed out by the examiner, and delusions that stubbornly resist to the examiner's demonstration (Feinberg et al. 2005). It is referred to fully-fledged somatoparaphrenia only in the second category of symptoms.

In sum, somatoparaphrenic phenomena do not imply a mental illness and can be characterized as follows (Vallar and Ronchi 2009):

the feeling of estrangeness and/or separation of the affected body parts;
delusional beliefs of disownership of the affected body parts;
delusional beliefs that the affected body parts belong to another person;
complex delusional misidentifications of the affected body parts;
associated disorders, such as supernumerary limbs, personification, and misoplegia (hatred for the affected limbs).

Overall, available data suggest that patients showing somatoparaphrenic symptoms suffer from impairments in the higher-level processes concerned with body awareness and ownership. Therefore it seems reasonable to hypothesize that if certain behaviors do not occur without specific conscious sensations accompanied by the beliefs which refer to them (i.e. mental representations of the body), then those specific conscious sensations and their consequent beliefs must play an important causal role in the process that produces this kind of behavior.

5. Conclusion

In specific scientific contexts, it seems mandatory to apply concepts which carry a commitment for a causal role for consciousness. For the sake of the unity of science, it seems justified to take the physical causal closure for granted; on the other hand, it does not seem as well justified to take for granted the clear-cut distinction traced by epiphenomenalism between the physical world and the conscious mind. However, neither the common version of epiphenomenalism (in which conscious states are contingent), nor its variant proposed by Edelman (in which consciousness and the physical world are necessarily intertwined), appear to be a valid theory to explain the nature of consciousness. The theoretical and empirical arguments advanced in this article show that it is likely for consciousness to play fundamental roles in the genesis of behavior. Undoubtedly much more is to be done, especially on the side of the empirical research, in order to unravel the actual brain mechanisms of conscious causal processes.

References

Baier B., Karnath H.O. (2008), Tight link between our sense of limb ownership and self-awareness of actions. Stroke: 486-488.

Bisiach E., Geminiani G. (1991), Anosognosia related to hemiplegia and hemianopia. Prigatano G.P., Schacter D.L. (eds.), Awareness of deficit after brain injury, Oxford: Oxford University Press.

Bremmer, J. (1983), The Early Greek Concept of the Soul, Princeton: Princeton University Press.

Critchley M. (1974), Misoplegia or hatred of hemiplegia. Mt.Sinai Journal of Medicine 41: 82-87.

Edelman, G.M. (1989), The Remembered Present: A Biological Theory of Consciousness, New York: Basic Books.

Edelman, G. M. (1993), Neural Darwinism: The Theory of Neuronal Group Selection. Neuron 10: 115-125.

Edelman, G.M. (2004), Wider than the Sky. The Phenomenal Gift of Consciousness, Yale University Press.

Edelman, G.M. (2007), Second Nature, Brain Science and Human Knowledge, Yale University Press.

Faye, J. (1991), Niels Bohr: His Heritage and Legacy. An Antirealist View of Quantum Mechanics, Dordrecht: Kluwer Academic Publisher.

Feinberg, T.E., DeLuca, J., Giacinto, J.T., Roane, D.M, Solms, M. (2005), Right-hemisphere pathology and the self. Feinberg, T.E., Keenan, J.P. (eds.) The lost self. Pathologies of the brain and identity, Oxford: Oxford University Press, pp. 10-130.

Flanagan, O. (1992), Consciousness reconsidered, MIT Press, Cambridge Mass. Fuster, J. M. (2003), Cortex and Mind, Oxford University Press.

Gomatam, R. (2007), Niels Bohr's Interpretation and the Copenhagen Interpretation — Are the two incompatible? Philosophy of Science, 74, December issue.

Heil, J. and Mele, A. eds. (1993), Mental Causation, Oxford University Press.

Heisenberg, W. (1955), The Development of the Interpretation of the Quantum Theory. In W. Pauli (ed.), Niels Bohr and the Development of Physics, 35, London: Pergamon.

Heisenberg, W. (1958), Physics and Philosophy: The Revolution in Modern Science, London: Goerge Allen & Unwin.

Howard, D. (1994), What Makes a Classical Concept Classical? Toward a Reconstruction of Niels Bohr's Philosophy of Physics. In Faye, J., and Folse, H., eds., Niels Bohr and Contemporary Philosophy. Series: Boston Studies in the Philosophy of Science, vol. 158. Dordrecht: Kluwer Academic Publisher.

Howard, D. (2004), Who Invented the "Copenhagen Interpretation?" A Study in Mythology. Philosophy of Science 71, pp. 669-682.

Huffman, C. A. (2009), The Pythagorean Conception of the Soul from Pythagoras to Philolaus. Body and Soul in Ancient Philosophy, D. Frede and B. Reis (eds.), Berlin: Walter de Gruyter.

Huxley, T.H. (1874), On the Hypothesis That Animals Are Automata, and Its Hystory. Fortnightly Review 95: 555-580. Reprinted in Collected Essays, London: Macmillan, 1893.

Huxley, T.H. (1884), Animal Automatism, and Other Essays, Humboldt Library of Popular Science Literature, New York: I. Fitzgerald.

Inwood, B. (2003), The Cambridge Companion to the Stoics, Cambridge: Cambridge University Press.

Jackson, F. (1982), Epiphenomenal qualia. Philosophical Quarterly32: 127-136.

James, W. (1890), The Principles of Psychology, reprint. New York: Dover, 1950.

Kerferd, G., 1971, Epicurus' doctrine of the soul. Phronesis 16: 80–96.

Kim, J. (2005), Physicalism, or Something Near Enough, Princeton University Press, Princeton.

Levine, D.N., Calvanio, R., Rinn, W.E. (1991), The pathogenesis of anosognosia for hemiplegia. Neurology 41: 1770-1781.

London, F., and Bauer, E. (1939), La théorie de l'observation en mécanique quantique. Hermann, Paris. English translation: The theory of observation in quantum mechanics. In Wheeler J.A., and Zurek, W.H., eds., (1983), Quantum Theory and Measurement, Princeton University Press, Princeton.

Lorenz, H. (2008), Plato on the Soul. The Oxford Handbook of Plato, G. Fine (ed.), Oxford: Oxford University Press.

Murdoch, D. (1987), Niels Bohr's Philosophy of Physics, Cambridge: Cambridge University Press.

Neumann, J. von (1932), Die mathematischenGrundlagen der Quantenmechanik, Springer, Berlin. Reprinted in English (1955), Mathematical Foundations of Quantum Mechanics. Princeton University Press, Princeton.

Nussbaum, M. C. & Rorty, A. O., eds., (1992) Essays on Aristotle's De Anima, Oxford: Clarendon Press.

Richardson, J.K. (1992), Psychotic behavior after right hemispheric cerebrovascular accident: a case report. Arch. Phys. Med. Rehabil. 73: 381-384.

Robinson, H. M. (1978), Mind and Body in Aristotle. The Classical Quarterly 28: 105-124.

Schwartz, J.M., Stapp, H.P., and Beauregard, M. (2005), Quantum theory in neuroscience and psychology: a neurophysical model of mind/brain interaction. Philosophical Transactions of the Royal Society B 360, 1309-1327.

Searle, J. R. (2004), Mind, a brief introduction, Oxford University Press.

Skinner, B. (1974), About Behaviorism, New York: Vintage.

Stapp, H.P. (1993), A quantum theory of the mind-brain interface. Mind, Matter, and Quantum Mechanics, Springer, Berlin, pp. 145-172.

Stapp, H.P. (1999), Attention, intention, and will in quantum physics. Journal of Consciousness Studies 6(8/9), pp. 143-164.

Stapp, H.P. (2006), Clarifications and Specifications In Conversation with Harald Atmanspacher. Journal of Consciousness Studies 13(9), pp. 67-85.

Starkstein, S.E., Berthier, M.L., Fedoroff, P., Price, T.R., Robinson, R.G. (1990), Anosognosia and major depression in 2 patients with cerebrovascular lesions. Neurology 40: 1380-1382.

Vallar, G., Ronchi, R. (2009), Somatoparaphrenia: a body delusion. A review of the neuropsychological literature. Experimental Brain Research 192: 533-551.

Wigner, E.P. (1967), Symmetries and Reflections, Indiana University Press, Bloomington.

14. Consciousness in the Universe: Neuroscience, Quantum Space-Time Geometry and Orch OR Theory

Roger Penrose, PhD, OM, FRS[1],
and Stuart Hameroff, MD[2]

[1]Emeritus Rouse Ball Professor, Mathematical Institute, Emeritus Fellow, Wadham College, University of Oxford, Oxford, UK
[2]Professor, Anesthesiology and Psychology, Director, Center for Consciousness Studies, The University of Arizona, Tucson, Arizona, USA

Abstract

The nature of consciousness, its occurrence in the brain, and its ultimate place in the universe are unknown. We proposed in the mid 1990's that consciousness depends on biologically 'orchestrated' quantum computations in collections of microtubules within brain neurons, that these quantum computations correlate with and regulate neuronal activity, and that the continuous Schrödinger evolution of each quantum computation terminates in accordance with the specific Diósi–Penrose (DP) scheme of 'objective reduction' of the quantum state (OR). This orchestrated OR activity (Orch OR) is taken to result in a moment of conscious awareness and/or choice. This particular (DP) form of OR is taken to be a quantum-gravity process related to the fundamentals of spacetime geometry, so Orch OR suggests a connection between brain biomolecular processes and fine-scale structure of the universe. Here we review and update Orch OR in light of criticisms and developments in quantum biology, neuroscience, physics and cosmology. We conclude that consciousness plays an intrinsic role in the universe.

KEY WORDS: Consciousness, microtubules, OR, Orch OR, quantum computation, quantum gravity

1. Introduction: Consciousness, Brain and Evolution

Consciousness implies awareness: subjective experience of internal and external phenomenal worlds. Consciousness is central also to understanding, meaning and volitional choice with the experience of free will. Our views of reality, of the universe, of ourselves depend on consciousness. Consciousness defines our existence.

Three general possibilities regarding the origin and place of consciousness in the universe have been commonly expressed.

(A) Consciousness is not an independent quality but arose as a natural evolutionary consequence of the biological adaptation of brains and nervous systems. The most popular scientific view is that consciousness emerged as a property of complex biological computation during the course of evolution. Opinions vary as to when, where and how consciousness appeared, e.g. only recently in humans, or earlier in lower organisms. Consciousness as evolutionary adaptation is commonly assumed to be epiphenomenal (i.e. a secondary effect without independent influence), though it is frequently argued to confer beneficial advantages to conscious species (Dennett, 1991; 1995; Wegner, 2002).

(B) Consciousness is a quality that has always been in the universe. Spiritual and religious approaches assume consciousness has been in the universe all along, e.g. as the 'ground of being', 'creator' or component of an omnipresent 'God'. Panpsychists attribute consciousness to all matter. Idealists contend consciousness is all that exists, the material world an illusion (Kant, 1781).

(C) Precursors of consciousness have always been in the universe; biology evolved a mechanism to convert conscious precursors to actual consciousness. This is the view implied by Whitehead (1929; 1933) and taken in the Penrose-Hameroff theory of 'orchestrated objective reduction' ('Orch OR'). Precursors of consciousness, presumably with proto-experiential qualities, are proposed to exist as the potential ingredients of actual consciousness, the physical basis of these proto-conscious elements not necessarily being part of our current theories of the laws of the universe (Penrose and Hameroff, 1995; Hameroff and Penrose, 1996a; 1996b).

2. Ideas for how consciousness arises from brain action

How does the brain produce consciousness? An enormous amount of detailed knowledge about brain function has accrued; however the mechanism by which the brain produces consciousness remains mysterious (Koch, 2004). The prevalent scientific view is that consciousness somehow emerges from complex computation among simple neurons which each receive and integrate synaptic inputs to a threshold for bit-like firing. The brain as a network of 10^{11} 'integrate-and-fire' neurons computing by bit-like firing and variable-strength chemical synapses is the standard model for computer simulations of brain function, e.g. in the field of artificial intelligence ('AI').

The brain-as-computer view can account for non-conscious cognitive functions including much of our mental processing and control of behavior. Such non-conscious cognitive processes are deemed 'zombie modes', 'auto-pilot', or 'easy problems'. The 'hard problem' (Chalmers, 1996) is the question of how cognitive processes are accompanied or driven by phenomenal conscious experience and subjective feelings, referred to by philosophers as 'qualia'. Other issues also suggest the brain-as-computer view may be incomplete, and that other approaches are required. The conventional brain-as-computer view fails to account for:

The 'hard problem' Distinctions between conscious and non-conscious processes are not addressed; consciousness is assumed to emerge at a critical level (neither specified nor testable) of computational complexity mediating otherwise non-conscious processes.

'Non-computable' thought and understanding, e.g. as shown by Gödel's theorem (Penrose, 1989; 1994).

'Binding and synchrony', the problem of how disparate neuronal activities are bound into unified conscious experience, and how neuronal synchrony, e.g. gamma synchrony EEG (30 to 90 Hz), the best measurable correlate of consciousness does not derive from neuronal firings.

Causal efficacy of consciousness and any semblance of free will. Because measurable brain activity corresponding to a stimulus often occurs after we've responded (seemingly consciously) to that stimulus, the brain-as-computer view depicts consciousness as epiphenomenal illusion (Dennett, 1991; 1995; Wegner, 2002).

Cognitive behaviors of single cell organisms. Protozoans like Paramecium can swim, find food and mates, learn, remember and have sex, all without synaptic computation (Sherrington, 1957).

In the 1980s Penrose and Hameroff (separately) began to address these issues, each against the grain of mainstream views.

3. Microtubules as Biomolecular Computers

Hameroff had been intrigued by seemingly intelligent, organized activities inside cells, accomplished by protein polymers called microtubules (Hameroff and Watt, 1982; Hameroff, 1987). Major components of the cell's structural cytoskeleton, microtubules also accounted for precise separation of chromosomes in cell division, complex behavior of Paramecium, and regulation of synapses within brain neurons (Figure 1). The intelligent function and periodic lattice structure of microtubules suggested they might function as some type of biomolecular computer.

Microtubules are self-assembling polymers of the peanut-shaped protein dimer tubulin, each tubulin dimer (110,000 atomic mass units) being composed of an alpha and beta monomer (Figure 2). Thirteen linear tubulin chains ('protofilaments') align side-to-side to form hollow microtubule cylinders (25 nanometers diameter) with two types of hexagonal lattices. The A-lattice has multiple winding patterns which intersect on protofilaments at specific intervals matching the Fibonacci series found widely in nature and possessing a helical symmetry (Section 9), suggestively sympathetic to large-scale quantum processes.

Along with actin and other cytoskeletal structures, microtubules establish cell shape, direct growth and organize function of cells including brain neurons. Various types of microtubule-associated proteins ('MAPs') bind at specific lattice sites and bridge to other microtubules, defining cell architecture like girders and beams in a building. One such MAP is tau, whose displacement from microtubules results in neurofibrillary tangles and the cognitive dysfunction of Alzheimer's disease (Brunden et al, 2011). Motor proteins (dynein, kinesin) move rapidly along microtubules, transporting cargo molecules to specific locations.

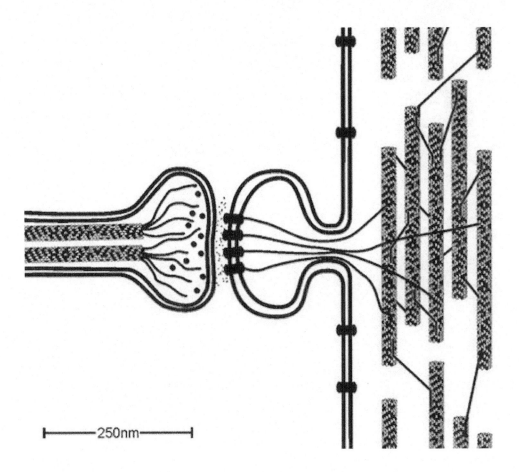

Figure 1. Schematic of portions of two neurons. A terminal axon (left) forms a synapse with a dendritic spine of a second neuron (right). Interiors of both neurons show cytoskeletal structures including microtubules, actin and microtubule-associated proteins (MAPs). Dendritic microtubules are arrayed in mixed polarity local networks, interconnected by MAPs. Synaptic inputs are conveyed to dendritic microtubules by ion flux, actin filaments, second messengers (e.g. CaMKII, see Hameroff et al, 2010) and MAPs.

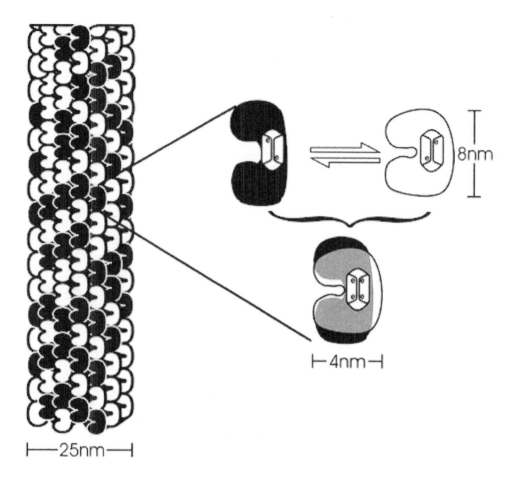

Figure 2. Left: Portion of single microtubule composed of tubulin dimer proteins (black and white) in A-lattice configuration. Right, top: According to pre-Orch OR microtubule automata theory (e.g. Hameroff and Watt, 1982; Rasmussen et al, 1990), each tubulin in a microtubule lattice switches between alternate (black and white) 'bit' states, coupled to electron cloud dipole London forces in internal hydrophobic pocket. Right, bottom: According to Orch OR, each tubulin can also exist as quantum superposition (quantum bit, or 'qubit') of both states, coupled to superposition of London force dipoles in hydrophobic pocket.

Microtubules also fuse side-by-side in doublets or triplets. Nine such doublets or triplets then align to form barrel-shaped mega-cylinders called cilia, flagella and centrioles, organelles responsible for locomotion, sensation and cell division. Either individually or in these larger arrays, microtubules are responsible for cellular and intra-cellular movements requiring intelligent spatiotemporal organization. Microtubules have a lattice structure comparable to computational systems. Could microtubules process information?

The notion that microtubules process information was suggested in general terms by Sherrington (1957) and Atema (1973). With physicist colleagues through the 1980s, Hameroff developed models of microtubules as information processing devices, specifically molecular ('cellular') automata, self-organizing computational devices (Figure 3). Cellular automata are computational systems in which fundamental units, or 'cells' in a grid or lattice can each exist in specific states, e.g. 1 or 0, at a given time (Wolfram, 2002). Each cell interacts with its neighbor cells at discrete, synchronized time steps, the state of each cell at any particular time step determined by its state and its neighbor cell states at the previous time step, and rules governing the interactions. In such ways, using simple neighbor interactions in simple lattice grids, cellular automata can perform complex computation and generate complex patterns.

Cells in cellular automata are meant to imply fundamental units. But biological cells are not necessarily simple, as illustrated by the clever Paramecium. Molecular automata are cellular automata in which the fundamental units, bits or cells are states of molecules, much smaller than biological cells. A dynamic, interactive molecular grid or lattice is required.

Microtubules are lattices of tubulin dimers which Hameroff and colleagues modeled as molecular automata. Discrete states of tubulin were suggested to act as bits, switching between states, and interacting (via dipole-dipole coupling) with neighbor tubulin bit states in 'molecular automata' computation (Hameroff and Watt, 1982; Rasmussen et al., 1990; Tuszynski et al., 1995). The mechanism for bit-like switching at the level of each tubulin was proposed to depend on the van der Waals–London force in non-polar, water-excluding regions ('hydrophobic pockets') within each tubulin.

Proteins are largely heterogeneous arrays of amino acid residues, including both water-soluble polar and water-insoluble non-polar groups, the latter including phenylalanine and tryptophan with electron resonance clouds (e.g. phenyl and indole rings). Such non-polar groups coalesce during protein folding to form homogeneous water-excluding 'hydrophobic' pockets within which instantaneous dipole couplings between nearby electron clouds operate. These are London forces which are extremely weak but numerous and able to act collectively in hydrophobic regions to influence and determine protein state (Voet and Voet, 1995).

London forces in hydrophobic pockets of various neuronal proteins are the mechanisms by which anesthetic gases selectively erase consciousness (Franks and Lieb, 1984). Anesthetics bind by their own London force attractions with electron clouds of the hydrophobic pocket, presumably impairing normally-occurring London forces governing protein switching required for consciousness.

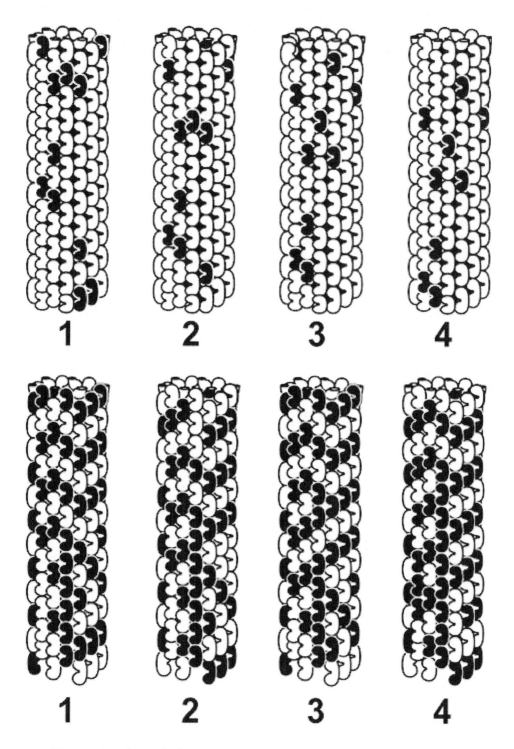

Figure 3. Microtubule automata (Rasmussen et al, 1990). Top: 4 time steps (e.g. at 8 megahertz, Pokorny et al, 2001) showing propagation of information states and patterns ('gliders' in cellular automata parlance). Bottom: At different

dipole coupling parameter, bi-directional pattern movement and computation occur.

In Figure 2, and as previously used in Orch OR, London forces are illustrated in cartoon fashion. A single hydrophobic pocket is depicted in tubulin, with portions of two electron resonance rings in the pocket. Single electrons in each ring repel each other, as their electron cloud net dipole flips (London force oscillation). London forces in hydrophobic pockets were used as the switching mechanism to distinguish discrete states for each tubulin in microtubule automata. In recent years tubulin hydrophobic regions and switching in the Orch OR proposal that we describe below have been clarified and updated (see Section 8).

To synchronize discrete time steps in microtubule automata, tubulins in microtubules were assumed to oscillate synchronously in a manner proposed by Fröhlich for biological coherence. Biophysicist Herbert Fröhlich (1968; 1970; 1975) had suggested that biomolecular dipoles constrained in a common geometry and voltage field would oscillate coherently, coupling, or condensing to a common vibrational mode. He proposed that biomolecular dipole lattices could convert ambient energy to coherent, synchronized dipole excitations, e.g. in the gigahertz (10^9 s^{-1}) frequency range. Fröhlich coherence or condensation can be either quantum coherence (e.g. Bose-Einstein condensation) or classical synchrony (Reimers et al., 2009).

In recent years coherent excitations have been found in living cells emanating from microtubules at 8 megahertz (Pokorny et al., 2001; 2004). Bandyopadhyay (2011) has found a series of coherence resonance peaks in single microtubules ranging from 12 kilohertz to 8 megahertz.

Rasmussen et al (1990) applied Fröhlich synchrony (in classical mode) as a clocking mechanism for computational time steps in simulated microtubule automata. Based on dipole couplings between neighboring tubulins in the microtubule lattice geometry, they found traveling gliders, complex patterns, computation and learning. Microtubule automata within brain neurons could potentially provide another level of information processing in the brain.

Approximately 10^8 tubulins in each neuron switching and oscillating in the range of 10^7 per second (e.g. Pokorny 8 MHz) gives an information capacity at the microtubule level of 10^{15} operations per second per neuron. This predicted capacity challenged and annoyed AI whose estimates for information processing at the level of neurons and synapses were virtually the same as this single-cell value, but for the entire brain (10^{11} neurons, 10^3 synapses per neuron, 10^2 transmissions per synapse per second = 10^{16} operations per second). Total brain capacity when taken at the microtubule level (in 10^{11} neurons) would potentially be 10^{26} operations per second, pushing the goalpost for AI brain equivalence farther into the future, and down into the quantum regime.

High capacity microtubule-based computing inside brain neurons could account for organization of synaptic regulation, learning and memory, and perhaps act as the substrate for consciousness. But increased brain information capacity per se didn't address most unanswered questions about consciousness (Section 2). Something was missing.

4. Objective Reduction (OR)

In 1989 Penrose published The Emperor's New Mind, which was followed in 1994 by Shadows of the Mind. Critical of AI, both books argued, by appealing to Gödel's theorem and other considerations, that certain aspects of human consciousness, such as understanding, must be beyond the scope of any computational system, i.e. 'non-computable'. Non-computability is a perfectly well-defined mathematical concept, but it had not previously been considered as a serious possibility for the result of physical actions. The non-computable ingredient required for human consciousness and understanding, Penrose suggested, would have to lie in an area where our current physical theories are fundamentally incomplete, though of important relevance to the scales that are pertinent to the operation of our brains. The only serious possibility was the incompleteness of quantum theory—an incompleteness that both Einstein and Schrödinger had recognized, despite quantum theory having frequently been argued to represent the pinnacle of 20th century scientific achievement. This incompleteness is the unresolved issue referred to as the 'measurement problem', which we consider in more detail below, in Section 5. One way to resolve it would be to provide an extension of the standard framework of quantum mechanics by introducing an objective form of quantum state reduction—termed 'OR' (objective reduction), an idea which we also describe more fully below, in Section 6.

In Penrose (1989), the tentatively suggested OR proposal would have its onset determined by a condition referred to there as 'the one-graviton' criterion. However, in Penrose (1995), a much better-founded criterion was used, now sometimes referred to as the Diósi–Penrose proposal (henceforth 'DP'; see Diósi 1987, 1989, Penrose 1993, 1996, 2000, 2009). This is an objective physical threshold, providing a plausible lifetime for quantum-superposed states. Other such OR proposals had also been put forward, from time to time (e.g. Kibble 1981, Pearle 1989, Pearle and Squires 1994, Ghirardi et al., 1986, 1990; see Ghirardi 2011, this volume) as solutions to the measurement problem, but had not originally been suggested as having anything to do with the consciousness issue. The Diósi-Penrose proposal is sometimes referred to as a 'quantum-gravity' scheme, but it is not part of the normal ideas used in quantum gravity, as will be explained below (Section 6). Moreover, the proposed connection between consciousness and quantum measurement is almost opposite, in the Orch OR scheme, to the kind of idea that had frequently been put forward in the early days of quantum mechanics (see, for example, Wigner 1961) which suggests that a 'quantum measurement' is something that occurs only as a result of the conscious intervention of an observer. This issue, also, will be discussed below (Section 5).

5. The Nature of Quantum Mechanics and its Fundamental Problem

The term 'quantum' refers to a discrete element of energy in a system, such as the energy E of a particle, or of some other subsystem, this energy being related to a fundamental frequency v of its oscillation, according to Max Planck's famous formula (where h is Planck's constant):

$$E = h\,v.$$

This deep relation between discrete energy levels and frequencies of oscillation underlies the wave/particle duality inherent in quantum phenomena. Neither the word "particle" nor the word "wave" adequately conveys the true nature of a basic quantum entity, but both provide useful partial pictures.

The laws governing these submicroscopic quantum entities differ from those governing our everyday classical world. For example, quantum particles can exist in two or more states or locations simultaneously, where such a multiple coexisting superposition of alternatives (each alternative being weighted by a complex number) would be described mathematically by a quantum wavefunction. We don't see superpositions in the consciously perceived world; we see objects and particles as material, classical things in specific locations and states.

Another quantum property is 'non-local entanglement,' in which separated components of a system become unified, the entire collection of components being governed by one common quantum wavefunction. The parts remain somehow connected, even when spatially separated by significant distances (e.g. over 10 kilometres, Tittel et al., 1998). Quantum superpositions of bit states (quantum bits, or qubits) can be interconnected with one another through entanglement in quantum computers. However, quantum entanglements cannot, by themselves, be used to send a message from one part of an entangled system to another; yet entanglement can be used in conjunction with classical signaling to achieve strange effects—such as the strange phenomenon referred to as quantum teleportation—that classical signalling cannot achieve by itself (e.g. Bennett and Wiesner, 1992; Bennett et al., 1993; Bouwmeester et al., 1997; Macikic et al., 2002).

The issue of why we don't directly perceive quantum superpositions is a manifestation of the measurement problem referred to in Section 4. Put more precisely, the measurement problem is the conflict between the two fundamental procedures of quantum mechanics. One of these procedures, referred to as unitary evolution, denoted here by U, is the continuous deterministic evolution of the quantum state (i.e. of the wavefunction of the entire system) according to the fundamental Schrödinger equation, The other is the procedure that is adopted whenever a measurement of the system—or observation—is deemed to have taken place, where the quantum state is discontinuously and probabilistically replaced by another quantum state (referred to, technically, as an eigenstate of a mathematical operator that is taken to describe the measurement). This discontinuous jumping of the state is referred to as the reduction of the state (or the 'collapse of the wavefunction'), and will be denoted here by the letter R. The conflict that is termed the measurement problem (or perhaps more accurately as the measurement paradox) arises when we consider the measuring apparatus itself as a quantum entity, which is part of the entire quantum system consisting of the original system under observation together with this measuring apparatus. The apparatus is, after all, constructed out of the same type of quantum ingredients (electrons, photons, protons, neutrons etc.—or quarks and gluons etc.) as is the system under observation, so it ought to be subject also to the same quantum laws, these being described in terms of the continuous and deterministic U. How, then, can the discontinuous and probabilistic R come about as a result of the interaction (measurement) between two parts of the quantum system? This is the measurement problem (or paradox).

There are many ways that quantum physicists have attempted to come to terms with this conflict (see, for example, Bell 1966, Bohm 1951, Rae 1994, Polkinghorne 2002, Penrose, 2004). In the early 20th century, the Danish physicist Niels Bohr, together with Werner Heisenberg, proposed the pragmatic 'Copenhagen interpretation', according to which the wavefunction of a quantum system, evolving according to U, is not assigned any actual physical 'reality', but is taken as basically providing the needed 'book-keeping' so that eventually probability values can be assigned to the various possible outcomes of a quantum measurement. The measuring device itself is explicitly taken to behave classically and no account is taken of the fact that the device is ultimately built from quantum-level constituents. The probabilities are calculated, once the nature of the measuring device is known, from the state that the wavefunction has U-evolved to at the time of the measurement. The discontinuous "jump" that the wavefunction makes upon measurement, according to R, is attributed to the change in 'knowledge' that the result of the measurement has on the observer. Since the wavefunction is not assigned physical reality, but is considered to refer merely to the observer's knowledge of the quantum system, the jumping is considered simply to reflect the jump in the observer's knowledge state, rather than in the quantum system under consideration.

Many physicists remain unhappy with such a point of view, however, and regard it largely as a 'stop-gap', in order that progress can be made in applying the quantum formalism, without this progress being held up by a lack of a serious quantum ontology, which might provide a more complete picture of what is actually going on. One may ask, in particular, what it is about a measuring device that allows one to ignore the fact that it is itself made from quantum constituents and is permitted to be treated entirely classically. A good many proponents of the Copenhagen standpoint would take the view that while the physical measuring apparatus ought actually to be treated as a quantum system, and therefore part of an over-riding wavefunction evolving according to U , it would be the conscious observer, examining the readings on that device, who actually reduces the state, according to R , thereby assigning a physical reality to the particular observed alternative resulting from the measurement. Accordingly, before the intervention of the observer's consciousness, the various alternatives of the result of the measurement including the different states of the measuring apparatus would, in effect, still coexist in superposition, in accordance with what would be the usual evolution according to U . In this way, the Copenhagen viewpoint puts consciousness outside science, and does not seriously address the nature and physical role of superposition itself nor the question of how large quantum superpositions like Schrödinger's superposed live and dead cat (see below) might actually become one thing or another.

A more extreme variant of this approach is the 'multiple worlds hypothesis' of Everett (1957) in which each possibility in a superposition evolves to form its own universe, resulting in an infinite multitude of coexisting 'parallel' worlds. The stream of consciousness of the observer is supposed somehow to 'split', so that there is one in each of the worlds—at least in those worlds for which the observer remains alive and conscious. Each instance of the observer's consciousness experiences a separate independent world, and is not directly aware of any of the other worlds.

A more 'down-to-earth' viewpoint is that of environmental decoherence, in which interaction of a superposition with its environment 'erodes' quantum states, so that instead of a single wavefunction being used to describe the state, a more complicated entity is used, referred to as a density matrix. However decoherence does not provide a consistent ontology for the reality of the world, in relation to the density matrix (see, for example, Penrose 2004, Sections 29.3-6), and provides merely a pragmatic procedure. Moreover, it does not address the issue of how R might arise in isolated systems, nor the nature of isolation, in which an external 'environment' would not be involved, nor does it tell us which part of a system is to be regarded as the 'environment' part, and it provides no limit to the size of that part which can remain subject to quantum superposition.

Still other approaches include various types of objective reduction (OR) in which a specific objective threshold is proposed to cause quantum state reduction (e.g. Kibble 1981; Pearle 1989; Ghirardi et al., 1986; Percival, 1994; Ghirardi, 2011). The specific OR scheme that is used in Orch OR will be described in Section 6.

The quantum pioneer Erwin Schrödinger took pains to point out the difficulties that confront the U-evolution of a quantum system with his still-famous thought experiment called 'Schrödinger's cat'. Here, the fate of a cat in a box is determined by magnifying a quantum event (say the decay of a radioactive atom, within a specific time period that would provide a 50% probability of decay) to a macroscopic action which would kill the cat, so that according to Schrödinger's own U-evolution the cat would be in a quantum superposition of being both dead and alive at the same time. If this U-evolution is maintained until the box is opened and the cat observed, then it would have to be the conscious human observing the cat that results in the cat becoming either dead or alive (unless, of course, the cat's own consciousness could be considered to have already served this purpose). Schrödinger intended to illustrate the absurdity of the direct applicability of the rules of quantum mechanics (including his own U-evolution) when applied at the level of a cat. Like Einstein, he regarded quantum mechanics as an incomplete theory, and his 'cat' provided an excellent example for emphasizing this incompleteness. There is a need for something to be done about quantum mechanics, irrespective of the issue of its relevance to consciousness.

6. The Orch OR Scheme

Orch OR depends, indeed, upon a particular OR extension of current quantum mechanics, taking the bridge between quantum- and classical-level physics as a 'quantum-gravitational' phenomenon. This is in contrast with the various conventional viewpoints (see Section 5), whereby this bridge is claimed to result, somehow, from 'environmental decoherence', or from 'observation by a conscious observer', or from a 'choice between alternative worlds', or some other interpretation of how the classical world of one actual alternative may be taken to arise out of fundamentally quantum-superposed ingredients.

It must also be made clear that the Orch OR scheme involves a different interpretation of the term 'quantum gravity' from what is usual. Current ideas of quantum gravity (see, for example Smolin, 2002) normally refer, instead, to some sort of physical scheme that is to be formulated within the bounds of standard quantum field theory—although no particular such theory, among the multitude that has so far been put forward, has gained anything approaching universal acceptance, nor has any of them found a fully consistent, satisfactory formulation. 'OR' here refers to the alternative viewpoint that standard quantum (field) theory is not the final answer, and that the reduction R of the quantum state ('collapse of the wavefunction') that is adopted in standard quantum mechanics is an actual physical phenomenon which is not part of the conventional unitary formalism U of quantum theory (or quantum field theory) and does not arise as some kind of convenience or effective consequence of environmental decoherence, etc., as the conventional U formalism would seem to demand. Instead, OR is taken to be one of the consequences of melding together the principles of Einstein's general relativity with those of the conventional unitary quantum formalism U, and this demands a departure from the strict rules of U. According to this OR viewpoint, any quantum measurement—whereby the quantum-superposed alternatives produced in accordance with the U formalism becomes reduced to a single actual occurrence—is real objective physical phenomenon, and it is taken to result from the mass displacement between the alternatives being sufficient, in gravitational terms, for the superposition to become unstable.

In the DP (Diósi–Penrose) scheme for OR, the superposition reduces to one of the alternatives in a time scale τ that can be estimated (for a superposition of two states each of which can be taken to be stationary on its own) according to the formula

$\tau \approx \hbar/E_G$.

Here $\hbar$ ($=h/2\pi$) is Dirac's form of Planck's constant h and E_G is the gravitational self-energy of the difference between the two mass distributions of the superposition. (For a superposition for which each mass distribution is a rigid translation of the other, E_G is the energy it would cost to displace one component of the superposition in the gravitational field of the other, in moving it from coincidence to the quantum-displaced location; see Disói 1989, Penrose 1993, 2000, 2009).

According to Orch OR, the (objective) reduction is not the entirely random process of standard theory, but acts according to some non-computational new physics (see Penrose 1989, 1994). The idea is that consciousness is associated with this (gravitational) OR process, but occurs significantly only when the alternatives are part of some highly organized structure, so that such occurrences of OR occur in an extremely orchestrated form. Only then does a recognizably conscious event take place. On the other hand, we may consider that any individual occurrence of OR would be an element of proto-consciousness.

The OR process is considered to occur when quantum superpositions between slightly differing space-times take place, differing from one another by an integrated space-time measure which compares with the fundamental and extremely tiny Planck (4-volume) scale of space-time geometry. Since this is a 4-volume Planck measure, involving both time and space, we find that the time measure would be particularly tiny when the space-difference measure is relatively large (as with Schrödinger's cat), but for extremely tiny space-difference measures, the time measure might be fairly long, such as some significant fraction of a second. We shall be seeing this in more detail shortly, together with its particular relevance to microtubules. In any case, we recognize that the elements of proto-consciousness would be intimately tied in with the most primitive Planck-level ingredients of space-time geometry, these presumed 'ingredients' being taken to be at the absurdly tiny level of 10^{-35}m and 10^{-43}s, a distance and a time some 20 orders of magnitude smaller than those of normal particle-physics scales and their most rapid processes. These scales refer only to the normally extremely tiny differences in space-time geometry between different states in superposition, and OR is deemed to take place when such space-time differences reach the Planck level. Owing to the extreme weakness of gravitational forces as compared with those of the chemical and electric forces of biology, the energy E_G is liable to be far smaller than any energy that arises directly from biological processes. However, E_G is not to be thought of as being in direct competition with any of the usual biological energies, as it plays a completely different role, supplying a needed energy uncertainty that then allows a choice to be made between the separated space-time geometries. It is the key ingredient of the computation of the reduction time τ. Nevertheless, the extreme weakness of gravity tells us there must be a considerable amount of material involved in the coherent mass displacement between superposed structures in order that τ can be small enough to be playing its necessary role in the relevant OR processes in the brain. These superposed structures should also process information and regulate neuronal physiology. According to Orch OR, microtubules are central to these structures, and some form of biological quantum computation in microtubules (most probably primarily in the more symmetrical A-lattice microtubules) would have to have evolved to provide a subtle yet direct connection to Planck-scale geometry, leading eventually to discrete moments of actual conscious experience.

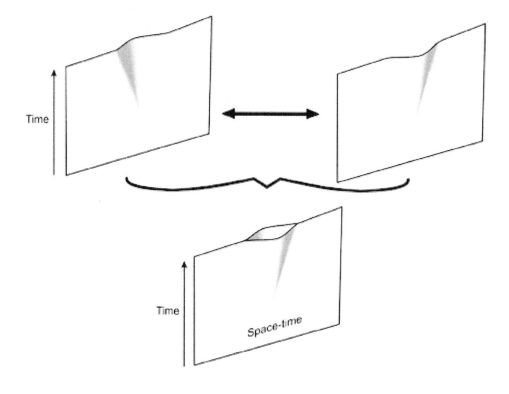

Figure 4. From Penrose, 1994 (P. 338). With four spatiotemporal dimensions condensed to a 2-dimensional spacetime sheet, mass location may be represented as a particular curvature of that sheet, according to general relativity. Top: Two different mass locations as alternative spacetime curvatures. Bottom: a bifurcating spacetime is depicted as the union ("glued together version") of the two alternative spacetime histories that are depicted at the top of the Figure. Hence a quantum superposition of simultaneous alternative locations may be seen as a separation in fundamental spacetime geometry.

The degree of separation between the space-time sheets is mathematically described in terms of a symplectic measure on the space of 4-dimensional metrics (cf. Penrose, 1993). The separation is, as already noted above, a space-time separation, not just a spatial one. Thus the time of separation contributes as well as the spatial displacement. Roughly speaking, it is the product of the temporal separation T with the spatial separation S that measures the overall degree of separation, and OR takes place when this overall separation reaches a critical amount. This critical amount would be of the order of unity, in absolute units, for which the Planck-Dirac constant ℏ, the gravitational constant G, and the velocity of light c, all take the value unity, cf. Penrose, 1994 - pp. 337-339. For small S, the lifetime $\tau \approx T$ of the superposed state will be large; on the other hand, if S is large, then τ will be small.

To estimate S, we compute (in the Newtonian limit of weak gravitational fields) the gravitational self-energy E_G of the difference between the mass distributions of the two superposed states. (That is, one mass distribution counts positively and the other, negatively; see Penrose, 1993; 1995.) The quantity S is then given by:

$$S \approx E_G$$
and $T \approx \tau$, whence

$$\tau \approx \hbar/E_G \text{ , i.e. } E_G \approx \hbar/\tau.$$

Thus, the DP expectation is that OR occurs with the resolving out of one particular space-time geometry from the previous superposition when, on the average, $\tau \approx \hbar/E_G$. Moreover, according to Orch OR, this is accompanied by an element of proto-consciousness.

Environmental decoherence need play no role in state reduction, according to this scheme. The proposal is that state reduction simply takes place spontaneously, according to this criterion. On the other hand, in many actual physical situations, there would be much material from the environment that would be entangled with the quantum-superposed state, and it could well be that the major mass displacement—and therefore the major contribution to E_G —would occur in the environment rather than in the system under consideration. Since the environment will be quantum-entangled with the system, the state-reduction in the environment will effect a simultaneous reduction in the system. This could shorten the time for the state reduction R to take place very considerably. It would also introduce an uncontrollable random element into the result of the reduction, so that any non-random (albeit non-computable, according to Orch OR) element influencing the particular choice of state that is actually resolved out from the superposition would be completely masked by this randomness. In these circumstances the OR-process would be indistinguishable from the R-process of conventional quantum mechanics. If the suggested non-computable effects of this

OR proposal are to be laid bare, if E_G is to be able to evolve and be orchestrated for conscious moments, we indeed need significant isolation from the environment.

As yet, no experiment has been refined enough to determine whether this (DP) OR proposal is actually respected by Nature, but the experimental testing of the scheme is fairly close to the borderline of what can be achieved with present-day technology (see, for example, Marshall et al. 2003). One ought to begin to see the effects of this OR scheme if a small object, such as a 10-micron cube of crystalline material could be held in a superposition of two locations, differing by about the diameter of an atomic nucleus, for some seconds, or perhaps minutes.

A point of importance, in such proposed experiments, is that in order to calculate E_G it may not be enough to base the calculation on an average density of the material in the superposition, since the mass will be concentrated in the atomic nuclei, and for a displacement of the order of the diameter of a nucleus, this inhomogeneity in the density of the material can be crucial, and can provide a much larger value for E_G than would be obtained if the material is assumed to be homogeneous. The Schrödinger equation (more correctly, in the zero-temperature approximation, the Schrödinger–Newton equation, see Penrose 2000; Moroz et al. 1998) for the static unsuperposed material would have to be solved, at least approximately, in order to derive the expectation value of the mass distribution, where there would be some quantum spread in the locations of the particles constituting the nuclei.

For Orch OR to be operative in the brain, we would need coherent superpositions of sufficient amounts of material, undisturbed by environmental entanglement, where this reduces in accordance with the above OR scheme in a rough time scale of the general order of time for a conscious experience to take place. For an ordinary type of experience, this might be say about $\tau = 10^{-1}$s which concurs with neural correlates of consciousness, such as particular frequencies of electroencephalograhy (EEG).

Penrose (1989; 1994) suggested that processes of the general nature of quantum computations were occurring in the brain, terminated by OR. In quantum computers (Benioff 1982, Deutsch 1985, Feynman 1986), information is represented not just as bits of either 1 or 0, but also as quantum superposition of both 1 and 0 together (quantum bits or qubits) where, moreover, large-scale entanglements between qubits would also be involved. These qubits interact and compute following the Schrödinger equation, potentially enabling complex and highly efficient parallel processing. As envisioned in technological quantum computers, at some point a measurement is made causing quantum state reduction (with some randomness introduced). The qubits reduce, or collapse to classical bits and definite states as the output.

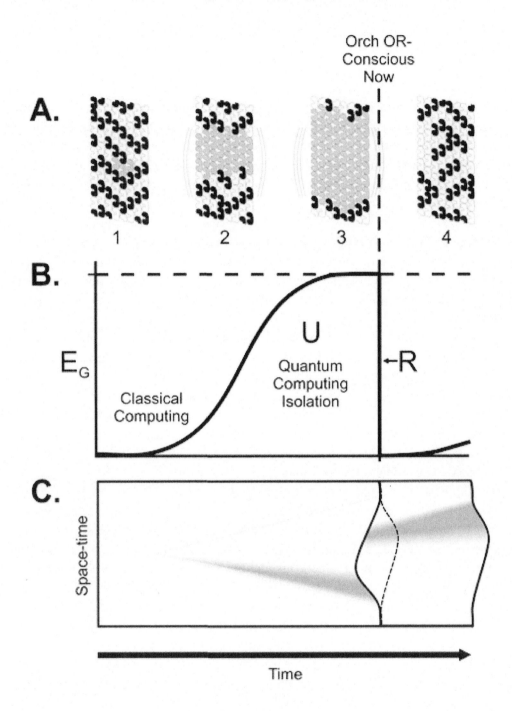

Figure 5. Three descriptions of an Orch OR conscious event by $E_G = \hbar/\tau$. A. Microtubule automata. Quantum (gray) tubulins evolve to meet threshold after Step 3, a moment of consciousness occurs and tubulin states are selected. For actual event (e.g. 25 msec), billions of tubulins are required; a small number is

used here for illustration. B. Schematic showing U-like evolution until threshold. C. Space-time sheet with superposition separation reaches threshold and selects one reality/spacetime curvature.

The proposal that some form of quantum computing could be acting in the brain, this proceeding by the Schrödinger equation without decoherence until some threshold for self-collapse due to a form of non-computable OR could be reached, was made in Penrose 1989. However, no plausible biological candidate for quantum computing in the brain had been available to him, as he was then unfamiliar with microtubules.

7. Penrose-Hameroff Orchestrated Objective Reduction ('Orch OR')

Penrose and Hameroff teamed up in the early 1990s. Fortunately, by then, the DP form of OR mechanism was at hand to be applied to the microtubule-automata models for consciousness as developed by Hameroff. A number of questions were addressed.

How does $\tau \approx \hbar/E_G$ relate to consciousness? Orch OR considers consciousness as a sequence of discrete OR events in concert with neuronal-level activities. In $\tau \approx \hbar/E_G$, τ is taken to be the time for evolution of the pre-conscious quantum wavefunction between OR events, i.e. the time interval between conscious moments, during which quantum superpositions of microtubule states evolve according to the continuous Schrödinger equation before reaching (on the average) the $\tau \approx \hbar/E_G$ OR threshold in time τ, when quantum state reduction and a moment of conscious awareness occurs (Figure 5).

The best known temporal correlate for consciousness is gamma synchrony EEG, 30 to 90 Hz, often referred to as coherent 40 Hz. One possible viewpoint might be to take this oscillation to represent a succession of 40 or so conscious moments per second (τ=25 milliseconds). This would be reasonably consistent with neuroscience (gamma synchrony), with certain ideas expressed in philosophy (e.g. Whitehead 'occasions of experience'), and perhaps even with ancient Buddhist texts which portray consciousness as 'momentary collections of mental phenomena' or as 'distinct, unconnected and impermanent moments which perish as soon as they arise.' (Some Buddhist writings quantify the frequency of conscious moments. For example the Sarvaastivaadins, according to von Rospatt 1995, described 6,480,000 'moments' in 24 hours—an average of one 'moment' per 13.3 msec, ~75 Hz—and some Chinese Buddhism as one "thought" per 20 msec, i.e. 50 Hz.) These accounts, even including variations in frequency, could be considered to be consistent with Orch OR events in the gamma synchrony range. Accordingly, on this view, gamma synchrony, Buddhist 'moments of experience', Whitehead 'occasions of experience', and our proposed Orch OR events might be viewed as corresponding tolerably well with one another.

Putting τ=25msec in $E_G \approx \hbar/\tau$, we may ask what is E_G in terms of superpositioned microtubule tubulins? E_G may be derived from details about the super-position separation of mass distribution. Three types of mass separation were considered in Hameroff–Penrose 1996a for peanut-shaped tubulin proteins of 110,000 atomic mass units: separation at the level of (1) protein spheres, e.g. by 10 percent volume, (2) atomic nuclei (e.g. carbon, ~ 2.5 Fermi length), (3) nucle-ons (protons and neutrons). The most plausible calculated effect might be separa-tion at the level of atomic nuclei, giving E_G as superposition of 2×10^{10} tubulins reaching OR threshold at 25 milliseconds.

Brain neurons each contain roughly 10^8 tubulins, so only a few hundred neurons would be required for a 25msec, gamma synchrony OR event if 100 per-cent of tubulins in those neurons were in superposition and avoided decoherence. It seems more likely that a fraction of tubulins per neuron are in superposition. Global macroscopic states such as superconductivity ensue from quantum coher-ence among only very small fractions of components. If 1 percent of tubulins within a given set of neurons were coherent for 25msec, then 20,000 such neurons would be required to elicit OR. In human brain, cognition and consciousness are, at any one time, thought to involve tens of thousands of neurons. Hebb's (1949) 'cell assemblies', Eccles's (1992) 'modules', and Crick and Koch's (1990) 'co-herent sets of neurons' are each estimated to contain some 10,000 to 100,000 neurons which may be widely distributed throughout the brain (Scott, 1995).

Adopting $\tau \approx \hbar/E_G$, we find that, with this point of view with regard to Orch-OR, a spectrum of possible types of conscious event might be able to occur, including those at higher frequency and intensity. It may be noted that Tibetan monk meditators have been found to have 80 Hz gamma synchrony, and perhaps more intense experience (Lutz et al. 2004). Thus, according to the viewpoint proposed above, where we interpret this frequency to be associated with a suc-cession of Orch-OR moments, then $E_G \approx \hbar/\tau$ would appear to require that there is twice as much brain involvement required for 80 Hz than for consciousness occurring at 40 Hz (or $\sqrt{2}$ times as much if the displacement is entirely coher-ent, since then the mass enters quadratically in E_G). Even higher (frequency), expanded awareness states of consciousness might be expected, with more neu-ronal brain involvement.

On the other hand, we might take an alternative viewpoint with regard to the probable frequency of Orch-OR actions, and to the resulting frequency of elements of conscious experience. There is the possibility that the discernable moments of consciousness are events that normally occur at a much slower pace than is suggested by the considerations above, and that they happen only at rough intervals of the order of, say, one half a second or so, i.e. ~500msec, rather than ~25msec. One might indeed think of conscious influences as perhaps being rather slow, in contrast with the great deal of vastly faster unconscious computing that might be some form of quantum computing, but without OR. At the present stage of uncertainty about such matters it is perhaps best not to be dogmatic about how the ideas of Orch OR are to be applied. In any case, the numerical assignments provided above must be considered to be extremely rough, and at the moment we are far from being in a position to be definitive about the precise way in which the Orch-OR is to operate. Alternative possibilities will need to be considered with an open mind.

How do microtubule quantum computation avoid decoherence? Technological quantum computers using e.g. ion traps as qubits are plagued by decoherence, disruption of delicate quantum states by thermal vibration, and require extremely cold temperatures and vacuum to operate. Decoherence must be avoided during the evolution toward time τ ($\approx \hbar/E_G$), so that the non-random (non-computable) aspects of OR can be playing their roles. How does quantum computing avoid decoherence in the 'warm, wet and noisy' brain?

It was suggested (Hameroff and Penrose, 1996a) that microtubule quantum states avoid decoherence by being pumped, laser-like, by Fröhlich resonance, and shielded by ordered water, C-termini Debye layers, actin gel and strong mitochondrial electric fields. Moreover quantum states in Orch OR are proposed to originate in hydrophobic pockets in tubulin interiors, isolated from polar interactions, and involve superposition of only atomic nuclei separation. Moreover, geometrical resonances in microtubules, e.g. following helical pathways of Fibonacci geometry are suggested to enable topological quantum computing and error correction, avoiding decoherence perhaps effectively indefinitely (Hameroff et al 2002) as in a superconductor.

The analogy with high-temperature superconductors may indeed be appropriate, in fact. As yet, there is no fully accepted theory of how such superconductors operate, avoiding loss of quantum coherence from the usual processes of environmental decoherence. Yet there are materials which support superconductivity at temperatures roughly halfway between room temperature and absolute zero (He et al., 2010). This is still a long way from body temperature, of course, but there is now some experimental evidence (Bandyopadhyay 2011) that is indicative of something resembling superconductivity (referred to as 'ballistic conductance'), that occurs in living A-lattice microtubules at body temperature. This will be discussed below.

Physicist Max Tegmark (2000) published a critique of Orch OR based on his calculated decoherence times for microtubules of 10^{-13} seconds at biological temperature, far too brief for physiological effects. However Tegmark didn't include Orch OR stipulations and in essence created, and then refuted his own quantum microtubule model. He assumed superpositions of solitons separated from themselves by a distance of 24 nanometers along the length of the microtubule. As previously described, superposition separation in Orch OR is at the Fermi length level of atomic nuclei, i.e. 7 orders of magnitude smaller than Tegmark's separation value, thus underestimating decoherence time by 7 orders of magnitude, i.e. from 10^{-13} secs to microseconds at 10^{-6} seconds. Hagan et al

(2001) used Tegmark's same formula and recalculated microtubule decoherence times using Orch OR stipulations, finding 10^{-4} to 10^{-3} seconds, or longer due to topological quantum effects. It seemed likely biology had evolved optimal information processing systems which can utilize quantum computing, but there was no real evidence either way.

Beginning in 2003, published research began to demonstrate quantum coherence in warm biological systems. Ouyang and Awschalom (2003) showed that quantum spin transfer through phenyl rings (the same as those in protein hydrophobic pockets) is enhanced at increasingly warm temperatures. Other studies showed that quantum coherence occurred at ambient temperatures in proteins involved in photosynthesis, that plants routinely use quantum coherence to produce chemical energy and food (Engel et al, 2007). Further research has demonstrated warm quantum effects in bird brain navigation (Gauger et al, 2011), ion channels (Bernroider and Roy, 2005), sense of smell (Turin, 1996), DNA (Rieper et al., 2011), protein folding (Luo and Lu, 2011), biological water (Reiter et al., 2011) and microtubules.

Recently Anirban Bandyopadhyay and colleagues at the National Institute of Material Sciences in Tsukuba, Japan have used nanotechnology to study electronic conductance properties of single microtubules assembled from porcine brain tubulin. Their preliminary findings (Bandyopadhyay, 2011) include: (1) Microtubules have 8 resonance peaks for AC stimulation (kilohertz to 10 megahertz) which appear to correlate with various helical conductance pathways around the geometric microtubule lattice. (2) Excitation at these resonant frequencies causes microtubules to assemble extremely rapidly, possibly due to Fröhlich condensation. (3) In assembled microtubules AC excitation at resonant frequencies causes electronic conductance to become lossless, or 'ballistic', essentially quantum conductance, presumably along these helical quantum channels. Resonance in the range of kilohertz demonstrates microtubule decoherence times of at least 0.1 millisecond. (4) Eight distinct quantum interference patterns from a single microtubule, each correlating with one of the 8 resonance frequencies and pathways. (5) Ferroelectric hysteresis demonstrates memory capacity in microtubules. (6) Temperature-independent conductance also suggests quantum effects. If confirmed, such findings would demonstrate Orch OR to be biologically feasible.

How does microtubule quantum computation and Orch OR fit with recognized neurophysiology? Neurons are composed of multiple dendrites and a cell body/soma which receive and integrate synaptic inputs to a threshold for firing outputs along a single axon. Microtubule quantum computation in Orch OR is assumed to occur in dendrites and cell bodies/soma of brain neurons, i.e. in regions of integration of inputs in integrate-and-fire neurons. As opposed to axonal firings, dendritic/somatic integration correlates best with local field potentials, gamma synchrony EEG, and action of anesthetics erasing consciousness. Tononi

(2004) has identified integration of information as the neuronal function most closely associated with consciousness. Dendritic microtubules are uniquely arranged in local mixed polarity networks, well-suited for integration of synaptic inputs.

Membrane synaptic inputs interact with post-synaptic microtubules by activation of microtubule-associated protein 2 ('MAP2', associated with learning), and calcium-calmodulin kinase II (CaMKII, Hameroff et al, 2010). Such inputs were suggested by Penrose and Hameroff (1996a) to 'tune', or 'orchestrate' OR-mediated quantum computations in microtubules by MAPs, hence 'orchestrated objective reduction', 'Orch OR'.

Proposed mechanisms for microtubule avoidance of decoherence were described above, but another question remains. How would microtubule quantum computations which are isolated from the environment, still interact with that environment for input and output? One possibility that Orch OR suggests is that perhaps phases of isolated quantum computing alternate with phases of classical environmental interaction, e.g. at gamma synchrony, roughly 40 times per second. (Computing pioneer Paul Benioff suggested such a scheme of alternating quantum and classical phases in a science fiction story about quantum computing robots.)

With regard to outputs resulting from processes taking place at the level of microtubules in Orch-OR quantum computations, dendritic/somatic microtubules receive and integrate synaptic inputs during classical phase. They then become isolated quantum computers and evolve to threshold for Orch OR at which they reduce their quantum states at an average time interval τ (given by by $\tau \approx \hbar/E_G$). The particular tubulin states chosen in the reduction can then trigger axonal firing, adjust firing threshold, regulate synapses and encode memory. Thus Orch OR can have causal efficacy in conscious actions and behavior, as well as providing conscious experience and memory.

Orch OR in evolution In the absence of Orch OR, non-conscious neuronal activities might proceed by classical neuronal and microtubule-based computation. In addition there could be quantum computations in microtubules that do not reach the Orch OR level, and thereby also remain unconscious.

This last possibility is strongly suggested by considerations of natural selection, since some relatively primitive microtubule infrastructure, still able to support quantum computation, would have to have preceded the more sophisticated kind that we now find in conscious animals. Natural selection proceeds in steps, after all, and one would not expect that the capability of the substantial level of coherence across the brain that would be needed for the non-computable OR of human conscious understanding to be reached, without something more primitive having preceded it. Microtubule quantum computing by U evolution which avoids decoherence would well be advantageous to biological processes without ever reaching threshold for OR.

Microtubules may have appeared in eukaryotic cells 1.3 billion years ago due to symbiosis among prokaryotes, mitochondria and spirochetes, the latter the apparent origin of microtubules which provided movement to previously immobile cells (e.g. Margulis and Sagan, 1995). Because Orch OR depends on $\tau \approx \hbar/E_G$, more primitive consciousness in simple, small organisms would involve smaller E_G, and longer times τ to avoid decoherence. As simple nervous systems and arrangements of microtubules grew larger and developed anti-decoherence mechanisms, inevitably a system would avoid decoherence long enough to reach threshold for Orch OR conscious moments. Central nervous systems around 300 neurons, such as those present at the early Cambrian evolutionary explosion 540 million years ago, could have τ near one minute, and thus be feasible in terms of avoiding decoherence (Hameroff, 1998d). Perhaps the onset of Orch OR and consciousness with relatively slow and simple conscious moments, precipitated the accelerated evolution.

Only at a much later evolutionary stage would the selective advantages of a capability for genuine understanding come about. This would require the non-computable capabilities of Orch OR that go beyond those of mere quantum computation, and depend upon larger scale infrastructure of efficiently functioning microtubules, capable of operating quantum-computational processes. Further evolution providing larger sets of microtubules (larger EG) able to be isolated from decoherence would enable, by $\tau \approx \hbar/E_G$, more frequent and more intense moments of conscious experience. It appears human brains could have evolved to having Orch OR conscious moments perhaps as frequently as every few milliseconds.

How could microtubule quantum states in one neuron extend to those in other neurons throughout the brain? Assuming microtubule quantum state phases are isolated in a specific neuron, how could that quantum state involve microtubules in other neurons throughout the brain without traversing membranes and synapses? Orch OR proposes that quantum states can extend by tunneling, leading to entanglement between adjacent neurons through gap junctions.

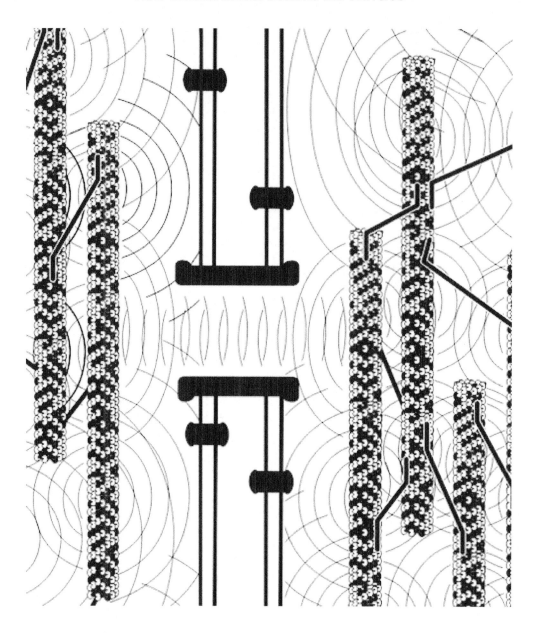

Figure 6. Portions of two neurons connected by a gap junction with microtubules (linked by microtubule-associated proteins, 'MAPs') computing via states (here represented as black or white) of tubulin protein subunits. Wavy lines suggest entanglement among quantum states (not shown) in microtubules.

Gap junctions are primitive electrical connections between cells, synchronizing electrical activities. Structurally, gap junctions are windows between cells which may be open or closed. When open, gap junctions synchronize adjacent cell membrane polarization states, but also allow passage of molecules between cytoplasmic compartments of the two cells. So both membranes and cytoplasmic interiors of gap-junction-connected neurons are continuous, essentially one complex 'hyper-neuron' or syncytium. (Ironically, before Ramon-y-Cajal showed that neurons were discrete cells, the prevalent model for brain structure was a continuous threaded-together syncytium as proposed by Camille Golgi.) Orch OR suggests that quantum states in microtubules in one neuron could extend by entanglement and tunneling through gap junctions to microtubules in adjacent neurons and glia (Figure 6), and from those cells to others, potentially in brain-wide syncytia.

Open gap junctions were thus predicted to play an essential role in the neural correlate of consciousness (Hameroff, 1998a). Beginning in 1998, evidence began to show that gamma synchrony, the best measureable correlate of consciousness, depended on gap junctions, particularly dendritic-dendritic gap junctions (Dermietzel, 1998; Draguhn et al, 1998; Galaretta and Hestrin, 1999). To account for the distinction between conscious activities and non-conscious 'auto-pilot' activities, and the fact that consciousness can occur in various brain regions, Hameroff (2009) developed the "Conscious pilot' model in which syncytial zones of dendritic gamma synchrony move around the brain, regulated by gap junction openings and closings, in turn regulated by microtubules. The model suggests consciousness literally moves around the brain in a mobile synchronized zone, within which isolated, entangled microtubules carry out quantum computations and Orch OR. Taken together, Orch OR and the conscious pilot distinguish conscious from non-conscious functional processes in the brain.

Libet's backward time referral In the 1970s neurophysiologist Benjamin Libet performed experiments on patients having brain surgery while awake, i.e. under local anesthesia (Libet et al., 1979). Able to stimulate and record from conscious human brain, and gather patients' subjective reports with precise timing, Libet determined that conscious perception of a stimulus required up to 500 msec of brain activity post-stimulus, but that conscious awareness occurred at 30 msec post-stimulus, i.e. that subjective experience was referred 'backward in time'.

Bearing such apparent anomalies in mind, Penrose put forward a tentative suggestion, in The Emperor's New Mind, that effects like Libet's backward time referral might be related to the fact that quantum entanglements are not mediated in a normal causal way, so that it might be possible for conscious experience not to follow the normal rules of sequential time progression, so long as this does not lead to contradictions with external causality. In Section 5, it was pointed out that the (experimentally confirmed) phenomenon of 'quantum teleportation' (Bennett et al., 1993; Bouwmeester et al., 1997; Macikic et al., 2002) cannot be explained in terms of ordinary classical information processing, but as a combination of such classical causal influences and the acausal effects of quantum entanglement. It indeed turns out that quantum entanglement effects—referred to as 'quantum information' or 'quanglement' (Penrose 2002, 2004)—appear to have to be thought of as being able to propagate in either direction in time (into the past or into the future). Such effects, however, cannot by themselves be used to communicate ordinary information into the past. Nevertheless, in conjunction with normal classical future-propagating (i.e. 'causal') signalling, these quantum-teleportation influences can achieve certain kinds of 'signalling' that cannot be achieved simply by classical future-directed means.

The issue is a subtle one, but if conscious experience is indeed rooted in the OR process, where we take OR to relate the classical to the quantum world, then apparent anomalies in the sequential aspects of consciousness are perhaps to be expected. The Orch OR scheme allows conscious experience to be temporally non-local to a degree, where this temporal non-locality would spread to the kind of time scale τ that would be involved in the relevant Orch OR process, which might indeed allow this temporal non-locality to spread to a time $\tau=500$ms. When the 'moment' of an internal conscious experience is timed externally, it may well be found that this external timing does not precisely accord with a time progression that would seem to apply to internal conscious experience, owing to this temporal non-locality intrinsic to Orch OR.

Measurable brain activity correlated with a stimulus often occurs several hundred msec after that stimulus, as Libet showed. Yet in activities ranging from rapid conversation to competitive athletics, we respond to a stimulus (seemingly consciously) before the above activity that would be correlated with that stimulus occurring in the brain. This is interpreted in conventional neuroscience and philosophy (e.g. Dennett, 1991; Wegner, 2002) to imply that in such cases we respond non-consciously, on auto-pilot, and subsequently have only an illusion of conscious response. The mainstream view is that consciousness is epiphenomenal illusion, occurring after-the-fact as a false impression of conscious control of behavior. We are merely 'helpless spectators' (Huxley, 1986).

However, the effective quantum backward time referral inherent in the temporal non-locality resulting from the quanglement aspects of Orch OR, as suggested above, enables conscious experience actually to be temporally non-local, thus providing a means to rescue consciousness from its unfortunate characterization as epiphenomenal illusion. Accordingy, Orch OR could well enable consciousness to have a causal efficacy, despite its apparently anomalous relation to a timing assigned to it in relation to an external clock, thereby allowing conscious action to provide a semblance of free will.

8. Orch OR Criticisms and Responses

Orch OR has been criticized repeatedly since its inception. Here we review and summarize major criticisms and responses.

Grush and Churchland, 1995. Philosophers Grush and Churchland (1995) took issue with the Gödel's theorem argument, as well as several biological factors. One objection involved the microtubule-disabling drug colchicine which treats diseases such as gout by immobilizing neutrophil cells which cause painful inflammation in joints. Neutrophil mobility requires cycles of microtubule assembly/disassembly, and colchicine prevents re-assembly, impairing neutrophil mobility and reducing inflammation. Grush and Churchland pointed out that patients given colchicine do not lose consciousness, concluding that microtubules cannot be essential for consciousness. Penrose and Hameroff (1995) responded point-by-point to every objection, e.g. explaining that colchicine does not cross the blood brain barrier, and so doesn't reach the brain. Colchicine infused directly into the brains of animals does cause severe cognitive impairment and apparent loss of consciousness (Bensimon and Chemat, 1991).

Tuszynski et al, (1998). Tuszynski et al (1998) questioned how extremely weak gravitational energy in Diósi-Penrose OR could influence tubulin protein states. In Hameroff and Penrose (1996a), the gravitational self-energy E_G for tubulin superposition was calculated for separation of tubulin from itself at the level of its atomic nuclei. Because the atomic (e.g. carbon) nucleus displacement is greater than its radius (the nuclei separate completely), the gravitational self-energy E_G is given by: $E_G = Gm^2/a_c$, where a_c is the carbon nucleus sphere radius equal to 2.5 Fermi distances, m is the mass of tubulin, and G is the gravitational constant. Brown and Tuszynski calculated E_G (using separation at the nanometer level of the entire tubulin protein), finding an appropriately small energy E of 10^{-27} electron volts (eV) per tubulin, infinitesimal compared with ambient energy kT of 10^{-4}eV. Correcting for the smaller superposition separation distance of 2.5 Fermi lengths in Orch OR gives a significantly larger, but still tiny 10^{-21}eV per tubulin. With 2×10^{10} tubulins per 25msec, the conscious Orch OR moment would be roughly 10^{-10}eV (10^{-29} joules), still insignificant compared to kT at 10^{-4}eV.

All this serves to illustrate the fact that the energy E_G does not actually play a role in physical processes as an energy, in competition with other energies that are driving the physical (chemical, electronic) processes of relevance. In a clear sense E_G is, instead, an energy uncertainty—and it is this uncertainty that allows quantum state reduction to take place without violation of energy conservation. The fact that E_G is far smaller than the other energies involved in the relevant physical processes is a necessary feature of the consistency of the OR scheme. It does not supply the energy to drive the physical processes involved, but it provides the energy uncertainty that allows the freedom for processes having virtually the same energy as each other to be alternative actions. In practice, all that E_G is needed for is to tell us how to calculate the lifetime τ of the superposition. E_G would enter into issues of energy balance only if gravitational interactions between the parts of the system were important in the processes involved. (The Earth's gravitational field plays no role in this either, because it cancels out in the calculation of E_G.) No other forces of nature directly contribute to E_G, which is just as well, because if they did, there would be a gross discrepancy with observational physics. Tegmark, 2000. Physicist Max Tegmark (2000) confronted Orch OR on the basis of decoherence. This was discussed at length in Section 7.

Koch and Hepp, 2006. In a challenge to Orch OR, neuroscientists/physicists Koch and Hepp published a thought experiment in Nature, describing a person observing a superposition of a cat both dead and alive with one eye, the other eye distracted by a series of images (binocular rivalry). They asked 'Where in the observer's brain would reduction occur?', apparently assuming Orch OR followed the Copenhagen interpretation in which conscious observation causes quantum state reduction. This is precisely the opposite of Orch OR in which consciousness is the orchestrated quantum state reduction given by OR.

Orch OR can account for the related issue of bistable perceptions (e.g. the famous face/vase illusion, or Necker cube). Non-conscious superpositions of both possibilities (face and vase) during pre-conscious quantum superposition then reduce by OR at time τ to conscious perception of one or the other, face or vase. The reduction would occur among microtubules within neurons interconnected by gap junctions in various areas of visual and pre-frontal cortex and other brain regions.

Reimers et al (2009) described three types of Fröhlich condensation (weak, strong and coherent, the first classical and the latter two quantum). They validated 8 MHz coherence measured in microtubules by Pokorny (2001; 2004) as weak condensation. Based on simulation of a 1-dimensional linear chain of tubulin dimers representing a microtubule, they concluded only weak Fröhlich condensation occurs in microtubules. Claiming Orch OR requires strong or coherent Fröhlich condensation, they concluded Orch OR is invalid. However Samsonovich et al (1992) simulated a microtubule as a 2-dimensional lattice plane with toroidal boundary conditions and found Fröhlich resonance maxima at discrete locations in super-lattice patterns on the simulated microtubule surface which precisely matched experimentally observed functional attachment sites for microtubule-associated proteins (MAPs). Further, Bandyopadhyay (2011) has experimental evidence for strong Fröhlich coherence in microtubules at multiple resonant frequencies.

Figure 7 (next page). Simulating Fröhlich coherence in microtubules. A) Linear column of tubulins (protofilament) as simulated by Reimers et al (2010) which showed only weak Fröhlich condensation. B) and C) 2-dimensional tubulin sheets with toroidal boundary conditions (approximating 3-dimensional microtubule) simulated by Samsonovich et al (1992) shows long range Fröhlich resonance, with long-range symmetry, and nodes matching experimentally-observed MAP attachment patterns.

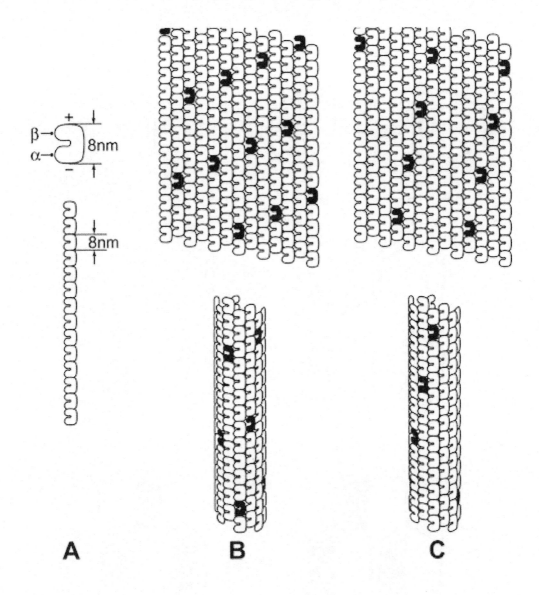

McKemmish et al (2010) challenged the Orch OR contention that tubulin switching is mediated by London forces, pointing out that mobile π electrons in a benzene ring (e.g. a phenyl ring without attachments) are completely delocalized, and hence cannot switch between states, nor exist in superposition of both states. Agreed. A single benzene cannot engage in switching. London forces occur between two or more electron cloud ring structures, or other non-polar groups. A single benzene ring cannot support London forces. It takes two (or more) to tango. Orch OR has always maintained two or more non-polar groups are necessary (Figure 8). McKemmish et al are clearly mistaken on this point.

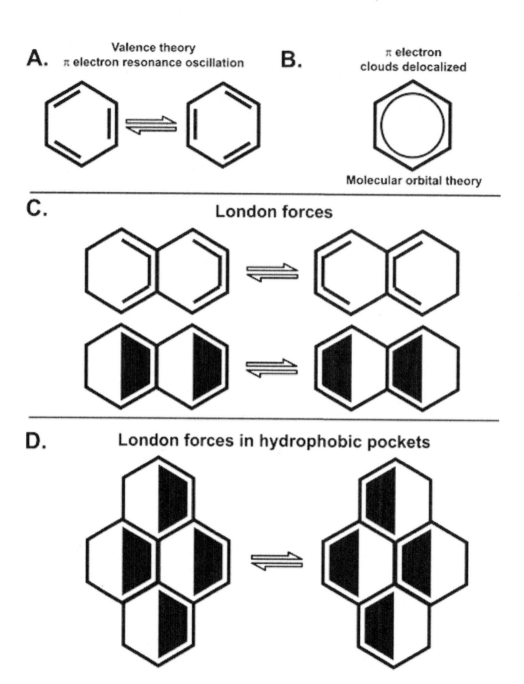

Figure 8. A) Phenyl ring/benzene of 6 carbons with three extra π electrons/ double bonds which oscillate between two configurations according to valence theory. B) Phenyl ring/benzene according to molecular orbital theory in which π electrons/double bonds are delocalized, thus preventing oscillation between alternate states. No oscillation/switching can occur. C) Two adjacent phenyl rings/ benzenes in which π electrons/double bonds are coupled, i.e. van der Waals London (dipole dispersion) forces. Two versions are shown: In top version, lines

represent double bond locations; in bottom version, dipoles are filled in to show negative charge locations. D) Complex of 4 rings with London forces.

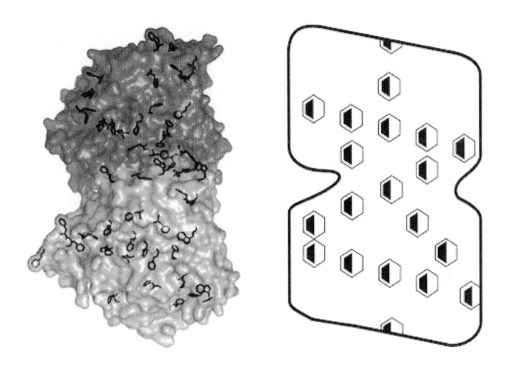

Figure 9. Left: Molecular simulation of tubulin with beta tubulin (dark gray) on top and alpha tubulin (light gray) on bottom. Non-polar amino acids phenylalanine and tryptophan with aromatic phenyl and indole rings are shown. (By Travis Craddock and Jack Tuszynski.) Right: Schematic tubulin with non-polar hydrophobic phenyl rings approximating actually phenyl and indole rings. Scale bar: 1 nanometer.

McKemmish et al further assert that tubulin switching in Orch OR requires significant conformational structural change (as indicated in Figure 2), and that the only mechanism for such conformational switching is due to GTP hydrolysis, i.e. conversion of guanosine triphophate (GTP) to guanosine diphosphate (GDP) with release of phosphate group energy, and tubulin conformational flexing. McKemmish et al correctly point out that driving synchronized microtubule oscillations by hydrolysis of GTP to GDP and conformational changes would be prohibitive in terms of energy requirements and heat produced. This is agreed. However, we clarify that tubulin switching in Orch OR need not actually involve significant conformational change (e. g. as is illustrated in Figure 2), that electron cloud dipole states (London forces) are sufficient for bit-like switching, superposition and qubit function. We acknowledge tubulin conformational switching as discussed in early Orch OR publications and illustrations do indicate significant conformational changes. They are admittedly, though unintentionally, misleading

The only tubulin conformational factor in Orch OR is superposition separation involved in E_G, the gravitational self-energy of the tubulin qubit. As previously described, we calculated E_G for tubulin separated from itself at three possible levels: 1) the entire protein (e.g. partial separation, as suggested in Figure 2), 2) its atomic nuclei, and 3) its nucleons (protons and neutrons). The dominant effect is 2) separation at the level of atomic nuclei, e.g. 2.5 Fermi length for carbon nuclei (2.5 femtometers; 2.5×10^{-15} meters). This shift may be accounted for by London force dipoles with Mossbauer nuclear recoil and charge effects (Hameroff, 1998). Tubulin switching in Orch OR requires neither GTP hydrolysis nor significant conformational changes.

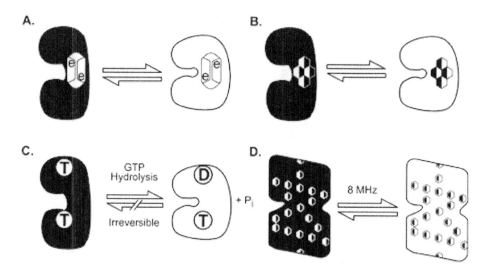

Figure 10. Four versions of the schematic Orch OR tubulin bit (superpositioned qubit states not shown). A) Early version showing conformational change coupled to/driven by single hydrophobic pocket with two aromatic rings. B) Updated version with single hydrophobic pocket composed of 4 aromatic rings. C) McKemmish et al (2009) mis-characterization of Orch OR tubulin bit as irreversible conformational change driven by GTP hydrolysis. D) Current version of Orch OR bit with no significant conformational change (change occurs at the level of atomic nuclei) and multiple hydrophobic pockets arranged in channels.

Schematic depiction of the tubulin bit, qubit and hydrophobic pockets in Orch OR has evolved over the years. An updated version is described in the next Section.

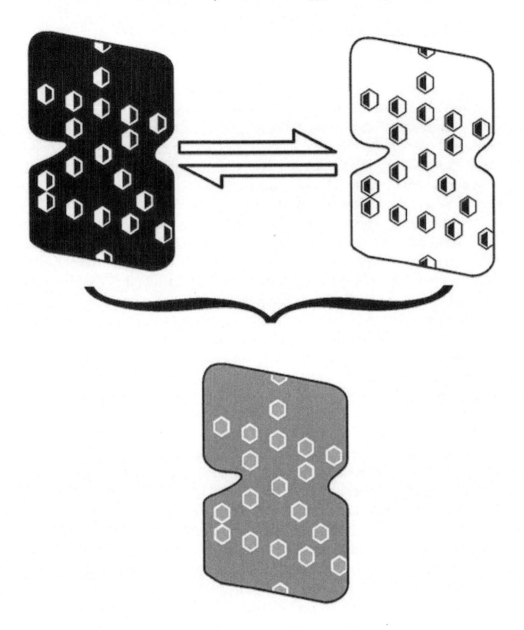

Figure 11. 2011 Orch OR tubulin qubit. Top: Alternate states of tubulin dimer (black and white) due to collective orientation of London force electron cloud dipoles in non-polar hydrophobic regions. There is no evident conformational change as suggested in previous versions; conformational change occurs at the level of atomic nuclei. Bottom: Depiction of tubulin (gray) superpositioned in both states.

9. Topological Quantum Computing in Orch OR

Quantum processes in Orch OR have consistently been ascribed to London forces in tubulin hydrophobic pockets, non-polar intra-protein regions, e.g. of π electron resonance rings of aromatic amino acids including tryptophan and phenylalanine. This assertion is based on (1) Fröhlich's suggestion that protein states are synchronized by electron cloud dipole oscillations in intra-protein non-polar regions, and (2) anesthetic gases selectively erasing consciousness by London forces in non-polar, hydrophobic regions in various neuronal proteins (e.g. tubulin, membrane proteins, etc.). London forces are weak, but numerous and able to act cooperatively to regulate protein states (Voet and Voet, 1995).

The structure of tubulin became known in 1998 (Nogales et al, 1998), allowing identification of non-polar amino acids and hydrophobic regions. Figure 9 shows locations of phenyl and indole π electron resonance rings of non-polar aromatic amino acids phenylalanine and tryptophan in tubulin. The ring locations are clustered along somewhat continuous pathways (within 2 nanometers) through tubulin. Thus, rather than hydrophobic pockets, tubulin may have within it quantum hydrophobic channels, or streams, linear arrays of electron resonance clouds suitable for cooperative, long-range quantum London forces. These quantum channels within each tubulin appear to align with those in adjacent tubulins in microtubule lattices, matching helical winding patterns (Figure 12). This in turn may support topological quantum computing in Orch OR.

Quantum bits, or qubits in quantum computers are generally envisioned as information bits in superposition of simultaneous alternative representations, e.g. both 1 and 0. Topological qubits are superpositions of alternative pathways, or channels which intersect repeatedly on a surface, forming 'braids'. Quasiparticles called anyons travel along such pathways, the intersections forming logic gates, with particular braids or pathways corresponding with particular information states, or bits. In superposition, anyons follow multiple braided pathways simultaneously, then reduce, or collapse to one particular pathway and functional output. Topological qubits are intrinsically resistant to decoherence.

An Orch OR qubit based on topological quantum computing specific to microtubule polymer geometry was suggested in Hameroff et al. (2002). Conductances along particular microtubule lattice geometry, e.g. Fibonacci helical pathways, were proposed to function as topological bits and qubits. Bandyopadhyay (2011) has preliminary evidence for ballistic conductance along different, discrete helical pathways in single microtubules

As an extension of Orch OR, we suggest topological qubits in microtubules based on quantum hydrophobic channels, e.g. continuous arrays of electron resonance rings within and among tubulins in microtubule lattices, e.g. following Fibonacci pathways. Cooperative London forces (electron cloud dipoles) in quantum hydrophobic channels may enable long-range coherence and topological quantum computing in microtubules necessary for optimal brain function and consciousness.

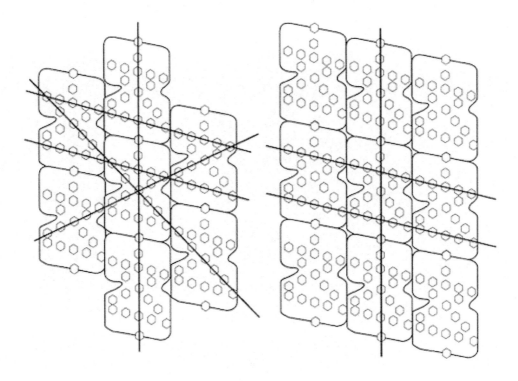

Figure 12. Left: Microtubule A-lattice configuration with lines connecting proposed hydrophobic channels of near-contiguous (<2 nanometer separation) electron resonance rings of phenylalanine and tryptophan. Right: Microtubule B-lattice with fewer such channels and lacking Fibonacci pathways. B-lattice microtubules have a vertical seam dislocation (not shown).

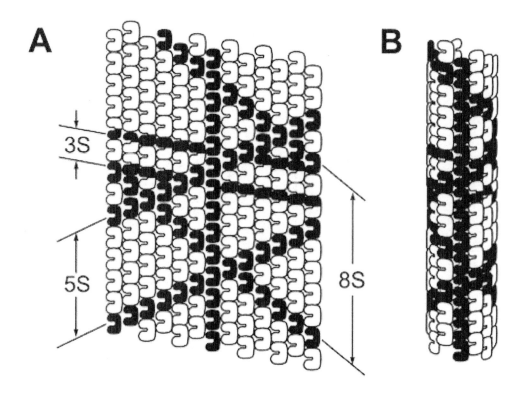

Figure 13. Extending microtubule A-lattice hydrophobic channels (Figure 12) results in helical winding patterns matching Fibonacci geometry. Bandyopadhyay (2011) has evidence for ballistic conductance and quantum inteference along such helical pathways which may be involved in topological quantum computing. Quantum electronic states of London forces in hydrophobic channels result in slight superposition separation of atomic nuclei, sufficient E_G for Orch OR. This image may be taken to represent superposition of four possible topological qubits which, after time T=tau, will undergo OR, and reduce to specific pathway(s) which then implement function.

10. Conclusion: Consciousness in the Universe

Our criterion for proto-consciousness is OR . It would be unreasonable to refer to OR as the criterion for actual consciousness, because, according to the DP scheme, OR processes would be taking place all the time, and would be providing the effective randomness that is characteristic of quantum measurement. Quantum superpositions will continually be reaching the DP threshold for OR in non-biological settings as well as in biological ones, and usually take place in the purely random environment of a quantum system under measurement. Instead, our criterion for consciousness is Orch OR, conditions for which are fairly stringent: superposition must be isolated from the decoherence effects of the random environment for long enough to reach the DS threshold. Small superpositions are easier to isolate, but require longer reduction times τ. Large superpositions will reach threshold quickly, but are intrinsically more difficult to isolate. Nonetheless, we believe that there is evidence that such superpositions could occur within sufficiently large collections of microtubules in the brain for τ to be some fraction of a second.

Very large mass displacements can also occur in the universe in quantum-mechanical situations, for example in the cores of neutron stars. By OR , such superpositions would reduce extremely quickly, and classically unreasonable superpositions would be rapidly eliminated. Nevertheless, sentient creatures might have evolved in parts of the universe that would be highly alien to us. One possibility might be on neutron star surfaces, an idea that was developed ingeniously and in great detail by Robert Forward in two science-fiction stories (Dragon's Egg in 1980, Starquake in 1989). Such creatures (referred to as 'cheelas' in the books, with metabolic processes and OR-like events occurring at rates of around a million times that of a human being) could arguably have intense experiences, but whether or not this would be possible in detail is, at the moment, a very speculative matter. Nevertheless, the Orch OR proposal offers a possible route to rational argument, as to whether life of a totally alien kind such as this might be possible, or even probable, somewhere in the universe.

Such speculations also raise the issue of the 'anthropic principle', according to which it is sometimes argued that the particular dimensionless constants of Nature that we happen to find in our universe are 'fortuitously' favorable to human existence. (A dimensionless physical constant is a pure number, like the ratio of the electric to the gravitational force between the electron and the proton in a hydrogen atom, which in this case is a number of the general order of 10^{40}.) The key point is not so much to do with human existence, but the existence of sentient beings of any kind. Is there anything coincidental about the dimensionless physical constants being of such a nature that conscious life is possible at all? For example, if the mass of the neutron had been slightly less than that of the proton, rather than slightly larger, then neutrons rather than protons would have been stable, and this would be to the detriment of the whole subject of chemistry. These issues are frequently argued about (see Barrow and Tipler 1986), but the Orch OR proposal provides a little more substance to these arguments, since a proposal for the possibility of sentient life is, in principle, provided.

The recently proposed cosmological scheme of conformal cyclic cosmology (CCC) (Penrose 2010) also has some relevance to these issues. CCC posits that what we presently regard as the entire history of our universe, from its Big-Bang origin (but without inflation) to its indefinitely expanding future, is but one aeon in an unending succession of similar such aeons, where the infinite future of each matches to the big bang of the next via an infinite change of scale. A question arises whether the dimensionless constants of the aeon prior to ours, in the CCC scheme, are the same as those in our own aeon, and this relates to the question of whether sentient life could exist in that aeon as well as in our own. These questions are in principle answerable by observation, and again they would have a bearing on the extent or validity of the Orch OR proposal. If Orch OR turns out to be correct, in it essentials, as a physical basis for consciousness, then it opens up the possibility that many questions may become answerable, such as whether life could have come about in an aeon prior to our own, that would have previously seemed to be far beyond the reaches of science.

Moreover, Orch OR places the phenomenon of consciousness at a very central place in the physical nature of our universe, whether or not this 'universe' includes aeons other than just our own. It is our belief that, quite apart from detailed aspects of the physical mechanisms that are involved in the production of consciousness in human brains, quantum mechanics is an incomplete theory. Some completion is needed, and the DP proposal for an OR scheme underlying quantum theory's R-process would be a definite possibility. If such a scheme as this is indeed respected by Nature, then there is a fundamental additional ingredient to our presently understood laws of Nature which plays an important role at the Planck-scale level of space-time structure. The Orch OR proposal takes advantage of this, suggesting that conscious experience itself plays such a role in the operation of the laws of the universe.

Acknowledgment We thank Dave Cantrell, University of Arizona Biomedical Communications for artwork.

References

Atema, J. (1973). Microtubule theory of sensory transduction. Journal of Theoretical Biology, 38, 181-90.

Bandyopadhyay A (2011) Direct experimental evidence for quantum states in microtubules and topological invariance. Abstracts: Toward a Science of Consciousness 2011, Sockholm, Sweden, HYPERLINK "http://www.consciousness.arizona.edu"www.consciousness.arizona.edu

Barrow, J.D. and Tipler, F.J. (1986) The Anthropic Cosmological Principle (OUP, Oxford).

Bell, J.S. (1966) Speakable and Unspeakable in Quantum Mechanics (Cambridge Univ. Press, Cambridge; reprint 1987).

Benioff, P. (1982). Quantum mechanical Hamiltonian models of Turing Machines. Journal of Statistical Physics, 29, 515-46.

Bennett C.H., and Wiesner, S.J. (1992). Communication via 1- and 2-particle operators on Einstein-Podolsky-Rosen states. Physical Reviews Letters, 69,

2881-84.

Bensimon G, Chemat R (1991) Microtubule disruption and cognitive defects: effect of colchicine on teaming behavior in rats. Pharmacol. Biochem. Behavior 38:141-145.

Bohm, D. (1951) Quantum Theory (Prentice–Hall, Englewood-Cliffs.) Ch. 22, sect. 15-19. Reprinted as: The Paradox of Einstein, Rosen and Podolsky, in Quantum Theory and Measurement, eds., J.A. Wheeler and W.H. Zurek (Princeton University Press, Princeton, 1983).

Bernroider, G. and Roy, S. (2005) Quantum entanglement of K ions, multiple channel states and the role of noise in the brain. SPIE 5841-29:205–14.

Bouwmeester, D., Pan, J.W., Mattle, K., Eibl, M., Weinfurter, H. and Zeilinger, A. (1997) Experimental quantum teleportation. Nature 390 (6660): 575-579.

Brunden K.R., Yao Y., Potuzak J.S., Ferrer N.I., Ballatore C., James M.J., Hogan A.M., Trojanowski J.Q., Smith A.B. 3rd and Lee V.M. (2011) The characterization of microtubule-stabilizing drugs as possibletherapeutic agents for Alzheimer's disease and related taupathies. Pharmacological Research, 63(4), 341-51.

Chalmers, D. J., (1996). The conscious mind - In search of a fundamental theory. Oxford University Press, New York.

Crick, F., and Koch, C., (1990). Towards a neurobiological theory of consciousness. Seminars in the Neurosciences, 2, 263-75.

Dennett, D.C. (1991). Consciousness explained. Little Brown, Boston. MA.

Dennett, D.C. (1995) Darwin's dangerous idea: Evolution and the Meanings of Life, Simon and Schuster.

Dermietzel, R. (1998) Gap junction wiring: a 'new' principle in cell-to-cell communication in the nervous system? Brain Research Reviews. 26(2-3):176-83.

Deutsch, D. (1985) Quantum theory, the Church–Turing principle and the universal quantum computer, Proceedings of the Royal Society (London) A400, 97-117.

Diósi, L. (1987) A universal master equation for the gravitational violation of quantum mechanics, Physics Letters A 120 (8):377-381.

Diósi, L. (1989). Models for universal reduction of macroscopic quantum fluctuations Physical Review A, 40, 1165-74.

Draguhn A, Traub RD, Schmitz D, Jefferys (1998). Electrical coupling underlies high-frequency oscillations in the hippocampus in vitro. Nature, 394(6689), 189-92.

Eccles, J.C. (1992). Evolution of consciousness. Proceedings of the National Academy of Sciences, 89, 7320-24.

Engel GS, Calhoun TR, Read EL, Ahn T-K, Mancal T, Cheng Y-C, Blankenship RE, Fleming GR (2007) Evidence for wavelike energy transfer through quantum coherence in photosynthetic systems. Nature 446:782-786.

Everett, H. (1957). Relative state formulation of quantum mechanics. In Quantum Theory and Measurement, J.A. Wheeler and W.H. Zurek (eds.) Princeton University Press, 1983; originally in Reviews of Modern Physics, 29, 454-62.

Feynman, R.P. (1986). Quantum mechanical computers. Foundations of Physics, 16(6), 507-31.

Forward, R. (1980) Dragon's Egg. Ballentine Books.

Forward, R. (1989) Starquake. Ballentine Books.

Fröhlich, H. (1968). Long-range coherence and energy storage in biological systems. International Journal of Quantum Chemistry, 2, 641-9.

Fröhlich, H. (1970). Long range coherence and the actions of enzymes. Nature, 228, 1093.

Fröhlich, H. (1975). The extraordinary dielectric properties of biological materials and the action of enzymes. Proceedings of the National Academy of Sciences, 72, 4211-15.

Galarreta, M. and Hestrin, S. (1999). A network of fast-spiking cells in the neocortex connected by electrical synapses. Nature, 402, 72-75.

Gauger E., Rieper E., Morton J.J.L., Benjamin S.C., Vedral V. (2011) Sustained quantum coherence and entanglement in the avian compass http://arxiv.org/abs/0906.3725.

Ghirardi, G.C., Rimini, A., and Weber, T. (1986). Unified dynamics for microscopic and macroscopic systems. Physical Review D, 34, 470.

Ghirardi, G.C., Grassi, R., and Rimini, A. (1990). Continuous-spontaneous reduction model involving gravity. Physical Review A, 42, 1057-64.

Grush R., Churchland P.S. (1995), 'Gaps in Penrose's toilings', J. Consciousness Studies, 2 (1):10-29.

Hagan S, Hameroff S, and Tuszynski J, (2001). Quantum Computation in Brain Microtubules? Decoherence and Biological Feasibility, Physical Review E, 65, 061901.

Hameroff, S.R., and Watt R.C. (1982). Information processing in microtubules. Journal of Theoretical Biology, 98, 549-61.

Hameroff, S.R.(1987) Ultimate computing: Biomolecular consciousness and nanotechnology. Elsevier North-Holland, Amsterdam.

Hameroff, S.R., and Penrose, R., (1996a). Orchestrated reduction of quantum coherence in brain microtubules: A model for consciousness. In: Toward a Science of Consciousness ; The First Tucson Discussions and Debates. Hameroff, S.R., Kaszniak, and Scott, A.C., eds., 507-540, MIT Press, Cambridge MA, 507-540. Also published in Mathematics and Computers in Simulation (1996) 40:453-480.

Hameroff, S.R., and Penrose, R. (1996b). Conscious events as orchestrated spacetime selections. Journal of Consciousness Studies, 3(1), 36-53.

Hameroff, S. (1998a). Quantum computation in brain microtubules? The Penrose-Hameroff "Orch OR" model of consciousness. Philosophical Transactions of the Royal Society (London) Series A, 356, 1869-1896.

Hameroff, S. (1998b). 'Funda-mentality': is the conscious mind subtly linked to a basic level of the universe? Trends in Cognitive Science, 2, 119-127.

Hameroff, S. (1998c). Anesthesia, consciousness and hydrophobic pockets – A unitary quantum hypothesis of anesthetic action. Toxicology Letters, 100, 101, 31-39.

Hameroff, S. (1998d). HYPERLINK "http://www.hameroff.com/penrose-hameroff/cambrian.html"Did consciousness cause the Cambrian evolutionary explosion? In: Toward a Science of Consciousness II: The Second Tucson Discussions and Debates. Eds. Hameroff, S.R., Kaszniak, A.W., and Scott, A.C., MIT Press, Cambridge, MA.

Hameroff, S., Nip, A., Porter, M., and Tuszynski, J. (2002). Conduction pathways in microtubules, biological quantum computation and microtubules. Biosystems, 64(13), 149-68.

Hameroff S.R., & Watt R.C. (1982) Information processing in microtubules. Journal of Theoretical Biology 98:549-61.

Hameroff, S.R. (2006) The entwined mysteries of anesthesia and consciousness. Anesthesiology 105:400-412.

Hameroff, S.R, Craddock TJ, Tuszynski JA (2010) Memory 'bytes' – Molecular match for CaMKII phosphorylation encoding of microtubule lattices. Journal of Integrative Neuroscience 9(3):253-267.

He, R-H., Hashimoto, M., Karapetyan. H., Koralek, J.D., Hinton, J.P., Testaud, J.P., Nathan, V., Yoshida, Y., Yao, H., Tanaka, K., Meevasana, W., Moore, R.G., Lu, D.H.,Mo, S-K., Ishikado, M., Eisaki, H., Hussain, Z., Devereaux, T.P., Kivelson, S.A., Orenstein, Kapitulnik, J.A., Shen, Z-X. (2011) From a Single-Band Metal to a High Temperature Superconductor via Two Thermal Phase Transitions. Science, 2011;331 (6024): 1579-1583.

Hebb, D.O. (1949). Organization of Behavior: A Neuropsychological Theory, John Wiley and Sons, New York.

Huxley TH (1893; 1986) Method and Results: Essays.

Kant I (1781) Critique of Pure Reason (Translated and edited by Paul Guyer and Allen W. Wood, Cambridge University Press, 1998).

Kibble, T.W.B. (1981). Is a semi-classical theory of gravity viable? In Quantum Gravity 2: a Second Oxford Symposium; eds. C.J. Isham, R. Penrose, and D.W. Sciama (Oxford University Press, Oxford), 63-80.

Koch, C., (2004) The Quest for Consciousness: A Neurobiological Approach, Englewood, CO., Roberts and Co.

Koch C, Hepp K (2006) Quantm mechanics in the brain. Nature 440(7084):611.

Libet, B., Wright, E.W. Jr., Feinstein, B., & Pearl, D.K. (1979) Subjective referral of the timing for a conscious sensory experience. Brain 102:193-224.

Luo L, Lu J (2011) Temperature dependence of protein folding deduced from quantum transition. http://arxiv.org/abs/1102.3748

Lutz A, Greischar AL, Rawlings NB, Ricard M, Davidson RJ (2004) Long-term meditators self-induce high-amplitude gamma synchrony during mental practice The Proceedings of the National Academy of Sciences USA 101(46)16369-16373.

Macikic I., de Riedmatten H., Tittel W., Zbinden H. and Gisin N. (2002) Long-distance teleportation of qubits at telecommunication wavelengths Nature 421, 509-513.

Margulis, L. and Sagan, D. 1995. What is life? Simon and Schuster, N.Y.

Marshall, W, Simon, C., Penrose, R., and Bouwmeester, D (2003). Towards quantum superpositions of a mirror. Physical Review Letters 91, 13-16; 130401.

McKemmish LK, Reimers JR, McKenzie RH, Mark AE, Hush NS (2009) Penrose-Hameroff orchestrated objective-reduction proposal for human consciousness is not biologically feasible. Physical Review E. 80(2 Pt 1):021912.

Moroz, I.M., Penrose, R., and Tod, K.P. (1998) Spherically-symmetric solutions of the Schrödinger–Newton equations:. Classical and Quantum Gravity, 15, 2733-42.

Nogales E, Wolf SG, Downing KH. (1998) HYPERLINK "http://dx.doi.org/10.1038/34465"Structure of the $\alpha\beta$-tubulin dimer by electron crystallography. Nature. 391, 199-203.

Ouyang, M., & Awschalom, D.D. (2003) Coherent spin transfer between molecularly bridged quantum dots. Science 301:1074-78.

Pearle, P. (1989). Combining stochastic dynamical state-vector reduction with spontaneous localization. Physical Review A, 39, 2277-89.

Pearle, P. and Squires, E.J. (1994). Bound-state excitation, nucleon decay experiments and models of wave-function collapse. Physical Review Letters, 73(1), 1-5.

Penrose, R. (1989). The Emperor's New Mind: Concerning Computers, Minds, and the Laws of Physics, Oxford University Press, Oxford.

Penrose, R. (1993). Gravity and quantum mechanics. In General Relativity and Gravitation 13. Part 1: Plenary Lectures 1992. Proceedings of the Thirteenth International Conference on General Relativity and Gravitation held at Cordoba, Argentina, 28 June - 4 July 1992. Eds. R.J.Gleiser, C.N.Kozameh, and O.M.Moreschi (Inst. of Phys. Publ. Bristol and Philadelphia), 179-89.

Penrose, R. (1994). Shadows of the Mind; An Approach to the Missing Science of Consciousness. Oxford University Press, Oxford.

Penrose, R. (1996). On gravity's role in quantum state reduction. General Relativity and Gravitation, 28, 581-600.

Penrose, R. (2000). Wavefunction collapse as a real gravitational effect. In Mathematical Physics 2000, Eds. A.Fokas, T.W.B.Kibble, A.Grigouriou, and B.Zegarlinski. Imperial College Press, London, 266-282.

Penrose, R. (2002). John Bell, State Reduction, and Quanglement. In Quantum Unspeakables: From Bell to Quantum Information, Eds. Reinhold A. Bertl-mann and Anton Zeilinger , Springer-Verlag, Berlin, 319-331.

Penrose, R. (2004). The Road to Reality: A Complete Guide to the Laws of the Universe. Jonathan Cape, London.

Penrose, R. (2009). Black holes, quantum theory and cosmology (Fourth International Workshop DICE 2008), Journal of Physics, Conference Series 174, 012001.

Penrose, R. (2010). Cycles of Time: An Extraordinary New View of the Universe. Bodley Head, London.

Penrose R. and Hameroff S.R. (1995) What gaps? Reply to Grush and Churchland. Journal of Consciousness Studies.2:98-112.

Percival, I.C. (1994) Primary state diffusion. Proceedings of the Royal Society (London) A, 447, 189-209.

Pokorný, J., Hasek, J., Jelínek, F., Saroch, J. & Palan, B. (2001) Electro-magnetic activity of yeast cells in the M phase. Electro Magnetobiol 20, 371–396.

Pokorný, J. (2004) Excitation of vibration in microtubules in living cells. Bioelectrochem. 63: 321-326.

Polkinghorne, J. (2002) Quantum Theory, A Very Short Introduction. Oxford University Press, Oxford.

Rae, A.I.M. (1994) Quantum Mechanics. Institute of Physics Publishing; 4th edition 2002.

Rasmussen, S., Karampurwala, H., Vaidyanath, R., Jensen, K.S., and Ham-eroff, S. (1990) Computational connectionism within neurons: A model of cyto-skeletal automata subserving neural networks. Physica D 42:428-49.

Reimers JR, McKemmish LK, McKenzie RH, Mark AE, Hush NS (2009) Weak, strong, and coherent regimes of Frohlich condensation and their applica-tions to terahertz medicine and quantum consciousness Proceedings of the Na-tional Academy of Sciences USA 106(11):4219-24

Reiter GF, Kolesnikov AI, Paddison SJ, Platzman PM, Moravsky AP, Ad-ams MA, Mayers J (2011) Evidence of a new quantum state of nano-confined water http://arxiv.org/abs/1101.499

Rieper E, Anders J, Vedral V (2011) Quantum entanglement between the electron clouds of nucleic acids in DNA. http://arxiv.org/abs/1006.4053.

Samsonovich A, Scott A, Hameroff S (1992) Acousto-conformational tran-sitions in cytoskeletal microtubules: Implications for intracellular information processing. Nanobiology 1:457-468.

Sherrington, C.S. (1957) Man on His Nature, Second Edition, Cambridge University Press.

Smolin, L. (2002). Three Roads to Quantum Gravity. Basic Books. New York.

Tegmark, M. (2000) The importance of quantum decoherence in brain pro-cesses. Physica Rev E 61:4194-4206.

Tittel, W, Brendel, J., Gisin, B., Herzog, T., Zbinden, H., and Gisin, N. (1998) Experimental demonstration of quantum correlations over more than 10 km, Physical Reiew A, 57:3229-32.

Tononi G (2004) An information integration theory of consciousness BMC Neuroscience 5:42.

Turin L (1996) A spectroscopic mechanism for primary olfactory reception Chem Senses 21(6) 773-91.

Tuszynski JA, Brown JA, Hawrylak P, Marcer P (1998) Dielectric polarization, electrical conduction, information processing and quantum computation in microtubules. Are they plausible? Phil Trans Royal Society A 356:1897-1926.

Tuszynski, J.A., Hameroff, S., Sataric, M.V., Trpisova, B., & Nip, M.L.A. (1995) Ferroelectric behavior in microtubule dipole lattices; implications for information processing, signaling and assembly/disassembly. Journal of Theoretical Biology 174:371–80.

Voet, D., Voet, J.G. 1995. Biochemistry, 2nd edition. Wiley, New York.

von Rospatt, A., (1995) The Buddhist Doctrine of Momentariness: A survey of the origins and early phase of this doctrine up to Vasubandhu (Stuttgart: Franz Steiner Verlag).

Wegner, D.M. (2002) The illusion of conscious will Cambridge MA, MIT Press.

Whitehead, A.N., (1929) Process and Reality. New York, Macmillan.

Whitehead, A.N. (1933) Adventure of Ideas, London, Macmillan.

Wigner E.P. (1961). Remarks on the mind-body question, in The Scientist Speculates, ed. I.J. Good (Heinemann, London). In Quantum Theory and Measurement, eds., J.A. Wheeler and W.H. Zurek, Princeton Univsity Press, Princeton, MA. (Reprinted in E. Wigner (1967), Symmetries and Reflections, Indiana University Press, Bloomington).

Wolfram, S. (2002) A New Kind of Science. Wolfram Media incorporated.

****
****
****

III. Consciousness, Quantum Physics, Relativity, Retrocausation, Precognition, Multiple Dimensions, Entanglement, and Time

****
****
****

15. The Theory of MindTime

John T. Furey[1] and Vincent J. Fortunato[2]

[1]The MindTime Project; [2]Walden University and The MindTime Project

Abstract

According to modern cosmologists, the evolution of consciousness corresponded with the evolution of matter into increasingly complex, elaborate, and interactive systems, with the human brain providing the highest level of complexity known. Psychological research shows that just about all of human experience is dependent upon and influenced by how individuals perceive time, localize themselves consciously within space and time, process their temporally-based perceptions and experiences, and utilize their episodic and semantic memory structures to engage in mental time travel. We propose that over the course of evolution, sensitivities toward perceiving potentially pleasurable/ appetitive and aversive/harmful environmental stimuli and the motivation to approach and/or avoid such stimuli moved beyond reflexive, innate, and learned associative neural networks and became increasingly influenced by, and in turn influenced, the cognitive structures associated with organisms' ability to perceive and conceptualize time. In this paper, we present a theory of consciousness and psychology in which we propose that three general yet distinct cognitive patterns, or thinking perspectives, exist, which we refer to as Past, Present, and Future thinking, and that these three patterns are universal conditions of consciousness and form the foundation and framework for understanding, in particular, all of human thought and interaction, from the individual to the collective, and from the formation of an idea to the creation of cultures and artifacts based on those ideas.

Keywords: Thinking perspective, Past thinking, Present thinking, Future thinking, mental time travel, time, temporal perspective, perception, consciousness, self-awareness, MindTime

1. Introduction

The ability to consciously localize experience temporally and engage in what Tulving (1985a) referred to as mental time travel is considered to be one of the most important evolutionary advancements of consciousness (e.g., Corballis, 2013; Jaynes, 1976; Liljenström, 2011; Suddendorf & Corballis, 1997, 2007). Although mental time travel—the ability to mentally project one's mind forward and backward in time—has been demonstrated in many animals (e.g., Corballis, 2013), in human beings, the ability to engage in mental time travel is especially advanced. Human beings, in particular, have the ability to "internalize" worlds through the formation of spatial and temporal patterns and form an understanding of the relationship between cause and effect (Liljenström, 2011).

Mental time travel appears to have coincided with the evolution of complex memory systems and self-awareness (e.g., Liljenström, 2011; Suddendorf & Corballis, 1997, 2007; Tulving, 1985a, 1985b) and, according to Suddendorf and colleagues (Suddendorf, 1999; Suddendorf & Corballis, 1997, 2007), provided Homo sapiens with a cognitive flexibility to respond to the cyclical nature of temporally-based experiences, draw upon past experiences and stored knowledge, creatively imagine an infinite set of hypothetical future possibilities and engage in "what if" theorizing, set short-term and long-term goals, develop strategies and action plans, and organize the resources needed to obtain long-term results; all with the goal of maximizing survival. Mental time travel also provides human beings with the boundless flights of imagination that typify the human species (e.g., Hejazi, 2012; Lombardo, 2006).

Mental time travel has become an increasingly popular construct of interest among developmental psychologists (e.g., Atance & O'Neill, 2005; Atance & Jackson, 2009), cognitive psychologists (e.g., Trope & Liberman, 2003, 2010), social psychologists (e.g., Gilbert & Wilson, 2007), and neuropsychologists (e.g., Addis, Wong, & Schacter, 2007; Hassabis, Kumaran, & Maguire, 2007) and there is increasing evidence that just about all of human experience is dependent upon and influenced by how individuals perceive time, process their temporally-based perceptions and experiences, and utilize their episodic and semantic memory structures. For example, the ability of human beings to project their minds forward and backward in time has been shown to influence the emotions people experience (D'Argembeau & Van der Linden, 2007), their goals and motivational intentions (Oettingen & Mayer, 2002), their attributions of others (Warner, VanDeursen, & Pope, 2012), their perceptions of physical, social, and psychological distance (Trope & Liberman, 2003, 2010), their performance on creative and analytical tasks (Förster & Becker, 2012; Förster, Friedman, & Liberman, 2004), how they perceive and process cognitive information (Liberman & Trope, 1998), and how they perceive themselves and imagine their future selves (Wilson, Buehler, Lawford, Schmidt, & Yong, 2012).

Moreover, the ability to localize experience temporally and engage in mental time travel is implicated in the dynamic social constructive process in which language evolved as a means of social interaction and collaboration (Corballis, 2011; Perrot-Clermont & Lamboltz, 2005), the development of personal and collective narratives (i.e., life scripts: Berntsen & Bohn, 2010; Bronckart, 2005), the development of social schemas, norms, and expectations (e.g., Levine, 2006), and the development and evolution of culture and cultural artifacts (Vale, Flynn, & Kendal, 2012; Trompenaars & Hampden-Turner, 1997). Indeed, Tattersall (2011) suggested that human beings are, arguably, the only creatures on earth capable of mentally disassembling the world into a vocabulary of abstract symbols and then recombining them to create alternative versions of reality and that the fact that each human being recreates the world differently is at the root of the complexities of human experience and of human society.

Relatedly, Gilead, Liberman, and Maril (2012) proposed that mental time travel in human beings is a special case of the ability to traverse psychological distance and that many higher order cognitive functions such as the ability to imagine hypothetical realities, deceive the mind of others, and engage in prospective theorizing and counterfactual thinking are all based on a common underlying mechanism that involves the human capacity for abstract–linguistic and disembodied representations. Indeed, cognitive psychology research (Liberman & Trope, 1998; Trope & Liberman, 2003, 2010) has shown that when individuals are asked to engage in mental time travel, the temporal direction (i.e., past or future) and distance (e.g., near-term or distal future) with which they imagine themselves profoundly affects the degree of abstraction with which objects of consciousness are mentally represented and how individuals perform on a variety of cognitive tasks. The greater the temporal distance an object or event is imagined to exist in time, either into the future or into the past, the more likely it is that individuals will mentally represent that object or event abstractly.

However, despite the inextricable relationship between time, consciousness, and human experience, with perhaps the exception of Lewin (1942, 1951), who proposed that individuals' develop their own personal psychology based on the totality of their views of their own psychological past and psychological future, little theoretical development exists incorporating human perception of time and awareness and the ability to engage in mental time travel into a general model of human psychology. In this manuscript, we present a framework—the theory of MindTime—that we believe provides a foundation for understanding human consciousness, personality, cognition and information processes, preferences, and behavior.

2. The Theory of MindTime

King (2011) stated that "the evolutionary key to consciousness may lie in the survival advantage it could provide in anticipating threats and strategic opportunities." King goes on to describe how these two characteristics of life—the motivation to avoid environmental threats and the motivation to approach opportunities—exist at all levels of life, from the eukaryote cell to human beings. Each form of life contains sense organs that are sensitive to feedback about its environment. However, over time, life evolved more intricate and complex methods of survival, including complex nervous systems, such as those associated with episodic and semantic memory systems, that allowed for increased capacity of information storage and processing (Liljenström, 2011), which in turn provided life forms the ability to, in varying degrees, (a) perceive the passage of time, (b) localize their awareness in time, and (c) engage in mental time travel (e.g., Corballis, 2013).

As Lombardo (2011) noted, consciousness is temporally based in that it is always opening into the future or looking backwards into the past. According to Lombardo, "conscious beings are aware of duration, relative stability, and patterns of change; of becoming and passing away; and of an experiential direction to time. The conscious now ... may be anchored at the level of perception, and contextualized within consciousness of the past (memories) and conscious anticipation of the future, all three phenomenologically blurring together at the edges."

We propose that over the course of evolution, sensitivities toward perceiving potentially pleasurable/appetitive and aversive/harmful environmental stimuli and the motivation to approach and/or avoid such stimuli moved beyond reflexive, innate, and learned associative neural networks and became increasingly influenced by, and in turn influenced, the cognitive structures associated with organisms' ability to perceive and conceptualize time.

Specifically, we propose that at the foundation of consciousness are three temporally- based, cognitive–perceptual, abstract–linguistic patterns of thinking, which we refer to as Past, Present, and Future thinking (see Fig. 1). These three thinking perspectives correspond with (a) innate representations of the past, present, and future as temporal realities; (b) the conceptual representations and concepts that emerge from those representations; and (c) how organisms, particularly human beings, localize themselves in time. Past, Present, and Future thinking form the foundation for understanding all of human perception, thought, and interaction, from the individual to the collective, and from the formation of an idea to the creation of cultures and artifacts based on those ideas. Past, Present, and Future thinking influence the personal (and collective) narratives that individuals (and groups) develop and how individuals (and collectives): (a) perceive the world around them; (b) process and then encode information in semantic and episodic memory; (c) mentally represent objects of consciousness; (d) formulate goals and intentions; (e) develop their preferences; and (f) communicate and interact with others.

At the level of the individual, we propose that the foundation of a personal identity (i.e., a me) and just about all stable trait-based individual differences, such as the personalities that individuals manifest, as well as individuals' perceptions, intentions, values, beliefs, motivations, and behaviors can be understood as the interaction of individuals' Past, Present, and Future thinking. We also propose that the theory of MindTime can be used to describe and explain the behaviors of increasingly aggregated higher-order and complex collections of individuals such as groups and work teams, organizations, and nations as well as the temporal origins of the cultural artifacts created by these aggregates. Thus, Past, Present, and Future thinking operate as collective cognitive filters that form the basis for the development of a group culture and the cultural norms and expectations that follow. In this way we believe these three patterns of thought to be universal in scope and fractal in nature.

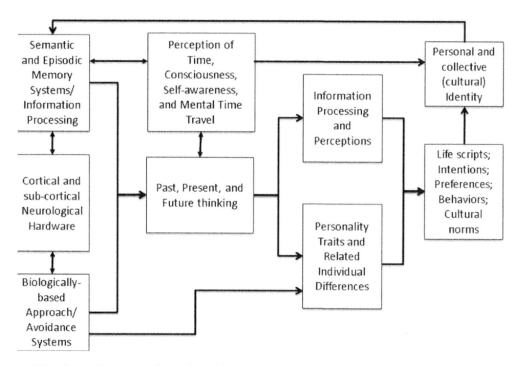

Fig. 1. An integrated model of human psychology and individual differences.

Finally, we propose that the degree to which any individual or collection of individuals resonates with any other individual or collection of individuals or with any artifact or product of human endeavor (e.g., culture, political and economic system[s], institution[s], technology, language, symbol[s], message[s], manufactured object[s], architecture, design[s]) will depend on the degree of similarity that exists between the thinking perspective characteristics of the subject and that of the object. That is, the theory of MindTime provides a basis for understanding the quality and nature of the interaction between any two individuals or collectives of individuals as well as the quality and nature of the interactions among the members of any collective and between any individual or collective and the products of human endeavor.

In the sections that follow, we briefly describe the three thinking perspectives, review some empirical evidence that support our descriptions and propositions involving Past, Present, and Future thinking, discuss a few theoretical and practical implications, and, in our closing remarks, seek to place our theory into a cosmological context.\

2.1 The Three Thinking Perspectives. Although it is customary to refer to the past, present, and future in that order (as we do throughout this manuscript), we discuss Past and Future thinking before we discuss Present thinking for reasons we hope will be apparent to the reader. Table 1 lists the key characteristics of the three thinking perspectives and Fig. 2 visually some key higher-order concepts that emerge from the interaction of Past, Present, and Future thinking.

Fig. 2. A visual depiction of the key higher-order concepts that emerge from the interaction of Past, Present, and Future thinking. Figure used with permission from the MindTime Project, LLC. Illustrated by Alden Bevington.

2.1.1 Past thinking. We use the term Past thinking to refer to the cognitive patterning that exists when memory processes are used by organisms to differentiate and dichotomize experienced reality. In human beings, the products of that dichotomization are the conceptual and social schemas, measurements, perceived phenomena, and qualities that facilitate our understanding of the world, the universe, and ourselves within it. Past thinking involves both abstract and concrete mental representations of objects and is used when individuals reflect, recollect, reconstruct, analyze, and critically evaluate experienced events and knowledge stored in memory. Past thinking is used to avoid threats, minimize risks, and maximize survival, by determining the relevance, validity, and truth of information and knowledge as well as those of prevailing personal, social, and cultural schemas, expectations, and norms. Past thinking is also used when individuals integrate ideas, observations, and information into conceptual schemas through assimilation and accommodation processes.

Our construct of Past thinking is similar to Dewey's (1910/1933) construct of reflective thinking. Dewey believed that reflective thinking had two critical components: sense-making and continuity. The former refers to the process in which individuals develop a deep understanding of the relationships and connections to experiences and ideas. The latter refers to how individuals make sense of each new experience based on the meaning derived from past experiences as well as prior knowledge of the world, such as what we have heard about and read of others' experiences and ideas. Although Dewey conceptualized reflective thinking as a process to be cultivated within the educational system in order to facilitate the moral, intellectual, and emotional growth of the individual, we conceptualize Past thinking as a stable individual difference variable, which, along with Present and Future thinking, influences how individuals perceive, process, and utilize information.

At the individual level, we hypothesize that Past thinking manifests as: (a) a sensitivity to the presence of potentially negative environmental stimuli and to gaps in knowledge; (b) a propensity to avoid risks; (b) slow and deliberate thinking; (c) principled, judicious, reflective, and thoughtful decision making; (d) a propensity to second guess decisions once made; (e) a cautious, skeptical outlook on life; (f) fair-mindedness; and (g) a propensity to experience psychological distress, such as depression and anxiety. Past thinking also manifests as the Big Five personality traits (e.g., Costa & McCrae, 1992a, 1992b) of introversion and neuroticism, a preference for quiet and studious environments, opportunities for contemplation, the need for few but deeply trusting friendships, a somewhat ideological leadership style, and careers that allow for independence of thought, opportunities for applying scientific and analytical inquiry, and working with information and knowledge.

We also propose that it is Past thinking at work when collections of individuals engage in the recollection, reconstruction, analysis, and critical evaluation of collectively experienced and/or communicated events and when such information is used to establish and maintain a sense of collective continuity as well as a sense of collective efficacy. Through the tools of science, reasoned discourse, logic, Socratic debate, inductive and deductive reasoning, propaganda, and historical storytelling, societies establish and maintain a sense of cultural identity and continuity as well as a sense of collective well-being and social efficacy. For example, the scientific method is the formal use of Past thinking to understand the physical universe and theology is the formal use of Past thinking to understand the spiritual universe. Past thinking is that aspect of consciousness that human beings utilize to understand reality and derive meaning regarding our experience of reality.

2.1.2 Future thinking. We use the term Future thinking to refer to the cognitive patterning that exists when organisms utilize their memory structures to perceive and imagine novel and innovative arrangements or solutions to personal and environmental challenges and opportunities. In human beings, Future thinking is systems-level thinking in which the higher-order properties of objects of perception, both physical and abstract, the relationships and interconnections among those objects of perception and mental activity are observed. Future thinking involves the abstract mental representation of objects and events and is used to speculatively generate alternate realities and possible future ("what if") scenarios.

Future thinking occurs when novel and innovative solutions to immediate problems are envisioned, solutions that are not limited by preexisting conceptual and social schemas or by the contents of memory. Future thinking also manifests as abstract, creative, open-ended, big-picture thinking oriented toward perceiving and pursuing opportunities, forward motion, the generation and exploration of future possibilities, ingenuity, the constructive disruption of current personal, social, and collective schemas, and the adaptation and reinvention of such schemas to accelerate the pace of personal, social, technological, cultural, and spiritual evolution. Thus, boundless uses of imagination, such as intuitive leaps in scientific thinking, the creation of novel art, music, dance, literature, and poetry, positive psychology, the visionary evolution of human ventures, inventive and innovative technological advancements, and the reimagining of human physical and mental possibilities are all products of Future thinking.

Our construct of Future thinking encompasses many related and overlapping constructs, such as episodic future thinking (e.g., Atance & O'Neill, 2005), episodic foresight(Martin- Ordas, Atance, & Louw, 2012; Suddendorf & Moore, 2011), episodic simulation (Schacter & Addis, 2007), semantic future thinking (Atance & O'Neill, 2005), semantic prospection (e.g., Gilbert & Wilson, 2007), and semantic fantasy (Merker, 2007). Our construct of Future thinking also encompasses the constructs of forward thinking, which is often used colloquially to describe new and innovative ideas, conceptual schemas, and/or methods as they apply to specific fields of inquiry or areas of application, and futures thinking, which involves thinking about the future and future trends from a broad contextual or societal perspective (a systems level of understanding) and the examination of the evolutionary processes associated with specific fields of endeavor or social trends that allow for the speculative imagination of a wide variety of future possibilities (Hejazi, 2012; Lombardo, 2006). Similarly, the term future thinker is often used to describe individuals who are considered pioneers in their respective fields and far ahead of their times (e.g., Lutzo, 2004), and who offer innovative approaches that transform thinking, research, and/or application in their respective fields (Honan, 1997).

At the individual level, we hypothesize that Future thinking manifests as (a) visionary, speculative thinking; (b) creativity and creative problem solving; (c) a perception of new environmental opportunities; (d) idealistic expectations; (e) flexibility and adaptability; (f) quick and often impulsive decision making; (g) a hopeful, optimistic, and resilient outlook on life; and (h) a tendency to engage in impulsive, spontaneous, and hedonistic behavior. We also hypothesize that Future thinking manifests as the Big Five personality traits of openness and extraversion as well as the tendency to be adventurous, charismatic and charming, dynamic, energetic, inventive and innovative, inspirational, and persuasive. Future thinking also manifests as a preference for flexible, social, and unrestricted environments with few rules and regulations and as a need to form relationships with a broad network of people with diverse ideas and interests.

At the collective level, we propose that Future thinking uses the mental spaciousness created by the concept of future for the generation and exploration of new ideas, approaches, and relationships as well as the generation of alternative conceptual, social, and cultural schemas, which in turn, may capture the imagination of the collective and stimulate cultural, technological, social, and political upheaval, innovation, and change. To paraphrase Hajazi (2012), Future thinking expands the universe of ideas, vistas, and realities, entertains the unthinkable and makes it thinkable, and opens the human mind to considering alternative visions of reality and existence (p. 4).

2.1.3 Present thinking. We use the term Present thinking to refer to the cognitive pattern that exists when organisms utilize their memory systems to impose control mechanisms on the environment in order to maximize biological survival. Present thinking is functional thinking in which the lower- order properties of objects and relationships among objects are observed. In human beings, Present thinking occurs when individuals impose complex cognitive and behavioral control mechanisms, such as plans, structures, processes, rules, and schemas on the physical environment and when cultural norms and expectations and individual and cultural life scripts based on those norms also are developed. Moreover, Present thinking occurs when individuals form concrete, contextualized, goal-oriented mental representations of objects and when individuals develop action plans and organize the resources needed to execute those plans.

Similarly, Present thinking occurs when individuals attempt to restore and/ or impose order when shifts in the status quo, cultural norms, and goals are perceived or anticipated.

Present thinking is also the cognitive patterning involved when the abstract products of Past and Future thinking are woven and manifested into reality. For example, Present thinking involves the organization of data, information, people, objects, and events into the conceptual schemas, standards, and best practices deemed valid by Past thinking. Present thinking is also involved when action and contingency plans are created that weave and manifest into reality existing ideas, solutions, and technologies that are logically derived from prevailing schemas and consistent with the status quo as well as novel and innovative ideas, solutions, and inventions (i.e., the creative products of Future thinking) that alter the status quo.

We propose that all planning activities are the domains of Present thinking, including those oriented toward (a) current circumstances or future goals; (b) maintaining harmony with the status quo and existing prevailing schemas; (c) applying the innovative ideas and solutions of Future thinking to existing processes and control systems; (d) making manifest the conceptual schemas and knowledge of Past thinking or the creative ideas and solutions generated by Future thinking; or (e) achieving personal or collective goals. As such, we argue (as did Merker, 2007; and Tulving & Kim, 2007) that activities such as planning for the future, which have been considered to belong to the construct domain of episodic future thinking and strategic planning, and have often been confused with strategic thinking (Mintzberg, 1981, 1994), are not activities that belong to the domain of Future thinking, but rather to the domain of Present thinking.

At the individual level, we hypothesize that Present thinking manifests as a tendency to: (a) classify objects and events concretely; (b) perform well on detailed-oriented tasks; (c) organize, plan, and structure one's environment and activities; (d) adopt and maintain predefined cultural, social, and personal schemas and life scripts; (e) make pragmatic decisions; (d) create stability, harmony, and good relations with others; and (f) approach life with pragmatic resilience and positive well-being. Present thinking also manifests as (a) the Big Five personality traits of conscientiousness and agreeableness; (b) the tendency to be highly practical, pragmatic, predictable, compliant, dependable, dogmatic, efficient, inflexible, methodical, task-oriented, and resourceful; and (c) the need to force conformity, both within oneself and among others, with prevailing cultural norms and expectations that have been adopted as well as to one's own plans and goals. Present thinking also manifests as a natural inclination to be drawn to social activities that involve community or social groups and memberships in clubs and organizations.

At the collective level, we propose that Present thinking is involved in the implementation and enactment of and conformity to cultural expectations, laws, and norms and occurs when communities, organizations, societies, and nations attempt to successfully navigate change and execute collective goals (e.g., achieving the goal of linking the Atlantic and Pacific oceans through Panama). Similarly, we propose that Present thinking involves attempts to create social equilibrium by synchronizing specific culturally shared expectations, life scripts, and agendas into a cohesive community (clubs, organizations, institutions, social networks), in order to facilitate cooperative, collaborative, and productive interactions among members of those communities. Present thinking at the collective level manifests as bureaucracies, logistical institutions (e.g., world governing bodies, national governments, education, civil defense, physical and technological infrastructure, public utilities), and planning and control systems (e.g., law enforcement, armed defense, auto and air traffic control systems, navigational systems, computer systems, bodies that manage and regulate financial markets, legal agreements, and national and international standards) as well as systems and institutions such as the United Nations, the World Bank, The World Trade Organization, and the International Organization for Standardization, which exist to maintain stability and order both within and between populations.

2.2 Empirical Support. Research findings have generally supported our propositions involving Past, Present, and Future thinking (Fortunato and Furey, 2009, 2010, 2011, 2012). For example, we found that scores on a measure of Future thinking correlated positively with scores on measures of extraversion and openness, hedonism and risk-taking, optimism and resilience, and negatively with neuroticism, and anxiety and depression. Conversely, scores on a measure of Present thinking correlated positively with scores on measures of conscientiousness and agreeableness, resiliency and optimism, and negatively with scores on measures of openness, cynicism, anxiety, and depression. Finally, scores on measures of Past thinking correlated positively with scores on measures of neuroticism, cynicism, anxiety and depression, and negatively with extraversion and agreeableness,, and optimism and resiliency.

Indirect support for some of our propositions comes from research that has shown that scores on measures of extraversion and openness—personality traits that we hypothesize are mediated by Future thinking—correlated positively with scores on measures of creative and divergent thinking (e.g., Furnham &Bachtiar, 2008; Gelade, 2002; George & Zhou, 2001), sexual risk taking (Turchik, Garske, Probst, & Irvin, 2010), financial risk taking (Hunter & Kemp, 2004), and risky decision-making (Lauriola & Levin, 2001; Nicholson, Soane, Fenton-O'Creevy, & Willman, 2005). Conversely scores on measures of introversion and neuroticism— personality traits that we hypothesize are mediated by Past thinking—correlated negatively with scores on measures of optimism and creativity (Fink & Neubauer, 2008; Gelade, 2002), sensation seeking and risk-taking behavior (Zuckerman & Kuhlman, 2000), and positively with analytical thinking (Gelade, 2002), and anxiety and depression (Costa & McCrae, 1992b; Williams, 1992). Moreover, individuals who score high on extraversion show greater cortical activation during creative tasks than individuals who score high on introversion (Fink & Neubauer, 2008). Conversely, individuals who score high on introversion show greater cortical activation during mental reasoning and memory tasks (Fink & Neubauer, 2008: Fink, Grabner, Neuper, & Neubauer, 2005). Finally, scores on measures of conscientiousness—a personality trait that we hypothesize is mediated by Present thinking—correlated positively with conformity and rule-following (Gelade, 2002), whereas low scores on openness, a characteristic of Present thinking, tends to be observed in individuals who prefer the familiar, the routine, and that status quo (McCrae, 1996) and who tend to be rigid, inflexible to change, and have difficulty adapting to dissimilar points of view (e.g., McCrae, 1987).

Indirect support for our hypotheses also comes from an extensive series of studies by Liberman, Trope, and associates (see Liberman & Trope, 1998; Trope & Liberman, 2003; 2010 for reviews of this literature). For example, when individuals are asked to adopt a distant future temporal perspective, compared to individuals who are asked to adopt a near-term temporal perspective, they tend to (a) classify objects and events into broad, rather than specific categories; (b) form super-ordinate, idealistic goals; (c) perform better on creative tasks than on analytical tasks; (d) display high levels of optimism and overconfidence when making decisions; (e) engage in risk-taking behavior; (f) minimize any delay of gratification of outcomes; and (g) be persuaded by messages that speak to possible opportunities inherent in the situation, context, or product.

Similarly, research has shown that nostalgic recollections of past events are characterized by both abstract and concrete mental representations (Stephan, Sedikides, & Wildschut, 2012).

According to Stephan et al. (2012), on the one hand, because past events are often idealized versions of events that endure over time and are characterized as having a distal psychological perspective, nostalgic recollections of the past tend to consist of high-level construals. On the other hand, because nostalgic recollections are often activated by current stimuli that engage comparative processing of the relevance of the event to present circumstances, nostalgic recollections of events involve low-level construals that are rich in details.

Finally, brain imaging studies have also provided indirect support for our theory. For example, Addis et al. (2007) found opposite patterns of activation when individuals engaged in mental time travel into the past versus mental time travel into the future. Specially, they found that although reconstructions of past events and episodic future thinking both engage the left hippocampus, episodic future thinking uniquely engages the right hippocampus, the right frontopolar cortex and left ventrolateral prefrontal cortex. Similarly, Weiler, Suchan, & Daum (2010, 2011a, 2011b) observed differences in both left hemispheric temporo-parietal and right hemispheric parieto-occipatal activation depending on whether individuals were engaged in reconstructing past events or imagining future ones. Weiler et al. (2011) also noted that the thalamus appeared to play a more important role in the executive aspects of memory required for the imagination of novel scenarios above and beyond those brain areas involved in episodic future thinking.

In summary, there is ample theoretical and empirical evidence to support the general propositions of our theory. However, further research is needed examining the direct relationships between Past, Present, and Future thinking and individual differences on personality traits, cognitive and perceptual tasks, and behaviors as well as corresponding brain activity differences using enhanced imaging techniques.

2.3 Integration. Although we propose that Past, Present, and Future thinking are three distinct patterns of temporally-based consciousness, we also propose that each is inextricably intertwined with the others. Past, Present, and Future thinking form three essential codependent and interdependent cognitive patterns understood to be human thinking. Thus, we propose that it is only when Past, Present, and Future thinking are consciously utilized in combination that they are truly effective in maximizing current and future survival at both the individual and collective levels. For example, when the products of Future thinking (ideas, solutions, and novel approaches) are made available to Past thinking for evaluation, understanding, and analysis, and the synthesized products of Past and Future thinking are made available to Present thinking for manifestation into reality, the highest level of adaptive and survival value of human thinking is realized. Human beings, perhaps not uniquely among all species, have the ability to become consciously aware of both conscious and previously unconscious thought processes and direct them as desired. Thus, human beings are capable of choice and of consciously applying, adapting, and utilizing their Past, Present, and Future thinking when needed in response to environmental, personal, and social contingencies. As Merker (2007) stated, the ability to speculatively imagine a variety of future scenarios is useful only to the extent to which the utility, probability, or certainty of each scenario can be determined.

We further propose that Past, Present, and Future thinking are the foundation for one's own personal identity that is located in space and time. Tulving (1985a, 1985b, 2002) made a similar point when he argued that episodic memory, in particular, and semantic memory, in general, provide the basis for the development of a personal identify that links all of the temporally-based experiences that form the foundation for one's own personal history. We propose that Past, Present, and Future thinking are the elements of and inseparable from one's own self or ego.

It is our view that the physical, cognitive, social, and cultural achievements of human beings could not have occurred without the combined use of all three thinking perspectives. Indeed, it is the interaction and resulting entanglement of these three discreet patterns of thought that has led to an ever-increasing level of abstraction in human beings' understanding of the world and the language used to symbolize and communicate that understanding with others, which in turn, has resulted in ever-increasing technological and social advancements and other artifacts of culture. It is only when Past, Present, and Future thinking are used in combination that human thought is brought into unity, for each of these thought patterns is but one aspect of a trilogy that, together, forms the entirety of human conscious awareness.

It is also our view that the ability to look backwards into the past, focus attention on the present, and imagine the future allowed human beings to direct their attention toward increasingly abstract and higher-order goals (e.g., Maslow, 1943) (see Fig. 3). Human beings, arguably, unique among all animals, seek to understand the nature of consciousness and existence and have learned to transcend their own physical and information processing limitations.

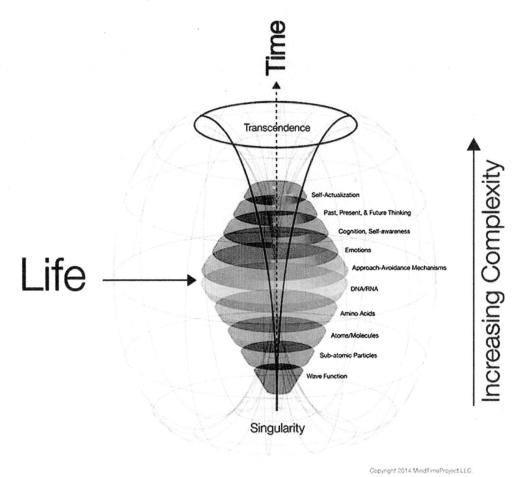

Fig. 3. Physical and temporal expansion of space–time and the evolution of differentiated consciousness from the singularity of the Big Bang to transcendence. Figure used with permission from the MindTime Project, LLC. Illustrated by Alden Bevington.

3. Theoretical and Practical Implications

The theory of MindTime can be applied across a broad spectrum of inquiry and that there are many theoretical and practical applications of the theory. For example, we suggest that the theory of MindTime may function as a meta-theory by providing a foundation for developing a holistic understanding of human psychology at both the individual and collective level and for connecting seemingly disparate fields of inquiry, such as psychology, education, sociology, social economics, cultural anthropology, political theory, governance, service science, organizational theory, and communication, even though each utilize different epistemologies, vocabulary, taxonomies, and methodologies.

At the practical level, we argue that the theory of MindTime has utility in understanding the interactions between people and the environmental domains in which they function. For example, according to Walsh, Craik, and Price (2000), the concept of person-environment fit is perhaps the most dominant conceptual force for understanding human behavior, and research in a variety of disciplines shows that the extent to which the characteristics of an individual are aligned, congruent, match, fit, or resonate with the characteristics of their surrounding physical, social, learning, and working environments influences how they react to that environment. Thus, by measuring individuals' Past, Present, and Future thinking as well as by identifying the Past, Present, and Future characteristics of environments and cultures, effective interactions between and among individuals and their environments can be facilitated. For example, in organizations, the theory can be used for hiring, placement and promotion of employees, leadership development, developing internal and external communications strategies, developing appropriate reward mechanisms, and facilitating work team effectiveness. In educational environments, the theory can be used to facilitate student learning by matching students with instructors based on their thinking perspective and by developing personalized instructional materials, curricula, and strategies based on how student think. In clinical and counseling contexts, the theory can be used to facilitate an enhanced understanding of clients' perceptual constructs and world views and to develop new therapeutic tools. In global politics, the theory of MindTime can be used to facilitate an understanding of the fundamental world views and cultures of different political parties, ideologies, peoples, and nations. This understanding can be used for both enhancing diplomatic relations and for resolving conflict.

Our theory also has implications for the digital age. Today, people are a part of an exponentially growing and continuous flow of digital data, in what has been called big data. In a recent book by Frank, Roehrig, and Pring (2014), the authors address the growing phenomenon whereby people have vast amounts of data attached to their identity and pertaining to their behavior, habits, preferences, educational, occupational, and health histories, interests, purchases, demographics, psychographics, and every other data point that can be captured digitally. The authors referred to these data as code halos. What has been missing from big data is a unifying theory that facilitates an understanding of the underlying patterns that exist within that data, both at the individual and collective levels. We propose that by examining individual and collective level data through the lens of the theory of MindTime, patterns will emerge that are consistent with Past, Present, and Future thinking, from which a whole new level of understanding of human behavior can be achieved. Preliminary cross-cultural data from North America, Europe, and Asia suggests that the theory of MindTime is generalizable across situations, domains, and cultures (MindTime Techologies,

Inc., 2012, 2013, 2014).

4. Closing Comments

In this paper, we presented a theory of consciousness and psychology in which perception of time is the fundamental process by which human beings perceive and process information and interact with the world and others. Specifically, we proposed that variation exists in how individuals utilize episodic and semantic memory structures to process information, form mental representations of temporally located objects and events, and engage in mental time travel. We proposed that Past, Present, and Future thinking are abstract–linguistic, perceptual–cognitive patterns that mediate the relationships between individuals' neurological responses to environmental and social stimuli and their perceptions, personality, intentions, values, beliefs, motivations, and behaviors. We also proposed that Past, Present, and Future thinking represent complex and abstract methods by which human beings are able to maximize survival by (a) avoiding negative stimuli, (b) approaching positive stimuli, and (c) controlling their environment.

Although we have focused in this paper on human beings, we speculate that Past, Present, and Future thinking also exist in other animals in various degrees. That is, Past, Present, and Future thinking are the mechanisms of consciousness, with human consciousness representing, arguably, the most complex form of consciousness known at this time (Liljenström, 2011). We surmise that perception of time, whether conscious or unconscious, narrow or infinite in extension, and the cognitive patterns associated with time perception, which we referred to as Past, Present, and Future thinking, no matter how evolutionarily advanced, are the fundamental driving mechanisms of consciousness and behavior as well as intra-species behavioral variation.

In a recent volume of this journal, several authors (e.g., Kafatos, Tanzi, & Chopra, 2011; Liljenström, 2011; Lombardo, 2011; Mitchell & Staretz, 2011; M. Cabanac, R. Cabanc, & Hammel, 2011) argued that consciousness and matter are two complementary aspects of one reality. On the one hand, for example, Kafatos et al (2011) proposed that consciousness is a field phenomenon, which they referred to as primordial consciousness that exists outside of space and time and which is characterized by generalized quantum physics principles, such as complementarity, non-locality, scale-invariance, and undivided wholeness. Similarly, Mitchell and Staretz (2011) wrote that "all matter seems interconnected with all other matter and this interconnection even transcends [italics are ours] space and time...and that at the lowest level resides the most basic aspects of undifferentiated awareness [italics are ours] built upon the quantum principles of entanglement, non-locality, and coherent emission/absorption of photons."

On the other hand, consciousness also exists within space and time. Kafatos et al (2011), King (2011), Liljenström, (2011), Mitchell and Staretz (2011) also all similarly proposed that the evolution of consciousness involved the evolution of matter into increasingly complex, elaborate, and interactive systems, with the human brain providing the highest level of complexity known. For example, Mitchell and Staretz wrote "We postulate that ...the most fundamental aspect of consciousness which we describe as undifferentiated awareness [forms the] mechanism of basic perception [and] extends up the entire evolutionary chain of increasing complexity of living organisms." According to Mitchell and Staretz, consciousness itself becomes increasingly complex as matter becomes increasingly complex; and that all organisms from the simplest to the most complex are interconnected at a very fundamental level using information obtained by nonlocal quantum coherence.

From the point of view of the human mind, we note a confounding and recursive paradox. According to quantum theory (see Penrose & Hammeroff, 2011, for example), the physical universe does not exist except as wave functions that collapse only when an observation is made by an observer or an instrument as an extension of an observer. Thus, any perception of space–time reality and, similarly, any attempt by any organism within this reality (e.g., human beings) to understand its own consciousness and the nature of the universe, are products of the very differentiation made possible by the perceptual apparatus that perceives space and time, apparatus which itself can only exist when observed. Thus, it is differentiating consciousness that is itself responsible for the apparatus that is doing the observing. Differentiating consciousness (for example, the human mind) creates itself and the very world it perceives.

Kafatos et al. (2011), based on a speech given by Werner Heisenburg in 1932, wrote that "the universe presents the face that the observer is looking for and when she looks for a different face, the universe changes its mask." Previously, we proposed that Past, Present, and Future thinking operate as cognitive patterns that form the foundation for individuals' perceptions of the world. We now take this one step further and suggest that Past, Present, and Future thinking, because they are integral in the encoding of our memories and the development of personal identities and belief systems, are the very mechanisms by which organisms collapse quantum wave functions and create the realities they observe and experience.

REFERENCES

Addis, D. R., Wong, A. T., & Schacter, D. L. (2007). Remembering the past and imagining the future: Common and distinct neural substrates during event construction and elaboration. Neuropsychologia, 45(7), 1363–1377. doi:10.1016/j.neuropsychologia.2006.10.016

Atance, C. M., & Jackson, L. K. (2009). The development and coherence of future-oriented behaviors during the preschool years. Journal of Experimental Child Psychology, 102(4), 379–391.

Atance, C. M., & O'Neill (2005). The emergence of episodic future thinking in humans. Learning and Motivation, 36(2), 126–144.

Berntsen, D., & Bohn, A. (2010). Remembering and forecasting: The relation between autobiographical memory and episodic future thinking. Memory & Cognition, 38(3), 265– 278. doi:10.3758/MC.38.3.265

Bronckart, J. (2005). The temporality of discourses: A contribution to the reshaping of human actions. In A. Perret-Clermont (Ed.) Thinking time: A multidisciplinary approach. Cambridge, MA: Hogrefe & Huber.

Buckner, R. L., & Carroll, D. C. (2007). Self-projection and the brain. Trends in Cognitive Sciences, 11(2), 49–57. doi:10.1016/j.tics.2006.11.004

Cabanac, M., Cabanac, R., & Hammel, H. T. (2011). Consciousness: The fifth influence. Journal of Cosmology, 14. Retrieved from http://journalofcosmology. com/Consciousness127.html

Carver, C. S., Sutton, S. K., & Scheier, M. F. (2000). Action, emotion, and personality: Emerging conceptual integration. Personality and Social Psychology Bulletin, 26(6), 741–751. doi:10.1177/0146167200268008

Corballis, M. C. (2011). The recursive mind: The origins of human language, thought, and civilization. Princeton, NJ: Princeton University Press.

Corballis, M. C. (2013). Mental time travel: A case for evolutionary continuity. Trends in Cognitive Sciences, 17(1), 5–6. doi:10.1016/j.tics.2012.10.009

Costa, P. T., & McCrae, R. R. (1992a). Four ways five factors are basic. Personality and Individual Differences, 13(6), 653–665. doi:10.1016/0191-8869(92)90236-I

Costa, P. T., & McCrae, R. R. (1992b). Normal personality assessment in clinical practice: The NEO Personality Inventory. Psychological Assessment, 4(1), 5–13. doi:10.1037/1040- 3590.4.1.5

D'Argembeau, A., & Van der Linden, M. (2007). Emotional aspects of mental time travel. Behavioral and Brain Sciences, 30(3), 320–321. doi:10.1017/S0140525X07002051

Dewey, J. (1933). How we think. Buffalo, NY: Prometheus Books. (Original work published 1910)

Fink, A., & Neubauer, A. C. (2008). Eysenck meets Martindale: The relationship between extraversion and originality from the neuroscientific perspective. Personality and Individual Differences, 44(1), 299–310. doi:10.1016/j.paid.2007.08.010

Fink, A., Grabner, R. h., Neuper, C., & Neubauer, A. c. (2005). Extraversion and cortical activation during memory performance. International Journal of Psychophysiology, 56(2), 129–141.

Förster, J., & Becker, D. (2012). When curiosity kills no cat—but mediates the relation between distant future thoughts and global processing across sensory modalities. European Journal of Social Psychology, 42(3), 334–341. doi:10.1002/ejsp.1856

Förster, J., Friedman, R. S., & Liberman, N. (2004). Temporal construal effects on abstract and concrete thinking: Consequences for insight and creative cognition. Journal of Personality and Social Psychology, 87(2), 177–189. doi:10.1037/0022-3514.87.2.177

Fortunato, V. J., & Furey, J. T. (2009). The theory of MindTime and the relationships between thinking perspective and the Big Five personality traits. Personality and Individual Differences, 47(4), 241–246.

Fortunato, V. J., & Furey, J. T. (2010). The theory of MindTime: The relationships between thinking perspective and time perspective. Personality and Individual Differences, 48(4), 436–441. doi:10.1016/j.paid.2009.11.015

Fortunato, V. J., & Furey, J. T. (2011). The theory of MindTime: The relationships between Future, Past, and Present thinking and psychological well-being and distress. Personality and Individual Differences, 50(1), 20–24.

Fortunato, V. J., & Furey, J. T. (2012). An examination of thinking style patterns as a function of thinking perspective profile. Personality and Individual Differences, 53(7), 849–856. doi:10.1016/j.paid.2012.06.017

Frank, M., Roehrig, P., & Pring, B. (2014). Code Halos: How the digital lives of people, things, and organizations are changing the rules of business. Hoboken, NJ: John Wiley & Sons.

Furnham, A., & Bachtiar, V. (2008). Personality and intelligence as predictors of creativity. Personality and Individual Differences, 45(7), 613–617. doi:10.1016/j.paid.2008.06.023

Gelade, G. A. (2002). Creative style, personality and artistic endeavor. Genetic, Social, and General Psychology Monographs, 128(3), 213–234.

George, J. M., & Zhou, J. (2001). When openness to experience and conscientiousness are related to creative behavior: An interactional approach. Journal of Applied Psychology, 86(3), 513–524. doi:10.1037/0021-9010.86.3.513

Gilbert, D. T., & Wilson, T. D. (2007). Prospection: Experiencing the future. Science, 317(5843), 1351–1354. doi:10.1126/science.1144161

Gilead, M., Liberman, N., & Maril, A. (2012). Construing counterfactual worlds: The role of abstraction. European Journal of Social Psychology, 42(3), 391–397. doi:10.1002/ejsp.1862 Hassabis, D., Kumaran, D., & Maguire, E. A. (2007). Using imagination to understand the neural basis of episodic memory. Journal of Neuroscience, 27(52), 14365–14374. doi:10.1523/JNEUROSCI.4549-07.2007

Hejazi, A. (2012). Futures metacognition: A progressive understanding of futures thinking. World Future Review, 4(2), 18-27.

Honan, W. H. (1997, November 2). Looking back at forward thinkers. The New York Times. Retrieved from www.nytimes.com.

Hunter, K., & Kemp, S. (2004). The personality of e-commerce investors.

Journal of Economic Psychology, 25(4), 529–537. doi:10.1016/S0167-4870(03)00050-3

Jaynes, J. (1976). The origin of consciousness and the breakdown of the bicameral mind. Houghton Mifflin: Boston, MA.

Kafatos, M., Tanzi, R. E., & Chopra, D. (2011). How consciousness becomes the physical universe. Journal of Cosmology, 14. Retrieved from http://journalofcosmology.com/Consciousness140.html

King, C. (2011). Cosmological foundations of consciousness. Journal of Cosmology, 14, 3706– 3725. Retrieved from http://journalofcosmology.com/Consciousness103.html

Lauriola, M., & Levin, I. P. (2001). Personality traits and risky decision-making in a controlled experimental task: An exploratory study. Personality and Individual Differences, 31(2), 215–226. doi:10.1016/S0191-8869(00)00130-6

Levine, R. (2006). A geography of time. Oxford, England: Oneworld Publications.

Lewin, K. (1942). Time perspective and morale. In G. Watson (Ed.), Civilian morale. Second yearbook of the S.P.S.S.L. Boston, MA: Houghton Mifflin.

Lewin, K. (1951). Field theory in social science. New York, NY: Harper and Row.

Liljenström, H. (2011). Intention and attention in consciousness dynamics and evolution. Journal of Cosmology, 14, 4839–4847. Retrieved from http://journalofcosmology.com/Consciousness138.html

Liberman, N., & Trope, Y. (1998). The role of feasibility and desirability considerations in near and distant future decisions: A test of temporal construal theory. Journal of Personality and Social Psychology, 75(1), 5–18. doi:10.1037/0022-3514.75.1.5

. Lombardo, T. (2006). The evolution of future consciousness, Bloomington, IN: AuthorHouse. Lombardo, T. (2011). The ecological cosmology of consciousness. Journal of Cosmology, 14, 4859–4868. Retrieved from http://journalofcosmology.com/Consciousness141.html

Lutzo, E. (2004). Are you a forward thinker? Weatherhead Coaches Corner, 1(9).

Martin-Ordas, G., Atance, C. M., & Louw, A. (2012). The role of episodic and semantic memory in episodic foresight. Learning and Motivation, 43(4), 209–219. doi:10.1016/j.lmot.2012.05.011

Maslow, A. H. (1943). A theory of human motivation. Psychological Review, 50(4), 370–396. Retrieved from http://psychclassics.yorku.ca/Maslow/motivation.htm

McCrae, R. R. (1987). Creativity, divergent thinking, and openness to experience. Journal of Personality and Social Psychology, 52(6), 1258–1265. doi:10.1037/0022-3514.52.6.1258

McCrae, R. R. (1996). Social consequences of experiential openness.

Psychological Bulletin, 120(3), 323–337. doi:10.1037/0033-2909.120.3.323

Merker, B. (2007). Memory, imagination, and the asymmetry between past future. Behavioral and Brain Sciences, 30(3), 325–326. doi:10.1017/S0140525X07002117 MindTime Techologies, Inc. (2012, 2013, 2014). Unpublished technical reports.

Mintzberg, H. (1981). What is planning anyway? Strategic Management Journal, 2(3), 319–324.

Mintzberg, H. (1994). Planning and Strategy. In H. Mintzberg (Ed.), Rise & fall of strategic planning (pp. 5–34). New York, NY: The Free Press.

Mitchell, E. D., & Staretz, R. (2011). The quantum hologram and the nature of consciousness. Journal of Cosmology, 14, Retrieved from http://journalofcosmology.com/Consciousness149.html

Nicholson, N., Soane, E., Fenton-O'Creevy, M., & Willman, P. (2005). Personality and domain- specific risk taking. Journal of Risk Research, 8(2), 157–176. doi:10.1080/1366987032000123856

Oettingen, G., & Mayer, D. (2002). The motivating function of thinking about the future: Expectations versus fantasies. Journal of Personality and Social Psychology, 83(5), 1198– 1212. doi:10.1037/0022-3514.83.5.1198

Penrose, R., & Hameroff, S. (2011). Consciousness in the universe: Neuroscience, quantum space-time geometry and Orch OR theory. Journal of Cosmology, 14. Retrieved from http://journalofcosmology.com/Consciousness160.html

Schacter, D. L., & Addis, D. R. (2007). On the constructive episodic simulation of past and future events. Behavioral and Brain Sciences, 30(3), 331–332. doi:10.1017/S0140525X07002178

Stephan, E., Sedikides, C., & Wildschut, T. (2012). Mental travel into the past: Differentiating recollections of nostalgic, ordinary, and positive events. European Journal of Social Psychology, 42(3), 290–298. doi:10.1002/ejsp.1865

Suddendorf, T. (1999). The rise of the metamind. In M. C. Corballis & S. E. G. Lea (Eds.), The descent of mind: Psychological perspectives on hominid evolution (pp. 218–260). Oxford University Press: New York, NY.

Suddendorf, T., & Corballis, M. C. (1997). Mental time travel and the evolution of the human mind. Genetic, Social, and General Psychology Monographs, 123(2), 133–167.

Suddendorf, T., & Corballis, M. C. (2007). Mental time travel across the disciplines: The future looks bright. Behavioral and Brain Sciences, 30(3), 335–351. doi:10.1017/S0140525X0700221X

Suddendorf, T., & Moore, C. (2011). Introduction to the special issue of episodic foresight. Cognitive Development, 26(4), 295–298. doi:10.1016/j.cogdev.2011.09.001

Tattersall, I. (2011). Evolution of modern human consciousness. Journal of Cosmology, 14, 4831–4838. Retrieved from http://journalofcosmology.com/Consciousness151.html

Trompenaars, F., & Hampden-Turner, C. (1997). Riding the waves of culture: Understanding cultural diversity in business. Finland: Werner Söderström Oy.

Trope, Y., & Liberman, N. (2003). Temporal construal. Psychological Review, 110(3), 403–421. doi:10.1037/0033-295X.110.3.403

Trope, Y., & Liberman, N. (2010). Construal-level theory of psychological distance. Psychological Review, 117(2), 440–463. doi:10.1037/a0018963

Tulving, E. (1985a). How many memory systems are there? American Psychologist, 40(4), 385–398. doi:10.1037/0003-066X.40.4.385

Tulving, E. (1985b). Memory and consciousness. Canadian Psychology/ Psychologie canadienne, 26(1), 1–12. doi:10.1037/h0080017

Tulving, E. (2002). Episodic memory: From mind to brain. Annual Review of Psychology, 53(1), 1–25. doi:10.1146/annurev.psych.53.100901.135114

Tulving, E., & Kim, A. (2007). The medium and the message of mental time travel. Behavioral and Brain Sciences, 30(3), 334–335. doi:10.1017/S0140525X07002208

Turchik, J. A., Garske, J. P., Probst, D. R., & Irvin, C. R. (2010). Personality, sexuality, and substance use as predictors of sexual risk taking in college students. Journal of Sex Research, 47, 411-419. doi: 10.1080/00224490903161621.

Vale, G. l., Flynn, E. g., & Kendal, R. l. (2012). Cumulative culture and future thinking: Is mental time travel a prerequisite to cumulative cultural evolution? Learning and Motivation, 43(4), 220–230. doi:10.1016/j.lmot.2012.05.010

Walsh, W. B., Craik, K. H., & Price, R. H. (Eds.). (2000). Person–environment psychology: New directions and perspectives (2nd ed.). Mahwah, NJ: Lawrence Erlbaum.

Warner, R. H., VanDeursen, M. J., & Pope, A. R. D. (2012). Temporal distance as a determinant of just world strategy. European Journal of Social Psychology, 42(3), 276–284. doi:10.1002/ejsp.1855

Weiler, J. A., Suchan, B., & Daum, I. (2010a). Foreseeing the future: Occurrence probability of imagined future events modulates hippocampal activation. Hippocampus, 20(6), 685–690. doi:10.1002/hipo.20695

Weiler, J. A., Suchan, B., & Daum, I. (2010b). When the future becomes the past: Differences in brain activation patterns for episodic memory and episodic future thinking. Behavioural Brain Research, 212(2), 196–203. doi:10.1016/j.bbr.2010.04.013

Weiler, J. A., Suchan, B., & Daum, I. (2011). What comes first? Electrophysiological differences in the temporal course of memory and future thinking. European Journal of Neuroscience, 33(9), 1742–1750. doi:10.1111/j.1460-9568.2011.07630.x

Williams, D. G. (1992). Dispositional optimism, neuroticism, and extraversion. Personality and Individual Differences, 13, 475-477.

Wilson, A. E., Buehler, R., Lawford, H., Schmidt, C., & Yong, A. G. (2012). Basking in projected glory: The role of subjective temporal distance in future self-appraisal. European Journal of Social Psychology, 42(3), 342–353. doi:10.1002/ejsp.1863

Zuckerman, M., & Kuhlman, D. M. (2000). Personality and risk-taking: Common biosocial factors. Journal of Personality, 68, 999-1029.

16. Consciousness of Continuity in Time

Steven Bodovitz

Principal, BioPerspectives,
1624 Fell Street, San Francisco, CA 94117 USA

Abstract

One of the defining characteristics, if not the defining characteristic of consciousness is the experience of continuity. One thought or sensation appears to transition immediately into the next, but this is likely an illusion. I propose that consciousness is broken up into discrete cycles of cognition and that the sense of continuity is the result of determining the magnitude and direction of changes between cycles. These putative consciousness vectors are analogous to motion vectors that enable us to perceive continuous motion even when watching a progression of static images. Detailed characterization of consciousness vectors, assuming they exist, would be a significant advance in the characterization of consciousness.

Key Words: brainstorming, consciousness, conscious vector, consciousness vector, continuity, creativity, delay, DLPFC, dorsolateral prefrontal cortex, motion vector, philosophical zombie, sports psychology

Time is the substance I am made of. Time is a river which sweeps me along, but I am the river; it is a tiger which destroys me, but I am the tiger; it is a fire which consumes me, but I am the fire. - Jorge Luis Borges (1946).

1. Introduction

To paraphrase the eloquence of Borges, we are made of time and consumed by time. The continuity of experience is one of the defining features, if not the defining feature of consciousness. To be more specific, as first explained by Karl Lashley, each thought or sensation is stable, but each is immediately present after the other, fully formed, with no experience of the underlying processing that led each to become conscious (Lashley, 1956).

Another way to think about the continuity is through a thought experiment of the inverse condition. Start by imagining a lower state of continuity, in which each individual thought is stable, but gaps are apparent. Each. Word. For. Example.

In. This. Sentence. Is. Separated. The extra breaks affect your experience of reading the sentence, because you have to think about the flow of the words to get the meaning. Now jump to a complete loss of continuity. Each. Word. Is. Completely. Frozen. In. Time. For. A. Moment. Each. Pops. Into. Cognition. And. Is. Replaced. By. Another. Without temporal integrity, we are repeatedly frozen in time. Frozen memories can inform us where we've been, but not where we are going. We become biological computers without sentience.

The concept of separating information processing from sentience has been proposed in a much more colorful manner by David Chalmers, who describes a philosophical zombie that roughly appears to be human, but otherwise has no awareness (Chalmers, 1996). This is not as abstract as it sounds, because one aspect of this concept has been demonstrated by Hakwan Lau and Richard Passingham (Lau & Passingham, 2006). These researchers used a variant of the well-known paradigm of masking. In a simple version, subjects are briefly shown an image, known as the target, followed quickly by a second brief image, known as the mask, and if the timing falls into well-defined parameters, the target is eliminated from conscious awareness (Koch, 2004a). Lau and Passingham used a more complex version known as a type II metacontrast masking, but the underlying principle is the same, and they tested the accuracy of identifying the target, in this case a square or a diamond, followed by asking the subjects to press keys to indicate whether they actually saw the identity of the target or simply guessed what it was. By using different lengths of time between the presentation of the target and the mask, the researchers were able to identify two conditions in which the accuracy of identifying the target was statistically the same, but the subjective assessments of awareness were significantly different (Lau & Passingham, 2006). Cognition (defined as high-level biological computation) and awareness can be separated, although presumably only under certain circumstances and for brief periods of time.

Taken together, the thought experiment and the actual experiment suggest that the output of cognitive processing is transferred into consciousness in a continuous or seemingly continuous process. The normal limit for information transfer is the speed of light, which is clearly faster than human perception, but not instantaneous. True continuity would presumably require a mechanism based on quantum mechanics. The possibility that microtubules mediate coherent quantum states across large populations of neurons was proposed by Stuart Hameroff and Roger Penrose (1996). This hypothesis has received indirect support in recent years. Physicists at the University of Geneva, for example, demonstrated quantum entanglement by observing two-photon interferences well above the Bell inequality threshold (Salart et al. 2008), but this was with isolated pairs of photons. Moreover, physicists at the University of California at Santa Barbara were able to coax a mechanical resonator into two states at once, which showed for the first time that quantum events could be observed in complex objects, but this required cooling to near absolute zero (Cho, 2010; O'Connell et al. 2010). Notwithstanding this recent progress, whether microtubules, which undergo constant remodeling, can be islands of quantum events in the biochemical and electrical cauldron of the human brain at 37 degrees Celsius remains to be observed. I propose an alternative hypothesis that, rather than true continuity, consciousness is broken up into discrete cycles of cognition and that the sense of continuity is the result of determining the magnitude and direction of changes between cycles.

2. Consciousness Is Likely Discontinuous

Even though the experience of continuity is a defining characteristic of consciousness, it is likely an illusion. The experimental evidence for the discontinuity is largely based on the delay between sensory perception and conscious awareness. Briefly, the pioneering work on the delay was performed by Benjamin Libet, in which he and his colleagues showed an undetectable stimulus could become conscious after approximately 500 msec (Libet et al. 1964; Libet et al. 1967; Libet et al. 1991), but it is not clear whether the delay was due to the processing time to reach consciousness or the time for summation of the stimulus to reach threshold, and others have criticized Libet's conclusions (for example, see Gomes, 1998; Pockett, 2002). A better study was designed by Marc Jeannerod and colleagues, in which subjects were trained to grasp one of three dowels following the appropriate signal and performed the task with a reaction time of 120 msec. When the subjects were asked to verbalize when they first became aware of the signal, the response time was 420 msec, or 300 msec longer (Castiello et al. 1991). Even allowing 50 msec for the required muscle contraction for verbalization, the delay is still a quarter of a second (Koch, 2004b). Thus, according to this experiment, the frequency of cycles of cognition is roughly 4 per second. A larger and arguably more compelling body of evidence for the delay comes from the well-established phenomena of masking, as described above, in which a mask eliminates and replaces the awareness of a target. The elimination is not the result of interfering with the sensory input because if a second mask is presented, the first mask can be eliminated and the awareness of the target can be restored (Dember & Purcell, 1967). The elimination is only possible with a delay between sensory perception and consciousness. The delay, in turn, indicates that consciousness is discontinuous (Koch, 2004c; Libet, 1999).

3. Continuity and Consciousness Vectors

If consciousness is discontinuous, but appears to be continuous, then the problem of understanding consciousness becomes better posed: what creates the continuity? I propose that the sense of continuity is the result of determining the magnitude and direction of changes between cycles (Bodovitz, 2008). These putative consciousness vectors, however, are largely undefined. They presumably track the magnitudes and directions of multiple changes in parallel and/or in aggregate. Moreover, they presumably track changes in inherently qualitative information, such as words and concepts. While these open questions leave the key tenet of this hypothesis unsubstantiated, they create opportunities for breakthroughs by experts in advanced mathematics, physics and/or computer science. At the very least, efforts to model consciousness vectors may provide insights into the value of using the flow of information as feedback for better organizing complex and dynamic data.

The most significant substantiation of consciousness vectors is through analogy to motion vectors, which add motion to a series of otherwise discrete images. The standard speed for movies based on film is 24 frames per second, but rather than strobing, we perceive smooth motion. This is because motion vectors are calculated by the visual system, most likely in visual area V5, also known as visual area MT (middle temporal). Without motion vectors, vision becomes a series of still images, a condition known as akinetopsia or visual motion blindness (Shipp et al. 1994; Zihl et al. 1983; Zihl et al. 1991). The strobe effect makes otherwise simple tasks, such as crossing a street, extremely difficult. The cars are a safe distance away, then bearing down, without any sense of the transition. Even though there is memory of where the cars were, there is no sense of where they are going. Likewise, without consciousness vectors, simple cognitive tasks involving even a limited series of steps would be extremely difficult.

Motion vectors, like consciousness vectors, appear relatively simple at first approximation. In fact, the retina is arguably even a two-dimensional, Euclidian array of detectors, and most objects in motion follow standard trajectories. Yet, the exact neural computations to generate motion vectors have been difficult to determine and are the subject of decades of debate (for review, see Born & Bradley, 2005), although there is consensus that they involve the mapping of retinal activity onto higher-order visual processors such as those in V1 and V5. Thus identifying the calculations for motion vectors may provide the ideal model system for identifying the calculations for the more complex consciousness vectors.

4. Continuity and the Awareness of Change

If consciousness vectors and a sense of continuity are necessary for consciousness, then the corollary is that changes in cognition are necessary for awareness. This corollary is supported by the fact that we only see changes in our visual field. Even though an image may be static, our eyes never are, even during fixation. Our eyes are in constant motion with tremors, drifts and microsaccades. If these fixational eye movements are eliminated, then visual perception fades to a homogenous field (Ditchburn & Ginsborg, 1952; Riggs & Ratliff, 1952; Yarbus, 1967). The significance of these fixational movements for visual processing has long been debated, and no clear consensus has emerged (for review, see Martinez-Conde et al. 2004). The best correlation of neuronal responses to fixational eye movements are specific clusters of long, tight bursts, which might enhance spatial and temporal summation (Martinez-Conde et al. 2004); in addition, a more recent study showed that fixational eye movements improve discrimination of high spatial frequency stimuli (Rucci et al. 2007). But a lack of enhancement or improved discrimination does not explain the complete loss of visual perception. A better explanation is that changes in cognition are necessary for awareness.

5. Discussion

If cognition is broken up into discrete cycles and consciousness vectors create the illusion of continuity, then conscious feedback has pitfalls. It is slow, such that any action that occurs in less than approximately 250 msec will be over before reaching consciousness. Moreover, if events are happening too quickly and/or you are thinking too fast, your conscious feedback will miss changes in cognition, and, to make matters worse, you will have no immediate awareness of any deficiencies and will only be able to deduce the errors afterwards (see figure 1).

In addition, according to this theory, conscious feedback is inherently subtractive. The feedback tracks the magnitude and direction of what has already happened, thereby constraining the introduction of new ideas. All things otherwise being equal, turning down the feedback should inspire more creativity by allocating more energy to new information. Of course, all things otherwise being equal, without feedback, thoughts will be much more disorganized.

Ideally, these practical benefits are only the beginning. If consciousness vectors are real, and if we can begin to understand how they are calculated, we will have a much deeper knowledge of the highest functions of the human brain and possibly be able to apply our insights to artificial intelligence. Unlocking consciousness vectors may unlock human consciousness.

Acknowledgment: I would like to thank Aubrey Gilbert for her insights and careful review. Some of the material in this review was previously published in Bodovitz, 2008. Whereas the previous review included an argument about the possible localization of the brain region responsible for calculating consciousness vectors, this review is focused more on the significance of continuity and the role of putative consciousness vectors.

References

Bodovitz, S. (2008). The neural correlate of consciousness. Journal of Theoretical Biology, 254(3), 594-598.

Borges, J.L. (1946). A New Refutation of Time.

Born, R.T., Bradley, D.C. (2005). Structure and Function of Visual Area MT. Annual Review of Neuroscience, 28, 157-189.

Castiello, U., Paulignan, Y., Jeannerod, M. (1991). Temporal dissociation of motor responses and subjective awareness. A study in normal subjects. Brain, 6, 2639-2655.

Chalmers, D.J. (1996). The conscious mind: in search of a fundamental theory. Oxford University Press, New York, US.

Cho, A. (2010). The first quantum machine. Science, 330(6011), 1604

Dember, W.N., Purcell, D.G. (1967). Recovery of masked visual targets by inhibition of the masking stimulus. Science, 157, 1335-1336.

Ditchburn, R.W., Ginsborg, B.L. (1952). Vision with a stabilized retinal image. Nature, 170, 36-37.

Gomes, G. (1998). The timing of conscious experience: a critical review and reinterpretation of Libet's research. Conscious and Cognition, 7(4), 559-595.

Hameroff, S.R., Penrose, R. (1996). Orchestrated reduction of quantum coherence in brain microtubules: a model for consciusness. In: Hameroff, S.R., Kaszniak, A.W., Scott, A. C. (Eds.) Toward a Science of Consciousness. MIT Press, Cambridge, MA, pp. 507- 540.

Koch, C. (2003). Lecture 15: On Time and Consciousness. In: California Institute of Technology course CNS/Bi 120. http://www.klab.caltech.edu/cns120/videos.php

Koch, C. (2004a). The quest for consciousness: a neurobiological approach. Roberts & Company, Englewood, Colorado, US, pp. 257-259.

Koch, C. (2004b). The quest for consciousness: a neurobiological approach. Roberts & Company, Englewood, Colorado, US, p. 214.

Koch, C. (2004c). The quest for consciousness: a neurobiological approach. Roberts & Company, Englewood, Colorado, pp. 249-268.

Lashley, K. (1956) Cerebral Organization and Behavior. In: Cobb, S. & Penfield, W. (Eds.) The Brain and Human Behavior. Williams and Wilkins Press, Baltimore, Maryland.

Lau, H.C., Passingham, R.E. (2006). Relative blindsight in normal observers and the neural correlate of visual consciousness. Proceedings of the National Academy of Sciences, 103(49), 18763-18768.

Libet, B. (1999). How does conscious experience arise? The neural time factor. Brain Research Bulletin, 50(5/6), 339-340.

Libet, B., Alberts, W.W., Wright, E.W., Jr., Feinstein, B. (1967). Responses of human somatosensory cortex to stimuli below threshold for conscious sensation. Science, 158, 2597-1600.

Libet, B., Alberts, W.W., Wright, E.W., Jr., Delattre, L.D., Levin, G., Feinstein, B. (1964). Production of threshold levels of conscious sensation by electrical stimulation of human somatosensory cortex. Journal of Neurophysiology, 27, 546-578.

Libet, B., Pearl, D.K., Morledge, D.A., Gleason, C.A., Hosobuchi, Y., Barbaro, N.M. (1991). Control of the transition from sensory detection to sensory awareness in man by the duration of a thalamic stimulus: the cerebral 'time-on' factor. Brain, 114, 1731-1757.

Martinez-Conde, S., Macknik, S.L. Hubel, D.H. (2004). The role of fixational eye movements in visual perception. Nat Rev Neurosci. 5(3), 229-240.

O'Connell, A.D., Hofheinz, M., Ansmann, M., Bialczak, R.C., Lenander, M., Lucero, E., Neeley, M., Sank, D., Wang, H., Weides, M., Wenner, J., Martinis, J.M., Cleland, A.N. (2010). Quantum ground state and single-phonon control of a mechanical resonator. Nature, 464, 697-703.

Pockett, S. (2002). On subjective back-referral and how long it takes to become conscious of a stimulus: a reinterpretation of Libet's data. Conscious and Cognition, 11(2), 144-161.

Riggs, L.A., Ratliff, F. (1952). The effects of counteracting the normal movements of the eye. J. Opt. Soc. Am. 42, 872-873.

Rucci, M., Iovin, R., Poletti, M., Santini, F. (2007). Miniature eye movements enhance fine spatial detail. Nature, 447, 851-854.

Salart, D., Baas, A., Branciard, C., Gisin, N., Zbinden, H. (2008). Testing the speed of 'spooky action at a distance'. Nature, 454, 861–864.

Shipp, S., de Jong, B.M., Zihl, J., Frackowiak, R.S., Zeki, S. (1994). The brain activity related to residual motion vision in a patient with bilateral lesions of V5. Brain, 117(5), 1023-38.

Yarbus, A.L. (1967). Eye Movements and Vision. New York: Plenum.

Zihl, J., von Cramon D., Mai, N., Schmid, C. (1991). Disturbance of movement vision after bilateral posterior brain damage. Further evidence and follow up observations. Brain, 114(5), 2235-2252.

Zihl, J., von Cramon, D., Mai, N. (1983). Selective disturbance of movement vision after bilateral brain damage. Brain, 106(2), 313-340.

17. The Time Machine of Consciousness. Past Present Future Exist Simultaneously. Entanglement, Tachyons, Relative Time, Circle of Time, Quantum Time, Dream Time, PreCognition, Retrocausation, Deja Vu, and Premonitions

Rhawn Gabriel Joseph

Cosmology.com / BrainMind.com

Abstract:

There is no "universal now." The distinctions between past present and future are illusions. As predicted by Einstein's field equations space-time may be a circle such that the future leads to the present and then the past which leads to the future, thereby creating multiple futures and pasts and which allows information from the future to effect the present. Causes may cause themselves. Coupled with evidence from entanglement where choices made in the future effect measurements made in the present and theoretical tachyons which travel at superluminal speeds from the future to the present and then the past, this may account for precognition, deja vu, and premonitions. In quantum mechanics, where reality and the quantum continuum are a unity, time is also a unity such that the future present past are a continuum which are linked and the same could be said of consciousness which exists in the future and in the present and past. If considered as a "world line" and in space-like instead of time-like intervals, then consciousness from birth to death would be linked as a basic unity extending not in time but in space and the same could be said of time. Time-space and consciousness are also linked and interact via the wave function and as demonstrated by entanglement and the Uncertainty Principle. Evidence from space-time contraction, atomic clocks and the twin paradox as functions of gravity and acceleration also demonstrate that the future already exists before it is experienced by consciousness in the present. Likewise, under conditions of accelerated consciousness (such as in reaction to terror) and dream states where various brain structures are in a heightened state of activity, space-time may also contract, such that time may slow down and consciousness may be given glimpses of the future in advance of other conscious minds thereby providing again for experiences such as precognition, premonitions, and deja vu. Closed time curves, conscious time, relative time, dream time, and quantum time are also discussed.

Keywords: Consciousness, retrocausation, Time Travel, Space-Time, Relativity, Quantum Physics, deja vu, premonitions, precognition, Length Contraction, twin paradox, atomic clocks, dreaming, tachyons, entanglement, Uncertainty Principle, Wave function, Everett Multiple Worlds, rotating universe, closed time curves, violations of causality.

Relativity: The Future is the Past. The Past is the Future

Time is relative to the observer (Einstein 1961). Since there are innumerable observers, due to gravity, velocity and other variables, there is no universal "past, present, future" (Einstein 1905a,b, 1906, 1915a, 1961) all of which overlap and are infinite in number and yet interconnected and entangled in the basic oneness of the spacetime quantum continuum. It is the unity and relativity of time which makes time travel possible as well as some of the unique features of consciousness such as "premonition" and deja vu during which an observer experiences or is effected by the future before it becomes the present.

Because time is relative, and due to entanglement (Lee et al. 2011; Matson 2012; Olaf et al. 2003), the future can effect the past and may be experienced in the present depending on the observer's frame of reference. Consider the moon, the sun, and the stars up above. From a vantage point on Earth, the moon we see is actually the moon from 1 second ago; the moon we see in the present is from the past. The sun we observe is a sun from 8 seconds in the past. Upon gazing at the nearest star, Alpha Centauri, the star we see is from years ago since it takes 4.3 light years for its light image to reach Earth. If you stand in front of a full length mirror, just 3 feet away, and since light travels at 1 foot per nanosecond, you see yourself as you looked 6 nanoseconds ago. You are staring into the past. You are always younger in a mirror because what you see is the "you" from moments before. Mirrors are gateways to the past even though the past image you see is experienced in the "present." However, although from the past, the images are in the future until they arrive in the present relative to an observer. Before the image from the past arrives it is still in the future, relative to the observer. A stream of photons which just left the surface of the sun will not arrive on Earth until the future, 8 seconds from now. Until the splash of light arrives, it is in the future, relative to those on Earth but in the past relative to the sun.

If an alien observer living on a planet in Alpha Centauri was gazing at Earth, then the present on Alpha Centauri overlaps with the past on Earth. The alien sees an Earth from 4.3 light years ago. The reverse is true for an observer on Earth gazing at this distant star. However, until those images from the past reach the observer, they are in the future relative to that observer and overlap and exist simultaneously. The past can be the future and both may exist before they arrive in the present only to again become the past thereby creating a circle of time. Innumerable futures, presents, and pasts exist simultaneously albeit in different locations within space-time all of which are in motion. Observers located in New York, Shanghai, Tokyo, Paris, Mexico City, and in distant galaxies, are also in motion, as planets spin and orbit the sun, the sun orbits the galaxy, and galaxies move about in the universe. Observers, regardless of what planet, solar system, or in what galaxy they reside, are continually moving though space-time, often at different velocities and effected by varying degrees of gravity, and all are continually coming into contact with different times which are effect by velocity as well as the consciousness and emotional state of the observer.

Contraction of Time: The Future and Present Come Closer Together

As predicted by relativity and quantum mechanics, the experience of time and the distinctions between the past, future and the "present" are shaped and affected by distance, gravity, acceleration, consciousness, and our emotions, contracting and speeding up under conditions of pleasure and slowing down and sometimes splitting apart or even running backwards under conditions of fear and terror (Joseph 1996, 2010a). Acceleration contracts space-time thereby decreasing the distance between the future and the now, albeit depending on the location and frame of reference of the observers (Einstein 1905c, 1961; Einstein et al. 1923; Lorentz 1892, 1905). When time-space contracts, more time is squeezed into a smaller space such that it may take one consciousness less time to reach the future (vs the consciousness of a second observer) if that consciousness experiences time contraction. Two observers, with two different inertial frames of reference, may experience time as slowing down or speeding up. Consciousness can also accelerate and contract the space-time continuum, particularly during dream states, or under conditions of terror in which case, time may speed up or slow down and there may be a splitting of consciousness (Joseph 1996, 2010a). Likewise, emotions such as pleasure can also speed up the experience of time; a phenomenon observed by Einstein nearly 100 years ago:

"Put your hand on a hot stove for a minute, and it seems like an hour. Sit with a pretty girl for an hour, and it seems like a minute. THAT'S relativity." -Einstein

Time is a dimension, not in Euclidian space, but in "Minkowski space" (Minkowski 1909). Euclidian space consists of 4 spatial dimensions which include movement and geometric space; but none of which encompass time. By contrast, in "Minkowski space" which is incorporated within Einstein's special relativity, time is the 4th dimension (Einstein 1961). More specifically, 3 of the Euclidian dimensions of space are combined with a dimension of time thereby creating a four-dimensional manifold known as "space-time." Space-time, however, is effected by gravity and acceleration, and can shrink and contract as gravity and velocity increase and in response to alterations in cerebral activity and thus, consciousness. As demonstrated in quantum mechanics, consciousness and the act of perceptual (or mechanical) registration directly impacts the quantum continuum through interactions via the wave function and through entanglement.

The relationship between time dilation and the contraction of the length of space-time can be determined by a formula devised by Hendrik Lorentz in 1895. As specified by the Lorentz factor, γ (gamma) is given by the equation $\gamma =$, such that the dilation-contraction effect increases exponentially as the time traveler's velocity (v) approaches the speed of light c.

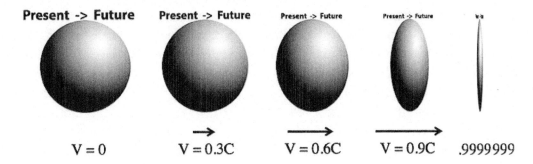

When time-space contracts more time is compacted into smaller spaces and it takes less time to reach the future which is squeezed closer to the present, whereas from the perspective of a dissociated consciousness, time may appear to slow down, thus paralleling some of the paradoxes of time travel: the time traveling consciousness experiences the future more quickly, and in less time, thereby providing the foundations of deja vu, premonitions, anticipation, and the ability to make accurate predictions and to plan for the future.

Not just space-time, but the time machine, the time traveler, and any ticking clocks inside also shrink with increased gravity and velocity such that the passage of time inside the time machine shrinks relative to time and any observer located outside and is looking inside the time machine. For those inside the time machine, time appears to pass at the same rate inside, and this is because everything inside the time machine has shrunk to the same degree. According to Einstein (1961), an observer inside the moving object or traveling alongside at the same speed would not notice this contraction. It is only apparent to an outside observer with a separate frame of reference; and the same appears to be true of dissociated consciousness under conditions of terror (Joseph 1996, REF). Time is relative and it is only an outside observer at a safe distance from the time machine (or the accelerated consciousness) who will perceive the contraction of time-space surrounding the time traveler and that the time traveler's clock has slowed. By contrast, if the time traveler were to look outside the time machine it would seem that the outside observer's clock is ticking faster. Thus as predicted by Einstein, clocks run more slowly (time contraction) as velocity and acceleration increase and a time traveler in a time machine would appear to be slowling down from the perspective of an outside observer, whereas from the perspective of the time traveler the outside observer would be speeding up.

This concept is brilliantly anticipated by H.G. Wells in "The Time Machine." Well's Time Traveler and his time machine began the voyage through time in his laboratory and looking outside the time machine he could see celestial events, people, and even a snail whiz by: "The laboratory got hazy and went dark. Mrs. Watchett came in and walked, apparently without seeing me, towards the garden door. I suppose it took her a minute or so to traverse the place, but to me she seemed to shoot across the room like a rocket." Well's Time Traveler also kept his eye on the laboratory clock and noted "a moment before it had stood at a minute or so past ten; now it was nearly half-past three!" A clock outside the time machine was therefore ticking away rapidly (relative to his clock inside the time machine), whereas his clock inside the time machine, from the perspective of Mrs. Watchett would run very slowly; exactly as predicted by Einstein's theories of relativity (Einstein 1914, 1915a,b, 1961). Although the laboratory clock sped up and Mrs. Watchet, the housekeeper, from the perspective of the Time Traveler, seemed to race across the room, from Mrs. Watchet's perspective the Time Traveler would appear to be frozen in time or moving exceedingly slowly. Likewise, victims subject to extreme terror may experience accelerated consciousness and from the perspective of an outside observer they may appear catatonic and frozen in time (Joseph 1996).

Twin Paradox

The shrinkage of space-time under accelerated conditions has given rise to the famous "twin paradox," a thought experiment based on special relativity (Langevin 1911; von Laue 1913. Because clocks inside the time machine run more slowly whereas the distance between the now and the future decreases, a time traveling twin will arrive more quickly in the future (since velocity does not shrink) and will age more slowly than her twin back on Earth. Consider for example, 30 feet of space which contracts to 10 feet. Those inside the time machine need only walk 10 feet whereas those outside the time machine must walk 30 feet. Likewise because the time traveler's clock runs more slowly, and since more time is contracted into a smaller space, it might take him 10 minutes to get 30 minutes into the future. Thus, the Earth-bound twin will be much older (as more time has passed) and may have already turned to dust if the time traveler arrived hundreds of years into the future. As summed up by Einstein (1911; see also Langevin 1911):

> "If we placed a living organism in a box ... one could arrange that the organism, after any arbitrary lengthy flight, could be returned to its original spot in a scarcely altered condition, while corresponding organisms which had remained in their original positions had already long since given way to

new generations. For the moving organism, the lengthy time of the journey was a mere instant, provided the motion took place with approximately the speed of light."

If one twin leaves Earth and accelerates toward light speed, that twin will arrive in the future in less time than the twin left behind on Earth (since more time passed for that twin whose clock ran faster). By contrast, because it took less time for the time traveling twin she does not age as much (since her clock ticked slower) whereas the twin left on Earth ages at the normal rate. Hence, the time traveling twin will be younger: it took her less time (clock ticks slower) whereas the twin on Earth took more time (clock ticks faster) to reach the same destination in the future. The time traveling twin arrives in the future more quickly--and the same can be said of accelerated and dissociated consciousness thereby providing the foundations of deja vu and premonitions.

Because of time dilation and the contraction of space, once the time traveler lands on Earth, and depending on how fast and far into the future she is propelled, all her friends and relatives back on Earth may have died and a completely new generation of Earthlings may greet the time traveler upon her return. By contrast, since time slows down and time-space become squeezed together, the time traveler who arrives in the future may not have aged appreciably.

For example, say the time traveler is born in the year 2100, had a life expectancy of 80 years and would have died in the year 2180 if she had never left on her journey into the future. If she began her journey at age 20 in the year 2120, achieved 0.999999999999999 light speed and arrived in the future date of 2180, she would still have a life expectancy of 60 years (minus the 20 she already lived and time spent in the time machine). Upon arriving in the year 2180, she would still be 20 years old instead of 80 and could now expect to live another 60 years until the year 2240 (vs the year 2180 if she had never left home).

This premise is based on achieving near light speeds almost instantaneously and is supported by experiments with non-living, ultra-short-lived particles. For example, the muon particle is given a new lease on life when accelerated to a velocity of 99.92% light speed and its life span is nearly 25 times longer (Houellebecq 2001; Knecht, 2003). The muon particle not only lives longer but travels 25 times further due to its expanded life span. Particles, including phi mesons, which have been accelerated to velocities of 99.9% light speed also achieve significant life span extensions with a γ factor of around 5,000 (Houellebecq 2001). Presumably particles live longer because they arrived in the future more quickly vs their counterparts traveling at their normal, slower speeds. Therefore, it could be predicted that a time traveler who journeys at near light speeds will live longer compared to friends left back on Earth; and this is because the contraction of time space enabled them to reach the future before those back on Earth. Premonitions and deja vu, work on the same principles.

A time traveling consciousness will also experience time as speeding up or slowing down depending not just on acceleration and gravity, but emotion and neural activity. The distance between the "present" and the future decrease because of the shrinkage of space. In consequence the time traveling consciousness gains access to information in the future more quickly than other observers.

These same principles can be applied when traveling great distances across space to other stars and planets. If the journey takes place at near lights speeds, the space-time traveler may visit a distant star and then return home still fresh and young whereas her relatives and friends will have grown old and infirm and may have already died.

For example, if Gaia stays on Earth and her twin, Aurora travels at 80% the speed of light to Proxima Centauri which is 4.2 light years away, then Aurora's trip will take 5.25 Earth years (4.2/0.8 = 5.25). One day in the time machine at 80% light speed is equal to 1.67 days on Earth. Thus 1,916.25 days in the time machine (5.25 years) is equal to 3,200 days on Earth (8.76 years). Hence, Aurora's clock will tick 0.599% more slowly than Gaia's clock on Earth (5.25/8.76) and Aurora will age only 3.15 years during the journey (0.599 x 5.25 = 3.146) whereas Gaia will age 5.25 years. If Aurora immediately returns to Earth at 80% light speed she will be 6.3 years older and her twin will be 10.5 years older.

Atomic Clocks

Alterations in consciousness, gravity, and velocity can shrink or stretch space-time. Therefore, time-space is also warped, shrunk, stretched, and may even curl up and fold upon and over itself depending on local conditions. Time is asymmetric. Like the weather, time is not the same everywhere, even when measured by atomic clocks.

Atomic clocks tick off time as measured by the vibrations of light waves emitted by atoms of the element cesium and with accuracies of billionths of a second (Essen & Parry, 1955). However, these clocks are also effected by their surroundings and run slower under conditions of increased gravity or acceleration (Ashby 2003; Hafele & Keating 1972a,b). In 1971 Joe Hafele and Richard Keating placed atomic clocks on airplanes traveling in the same direction of Earth's rotation thereby combining the velocity of Earth with the velocity of the planes (Hafele & Keating 1972a,b). All clocks slowed on average by 59 nanoseconds compared to atomic clocks on Earth. These clocks arrived in the future in less than than their counterparts.

It has also been demonstrated that atomic clocks at differing altitudes will show different times; a function of gravitational effects on time. The lower the altitude the slower the clock, whereas clocks speed up as altitude increases; albeit the differences consisting of increases of only a few nanoseconds (Chou et al. 2010; Hafele & Keating, 1972; Vessot et al. 1980). "For example, if two identical clocks are separated vertically by 1 km above the surface of Earth, the higher clock gains the equivalent of 3 extra seconds for each million years (Chou et al., 2010). The speeding up of atomic clocks at increasingly higher altitudes has been attributed to a reduction in gravitational potential which contributes to differential gravitational time dilation.

Accelerated Consciousness: Dissociative Mind And The Slowing Of Time

Evidence from relativity, quantum mechanics, atomic clocks, and space-tome contraction, demonstrates that the future, or at least, "a" future must have existed so this future could contract closer to the present experienced by the time traveler;. This is also proved by experiments in entanglement (REF), and Einstein's field equations which demonstrate that time is a circle (REF) where the present leads to a future which already exists and that this future leads to the present and then the past. That is, instead of the present moving toward a future which does not yet exist, the future already exists and streams toward consciousness, becoming the present, and then continues into the past relative to that observing consciousness. However, consciousness may also accelerate as reflected by increased brain activity, and this too would contract space-time. Buried deep within the brain are a series of structures referred to collectively as the limbic system, and which includes the amygdala, hippocampus, and hypothalamus. The limbic system governs all aspects of sexual behavior and emotion, including emotional and non-emotional memory as well as anxiety, fear, and the ability to visualize one's self (Joseph, 1992, 2011). Limbic system structures, such as the amygdala are able to receive sensory information from multiple modalities at the same time and excessive activity in these areas, as reflected by increased EEG activity, are associated with the the reception of information which is normally inhibited and filtered, including the experience of deju vu and other precognitive phenomenon (Daly, 1958; Halgren 1990, Gloor, 1990; Joseph, 1996, 2011; Penfield, 1952; Penfield & Perot 1963; Williams, 1956), such as a splitting of consciousness where time slow down and the dissociated consciousness can observe itself as if up in the air looking down.

> "I had a clear image of myself... as though watching it on a television screen." "The next thing I knew...I was looking down from 50 to 100 feet in the air...I had a sensation of floating. It was almost like stepping out of reality. I seemed to step out of this world."

Electrode stimulation, or other forms of heightened activity within limbic system structures such as the amygdala, hippocampus and overlying temporal lobe can also cause time to speed up or slow down (Joseph, 1998, 1999b, 2001). Likewise, in response to extreme trauma, stress and fear, the amygdala, hippocampus and temporal lobe become hyper activated resulting not only in a "splitting of consciousness" but the sensation that time has slowed down while the dissociated consciousness seems to speed up (Courtois, 2009; Grinker & Spiegel, 1945; Noyes & Kletti, 1977; van der Kolk 1987).

One individual, after losing control of his Mustang convertible while during over 100 miles per hour on a rain soaked freeway, reported that:

"time seemed to slow down and then... part of my mind was a few feet outside the car zooming above it and then beside it and behind it and in front of it, looking at and analyzing the respective positions of my spinning Mustang and the cars surrounding me. Simultaneously I was inside trying to steer and control it in accordance with the multiple perspectives I was given by that part of my mind that was outside. It was like my mind split and one consciousness was inside the car, while the other was zooming all around outside and giving me visual feedback that enabled me to avoid hitting anyone or destroying my Mustang."

"Tiffany" describes her experience as follows:

"I was a passenger in my boyfriend's sports car and we were laughing and racing along highway 17, going 80, 90 mph. I remember he reached his cigarettes when we were going around a corner and then the car began to slide sideways toward the embankment and all the trees. Everything just suddenly slowed down, like in slow motion, and I could see the car sliding very slowly toward the trees, and I turned and looked at my boyfriend and he had this look of fear and determination on his face. He was gritting his teeth which were very white. I remember looking at his hands tightly gripped on the steering wheel, and I could see the ring I gave him. And outside the car there were other cars and they were also moving in slow motion. We were still sliding, and I turned my head and I could see we were going to slide right into this big tree, and everything was still so slow, and I could see the trunk and bark of the tree, the tree limbs, coming closer and I could see this bird flying out of the tree flapping its wings real slow, then we hit the tree with the back of the car which made the car spin around the tree, but it was all in slow motion, and all this glass blew out the side and back window and I could see little pieces of glass going everywhere moving very slowly through the air. I was wearing my seat belt and was spun toward my boyfriend but he wasn't there. Instead, the driver's side door was open and the car was turning upside down and I could see my purse falling upward and my wallet and phone and eyeliner and lipstick and a pencil were all falling out but going upward very slowly, like floating right in front of me, and I remember thinking that I hoped that pencil did not stick me in the eye, and then the air bags popped out and it was also going in slow motion billowing out toward me and I could see the trees down below because we were falling over and down the embankment and everything was upside down and going sideways and then the airbag hit me in the chest and time suddenly sped up and the car landed upside down and slid down the embankment and hit some trees."

The slowing down of time and the splitting of consciousness, creating twin consciousnesses, are not uncommon under conditions of terror. Terror can accelerate the mind and brain by releasing a cascade of "fight or flight" neurochemicals such as norepinephrine (Joseph 1992, 1994, 1996, 20011). When the brain and mind are accelerated under these conditions one aspect of consciousness may split off and observe itself and the body which houses it. Under certain accelerated conditions, time will also slow down for the dissociated consciousness which has split off and is observing (Joseph 1996, 2000); exactly as predicted by relativity and the twin paradox: acceleration slows time for one observer and speeds it up for the other (Einstein et al. 1927; Einstein 1961).

In fact, time slows down under conditions of terror and accelerated, hyper-brain activity to such a degree that seconds may last minutes, and minutes hours (Joseph 1996). Individuals may become completely motionless, almost catatonic from the perspective of outside observers and may fail to make any effort to save their lives or to respond to assistance such as attempting to evacuate a burning plane or sinking ship even though they have been uninjured (Courtois, 1995; Galliano et al., 1993; Miller, 1951; Nijenhuis et al., 1998). From the perspective of outside observers, those so afflicted appear to be frozen in time; which is exactly how a time traveler accelerating toward light speed would appear to those outside the time machine. Likewise, from the perspective of the dissociated consciousness time also appear to slow down and to contract which gives that dissociated consciousness more time in less space to observe its surroundings; and this too is predicted by relativity and the Lorentz transformations of length and space-time contraction. Under accelerated conditions space-time shrinks and more time is compacted into less space.

> "I began moving at a tremendous speed... and I was aware of trees rushing below me. I just thought of home and knew I was going there... I saw my husband sitting in his favorite armchair reading the newspaper. I saw my children running up and down the stairs... I was drawn back to the hospital, but I don't remember the trip; it seemed to happen instantaneously" (Eadie & Taylor 1992).

Thus time slows down for the consciousness attached to the body, but may speed up for the dissociated consciousness. However, this multiplicity of mind, although dissociated, is still entangled, and as such, time may speed up and slow down simultaneously.

In fact, under conditions of extreme fear and terror and accelerated consciousness, time slows to such a degree and corresponding movements becomes slowed to such a degree that to outside observers the person may appear to be dead: "Far down below I could see houses and towns and green land and streams... I was very happy now. I kept on going very fast... then I started back, going very fast...Then I was lying on my back in bed and the girl and her father and a doctor were looking at me in a queer way...I had been dead three days (they told him)...and they were getting ready to buy my coffin" (Neihardt 1989).

Consider the case of Lisa, a wild blonde 22 year old beauty, a passenger in a sport's car with the top down that struck a telephone pole:

"It felt like a movie in slow motion and everything slowed down just before we crashed. I had a seat belt and my arms and hands stretched out in front on the dashboard... and the windshield shattered and I could see all these cracks forming in the glass in slow motion. Everything was slowed down and the windshield just broken in half and it fell toward me all in slow motion and cut off my arm....I could see it cutting the skin and droplets of blood and then all this blood and my arm falling slowly to the floor of the car. Everything was so slow... and I got out of the car and my arm was spraying blood everywhere. I walked only a few feet and in slow motion fell down.... Then I was in the air, watching everything. Part of the time I was on the ground looking up and at the same time I was in the air looking down at me. I could see people getting out of their cars. They were all around me and I could see them while I was on the ground and at the same time I could see them like I was 50 feet in the air looking down at them. Then the ambulance came and they put a tourniquet on my arm and put me inside... and then everything started going real fast. I was outside the ambulance, like I was inside sticking out and my mind was racing up and down the streets, like I was running very fast alongside.... then I was in the hospital. But I was no longer part of my body. I was racing along, tripping out, bobbing up and down the halls, just checking everything out and everything was going very fast. Then I saw all these doctors and nurses working on this body of a girl. I peaked over their shoulders and then I realized it was me, that girl was me and I could see that my hair was all bloody and this bothered me. It needed to be washed. But I wasn't moving. I looked dead.... The doctors also thought I was dead.... and that's when I fell back into my body with this thump and I started moving and that's when the doctors and nurses realized I was still alive."

Of course, time can also slow down under conditions of extreme boredom. However, boredom does not induce a splitting of the mind or dissociated states of consciousness. Instead of more time in less space, there is less time in more space. The clock ticks more slowly for the consciousness of the observer and more slowly external to that observer. Conversely, under conditions of pleasure, time speeds up and passes more quickly as so eloquently summed up by Einstein.

Time is entangled with and relative to consciousness and the multiplicity of mind.

The Event Horizon of Consciousness: The Eternal Now

As a thought experiment Einstein imagined that if he flew away from a big clock in the town square precisely at 12 noon, and traveled at the speed of light, the clock would appear to stop and would remain 12 noon forever--and this is because Einstein would be traveling at the same rate of speed as the light coming from the clock, in tandem and in parallel with it. Time would also essentially stop for Einstein, for if he were looking at the light beams on either side of him, they would look like stationary waves of electromagnetic activity consisting of crests and valleys--and this is because he would be moving in tandem and relative to these light beams; like two trains traveling at exactly the same speed, side by side and the only view is of the other train. At light speed Einstein would be captured in an "eternal now" with the future on one side and the past on the other.

All observers in uniform motion (like two trains traveling side by side) view themselves as at rest (so long at they can only see the two trains). If traveling at the speed of light, a light from a flashlight held in that time traveler's hand will never escape from the flashlight. The light from the flashlight will be frozen in place, in an eternal now.

If a star, astronaut, or space-time machine were to approach a supermassive black hole at the center of this galaxy, they would accelerate toward the "event horizon" at light speed (Dieter 2012; McClintock, 2004)--the "event horizon" being the point of no-return, the vortex forming the mouth of the hole. The Time Traveler's clock would tick increasingly slower and light trailing behind would become redder (red shifted) as the event horizon is approached. However, for the time traveler, time continues as before.

Once caught by the gravitational grip of the vortex spinning round the event horizon, the star, astronaut, or space-time machine would have a velocity of light speed (Dieter 2012). Time stops. They would be captured and held in the grip of what could best be described as an "eternal now." Light could not escape, and the outside of the hole would appear black, whereas the event horizon would be blazing brightly illuminated with light.

Just as a star will accelerate toward light speed as it approaches the event horizon of a supermassive black hole in the fabric of space-time (Bethe et al. 2003; Dieter 2012; McClintock, 2004), the multiple futures flowing toward the event horizon of consciousness may also accelerate toward light speed. Once captured by the event horizon of consciousness these futures have a velocity of light speed becoming the "eternal now." Consciousness of the "present" could be likened to an event horizon illuminated with light. The present, the "eternal now" is the illumination of the event horizon of consciousness at light speed. On one side of the event horizon of "now" would be the future, and on the other, the past.

Predicting A Future Which Exists Before It Is Experienced

Relativity and quantum physics both predict the future exists before it is experienced. However, due to the fact that time is entangled in the frenzied activity of the quantum continuum, the future, or rather "a" future may continually change until the moment it is perceived by consciousness.

Since futures and pasts overlaps and as time-space is coextensive, then time, including local time relative to a single observer, is entangled. The past may effect the future, the future can effect the past, time effects consciousness and alterations in consciousness effect the passage of time.

As a "future" flows toward Earth it can also be effected by whatever it encounters on the way to the consciousness of "now," relative to an observer on Earth--exactly as befalls light. All futures are also entangled with space-time, the quantum continuum, and subject to the Uncertainty Principle. Therefore, future time may be continually altered until perhaps just moments before these futures are experienced by observers who are also entangled with what they experience. Hence, although one may anticipate and predict the future, just like they may predict the weather, the ability to accurately anticipate and predict the future, like predicting future weather, may increase the closer that future is to the present. Planning skills, goal formation, strategy, long term investments, concern for consequences, and even the most basic of calendars, all rest upon the ability to make predictions about the future.

The future is like the weather, with the ability to forecast the weather decreasing in accuracy as time and distance from the present increases. In other words, and because of entanglement and classic concepts governing "cause and effect", the future is not already determined but is in flux and subject to continual alteration. The act of observing and other forces related to cause and affect alter the quantum continuum and continually change the future as it approaches. The future may not become fixed until the moment it is perceived by an observer relative to that observer, at which point it is in the present. Hence, predictions about the future will seldom be completely accurate, and become less accurate regarding increasingly distant events in the future, but more accurate but not completely accurate regarding events in the immediate future; a consequence of entanglement and the Uncertainty Principle.

Since the past is also relative and can exist in the future for some observers and in the present for others, and as the past is entangled with the quantum continuum, then the past is also subject to change after it has been experienced and before it is experienced by another observer at a downstream location in space-time. Two historians writing about history interpret and experience the past differently. A husband and wife discussing what happened at a party the night before, disagree. Eye-witness accounts differ among eye-witnesses (REF). A peasant living in a small village in western China in 1963 may have never heard of the assassination of president John F. Kennedy. The past is relative. There is no universal "past."

Time is entangled and is affected by consciousness and relative to and effected by the act of observation and measurement--as predicted by quantum mechanics (Bohr, 1958, 1963; Dirac, 1966a,b; Planck 1931, 1932, Heisenberg 1927, 1958; Neumann 1937, 1955).

Causes and Effects Are Relative To Consciousness

Every particle, person, planet, star, galaxy, has a wave function. The brain and consciousness have a wave function (Penrose & Hameroff 2011). Reality, including the reality of time, is a manifestation of wave functions and alterations in patterns of activity within the quantum continuum which are perceived as discontinuous (Bohr, 1958, 1963; Planck 1931; Heisenberg, 1958). This also gives rise to the perception of temporal order and what comes first, second, third, and what is in the present and in the past. The perception of temporal order, and structural units of information are not just perceived, but inserted into the quantum state which causes the reduction of the wave-packet and collapse of the wave function.

The brain and mind of a time traveler also has a wave function. As predicted by Einstein's field equations, consciousness can be accelerated into the future, and from the future, into the past. The Time traveler, upon observing his surroundings causes a collapse of the wave function, as predicted by the Copenhagen school of quantum physics: "The discontinuous change in the probability function takes place with the act of registration...in the mind of the observer" (Heisenberg, 1958).

The loss of coherence, the creation of discontinuous states in the quantum continuum is the result of entangled interactions within the environment which results in an exchange of energy and information: quantum entanglements. These entanglements, or blemishes in the quantum continuum, may be observed as shape, form, cause, effect, past, present, future, first, second, last, an so on, all of which are the result of a decoupling of quanta from the quantum (coherent) continuum which leaks out and then couples together in a form of knot which is observed as a wave form collapse. Every moment in time, is a wave form collapse of space-time at the moment of observation (Bohr, 1958, 1963; Heisenberg 1958; Von Neumann 1932, 1937).

However, in the Copenhagen model, the observer is external to the quantum state and is not part of the collapse function but a witness to it (Bohr, 1958, 1963; Heisenberg 1958). The observer is not the creator of reality but registers the transition of the possible to the actual: "The introduction of the observer must not be misunderstood to imply that some kind of subjective features are to be brought into the description of nature. The observer has, rather, only the function of registering decisions, i.e., processes in space and time, and it does not matter whether the observer is an apparatus or a human being; but the registration, i.e., the transition from the possible to the actual, is absolutely necessary here and cannot be omitted from the interpretation of quantum theory" (Heisenberg 1958).

As summed up by Von Neumann (1932), the "experiential increments in a person's knowledge" and "reductions of the quantum mechanical state of that person's brain" corresponds to the elimination of all those perceptual functions that are not necessary or irrelevant to the knowing of the event. Consciousness, therefore, could be viewed as a filter, which selectively attends to fragments of the quantum continuum which are perceived as real: the transition from the possible to the actual.

Therefore, according to the Copenhagen interpretation, the observing consciousness is external and separate from (albeit entangled with) what is observed and external to the ensuing collapse of the wave function which is collapsed by being measured and observed and this includes the observation and experience of time. However, consciousness can also be conscious of consciousness and thus consciousness can be subject to wave form collapse when observed by consciousness (Joseph 2011).

Consciousness and Mind

In a quantum universe all of existence, including consciousness, consists of a frenzy of subatomic activity which can be characterized as possessing pure potentiality and all of which are linked and entangled as a basic oneness which extends in all directions and encompasses all dimensions including time (Bohr, 1958, 1963; Dirac, 1966a,b; Planck 1931, 1932, Heisenberg 1955, 1958; von Neumann 1937, 1955). Hence, consciousness and the act of observation be it visual, auditory, tactile, mechanical, digital, are entangled with the quantum continuum and creates a static and series of impressions of just a fragment of that quantum frenzy that is registered in the mind of the observer as length, width, height, seconds, minutes, hours, days, weeks, months, first, second, third, and so on; like taking a series of pictures of continual motion and transformation and then believing it consists of temporal sequences when in fact, the conscious mind imposes temporal order (Joseph 1982, 1996, 2010). Just as, according to the quantum physics, the observing mind interacts with the quantum continuum and makes it possible to perceive shape and form, the conscious mind (and the dreaming mind) can perceive temporal sequences where there is none (Joseph 1982, 1986, 2010a); and those sequences include the illusion of future and past. That is, the act of sensory registration, be it a function of a single cell, or the conscious mind of a woman or man, selects a fragment of the infinite quantum possibilities and experiences it as real, and it is real but only to that mind or that cell at the moment of registration (Heisenberg 1955, 1958). Hence, "past present future" are a manifestation of consciousness which is entangled with time-space and the quantum continuum.

"I regard consciousness as fundamental. I regard matter as derivative from consciousness" (Max Planck, 1931).

As demonstrated by quantum mechanics and formalized by the Uncertainty Principle (Heisenberg 1925, 1927), what is known, is imprecise (Bohr, 1958, 1963; Dirac, 1966a,b; Planck 1931, 1932, Heisenberg 1955, 1958; Neumann 1937, 1955) and this includes time. To know something in its totality, would require a multi-dimensional all encompassing infinite "god's eye" view.

It could be said that consciousness is consciousness of something other than consciousness (Joseph 1982, 2011). Consciousness and knowledge of an object, such as a chair, are also distinct and separate. Consciousness is not the chair. The chair is not consciousness. The chair is an object of consciousness, and thus become discontinuous from the quantum state and entangled with consciousness.

Consciousness is consciousness of something and consciousness can be conscious of not being that object that it is conscious of. By knowing what it isn't, consciousness may know what is not, which helps define what is. This consciousness of not being the object can be considered the "collapse function" which results in discontinuity within the continuum: consciousness of consciousness being conscious.

Moreover, as demonstrated by neuroscience, the mind is not a singularity, but a multiplicity with different aspects of consciousness and awareness directly associated with specific regions of the brain (Joseph, 1992, 1996, 2011). These different mental realms and brain areas can perceive time and the quantum continuum differently. Time may be perceived by one brain region as lacking temporal order but as a continuum or gestalt. The mind is a multiplicity, which can become a duality, and which is often experienced as a singularity referred to as consciousness.

Further, it could be said that consciousness of consciousness, that is, self-consciousness, also imparts a duality, a separation, into the fabric of the quantum continuum. Hence, this consciousness that is the object of consciousness, becomes an abstraction, and may create a collapse function in the quantum continuum (Heisenberg, 1958; Joseph 2011; von Neurmann 1955, 2001). Consciousness may cause itself. That is, continuum which is consciousness, and which exists as entangled in the quantum continuum which includes time, may cause itself to experience the "eternal now" which is simply a collapse of the wave function of time.

Entanglement: The Future Causes the Past

Time, the fragmentation of time into temporal sequential units and where "causes" precede "effects," are also a "derivative of consciousness." If time is a feature of the quantum continuum, and if considered independent of "consciousness" then causes and effects may be one and the same, a unity and simultaneity, such that causes may cause themselves, or effects may be responsible for the causes.

Sometimes the association between and the classification of one event as coming first or second, or as a "cause" and the other an "effect" are also little more than illusion, as demonstrated by quantum entanglement and "spooky action at a distance" (Francis 2012; Lee et al. 2011; Matson 2012; Olaf et al. 2003; Plenio 2007; Juan et al. 2013). If time is a circle and due to entanglement, there are "effects" without any apparent "cause;" a possible consequence of the future effecting the present and the consciousness mind which experiences a premonition (Aharonov et al. 1988; Bem 2011; Radin 2006' Cho 2011). If time has a wave function and is an integral aspect of the quantum continuum which extends in all direction, not only would the future be linked to the past as a unity, but the conscious mind (with its own wave function) would be linked to the future and the past, thereby accounting for premonitions as well as anticipation of what is going to take place; and this is because what will take place has already taken place. The future is entangled with and causes the premonition. And just as likely, the premonition may cause the future due to entanglement.

However, typically, these "effects" (or premonitions) are written off as "mistakes" or due to "coincidence." Nevertheless, in an entangled universe the wave function of time representing the future can be predicted to interact with the wave function of the present (and vice versa) thereby inducing a causality-violating reduction of the wave form as perceived by the conscious mind.

If the future already exists, and if superluminal particles or information can arrive in the present from the future before they are perceived, this, coupled with entanglement (Plenio 2007; Juan et al. 2013; Francis 2012), may result in causes becoming confused with effects, whereas it is the future which is causing and effecting the present (Bem 2011; Radin 2006).

Consciousness is entangled with the space-time continuum which includes the future. Conscious observers can also engage in "mental time travel" (Suddendorf & Corballis 2007). Upon anticipating or looking into the future the observing consciousness can then engage in behaviors that are shaped and directed by that future. What constitutes a cause and what constitutes an effect, are relative and not uncommonly it is the anticipation of the future which causes the cause in the present.

A man buys a beautiful woman flowers, candy, jewelry, and an expensive dinner at a five star restaurant. He doesn't lavish these gifts upon the lucky maiden because he loves her, but because he is hoping she will reciprocate, after the date, by giving him sex. The expectation of sex in the future, and thus an event in the future, is the cause of his behavior in the present. The future is the cause which effects and causes his behavior in the present.

Before he bought her these gifts the man may have fantasized about the date, how he would take her to his home, what he would say, what he would do, how she would respond. This could be described as "mental time travel; rehearsing and practicing for a future event before it occurs. As demonstrated by Bem (2011), future practice can effect performance in the present before the practice occurs.

Time is also relative. Hence, when the beautiful woman received these gifts she decided to reward him. Therefore, relative to and from the perspective of the lucky maiden, the effect (sex) is a direct consequence of the cause (his gifts). On the other hand, she also knew that she could cause him to give her gifts by giving him sex in the future. Future sex caused his behavior.

Consciousness is also part of the quantum continuum and so too is the future, present, and past. Thus, consciousness, like gravity and electromagnetic waves, is relative and can affect distant objects and events, including, perhaps, those in the future and the past (Planck 1931, 1932). Moreover, all have a wave function, and time and consciousness are entangled. However, since consciousness is also entangled, then consciousness may also perceive a future event before it occur; a phenomenon known as "precognition"

Precognition: Experimental Proof

Precognition is a form of conscious cognitive awareness which involves the acquisition of future knowledge just prior to its occurrence. Premonitions are a form of presentiment or an emotional feeling that something may happen in the near future, but without conscious knowledge of exactly what it is that is going to happen. Both can be considered forms of quantum entanglement (Radin 2006; Bem, 2011) where some near future event exerts and makes an impression on consciousness before the event occurs even when there is absolutely no way the future event could be inferred as about to happen.

Various surveys have indicated that over 50% of adults have experienced premonitions or phenomenon which could be classified as precognition (Kennedy et al., 1994; Radin 2006). Moreover, numerous rigorous, scientifically controlled experiments and meta-analyses of these experiments have demonstrated statistically significant evidence for precognition and premonitions (Honorton & Ferrari 1989; Radin 2006). For example Honorton and Ferrari (1989) performed a meta-analysis of 309 forced-choice precognition experiments involving over 50,000 subjects, and which had been published in scientific journals between 1936 and 1997. They found a consistent, statistically significant hit rate, meaning that the results could not be due to chance.

As with deja vu, increased brain activity or arousal contributes to precognitive activity (Bem, 2011; Radin 1997, 2006; Spottiswoode & May, 2003). Presentiment effect has also been directly related to increased brain activity as demonstrated in fMRI experiments (Bierman & Scholte, 2002) and with other physiological indices of participants' emotional arousal in which case they become aroused before they see the stimulus (Radin 1997). For example, when participants viewed a series emotionally neutral or emotionally arousing pictures on a computer screen, strong emotional arousal occurred a few seconds before the picture appeared, even before the computer had selected which emotional picture was to be displayed (Radin 1997, 2006).

In 2011, a well respected scientist, Daryl Bem published extensive statistically significant evidence for the effects of future events on cognition and emotion, demonstrating that the effect is in the present whereas the cause can still be in the future. For example, Bem had subjects perform a memory test which required that each subject look at a long list of words and to remember as many as possible. After completing the memory test he had the subjects type various words from that list which were randomly selected. Subjects showed statistically superior memory for the words which they were later asked to type. That is, the practice effect was retrocausal. The practice which was to take place in the future (the typing of words they had already seen) improved their memory of those words before they typed them. Thus, rehearsing a set of words makes them easier to recall even when the rehearsal occurs in the future and after subjects recall the words.

In another set of experiments Bem (2011), allowed a computer to control the entire procedure which involved showing each subject "explicit erotic images." The instructions were as follows: "on each trial of the experiment, pictures of two curtains will appear on the screen side by side. One of them has a picture behind it; the other has a blank wall behind it. Your task is to click on the curtain that you feel has the picture behind it." Statistical analysis of the results demonstrated that based on "feelings" subjects picked the location of the pornographic image at well above chance (even though they couldn't see it), whereas the location of the non-erotic neutral pictures were chosen at the rate of chance, i.e. 49.8% of the time.

Bem (2011) performed nine rigorously controlled experiments involving over 1000 subjects involving erotic stimuli, the avoidance of negative stimuli, and retroactive priming effects on memory and recall. Eight of the nine experiments yielded statistically significant results, and thus evidence for precognition and premonition.

Criticism of Precognition Experimental Results: The Baseball Analogy

A common criticism regarding the validity of research on premonitions and precognition is: if it exists, why doesn't it happen all the time? Why doesn't everyone have these experiences?

Consider major league baseball. In 2013, Miguel Cabrera had a batting average of .348 which was the best of all major league players. Although he is the best hitter in major league baseball, he hit the ball less than 50% of the time when he was at bat, and was able to get a "base hit" less than 35% of the time. Out of 750 major league players, 726 of them got a base hit less than 30% of the time in 2013 during regular season play (http://espn.go.com/mlb/stats/batting). Given that these players had up to 5 opportunities to hit the ball each time at bat, and 3 opportunities to swing, it can be said that professional baseball players actually hit the ball less than 30% of the time. Bem (2011), Raden (1996, 2006) Bonorton and Ferrari (1989) and others have shown a precognition hit rate above 50%. But unlike major league baseball players, those displaying precognition get their hits before they see what is being thrown at them.

Precognition should be treated like all other measures of ability. We should not be surprised that there is variation (Carpenter 2004, 2005; Schmeidler, 1988). Indeed, the same complaints can be made about memory and past events: If it really happened, why does everyone remember it differently. Why do some people have a great memory and others are more forgetful? Why do different eye-witnesses remember the same event differently?

Even highly arousing and emotionally significant "flashbulb memories" are subject to considerable forgetting. For example, Neisser and Harsch (1992) had subjects fill out a questionnaire regarding where they were and how they heard about the Challenger space craft explosion soon after this national tragedy occurred in 1986. When these subjects were questioned again 32-34 months later, 75% could not recall filling out the questionnaire. Many of the subjects in fact had forgotten considerable detail regarding the Challenger explosion and where they were when the heard about it. According to Neisser and Harsch (1992), "As far as we can tell, the original memories are just gone."

Memory is poor. Batting averages are dismal. Should it be any surprise that premonitions and the experience of precognition is also variable?

The Quantum Physics of Premonition and Retrocausation

The phenomenon of premonition must be considered from the perspective of quantum physics not Newtonian physics or Einstein's theories of relativity. As summarized by John Stewart Bell in his 19964 ground breaking paper ("On the Einstein Podolsky Rosen paradox") "any physical theory that incorporates local realism, favoured by Einstein cannot reproduce all the predictions of quantum mechanical theory."

In 2006, the American Association for the Advancement of Science organized an interdisciplinary conference of research scientists and physicists to discuss evidence for retrocausation as related to quantum physics, the conclusions of which were published in 2006: "it seems untenable to assert that time-reverse causation (retrocausation) cannot occur, even though it temporarily runs counter to the macro-scopic arrow of time" (Sheehan, 2006, p vii).

As demonstrated by quantum physics and entanglement, the future may effect and even direct the past or the present. Consider again entanglement between photons. In delayed choice experiments, entanglement was demonstrated among photons even before there was a decision to make a choice regarding these photons, that is, before it was decided to do a measurement (Ma et al., 2012; Peres 2000). Entanglement has also been demonstrated among photons which do not yet exist, where the choice has not even been made to create or measure future photons. Nevertheless, decisions which will be made in the future effect the measurement of photons in the present (Megidish et al 2013). The same principles can be applied to precognition. Information in the future, information which does not yet exist in the present, can effect and is entangled with the consciousness which will directly perceive that information even before it arrives in the present.

The future, past, present, and consciousness are entangled within the quantum continuum. The future exists before it arrives and some people consciously perceive a future before it becomes the present; phenomenon which can be classified as evidence of entanglement and which are variably experienced as deja vu, premonitions, and precognition and which would only be possible if the future already exists, and if time is a circle.

The Circle of Time: The Future Leads to the Past

Einstein (1915a,b, 1961) theorized that time and space can be unified in the 4th dimension. Like the unification of mass and energy, space-time are two aspects of the same quantity, such that space can be converted into time, and time into space in the 4th dimension. Space-time and time, therefore, have energy, and can be experienced and perceived, and in this respect, time also shares characteristics with light and may have a particle wave duality.

A fundamental principle of physics is that a beam of light takes the shortest path between two points which is a straight line (Fermat's least time principle). However, light bends due to the influence of gravity (Einstein 1911), which means the path is not straight, but curved. Likewise, according to Einstein (1914, 1915a, 1961), space is curved. That curvature would not be a round circle, however,, but would have different geometric characteristics depending on and due to differences in gravity in various regions of the cosmos.

Einstein's curved universe could not be a perfect circle, as galaxy distribution is asymmetry and includes great "walls" of galaxies throughout the cosmos which have clustered together. It is this clustering, and these galactic walls which contribute to the unequal distribution of gravity, which causes space-time not just to curve, but to fold and curl up and to asymmetrically effect the flow of time.

Gravity is always strongest at the center of gravity where its most concentrated. Time-space is also pulled toward the center of gravity, which is why Einstein proposed his "Cosmological constant" a repulsive force which would prevent the universe from collapsing. Einstein later rejected his "cosmological constant" calling it "the biggest blunder" of his life, when in 1929 Hubble reported the universe was expanding. Einstein believed that if not for his "cosmological constant" he could have predicted an expanding universe. Instead, the prediction was made by Alexander Friedmann in papers published in 1922 and 1924.

However, as pointed out by Godel (1949a,b), Einstein's equations do not predict an expanding universe, but a rotating universe; a conclusion that Gamov (1946) also arrived at years before based in part of his observations of rotational patterns throughout the cosmos.

Earth orbits around the sun in a curve. This solar system has curvature and its motion follows a curving path as it orbits this galaxy. Likewise, space-time is curved and light and time follow that curvature (Einstein 1915a,b, 1961; Gödel 1949a,b). All is in motion and has velocity, but because of this curvature, one may travel in a circle and arrive where they began; and the same is true of time. Time is a circle (Gödel 1949a,b). The past leads to the future and the future can lead to the past.

If the entire universe is curved, as predicted by Einstein's theories, then just as traveling in a straight line on Earth will bring the traveler full circle to his starting point, the same could be applied to a curved universe as well as to the trajectory of light and time. Time, like time-space, has curvature; and just as a journey in a "straight" line will bring a voyager full circle around the globe, the same could be said of a journey across space-time. Time may be a circle; a cosmic clock which ticks at different speeds depending on gravity and the geometry of space-time relative to an observer's velocity and frame of reference. However, what this also implies is that a journey across time will bring the voyager full circle, such that the present leads to the future, and the future leads to present and then the past.

Because gravitational influences vary throughout the cosmos, then every infinitesimal region of space-time may have its own proper time relative to observers in different locations. The present on a distant galaxy, as conveyed by images of time-light, does not arrive on Earth until the future, such that the future and the past overlap in time-space. A logical corollary is that there is no universal "now" past or present, and that "absolute time" does not exist (Gödel 1949a,b).

Beginning in 1949, Kurt Gödel, in a series of papers based on Einstein's field equations of gravity, rejected the Newtonian conception of time and the belief that the "present" consists of infinite layers of 'now' coming into existence in continual successive and immediate sequences. According to Gödel (1949a,b, 1995) if space–time is curved, then the experience of time could be considered a consequence of that curvature.

As based on Einstein's field equations, Gödel (1949a,b) discovered that a particle traveling through space would circle round from the present to the future and then continue to circle around and meet itself in the past; and from the past that particle would circle round and meet itself in the future and from the future it would again travel round and meet itself in the past; an infinitely repeating pattern. Gödel argued, since space-time is curved, then the future and past may also be curved and circle round thereby completing the circle which then continues in an endless loop. Time is a circle.

According to Godel, because of the curvature of time and space it is possible to travel through time: "By making a round trip on a rocket ship in a sufficiently wide curve, it is possible in these worlds to travel into any region of the past, present, and future and back again."

Gödel's formulations also borrowed from George Gamow's (1946) conception of a universe which, like all astral bodies in space-time, is in orbital motion. As pointed out by Gamow, and Pythagoras 2000 years before, patterns repeat themselves in nature from the subatomic to entire galaxies (Joseph 2010c). Electrons orbit the nucleus of the atom. Planets orbit the sun. The sun is just one of billions of stars located throughout the spiral arms of the Milky Way Galaxy, and the entire galaxy is rotating. Perhaps the entire universe is also rotating and thus space-time is rotating, such that time is a circle and the future leads to the present, then the past, which leads back to the future.

Closed Time Curves In A Rotating Universe: The Future Leads to the Past

Gödel (1949a,b) explained that if the universe was rotating and space-time is curved, time should also be curved and curve back upon itself, forming infinitely repeating closed time-like curves (CTCs). Just as it is possible to circle the Earth and return to where one began, if time and time-space circles back on itself in Pythagorean endless loops thereby giving rise to CTCs, it would be possible to journey in a circle back to where one began; which means, one can travel into the future and into their own past.

In a "rotating universe" time is a circle where the future leads to the past and effects precede causes; the future can effect the present, and the past. However, the time-traveler journeying along such a loop does not experience a slowing of time as there is no contraction of space-time. Time would remain the same for the time-traveler and all those on Earth, as the time traveler is merely going in a circle.

A rotating universe and closed time-like curves violate the rules of causality. If time can circle back on itself, then the future can effect the past and the temporal discontinuity between past, present, and future is abolished. Hypothetically, and based on the concept of Karma, since cause and effect are abolished, if, as a child, you do something bad in the future when you become an adult, you may be punished for that future indiscretion while you are a still a child; "karma" in reverse.

Gödel (1949a,b) developed Gamow's (1946) concept of rotating universes as a thought experiment and as a logical extension of Einstein's field equations of gravity. However, the implications were so profound, and so contrary to the predictions of Newtonian physics, Einstein's concept of relativity, and what is now referred to as the "Standard Model" that the possibility of a rotating universe has been almost universally rejected (Buser et al. 2013). Even Gödel (1949a,b, 1995) who published his observations in the 1940s and 1950s, pointed out that there was a yet no evidence of red shifts in the distant regions of the cosmos which would support a rotation model.

Gamow (1946) who first proposed a model of a rotating universe blamed the lack of evidence on the insufficient power of the telescopes available to astronomers and physicists at that time and proposed that proof of rotating universes would have to wait until advanced telescopes became available.

As based on the observation of planets, stars, and the rotation and combined gravity of mass aggregations such as entire galaxies, Gamow (1946) thought it was only logical that the entire universe must also be rotating around some axial point in space. As pointed out by Gamow, "galaxies are found in the state of more or less rapid axial rotation" contrary to the Big Bang theory and in contradiction to the belief that galaxies formed following the condensation and angular momentum of the primordial matter. Gamow posed this question: since planets, stars, and galaxies are rotating then perhaps "all matter in the visible universe is in a state of general rotation around some centre located far beyond the reach of our telescopes?" As detailed elsewhere (Joseph REF) in the 1998, observations published by two separate teams inadvertently provided that evidence, as based on the red shifts of distant stars which had undergone supernova (Perlmutter et al., 1998; Schmidt, et al., 1998); i.e. the observable "Hubble Length Universe" appears to be in orbit around a universe-in-mass black hole (Joseph 2010REF).

Gamow (1946) based his rotating universes model on the rotation and angular momentum of galaxies which appear to orbit an axial point in space. Any rotating body, be it a galaxy, a merry-go-round, or the planets orbiting the sun, shows differential speeds of acceleration and velocity depending on how far away they are from the axial center of rotation. For example, in the inner galaxy, the rotation speed rises with the radius. By contrast, in the outer galaxy the rotation speed remains constant (Petrovskaya, 1994; Teerikorpi, 1989). The point closest to the axis rotates faster than points closer to the outer rim which rotate at a similar velocity. For example, Earth and our solar system, located on an outer arm of the Milky Way galaxy, orbit the supermassive black hole at the axial center of the galaxy, at a speed of approximately 155 miles/sec (250 km/sec) (or from 965,600 km/h, to 804,672 km/h), taking around 240 million years to complete an orbit. However, those stars closest to the axial galactic center, relative to the stars on the outer rims, are moving more rapidly and display accelerating velocities as they come closer to the central axis (Ghez et al., 2005; Petrovskaya, 1994; Teerikorpi, 1989). In fact, the speeds are so high they are beyond what would be predicted based on the universal law of gravitation (Schneider, 2006); observations which also led Gamow (1946) to question the Big Bang origins model and to propose that the universe may be in rotation.

In 2010, additional evidence, based on red shifts of exploding supernovas, appears to support Gamow's predictions. The entire Hubble Length (observable) universe, appears to be rotating around a universe-in-mass black holes, with those closest to the hole rotating at a faster rate than those future away; exactly as described for stars in the Milky Way galaxy which are closer vs further away from the black hole at the center of this galaxy (Joseph, 2010a,b). If pattern repeat, the the Hubble Length (observable galaxy) is just a spec of dust in an infinitely curved universe where time-space and thus time, are a circle, with the future leading to the present and then the past.

Multiple Earth's In the Circle of Time: Patterns Repeat

A pattern, be it recurring numbers, events, or objects, repeats itself in a predictable manner down to its essential elements (Ball 2009; Novak 2002; Wille 2010). The entire field of mathematics is the "Science of Patterns" and any sequence of numbers that may be described by a mathematical function has a pattern (Wille 2010). The pattern at the elementary level is the basis, model, or template which is repeated on a larger scale to generate larger objects or series of events all of which exhibit the same or similar underlying pattern. Hence, elementary particles have orbits, planets have orbits, stars have orbits, and it can be assumed that, collectively, galaxies have orbits which would mean the "known" Hubble length universe, is also in a rotational orbit as all share similar patterns (Joseph 2010b).

In Euclidean geometry, a pattern known as a translation involves movement of every point at a constant distance in a specified direction and the same can be said of rotation (Johnson 2007). The symmetry of the cosmos is based on the repetition of patterns found throughout nature, from sea shells to spiral galaxies (Joseph 2010b). For example, snail shells, sea shells, vortices, the cochlear nucleus of the inner ear, etc., show similar repeating patterns around an axial center or "eye." The patterns intrinsic to the shell of a snail are replicated repeatedly in nature and typify the structure of whirlpools, cyclones, hurricanes, the Milky Way galaxy and every spiral galaxy so far observed all of which rotate around an axial point (a "black hole") at their center.

Since rotating patterns repeat, as pointed out by Gamov (1946) and 2000 years earlier by Pythagoras, then the universe (including an expanding universe) and time-space would be part of this pattern. The entire universe, therefore, must orbit and rotate around an axial point, as predicted by Einstein's field equations (Gödel 1949a,b). Again, however, Einstein's equations do not predict a perfectly curved universe, but a lumpy universe with waves and crests which circles round and which would be pulled inward toward the center of gravity; that is, if the cosmos is considered as a collective single entity. If correct, then curvature of space-time would continue as a repeating pattern of curvature, curving forever inward and outward; which leads to Pythagoras and the "golden ratio" (Joseph 2010b).

Because of gravity, time-space can also be bent backwards in a circle, as happens with whirlpools and eddies along river banks where water flows in a circular motion. If the implications of Einstein's field equations are correct, then the river of time is bent round in a circle and it has no ending or beginning and may include pockets or vortexes of time which pop in and out of existence like vortexes and eddies along the river banks.

Einstein's time-space curvature coupled with gravity and the principle of repeating patterns, and the concept of close-time-like curves, raises the possibility that space-time is like a spiral staircase, so that when circling round at 360 degrees one does not end up in the same space or spot where they began, but above or below it (Buser et al. 2013; Gödel 1995). From the perspective of the Time Traveler, this spiraling circle can lead to the future or the past, or to multiple futures and pasts which may coexist, in parallel, side by side.

One feature of a CTC is that it opens the possibility of a world-line which is not connected to earlier times in this past, but to multiple possible pasts, and futures, which exist in parallel, above, or below, or alongside one another-- multiple spiraling staircases of time which lead to parallel worlds of time (Buser et al. 2013; Gödel 1949a,b); and each of which may have probable existences as predicted by Everett's "many worlds" interpretation of quantum physics. Therefore, if one were to travel in a circle across space-time, they may be taken to "a" future and then to "a" past, but not to "the" future or past--rather, to multiple possible futures and pasts some of which may exist side by side or one on top of the other--parallel times existing simultaneously.

A Gödel rotating universe implies duality, if not multiplicity; and the same is true of the bending of light. Because gravity increases the curvature of space-time and can bend and split images of light, as illustrated by galactic lensing (Renn et al., 1997; van der Wel et al. 2013), then light reflected from Earth may also be split apart as it curves through space. When these light-images of Earth cross paths with stellar objects of sufficient gravitational strength, these beams of light may be curved round in an 180 degree arc with Earth as its target. That is, light-images, or time-light, may be split apart and circle around numerous gigantic galaxies, and some of these light images will be reflected back toward Earth and become mirror images of Earth's past. Therefore, as we gaze at the various stars which twinkle in the darkness of night, some of those stars may be mirror images of Earth and our solar system from the long ago. Likewise, we may exist in the past relative to other observers on Earths which exist in the future--observers which are then looking upon an mirror image of Earth which exists in our "now" but which also exists in the past of those Earths in the future.

In a Godel spinning universe where time is a circle, the mirror would also be gazing back; meaning that this Earth could also be a mirror from the past of a future Earth; a reflection that those on a future Earth can look back upon.

The same can be said of consciousness which can anticipate the future, remember the past, and reflect upon itself.

Closed Time Light Curves: The Future Causes the Past

There are two conceptions of time-like curves, open or closed (Bonor & Steadman, 2005; Buser et al. 2013; Friedman et al. 1990). Open time-like curves follow an arrow of time straight into the future, and there is no return to the past unless one can exceed the speed of light.

Time-like curves which are closed, loop back in a circle; meaning that future events could affect past ones. A closed time-like curve (CTC) is a world line in a Lorentzian manifold, such that a particle or time traveler returns to its starting point (Buser et al. 2013). That is, because light is curved, then light can loop back on itself, and it would be possible for an object to move around this loop and return to the same place and time that it started. An object in such an orbit would repeatedly return to the same point in space-time.

The circle of space-time points forwards and backwards in time. If CTCs exist then it would be possible to travel backwards in time. The question becomes: how far back or forward in time? For example, it may be possible to follow the CTC in a negative direction and revisit the day President Abraham Lincoln was assassinated, the morning when Jesus was nailed to a cross, 65 million years ago when a giant asteroid struck this planet exterminating the last of the dinosaurs, and further back still to the Cambrian Explosion 500 million years ago when all manner of complex species with bones and brains appeared almost simultaneously in every ocean of Earth, and to the time when Earth was hellishly hot and populated by only microbes some 4.2 billion years ago.

Although seemingly paradoxical, Einstein's theories of relativity (despite his posting of a cosmic speed limit) predicts that the only way to travel into the past is to travel first to the future and then exceed the speed of light. Upon accelerating toward light speed, space-time contracts and the space-time traveler is propelled into the future. For example, because of the contraction of space-time, each day in the time-space machine at 90% light speed would propel the time traveler 2.29 days into the future of Earth.

Specifically, and if we accept that time and the speed of light are related, then if the time traveler journeys at 80% speed of light, then one day (1.197 days) from the perspective of the time traveler would be the equivalent of 2 days back on Earth. If he achieves 99% light speed, then 104 days in the time machine (time contraction) would be the equivalent of about 2 years on Earth. At 99.9% the speed of light, then 1 day (26 hours) in the time machine would be the equivalent of 6 years on Earth. If the time traveler wished to experience a future 2190 years distant she would have to spend one year in the time machine traveling at 99.999% light speed. At 99.999999% the speed of light, almost two years pass for every day in the time machine. At 99.99999999999999 % of c for every day on board, nearly twenty thousand years pass back on Earth. However, upon reaching light speed, time stops and the contraction of space-time comes close to a zero point, i.e. smaller than a Planck Length. At 100.0000000001% light speed, contraction continues in a negative direction, and time runs backward. The time traveler has entered the mirror universe of the past. It is only upon accelerating beyond light speed, that time runs in reverse and the contraction of space-time

continues in a negative direction. One must accelerate toward the future to reach the past. Einstein's general theory of relativity predicts that the future leads to the past. Likewise, as shown by Gödel (1949a,b), Einstein's field equations predict that time is a circle; and this violates the laws of causality (Buser et al. 2013). Therefore, upon reaching superluminal speeds, the time traveler would be headed backwards in time from the future and would pass himself journeying from the past into the future. And the time traveler voyaging toward the future and then the past, would pass himself heading back from the future. And the time traveler heading from the future to the past, could therefore, theoretically alter the past, thereby giving rise to innumerable paradoxes (Joseph 2014).

If time is a circle, then effects cannot always be traced to an earlier cause, for the cause may occur in the future; and this is because, in a closed loop, the future can come before the past and can even catch up with itself in the past so that an an event can be "simultaneous" with its cause or occur before its cause. An event may be able to cause itself.

These are not just thought experiments. There is considerable evidence of what Einstein (1955) referred to as "spooky action at a distance" and what is known in quantum physics as "entanglement" (Plenio 2007; Juan et al. 2013; Francis 2012). It is well established that causes and effects can occur simultaneously and ever faster than light speed (Lee et al. 2011; Matson 2012; Olaf et al. 2003); a consequence of the connectedness of all things in the quantum continuum including time which flows in all directions and which can circle round such that events in the future effect events in the present and in the past. The circle of time predicts that the future, present, and past exist simultaneously as a unity, and that this interconnectedness can result in effects in the future causing themselves.

Time is a circle, and this too is predicted by Einstein's theories of relativity, where accelerating toward light speed takes the voyager to the future, and upon exceeding the speed of light, the traveler heads back from the future into the past and thus effect the present and the past, as demonstrated by experiments in entanglement.

Quantum Entanglement And Causality: The Future Effects the Past

The river of time is bent round in a circle and it may have no beginning and no end. Since space-time is curved, warped and littered with vortexes surrounding black holes and effected by the gravity of innumerable stellar objects, the river of time may also be split apart and bent backwards in a circle, with circles within circles, as happens with whirlpools and eddies along river banks. Likewise, the geometry of time may flow differently in various regions of the cosmos and split off into innumerable tributaries of time each with their own unique trajectory and velocity.

Because space is "isotropic" there is nothing in the law of physics indicating that a particular direction is preferred; down, up, sideways, backwards, its all the same. Why should space-time, or time, be any different? Since the past, present and future overlap and are relative to observers and differ according to location, gravity, and speed of movement, then as Einstein stated, the distinctions between the past present and future are an illusion. If time is a circle, then time is a unity and there is no future, past, or present, except from the perspective of an observer.

The laws of electromagnetism do not make a distinction between past and future (Pollack & Stump, 2001; Slater & Frank, 2011). And yet, although light waves travel in a direction, it is assumed that these waves are traveling from the present into the future, when in fact they are traveling into the past and the future and from the future and from the past relative to different observers on different worlds and even on the same planet.

A light wave from Earth takes 4.2 light years to reach Proxima. However, since it will not be received on Proxima for 4.2 light years it will not arrive until some future date on Proxima. The light wave from Earth is in the future relative to observers on Proxima, although it is from the past relative to those on Earth. Likewise, light-images which just left Proxima are from Proxima's past but will not arrive on Earth until some day in their future. The future and the past are relative. Moreover, once light-images from Proxima arrive on Earth, they continue into the past relative to those on Earth, but not relative to those on a planet 4.2 light years in the opposite direction from Earth and 8.4 light years from Proxima, in which case although they are from the past relative to Earth and Proxima. However, these same light waves will not be received until some future date for those denizens of that more distant alien world. This conception of time is entirely consistent with Einstein's theories of relativity and Maxwell's equations of electromagnetism.

The past and future exist simultaneously in different and overlapping locations in space. Since space is isotropic, then, theoretically, there are no roadblocks to prevent a time traveler from choosing a location at will and then speeding into the future or the past; just as he may decide to go up-river or down-river.

The past, present and future, however, are like the weather, and differ in distant locations. There is no universal "now" and there are innumerable pasts, presents and futures which increasingly diverge as distance from any particular observer increases. Time is relative and the same can be said of the future and the past which only remains approximately and generally similar relative to observers sharing the same local, or personal, frames of references. Only when frames of reference are shared locally can observers agree on what took place first and last and what is in the past and what is still in the future.

Entanglement: The Future Effects the Present and the Past

Light can travel to the future and from the past relative to the observer's frame of reference. However, light and time are not the same. The speed of light, and time, be it past or future, are not synonymous, though both may be affected by gravity (Carroll 2004; Einstein 1961). Moreover, just as light has a particle-wave duality and can physically interact with various substances, time also can be perceived and therefore must have a wave function if not a particle-wave duality.

Time-space is interactional, and can contract to near nothingness and then continue to contract in a negative direction such that the time traveler can journey into the past. Therefore, time, and time-space are embedded in the quantum continuum and can effect as well as be effected by other particle-waves even at great distances; a concept referred to as "entanglement." Time and space-time are entangled.

It is well established that particles respond to and can influence and affect distant particles at speeds faster than light. This "spooky action at a distance" has been attributed to "fields," "mediator particles," gravity, and "quantum entanglement" (Bokulich & Jaeger, 2010; Juan et al. 2013; Sonner 2013).

For example, it is believed that an electric "field" may mediate "electrostatic" interactions between electromagnetic charges and currents separated by great distances across space. However, these changes can also take place at faster than light speeds. Charged particles, for example, produce an electric field around them which creates a "force" that effects other charges even at a distance without any time lapse. Maxwell's theories and equations incorporate these electrostatic physical "fields" to account for all electromagnetic interactions including action at a distance.

Since mass can become energy and energy mass, the "field" is therefore a physical entity that contains energy and has momentum which can be transmitted across space. Therefore, "action at a distance" may be both distant and local, a consequence of the interactions of these charges within the force field they create. However, the problem is: the effects can be simultaneous, even at great distances, and occur faster than the speed of light (Plenio 2007; Juan et al. 2013; Francis 2012; Schrödinger & Dirac 1936), effecting electrons, photons, atoms, molecules and even diamonds separated by great distances instantaneously (Lee et al. 2011; Matson 2012; Olaf et al. 2003; Schrödinger & Born 1935). The effect may even precede the cause since it takes place faster than light.

For example, photons are easily manipulated and preserve their coherence for long times and can be entangled by projection measurements (Kwiat et al. 1995; Weinfurter 1994). A pump photon, for example, can split light into two lower- energy photons while preserving momentum and energy, and these photons remained maximally entangled although separated spatially (Goebel et al 2008; Pan et al. 1998); the measurement of one simultaneously effects the measurement of another although separated by vast distances. It has been repeatedly demonstrated that entanglement swapping protocols can entangle two remote photons without any interaction between them and even with a significant time-like separation (Ma et al., 2012; Megidish et al. 2013; Peres 2000). Another example, two particles which are far apart have "spin" and they may spin up or down. However, an observer who measures and verifies the spin of particle A will at the same time effect the spin of particle B, as verified by a second observer. Measuring particle A, effects particle B and changes its spin. Likewise observing the spin of B determines the spin of A. There is no temporal order as the spin of one effects the spin of the other simultaneously through the simple act of measurements. Even distant objects are entangled and have a symmetrical relationship and a constant conjunction (Bokulich & Jaeger, 2010; Plenio 2007; Sonner 2013). If considered as a unity with no separations in time and space, then to effect one point in time-space is to effect all points which are entangled; and one of those entangled connections is consciousness (Joseph 2010a). And this gives rise to the uncertainty principle (Heisenberg, 1927) as the laws of cause and effect are violated. Correlation is not causation and it can't always be said with certainty which is the cause and which is the effect and this is because the cosmos is entangled.

Moreover, the decisions and measurements made in the future can effect the present. In one set of experiments entanglement was demonstrated following a delayed choice and even before there was a decision to make a choice. Specifically, four photons were created and two were measured and which became entangled such that the measurement of one effected the other simultaneously. However, if at a later time a choice was then made to measure the remaining two photons, all four became entangled before it was decided to do a second measurement, before the choice was even made in the future (Ma et al., 2012; Peres 2000).

Entanglement can occur independent of and before the act of measurement and choices made in the future can effect the present. "The time at which quantum measurements are taken and their order, has no effect on the outcome of a quantum mechanical experiment" (Megidish et al. 2013). Moreover, "two photons that exist at separate times can be entangled" (Megidish et al. 2013). As detailed by Megidish et al (2013): "In the scenario we present here, measuring the last photon affects the physical description of the first photon in the past, before it has even been measured. Thus, the "spooky action" is steering the system's past. Another point of view...is that the measurement of the first photon is immediately steering the future physical description of the last photon. In this case, the action is on the future of a part of the system that has not yet been created."

Hence, entanglement between photons has been demonstrated even before the second photon even exists; "a manifestation of the non-locality of quantum mechanics not only in space, but also in time" (Megidish et al 2013). In other words, a photon may become entangled with another photon even before that photon is created, before it even exists. Even after the first photon ceases to exist and before the second photon is created, both become entangled even though there is no overlap in time. Photons that do not exist can effect photons which do exist and photons which no longer exist and photons which will exist (Megidish et al. 2013); and presumably the same applies to all particles, atoms, molecules (Wiegner, et al 2011).

The same principles can be applied to conscious phenomenon, including the experience of deja vu and premonitions; i.e. experiencing an event before it occurs. In fact, the same could be said of feelings such as "anxiety" about what may happen before it happens, or logical thought processes of predicting what will happen before it happens--all of which may be made possible not by anticipation but by the future effecting the present. Premonitions and entanglement also prove the future exists before it becomes the present.

Deja Vu

Entanglement commonly occurs at superluminal speeds (Francis 2012; Juan et al. 2013; Plenio 2007; Lee et al. 2011; Matson 2012; Olaf et al. 2003). However, if an entangled consciousness is effected by the passage of that superluminal information from the future into the present, this can give rise to retro-cognition (Bem 2011; Radin 2006); knowing something has happened or will happen before it happens.

As illustrated by light-images from distant stars which are from the past but which will arrive on Earth in the future, various "futures" exist prior to being experienced by various observers. If time has a wave function and is entangled with space-time and the quantum continuum, and as the brain and consciousness are part of that continuum (Heisenberg 1958; Planck 1931, 1932), then under certain circumstances a future may effect consciousness prior to being experienced by consciousness due to entanglement of their wave functions. However, as discussed, consciousness too may exist in the future which is coextensive with the consciousness existing in the now. Since entanglement takes place faster than light speed, the leading edge of a future experience may be registered in various conscious minds at superluminal speeds before the future actually arrives in the now. The experience of this "time echo" is not uncommon, and has been referred to as deja vu, pre-cognition, and premonitions.

Deja vu is the conscious experience of having experienced some events just moments before the events take place. For example, a man opens the front door, step outsides, drops his keys and then a dog barks and the phone rings, and then he again experiences himself opening the door dropping his keys and then hearing a dog bark and then the ringing of his phone; like a time echo. He thus has the experience that all this has happened before or that he has done this before it happens. He may even say: "I've done this before" and then a few nanoseconds later he experiences himself saying "I've done this before."

Deja vu has been attributed to a delay in the transfer of sensory experiences from one region of the brain to another which receives that information twice, or the transmission of the same experience to the same area of the brain by two different brain areas such that the information is received twice following a brief delay (Joseph 1996). Hence, someone may experience deja vu because two or more areas of the brain are receiving or processing the same message with a slight delay between them. For example, the right and left halves of the brain are interconnected by a massive rope of nerve fibers called the corpus callosum. Each half of the brain is capable of conscious experience (Joseph 1988a,b; 2010a). Usually information is shared between the cerebral hemispheres. However, if there is a delay in transferring these signals, then one or both halves of the brain may sense it has had this experience just moments before thereby giving a sense of familiarity (Joseph 1996).

Brain areas communicate via neurons, and neurons communicate with each other by sending signals over axons which are transmitted to and received by dendrites (at the synaptic junction) belonging to other neurons which in turn may transmit message via their axons at synaptic junctions to the dendrites of other neurons. Impulses between neurons travel at various speeds, ranging from 10 to 50 m / s (Joseph 1996) whereas the speed of light is 300,000 km/sec.

The experience of deja vu has been reported under conditions of altered and heightened brain activity (Bancaud et al., 1994; Gloor 1990; Joseph 1996). Moreover, deja vu has been reported in cases involving the ingestion of anti-viral flu vaccines, such as amantadine and phenylpropanolamine (Taiminen & Jääskeläinen 2001) which increases brain activity by acting on dopamine receptors and increasing dopamine activity.

Heightened brain activity can be likened to an accelerated state of consciousness. Accelerated states are also associated with the contraction of space-time such that future arrives more quickly.

Deja vu, is also associated with heightened and accelerated activity in the inferior temporal lobe which houses the limbic striatum and amygdala, the later of which receives multi-modal sensory information and which normally filters out most of these sensations so the brain is not overwhelmed (Joseph 1996, 2011). Deja vu has been reported by patients when these areas of the brain have been activated due to direct electrode stimulation (Halgren 1990; Gloor 1990), drug ingestion (Taiminen & Jääskeläinen 2001) or seizure activity (Joseph 1996).

Therefore, when brain activity increases and neurons fire more rapidly and process more information, one of the consequences is Deja vu. In other words, just as a Time Traveler will come closer to the future as he accelerates toward light speed, when brain activity accelerates the future may also come closer such that the leading edge of a future event is experienced by this accelerated state of consciousness just before the event happens in the present.

Consciousness and Entanglement

As demonstrated in quantum physics, the act of observation, measurement, and registration of an event, can effect that event, causing a collapse of a the wave function (Dirac 1966a,b; Heisenberg 1955), thereby registering form, length, shape which emerges like a blemish on the face of the quantum continuum. Likewise, a Time Traveler or particle/object speeding toward and then faster than light and from the future into the past will affect the quantum continuum. By traveling into the future or the past, the Time Traveler will interact with and alter every local moment within the quantum continuum and thus the future or the past.

If the past or the future are not altered, this means that these dimensions of time are hardwired as part of the quantum continuum, that these events were already woven into the fabric of time and had always happened and always will happen and cannot be altered because they already happened, albeit in different distant locations of space-time which are linked as a unity within the quantum continuum.

If the future/past are not altered by voyaging through time then this is because the Time Traveler had already journeyed into the past and future before he journeyed into it. Likewise, a person not only exists in the present, but they will exist in the future. Thus, a future self would also be entangled with a past self and that self which exists in the present. Consciousness is thus entangled in time, and consciousness is entangled with its own consciousness which exists in the future, present, or past--such that a future self can effect a past self, including what the past self thinks and feels and anticipates.

The future already exists; a concept which is intrinsic to space-time relativity and Einstein's field equations. The future and the past exist in various overlapping locations in space-time which are in motion. And the same can be said of consciousness. Therefore, just as the end of a movie already exists as one begins watching the movie, then perhaps the same may be said of the river of time and consciousness as related to the future and the past. If this premise is correct, then one's consciousness also exists in the future and in the past.

World Lines, Causality, and Entanglement

Time is entangled. Future, past, present, are relative and overlap, and what is the future in one galaxy can be the past in another; all are entangled in the fabric of space-time and the quantum continuum. To get to the past, the Time Traveler must accelerate toward light speed into the future, and then, upon achieving superluminal velocities length contraction continues in a negative direction, time runs in reverse, and the destination becomes the past. Time is a circle and the future flows to the present, and the past and this is because time is entangled in the oneness of the quantum continuum.

If time is conceived as a spatial gestalt, an interconnected continuity of length, width, height, and extent but without temporal order, then what takes place in one location of space-time can effect what takes place in another, even if the distance is measured in miles, minutes, hours, light years, or as the future vs the past.

For example, in the Great Basin, White Mountains of California, there are "bristlecone pine" trees over 5000 years old, and which stand over 50 feet high. However, if the tree is measured in space-like intervals and not time-like intervals these same trees could be viewed as having a length of 5000 years. That is, if its "world line" is visualized as a thick strand of rope moving through space, that rope would begin with the seed and extend to the top of the tree.

The "world line" of the tree, encompasses it's entire history and although the tips of some branches and roots may have only recently grown, they are connected with the entire tree from the roots to the crown, and thus to the youngest and oldest parts of the tree. And what takes place in the roots can effect the twigs, branches, and crown of the tree, and the condition of the crown can effect the roots, branches and twigs. However, if viewed from a space-like intervals, the seeds of the tree and the 50 foot tree also becomes an interconnected continuity.

Likewise, if the orbit of Earth was viewed as a strand of rope, that rope would circle around the sun; for in fact, the movement of Earth is a continuity and is not separated into intervals which take place one after another like the ticking of a clock. If the genes of the first life forms to take root on Earth were viewed as a rope, then it would extend from the present to 4.2 billion years ago and perhaps even to the DNA of life forms whose bacterial ancestors journeyed here from the stars.

If time is considered from the perspective of space-like intervals and not time-like intervals, then causality can be forward, backward, or simultaneous (Bonor & Steadman, 2005; Buser et al. 2013; Carroll 2004; Gödel 1995). The future and the past are entangled as a continuity in space-time and this means information can be transmitted from the past to the future, and from the future to the past simultaneously.

Consciousness, however, would also have a world line, which extends from the birth to the death of that consciousness. Consciousness is therefore entangled with itself, and could transmit information from itself to itself, even if that consciousness exists in the illusionary present, past, or future.

Tachyons: Messengers From The Future

It is well established that various particles have a velocity close to or at the speed of light (Houellebecq 2001). Many of these high speed particles were hypothetical until their existence was verified experimentally. Photons and electromagnetic waves travel at light speed whereas some particles, such as positrons, and hypothetical "tachyons" are, or were believed to travel faster than light (Bilaniuk & Sudarshan 1969; Chodos 2002; Feinberg, 1967; Feynman 1949; Sen 2002) whereas others, such as . Superluminal tachyons, however, if they exist, may have negative energy and negative mass (Chodos 2002; Feinberg, 1967) and this may be a requirement for traveling at superluminal speeds where time flows in reverse.

Electromagnetic waves are a fundamental quality of matter and are subject to the effects of gravity as exemplified by galactic lensing (Slater & Frank, 2011; van der Wel 2013). When the electromagnetic force is stripped of its particle, it has no mass, and this is what is believed to occur when particles, or time machines enter a black hole (Everett & Roman 2012); what emerges has no mass, and it may possses negative mass and negative energy and may journey at faster than light speeds.

Wheeler and Feynman argued in 1945 that electromagnetic waves emitted by an electron proceed into the future and the past (Wheeler & Feynman 1945, 1949). When these waves collide with waves in the future they send waves back in time and further into the future due to the collision. Those sent to the past can also collide with those in the past sending them again in opposite directions, into the future and further into the past. Depending on if these waves collide crest to trough their energy levels may double, but if they collide crest to crest (or trough to trough) they cancel each other out; a phenomenon referred to, respectively, as constructive and destructive interference.

Some hypothetical particles, such as the "tachyon" are believed to be time-independent and to travel faster than light speed (Bilaniuk & Sudarshan 1969; Chodos 2002; Feinberg, 1967; Sen 2002); meaning that these particles are constantly arriving in the present from the future and continue their high speed journey into the distant past.

In contrast to slower than light particles which have "time-like four-momentum" tachyons and other hypothetical superluminal particles have "space-like four-momentum." For example, if two events have a greater separation in time than in space, they have a time-like separation which is indicated by a negative (minus) sign. If the sum is positive, the two events have a space-like separation which is greater than their separation in time. If the result is 0, then the two events have a light-like separation and are connected only by a beam of light.

Tachyons are believed to have worldlines which are space-like and not time-like such that the temporal order of events would not be the same in all inertial frames (Bilaniuk & Sudarshan 1969; Chodos 2002; Feinberg, 1967; Gibbons, 2002; Sen 2002); meaning cause and effect would be reversed or abolished. Tachyons, because they travel from the future to the past, would violate the laws of causality.

The existence of a tachyon particle was first proposed by Gerald Feinberg in 1967. According to Feinberg's theories and calculations, a tachyon could be similar to a "quanta" of a quantum field but with negatively squared mass; that is, it would have no mass or anti-mass. Its energy, nevertheless, would be real. Objects traveling toward light speed gain energy and mass, only to implode and come to consist of negative energy and negative mass (Joseph 2014). Tachyons would have negative mass and negative energy, thus avoiding any violation of the laws of thermodynamics. If the tachyon increases it superluminal speed it loses energy as it journeys faster into the past. If it accelerates to 200% light speed its negative energy diminishes to zero, time stands still and its negative mass becomes smaller than a Planck Length due to length contraction. Upon accelerating to 200.00001 light speed, what had been a negative contraction implodes and it contracts in a positive direction and gains positive energy and positive mass and turns around and travels from the past back to the future.

Therefore, whereas objects are believed to reach "infinite velocity" upon attaining light speed, the tachyon can only reach infinite velocity upon accelerating to speeds twice that of the speed of light, at which point there would be another time reversal and the tachyon would journey from the past into the future.

Einstein's field theories predict the curvature of space-time, such that the universe and time circles back upon itself (Gödel 1949a,b). The future leads to the past; a realization which greatly troubled Einstein. The existence of particles which travel from the future to the past are a logical extension of Einstein's theories and field equations (Gödel 1949a,b). Time is a circle which may be orbited by positive and negatively charged particles. If correct, then these negative and positively charged particles would also create a neutral state of equilibrium (Feynman 2011; Pollack & Stump, 2001; Slater & Frank, 2011; Wheeler & Feynman 1949); much like the positively charged nucleus of an atom counters the negative charge of an electron--the amount of positive charge determining the number of electrons.

Electrons may also circle in and out of time and changing charges as they do so, with negatively charged electrons directed toward the past and positively charged electrons, referred to as "positrons" directed toward the future. John Wheeler proposed that all electrons and positrons (the antiparticle to the electron) have identical mass but opposite charges (see also Feynman 1949). According to Wheeler (2010; Wheeler & Feynman 1949), all electrons in the universe zig zag backward and forward in time, and when zigging backward it is an electron and when zagging forward it is a positron. And when zigging and zagging they interact as an electron-positron pair, moving in and out of the past and future. Richard Feynman (2011) incorporated these ideas in his formulations for quantum electrodynamics which earned him a Nobel Prize. However, these pairs are not necessarily being created or annihilated; though annihilation could be predicted if they were to come in contact. Rather, like the positive and negative charged tachyon, they chase each other in a circle of time.

If we were building an atom-of-time, then it could be proposed that positively charged positrons and negatively charged tachyons circle toward the past, maintaining an equilibrium of charges in the past, whereas negatively charged electrons and positively charged tachyons do the same in the future; with all four circling around each other, in and out of the future and the past and without violating the laws of conservation of energy and mass.

Therefore, if a negative energy negative mass tachyon and a positron traveling from the future to the past was able to circle round and go from the past back toward the future, the tachyon would become a positive energy anti-tachyon and the positron a negatively charged electron. If time is a circle, the positron/electron and tachyon/anti-tachyon may circle from the future to the past to the future and back again; as if time was composed of particles which orbit the nucleus of "eternal now." Positrons, electrons, and tachyons would therefore provide time with the energy and atomic structure to emerge from the quantum continuum and be perceived as something real.

The existence of "tachyon" like particles has been rejected because they would violate the laws of causality and Einstein's theory of special relativity (Aharonov et al. 1969). Feinberg (1967), however, determined that special relativity did not prohibit faster than light travel so long as the object had always maintained superluminal velocities and had never had a velocity below the speed of light. According to special relativity (but not general relativity or quantum mechanics) the acceleration of matter to beyond light speed could cause the energy of this mass to becomes infinite and the Lorentz transformations would then have no meaning. However, if superluminal velocities are the norm for these faster than light particles, then there would be no need to break the cosmic speed limit except at 200% light speed. By the same token, these particle would never be able to reduce velocity to below light speed. Therefore, if these and other particles are traveling beyond the velocity of light they may have always journeyed at superluminal speeds and never had a velocity below light speed.

Others have argued that particles with negative mass cannot travel faster than light and would have negative energy and become unstable and undergo condensation (Ahraonov et al. 1969). These arguments were countered by Chodos (1985) who proposed that neutrinos can behave like tachyons and travel at superluminal speeds. By violating Lorentz invariance, neutrinos and other particles would undergo Lorentz-violating oscillations and travel faster than light while maintaining high energy levels. However, over time superluminal neutrinos would also lose energy, probably as Cherenkov radiation (Bock 1998).

Although theoretical, the implications are that information can travel from the future to the past; thus making it possible to anticipate, or see the future before it becomes the present, thereby giving rise to premonitions and related conscious experiences, including perhaps, anxiety, or conversely, an uncanny ability to correctly plan future courses of action which almost always lead to success and follow a course or result in a specific outcome exactly as predicted.

Although there have been numerous proposals and arguments to and fro it appears that objects or particles would lose mass and energy upon reaching superluminal speeds and those which travel faster than light would have negative mass and negative energy. Further, it could be said that tachyon-like particles once they accelerate to superluminal velocities, or, if they have always journeyed at faster than light speeds, may be unable to slow down to a velocity less than the speed of light. It has also been theorized that tachyons must maintain a constant speed, for if the Tachyon were to accelerate and increase velocity it loses energy which becomes zero if the speed reaches infinite velocity; i.e. 200% light speed; a velocity which would trigger a time reversal with negative contraction imploding and continuing in a positive direction back toward the future from the past.

According to some theories, if a tachyon were to slow toward light speed, the energy of a tachyon would increase and would becomes infinite as its velocity equals the speed of light; and the same would be true at 200% the speed of light. This is a mirror image of what is theorized to occur when particles or objects reach light speed as they are also supposed to gain infinite mass and infinite energy. Thus particles which always travel above and those which always travel below light speed are mirror images of each other and may have the same barriers and non-traversable event horizon, with the past on one side and the future on the other.

In other words, the transformation from positive to negative energy/mass, may be the event horizon which separates the future from the past. Thus, relative to a conscious observer, the future may consist of positive energy, and the past becomes the negative.

The Future and Past Exist Simultaneously: Circle of Time

As implied by the Lorentz transformation (Einstein et al 1923), a tachyon would always have negative energy. The Lorentz transformation indicates that the sign of a particle's energy is the same in all inertial frames, just as the sign of the temporal order of two points on the world line remain the same. All observers will see that the particle has positive or negative energy, though they may disagree on how much energy it has. However, if the particle has positive energy according to one observer, and negative according to another, then the observers, or the particles, are occupying different inertial frames (e.g. one in the present the other in the future/past; and this implies duality.

If tachyons or other objects did not have the same energy sign in all inertial frames, that is, if they were sometimes positive and at other instances negative, then perhaps they are looping in and out of the past and future, becoming positive when below the speed of light and negative above it as predicted by superluminal Lorentz transformations (Everett & Roman 2012). Because they would have positive energy when heading toward the future and negative energy when traveling into the past they could both exist even in the same inertial frame. The future and the past would exist simultaneously.

The dichotomy between positive vs negative energy and mass implies duality; the tachyon which voyages beyond light speed is the antithesis of the tachyon or time machine at a velocity below light speed. For example, the tachyon below light speed could be considered an anti-tachyon. The antiparticle of a tachyon would be a positive energy tachyon which is traveling forward in time. The negative energy tachyon would be coming from future heading into the past. As such, they would seem to be continually circling around each other from the perspective of an observer: one coming the other going in parallel continuously.

Negative energy and positive energy are repulsive and attractive. Therefore, if the future consists of positive energy and the past negative energy, and both consist of particles with positive vs negative energy/mass respectively, then the future and the past would be continually chasing and escaping from each other, with the positive energy tachyon showing attraction and the negative repulsion and with both maintaining the same distance from each other. Positive and negative tachyons, or a positive vs negative future and past, therefore, would create a circle of time.

For example, if a negative object and a positive object of the same size came into contact, the negative would be repelled away and the positive would accelerate toward--a push pull scenario which could result in the negative and positive objects circling round and round each other as they are attracted and repelled at the same time--like a very bad romantic relationship.

An object with negative energy falls down just like an object with positive energy. However, if a negative particle swerved near a planet, the gravitational effect would be repulsive and it would be pushed away. Negative mass is repelled by positive mass and vice versa. If both were negative, they would also be repelled and this is because the two minus signs (-m and -m) cancel each other out.

Positive energy would propel the negative energy object to accelerate in the direction it is already going. If the universe and time are curved and lead back to their starting point in a circle, then the positive (heading toward the future) and the negative (head from the future to the past) would also circle round each other, with the future leading to and following into the past. If the positive particle actually caught up with and bumped into the negative particle, such as might be expected at the event horizon, the positive would force the negative to speed up in the negative direction it is already going.

Moreover, although the the positive and the negative particles might maintain the same distance from each other, they would accelerate to greater and greater speeds--and this is because both have acceleration; despite the fact that this seemingly violates the conservation laws of momentum and energy which requires that they remain constant.

For example, the positively charged anti-tachyon would accelerate toward the future coming closer and closer to light speed, and upon crossing the event horizon separating future from past, would lose positive energy and attain negative mass and then accelerate backwards into the past at superluminal values. However, they would also chase one another, such that both increase in speed; the positively charged tachyon toward the velocity of light, and negatively charged tachyon to twice the speed of light; or, in a mirror universe where all is reversed, the negative would be forced to below the speed of light. That is, as the positive speeds up, the negative, going in a negative direction, might slow down, with both exchanging energy at the event horizon of "eternal now." Alternatively, the tachyon may accelerate until reaching twice the speed of light thereby losing negative energy and gaining positive energy as the contraction of time-space implodes and collapses in a positive direction.

At this juncture, we can only theorize and hypothesize: negative energy tachyons become positive energy anti-tachyons and positrons become electrons; and the circle of time continues to circle around with the positive chasing the negative which is chasing the positive, like the hands of a clock.

Coupled with Einstein's field equations which predict time is a circle, if tachyon-like particles exist, this would mean the future could effect and alter the present and the past. If true, then the past present and future would be in continual flux and undergoing constant change--which is exactly what might be expected if time is merely a perceived aspect of the quantum continuum (a function of wave form collapse)--such that even events which already occurred in the past may or may not have occurred. Time therefore becomes uncertain and what has or will take place can only be determined imprecisely by means of a probability distribution; all of which leads to the Many Worlds Interpretation of quantum physics. If true, this may explain why premonitions of future event are not always accurate; since that future may rapidly change, and may represent just one of many futures.

The Wave Function of Conciousness of Consciousness

Quantum mechanics, in theory, governs the behavior of all systems regardless of size (Bohr, 1934, 1947, 1958, 1963; Dirac 1966a,b; Heisenberg, 1930, 1955, 1958). Central to quantum mechanics is the wave function (Bohr, 1963; Heisenberg, 1958). All of existence has a wave function, including light. Every aspect of existence can be described as sharing particle-like properties and wave-like properties. The wave function is the particle spread out over space and describes all the various possible states of the particle. According to quantum theory the probability of findings a particle in time or space is determined by the probability wave which obeys the Schrodinger equation. Everything is reduced to probabilities. Moreover, these particle/waves and these probabilities are entangled.

Reality is a manifestation of wave functions and alterations in patterns of activity within the quantum continuum which are entangled and perceived as discontinuous, and that includes the perception of time: past, present, future, and consciousness. The perception of a structural unit of information is not just perceived, but is inserted into the quantum state which causes the reduction of the wave-packet and the collapse of the wave function. It is this collapse which describes shape, form, length, width, and future and past events and locations within space-time (Bohr, 1963; Heisenberg, 1958).

Consciousness can also reflect upon and become conscious of being conscious, and in so doing, creates a collapse of the wave function which is experienced as a dissociated consciousness observing itself; conditions which are not uncommon during accelerated states of brain-mind activity typical of terror and other emotional extremes. Consider the case of U.S. Army Specialist Bayne:

> "I could see me... it was like looking at a mannequin laying there... I was burnt up and there was blood all over the place... I could see the Vietcong. I could see the guy pull my boots off. I could see the rest of them picking up various things... I was like a spectator... It was about four or five in the afternoon when our own troops came. I could hear and see them approaching... I could see me... It was obvious I was burnt up. I looked dead... they put me in

a bag... transferred me to a truck and then to the morgue. And from that point, it was the embalming process....I was on that table and a guy was telling a couple of jokes about those USO girls... all I had on was bloody undershorts... he placed my leg out and made a slight incision and stopped... he checked my pulse and heartbeat again and I could see that too...It was about that point I just lost track of what was taking place.... [until much later] when the chaplain was in there saying everything was going to be all right.... I was no longer outside. I was part of it at this point" (Wilson, 1987).

One woman stated: "it was though I were two persons, one watching, and the other having this happen to me." Another patient stated "it was as though the patient were attending a familiar play and was both the actor and audience."

"I was struck from behind...That's the last thing I remember until I was above the whole scene viewing the accident. I was very detached. Everything was very quiet. This was the amazing thing about it to me... I could see my shoe which was crushed under the car and I thought: Oh no. My new dress is ruined... I don't remember hearing anything. I don't remember anybody saying anything. I was just viewing things...like I floated up there..." (Sabom, 1982; p. 90).

In instances of dissociation, consciousness is also conscious of itself as a consciousness. The dissociated consciousness creates a collapse of the wave function which includes the body, its brain, consciousness, and the surrounding space-time continuum which includes time; time which may speed up or slow down. Similar phenomenon also occur when dreaming and can be attributed to a collapse of the wave function; consciousness creating itself by dissociating itself form the quantum continuum.

In quantum physics, the wave function describes all possible states of the particle and larger objects, thereby giving rise to probabilities, and this leads to the "Many Worlds" interpretation of quantum mechanics (Dewitt, 1971; Everett 1956, 1957). That is, since there are numerous if not infinite probable outcomes, each outcome and probable outcome represents a different "world" with some worlds being more probable than others.

For example, an electron may collide with and bounce to the left of a proton on one trial, then to the right on the next, and then at a different angle on the third trial, and another angle on the fourth and so on, even though conditions are identical. This gives rise to the Uncertainty Principle and this is why the rules of quantum mechanics are indeterministic and based on probabilities. The state of a system one moment cannot determine what will happen next. Instead, we have probabilities which are based on the wave function. The wave function describes all the various possible states of the particle (Bohr, 1963; Heisenberg, 1958).

Since the universe, as a collective, must also have a wave function, then this universal wave function would describe all the possible states of the universe and thus all possible universes, which means there must be multiple universes which exist simultaneously as probabilities (Dewitt, 1971; Everett 1956, 1957). And the same would be true of time. Why shouldn't time have a wave function?

The wave function of time means there are infinite futures, presents, pasts, with some more probable than others.

Everett's Many Worlds

As theorized by Hugh Everett the universal wave function is "the fundamental entity, obeying at all times a deterministic wave equation" (Everett 1956). Thus, the wave function is real and is independent of observation or other mental postulates (Everett 1957), though it is still subject to quantum entanglement.

In Everett's formulation, a measuring apparatus MA and an object system OS form a composite system, each of which prior to measurement exists in well-defined (but time-dependent) states. Measurement is regarded as causing MA and OS to interact. After OS interacts with MA, it is no longer possible to describe either system as an independent state. According to Everett (1956, 1957), the only meaningful descriptions of each system are relative states: for example the relative state of OS given the state of MA or the relative state of MA given the state of OS. As theorized by Hugh Everett what the observer sees, and the state of the object, become correlated by the act of measurement or observation; they are entangled.

However, Everett reasoned that since the wave function appears to have collapsed when observed then there is no need to actually assume that it had collapsed. Wave function collapse is, according to Everett, redundant. Thus there is no need to incorporate wave function collapse in quantum mechanics and he removed it from his theory while maintaining the wave function, which includes the probability wave.

According to Everett (1956) a "collapsed" object state and an associated observer who has observed the same collapsed outcome have become correlated by the act of measurement or observation; that is, what the observer perceives and the state of the object become entangled. The subsequent evolution of each pair of relative subject–object states proceeds with complete indifference as to the presence or absence of the other elements, as if wave function collapse has occurred. However, instead of a wave function collapse, a choice is made among many possible choices, such that among all possible probable outcomes, the outcome that occurs becomes reality.

Everett argued that the experimental apparatus should be treated quantum mechanically, and coupled with the wave function and the probable nature of reality, this led to the "many worlds" interpretation (Dewitt, 1971). What is being measured and the measuring apparatus/observer are in two different states, i.e. different "worlds." Thus, when a measurement (observation) is made, the world branches out into a separate world for each possible outcome according to their probabilities of occurring. All probable outcomes exist regardless of how probable or improbable, and each outcome represent a "world." In each world, the measuring apparatus indicates which of the outcomes occurred, which probable world becomes reality for that observer; and this has the consequence that later observations are always consistent with the earlier observations (Dewitt, 1971; Everett 1956, 1957).

Predictions, therefore, are based on calculations of the probability that the observer will find themselves in one world or another. Once the observer enters the other world he is not aware of the other worlds which exist in parallel. Moreover, if he changes worlds, he will no longer be aware that the other world existed (Everett 1956, 1957): all observations become consistent, and that includes even memory of the past which existed in the other world.

The "many worlds" interpretation (as formulated by Bryce DeWitt and Hugh Everett), rejects the collapse of the wave function and instead embraces a universal wave function which represents an overall objective reality which consists of all possible futures and histories all of which are real and which exist as alternate realities or in multiple universes. What separates these many worlds is quantum decoherence and not a wave form collapse. Reality, the future, and the past, are viewed as having multiple branches, an infinite number of highways leading to infinite outcomes. Thus the world is both deterministic and non-deterministic (as represented by chaos or random radioactive decay) and there are innumerable futures and pasts.

As described by DeWitt and Graham (1973; Dewitt, 1971), "This reality, which is described jointly by the dynamical variables and the state vector, is not the reality we customarily think of, but is a reality composed of many worlds. By virtue of the temporal development of the dynamical variables the state vector decomposes naturally into orthogonal vectors, reflecting a continual splitting of the universe into a multitude of mutually unobservable but equally real worlds, in each of which every good measurement has yielded a definite result and in most of which the familiar statistical quantum laws hold."

DeWitt's many-worlds interpretation of Everett's work, posits that there may be a split in the combined observer–object system, the observation causing the splitting, and each split corresponding to the different or multiple possible outcomes of an observation. Each split is a separate branch or highway. A "world" refers to a single branch and includes the complete measurement history of an observer regarding that single branch, which is a world unto itself. However, every observation and interaction can cause a splitting or branching such that the combined observer–object's wave function changes into two or more non-interacting branches which may split into many "worlds" depending on which is more probable. The splitting of worlds can continue infinitely.

Since there are innumerable observation-like events which are constantly happening, there are an enormous number of simultaneously existing states, or worlds, all of which exist in parallel but which may become entangled; and this means, they can not be independent of each other and are relative to each other. This notion is fundamental to the concept of quantum computing.

Likewise, in Everett's formulation, these branches are not completely separate but are subject to quantum interference and entanglement such that they may merge instead of splitting apart thereby creating one reality.

Many Worlds of Quantum Dream-Time

When considered as a unity within the quantum continuum, time and consciousness exist in the future, past, present, simultaneously. Consciousness which exists in the future is entangled with consciousness which exists in the present and the past--like a rope of string stretched out and extending in all directions from the birth to death of that consciousness. Therefore, just as the hypothetical tachyons can travel from the future to the past, and the circle of time circles round from the present to the future and back again, information may also be conveyed from the future to the past, perhaps along the rope of consciousness which extends in all directions and dimensions and is an aspect of the quantum continuum.

Acceleration leads to a compression of time-space, such that the future comes closer to the present. The same can be said of accelerated consciousness, thereby giving rise to phenomenon such as deja vu, premonitions, precognition, as well as anticipation and prediction about the immediate future. Dream time is a form of accelerated consciousness; i.e. dream consciousness.

Consciousness and dreaming are not synonymous. Dreams may be observed by consciousness and as such, dreaming and consciousness are entangled as dream-consciousness. However, consciousness is generally little more than a passive witness during dreaming, an audience before the stage upon which the dreams are displayed in all their mystery and majestic glory. It is rare for consciousness to become conscious that "it" is observing a dream, and when such rarities occur the dreamer may awaken or briefly take an active role in what has been described as "lucid dreaming" (LaBerge, 1990).

Unlike conscious-time and the conscious mind, the dream-kaleidescape of dream-time and dream-consciousness could best be described as manifestation of the "Many worlds" interpretation of quantum physics where all worlds are possible and past and future and time and space are juxtaposed and intermingled; time can run backward and forward simultaneously and at varying speeds, and multiple realities come and go no matter now improbable.

During dream-time the brain is in a "paradoxical" state of accelerated activity, known as paradoxical sleep, as demonstrated by rapid eye movement (REM) and electrophysiological activity (Frank, 2012, Pagel, 2014, Stickgod & Walker, 2010). As predicted by Einstein's (1961) relativity, under accelerated states time contracts and the future arrives more quickly. Dream-time represents accelerated states of brain activity and is entangled with the "many worlds" and the space-time quantum continuum of future and past, and as such, while dreaming, the dreamer may obtain a glimpse of the future before it arrives. Therefore, in dream-time and dream consciousness one may visit the future or the past during the course of the dream.

It is through dreams that we may be transported to worlds that defy the laws of physics and which obey their own laws of time, space, motion and conscious reality, where the future is juxtaposed with the past and where time runs backwards and forwards (Campbell, 1988; Freud, 1900; Jung, 1945, 1964). Throughout history it has been believed that dreams open doors to alternate realities, to the future, to the past, and the hereafter, where the spiritual world sits at the boundaries of the physical; hence the tendency to bury the dead in a sleeping position even 100,000 years ago (Joseph 2011a,b). Although but a dream, the dream is experienced during dream consciousness much as the waking world is experienced by waking consciousness. The dream is real. Thus, throughout history dreams have been taken seriously especially when they gave glimpses of the future.

Dreams are often of events from the previous day and may concern the future. It is through dreams that the dreamer may gain insight into problems which have plagued him or which he anticipates encountering in the near future. Just as one can think about the future or the past and make certain deductions and predictions, a dream may include anticipations regarding the future, and in this respect, the dream could be considered an imaginal means of preparation for various possible realities. As such, dream-time and dream-consciousness could be considered obvious manifestations of the "Many Worlds" theory of quantum physics.

Not uncommonly the dream will include so many branching and overlapping multiple realities that it makes no sense at all, except to those skilled in the art of interpreting dream symbolism (Freud 1900; Jung 1945, 1964). Indeed, it is due to the non-temporal, often gestalt nature of dreams which require that they be consciously scrutinized from multiple angles in order to discern their meaning, for the last may be first and what is missing may be just as significant as what is there.

Relativity predicts that observers with an accelerated frame of reference experience time-contraction and a shrinking of time-space such that the future and the present come closer together relative to those with a different frame of reference (Einstein et al. 1923, Einstein 1961). Thus, since dream-consciousness and dream-time are also associated with accelerated levels of brain activity, during dream-time, the dreamer may see or experience the future before that future is experienced by the awake conscious mind or the consciousness of those external observers who have a different frame of reference as regard to the contraction of time.

Abraham Lincoln Dreams Of His Death

In April of 1965, less than two weeks before he was gunned down by an assassin's bullet, President Abraham Lincoln dreamed of his own assassination (Lamon 1911). Lincoln told this dream to his wife and to several friends including Ward Hill Lamon who was Lincoln's personal friend, body guard and former law partner. According to Lincoln:

"About ten days ago, I retired very late. I had been up waiting for important dispatches from the front. I could not have been long in bed when I fell into a slumber, for I was weary. I soon began to dream. There seemed to be a death-like stillness about me. Then I heard subdued sobs, as if a number of people were weeping. I thought I left my bed and wandered downstairs. There the silence was broken by the same pitiful sobbing, but the mourners were invisible. I went from room to room; no living person was in sight, but the same mournful sounds of distress met me as I passed along. I saw light in all the rooms; every object was familiar to me; but where were all the people who were grieving as if their hearts would break? I was puzzled and alarmed. What could be the meaning of all this? Determined to find the cause of a state of things so mysterious and so shocking, I kept on until I arrived at the East Room, which I entered. There I met with a sickening surprise. Before me was a catafalque, on which rested a corpse wrapped in funeral vestments. Around it were stationed soldiers who were acting as guards; and there was a throng of people, gazing mournfully upon the corpse, whose face was covered, others weeping pitifully. 'Who is dead in the White House?' I demanded of one of the soldiers, 'The President,' was his answer; 'he was killed by an assassin.' Then came a loud burst of grief from the crowd, which woke me from my dream. I slept no more that night; and although it was only a dream, I have been strangely annoyed by it ever since."

Dream-Time and the Many Worlds of Quantum Physics

In dream-time past-present-future and the three dimensions of space may exist simultaneously as a gestalt thereby violating all the rules of causality abut not the laws of quantum physics. During dream-time events may occur in a logical or semi-logical temporal sequence, or they may be juxtaposed and make no sense at all to an external consciousness which is dependent on temporal sequences to achieve understanding. Because the future past present may exist simultaneously and as the future may be experienced in a dream during accelerated states of brain activity, then during dream consciousness the dreamer may get glimpses of future events which may occur within days, the next morning, or which may even trigger wakefulness. In other words, just as increased velocity causes a contraction of space-time thereby decreasing the distance between the present and the future (Einstein 1961, Einstein et al. 2913), accelerated dream-consciousness has the same effect.

In dream-time and dream-consciousness all worlds are possible simultaneously and in parallel. These many worlds include those of the future and the past and where time and space are juxtaposed and every probable outcome is equally likely, and where the world is continually splitting into alternate worlds. Dream-time-consciousness is a manifestation of and in many respects obeys the laws of the "Many Worlds" theory of quantum physics as first proposed by Hugh Everett (1956, 1957).

Hugh Everett's "theory of the universal wavefunction" (Many Worlds) is distinguished from the Copenhagen model, as there is no special role for an observing consciousness. Everett also removed the "wave function" collapse which he believed to be redundant, and instead insisted that what is observed must be clearly defined (thereby answering one of Einstein's criticism of quantum theory). According to Everett's theory, every action, every measurements, every behavior, every choice, even not choosing, can create a new reality, another world, generating a bifurcation between what happened and what did not happen, such that innumerable possibilities and possible worlds arise from every action, including realties which do not obey the laws of physics and cause and effect.

As conceived by Everett (1956, 1957) and Dewitt (1971), when a physicist measures an object, the universe splits into two distinct universes to accommodate each of the possible outcomes. In one universe, the physicist measures the wave form, in the other universe the physicist measures the object as a particle. Since all objects have a particle-wave duality, this also explains how an object can be measured as a particle and can be measured as a wave, but not both at the same time in the same world, and how it can be measured in more than one state, each of which exists in another world. The simple act of measurement creates two worlds both of which exist at the same time in parallel, and each separate version of the universe contains a different outcome of that event.

Instead of one continuous timeline, the universe under the many worlds interpretation looks more like a forest of trees with innumerable branches and twigs each of which represents a different possible world. According to Everett the entire universes continuously exists in a superposition and juxtaposition of multiple states. In many respects, Everett's theory defines dream-time and dream-consciousness.

According to Everett (1957), observation and measurement does not force the object under observation to take any specific form or to have any specific outcome. Instead, all outcomes are possible; much like a dream. For example, an NFL football player, a receiver, is running down the field and the quarterback throws him the ball. According to the "Many Worlds" interpretation of quantum physics, every conceivable and incomprehensible outcome is possible: The receiver catches or doesn't catch the ball. A female cheerleader runs out into the field and catches the ball. The receiver and the cheerleader ignore the ball and take off their clothes and have sex on the field. The head coach takes out a shotgun and begins shooting at the football. Spectators run onto the football field and erect circus tents and it becomes a giant carnival with rides. Some of the football players dress up as clowns and circus performers. Players and spectators lay on the grass and swim toward the goal posts. An alien space ship crashes into the football stadium and aliens emerge selling popcorn. Terrorists attack the football players and steal the football, and so on.

All outcomes are possible in Multiple Worlds, from the most probable to the least probable (Dewitt 1971). Every probable outcome is possible; trillions of outcomes including those where the defiance of physics may become the law of the land. Moreover, each of these multiple realities exist, simultaneously, side-by-side, in parallel. They exist simultaneously with the reality in which the observer resides; and whatever reality houses the observer is just one probable reality.

PreCognition in Dream-Time and Dream-Consciousness

During dream-time and during dream-consciousness the reality being dreamed is characterized by every possible outcome. Some dream worlds exist in the future, others in the past, and yet others in a world where past, present and future are juxtaposed and exist simultaneously and where every possible outcome is possible. Thus, in dream-time, the dream-consciousness can witness any number of these possible worlds including those which exist in the future.

However, these futures and possible futures which are observed by dream-consciousness are not "just a dream." According to the Many Worlds interpretation, they actually exist. In terms of space-time, these future worlds exist in the future, in a distant location. As predicted by quantum mechanics, the observer is entangled with that future. However, in dream-time the observer (dream consciousness) directly observes that future; including those futures which are improbable or most probable.

The Many Worlds of dream-consciousness provides the foundation for dream-time precognition. The dreamer may dream of the future just before it occurs. And upon waking from that dream of the future, the conscious mind may remember it and then experience it as it occurs in real time.

Dream-time access to the future is made possible because the brain is in a state of accelerated activity during the course of the dream. As predicted by Einstein (1961) an accelerated frame of reference brings the future closer to the present and makes time travel possible. Accelerated states of consciousness not only bring the future closer, but provide glimpses of those futures before they occur; a phenomenon best described as pre-cognition in dream time.

Aberfan Disaster Dream-Time Precognition

Aberfan is a small village in South Wales. Throughout late September and October 1966, heavy rain lashed down on the area and seeped into the porous sandstone of the hills which surrounded the town and against which abutted the village school (Barker 1967).

On September 27 1966, Mrs SB of London dreamed about a school on a hillside, and a horrible avalanche which killed many children.

On October 14, 1966 Mrs GE from Sidcup, dreamed about a group of screaming children being covered by an avalanche of coal.

On October 20, 1966 Mrs MH, dreamed about a group of children who were trapped in a rectangular room and the children were screaming and trying to escape.

On October 20, 1966, a 10 year old child living in Aberfan woke up screaming from a nightmare. She told her parents that in her dream she was trying to go to school when "something black had come down all over it" and there was "no school there."

On October 21, 1966, part of the rain soaked hills of Aberfan gave way and half a million tons of debris slid toward the village of Aberfan and slammed into the village school. The 10 year old girl who dreamed of the tragedy and 115 other schoolchildren and 28 adults lost their lives when the school was smashed and covered with mud. There were less than a dozen survivors (Baker, 1967).

Assassination of Archduke Francis Ferdinand: Dream-Time Precognition

In June of 1914, Austria was seeking to expand it's central European empire; plans which were resented by neighboring states, including Serbia, who wished to remain independent. That same month, the Archduke Francis Ferdinand, nephew of the Austrian Emperor Francis Joseph, went on a diplomatic tour accompanied by his wife, to build alliances with the leaders of these independent nations. In late June he and his wife arrived in Sarajevo, Serbia.

On the evening of June 27, 1914, Bishop Joseph Lanyi prepared for bed and upon falling asleep he began to dream. The Archduke Franz Ferdinand of Austria, heir to the throne of Austria, had been the Bishop's student and pupil, and late that night the Archduke appeared in Bishop Lanyi's dream. The dream became a nightmare and at 3:15 AM Bishop Joseph Lanyi awoke, frightened, upset and in tears. He glanced at the clock, dressed himself, and because the dream was so horrible, he wrote it down:

> "At a quarter past three on the morning of 28th June, 1914, I awoke from a terrible dream. I dreamed that I had gone to my desk early in the morning to look through the mail that had come in. On top of all the other letters there lay one with a black border, a black seal, and the arms of the Archduke. I immediately recognized the letter's handwriting, and saw at the head of the notepaper in blue colouring a picture which showed me a street and a narrow side-street. Their Highnesses sat in a car, opposite them sat a General, and an Officer next to the chauffeur. On both sides of the street there was a large crowd. Two young men sprang forward and shot at their Highnesses."

In the dream, Bishop Lanyi read the dream-letter, which had been written by the Archduke. According to the Bishop's account, which he wrote down in the early predawn hours of June 28, the dream letter from the Archduke was as follows: "Dear Dr Lanyi: Your Excellency. I wish to inform you that my wife and I were the victims of a political assassination. We recommend ourselves to your prayers. Cordial greetings from your Archduke Franz. Sarajevo, 28th June, 3.15 a.m." Bishop Joseph Lanyi was convinced that the Archduke had been assassinated, and called his parishioners and household staff to tell them of the terrible news. Later that morning of June 28, 1914, the Bishop held a mass for the Archduke and his wife. But, the Archduke were still alive and would not be shot dead for another 2 hours.

On June 28, 1914, at 11 a.m., as the Archduke and his wife were leaving a ceremony at Sarajevo, a Serbian nationalist leaped from the crowd and killed them both. It was the Archduke's assassination which triggered World War One.

Death of Mark Twain's Brother: Dream-Time Precognition

In May of 1858, Mark Twin had a dream about his younger brother Henry who was working on a riverboat as a "mud clerk." As related by Mark Twain:

> "The dream was so vivid, so like reality, that it deceived me, and I thought it was real. In the dream I had seen Henry a corpse. He lay in a metallic [burial case]. He was dressed in a suit of my clothing, and on his breast lay a great bouquet of flowers, mainly white roses, with a red rose in the [centre]. The casket stood upon a couple of chairs...it suddenly flashed upon me that there was nothing real about this--it was only a dream. I can still feel something of the grateful upheaval of joy of that moment, and I can also still feel the remnant of doubt, the suspicion that maybe it [was] real, after all. I returned to the house almost on a run, flew up the stairs two or three steps at a jump, and rushed into that [sitting-room]--and was made glad again, for there was no casket there."

A few days later, Twain's brother left on a river boat from New Orleans. As related by Mark Twain:

> "Two or three days afterward the boat's boilers exploded at Ship Island, Memphis. I found Henry stretched upon a mattress on the floor of a great building, along with thirty or forty other scalded and wounded persons... his body was badly scalded... I think he died about dawn. The coffins provided for the dead were of unpainted white pine, but in this instance some of the ladies of Memphis had made up a fund of sixty dollars and bought a metallic case, and when I came back and entered the [dead-room] Henry lay in that open case, and he was dressed in a suit of my clothing. He had borrowed it without my knowledge during our last sojourn in St. Louis; and I recognized instantly that my dream of several weeks before was here exactly reproduced, so far as these details went--and I think I missed one [detail;] but that one was immediately supplied, for just then an elderly lady entered the place with a large bouquet consisting mainly of white roses, and in the [centre] of

it was a red rose, and she laid it on his breast."

The Dream-Murder of Tanya Zachs

In a legal case investigated and reported by Joseph (2000), a beautiful young woman, Tanya Zachs, disappeared on her way home in San Jose from her job in Santa Cruz in September of 1984. Her car was found abandoned along highway 17 midway between the two cities and which courses through the Santa Cruz mountains. That night, a young woman "Sunshine" who lived in a nudist colony, Lupin Lodge, situated in the Santa Cruz Mountains, had a nightmare: A woman was being brutally murdered. The next day, Sunshine read the story of Tanya's disappearance in the local newspaper, and that night she had the dream again, but this time the victim appeared to her quite clearly. It was Tanya.

In the dream Tanya showed "Sunshine" a narrow mountain road off highway 17, one of many leading from the long and winding highway between San Jose and Santa Cruz. Tanya led the dreamer down the mountain road which was bordered by a thick canopy of redwood trees and pines, and then to an isolated spot alongside. Tanya then beckoned the dreamer to follow her down a rather steep incline leading from the mountain road into the forest and thick brush, and then along a forested trail. Finally, Tanya stopped and pointed out her naked body, lying spread eagle on a huge slab of rock surrounded by trees.

Sunshine was convinced she knew where Tanya's body lay hidden. On the morning of 9/15/84, she contacted Tanya's family, told them of her dreams, and that same day led them and the police to the mountain side road Tanya had showed her and finally to the isolated spot. The police climbed down the tree-covered steep incline, and just as Sunshine had dreamed, they found the trail leading into the forest. But, there was no body.

That night Sunshine had another dream and Tanya took her to the same spot, down the same trail, then pointed at and emphasized a little deer trail that forked off to the right between the trees, and which led directly to her body. The next day, Sunshine and the family met again, and then climbed down the incline, took the trail to the right, and there was Tanya's body laid out exactly as revealed to Sunshine when dreaming.

The murder remained unsolved, however, until four years later. Damon Wells, beset by horrible nightmares where the victim kept accusing him of her murder, sought psychiatric treatment and confessed (Joseph 2000).

Precognition Dreams Are Common

Precognition dreams are common (Fukuda 2002; Haraldsson, 1985; Lange et al. 2001; Ross & Joshi, 1992; Stowell, 1995; Thalbourne, 1994) and often involve negative, unhappy, unpleasant events such as deaths, disasters and other calamities (Ryback & Sweitzer, 1990). About 40% of precognitive dreams are linked to an event the following day (Sondow, 1988), or take place several days or weeks later. However, anecdotal evidence indicates that the dreamed events may occur just prior to waking, even triggering wakefulness.

Precognition dreams can be about mundane affairs of concern only to the dreamer. A colleague of this author admits to frequently having had precognitive dreams and relates the following:

"I dreamed that my water heater busted and that water was flooding out onto the floor. Three days later, the water heater sprung a leak." "I dreamed about getting a flat tire while driving on the freeway. It was the rear tire on the driver's side. A couple days later, the car's dashboard-computer informed me that the rear tire on the driver's side was low in air." "I dreamed that I took a girlfriend to my hot tub in the back yard, but it was empty and there was no water. When I tried to turn the water on nothing would happen. In the dream I was irritated because it would have to be replaced. A few days later the hot tub on-switch broke and after several failed attempts to fix it, I had it junked."

Several studies indicate that precognitive dreams are more common in younger than older individuals and that women report more precognitive dreams than men (Lange et al. 2001). It has also been found that those who have experienced deja vu are more likely to have precognitive dreams (Fakuda, 2002).

In large samples, anywhere from 17.8 % to 66% of individuals report that they experienced at least one precognitive dream (Fukuda 2002; Palmer, 1979; Haraldsson, 1985; Ross & Joshi, 1992; Ryback, 1988; Thalbourne, 1994) whereas over 60% of the general population believe such dreams are possible (Thalbourne, 1984; Haraldsson, 1985). However, Ryback (1988) after investigating 290 case reports of paranormal dreams, dismissed most of these precognitive dreams as coincidence and concluded that only 8.8% of the population actually have these dreams.

PreCognitive Dream Skepticism and Professional Baseball

Over 2000 years ago Aristotle wrote a book expressing his disbelieve in precognitive dreams: "On Divination in Sleep." Aristotle complained that most of those having precognitive dreams were unworthy of the honor of receiving advanced information and "are not the best and wisest, but merely commonplace persons." Aristotle argued that "the sender of such dreams should be God." According to Aristotle "most dreams are to be classed as mere coincidences..." and do not take "place according to a universal or general rule" and have no causal connection to actual events in the future.

"Coincidence" has been the major objection to claims of precognitive dream activity (Caroll 2000; Wiseman 2011). Caroll (2000) refers to the "law of large numbers" and dismisses all claims as being a function merely of coincidence. For example, the odds, are with so many dreamers having dreams about so many different themes, that a few of them will have dreams about an airplane crash or a ship that sinks. If the next day a ship sinks or a plane crashes, this is merely coincidence. According to Caroll and others, if precognitive dreams were real, they should be more commonplace, with more dreamers coming forward, and thus there should be a high "hit rate" and there is not; and as such "precognitive dreams do not exist."

However, if we applied the same reasoning to professional baseball, then professional baseball does not exist. Consider, from 2000 until 2013, the average baseball batting average ranged around 267. During regular season play during 2013, out of 750 major league players, 726 had a batting average of less than 30% (http://espn.go.com/mlb/stats/batting). Taking into considering fowl balls and hits which result in "outs", but considering that each player has at least 3 opportunities each time at bat to hit the ball, and then taking that .267 average, it could be said that the average professional baseball player actually gets a base hit less than 20% of the time. Be it a 20% or 30% hit rate, obviously this does not mean no one in professional baseball is able to hit the ball, or that when they do it is merely a coincidence. The same standard must be applied to precognitive dreams.

Precognitive dreams need not be about Earth-shaking national tragedies and it is unknown how many dreamers would ever come forward to report their dreams even if they did have national implications. In fact, most dreams are forgotten upon waking (Frank, 2012, Pagel, 2014, Stickgold & Walker, 2010). Further, many precognitive dreams may be related to mundane matters like a "flat tire," or a phone call or visit from a friend the next day; or they may be entangled with events which are about to occur just minutes or seconds into the future, i.e. backward/precognitive dreams. Since most people forget their dreams upon waking and most dreams are forgotten, how often precognitive dreaming occurs, and how many people have them, is unknown. What is known is that such dreams can be explained by quantum physics and the neurological foundations for dream activity and dream-time.

PreCognitive Backward Dreams

Precognitive experiences occurring during waking may be entangled with innocuous event which are just about to occur, such as thinking of a friend and then getting a phone call or email from that friend minutes or hours later. Just as a professional baseball player is more likely to swing and miss than hit the ball, the fact that one might think of a friend who does not call is not evidence against precognition.

During accelerated states associated with dream-time, precognitive dreams may be for events which will soon happen, or are just about to happen, perhaps seconds, or minutes away. These latter-type of dreams care best described as precognitive-backward dreams.

A case in point, "Katherine" dreams she and a friend "Sheryl" are shopping in Boston. They go from store, lugging shopping bags. "Katherine" in her dreams feels this sense of urgency to go home as if she is late for something and someone is waiting for her so she sets her bags down on the sidewalk and sits on a bench to wait for a cab or a the bus. She then realized her friend "Sheryl" is gone. Katherine looks for her, goes in and out of stores, but can't find her. "Katherine" sees a bus-like street car coming down the cobbled street and she picks up her packages and steps out onto the curb. As the street car pulls up and stops "Katherine" is surprised to see that Sheryl is driving and is ringing its bell. The sound of the bell grows louder and louder and then jolts "Katherine" from her dream. Katherine realizes that her phone is ringing. She picks it up and it is her friend "Sheryl" who is calling. Sheryl and Katherine are going shopping that day.

That "Katherine" dreamed about going shopping with "Sheryl" is not remarkable in-itself. That "Sheryl" was ringing the bell and it was Sheryl who was calling can be explained away as interesting coincidence. It is no surprise that Sheryl called. What seems paradoxical, however, is that the dream of shopping and walking down the streets of Boston laden with packages, the desire to go home, then looking for her missing friend and then seeing the bus-like street car all seemed to lead up to the ringing of the bell in a logical order of events so that its ringing made sense in the context of the dream. Hearing the ringing bell seemed to be a natural part of the dream, and it is. However, the dream did not lead up to the bell. Rather, the ringing of the bell initiated the dream. The effect (ringing bell) and the cause (the ringing phone) are identical. The effect caused itself.

There are two explanations for these quite common "backward" dreams. Dream-time and dream-consciousness does not obey the laws of physics. In dream-time, dream-consciousness may attempt to impose temporal order on a dream which has no temporal order and which may be experienced as a gestalt. In other words, in dream-time the entire dream was instantaneous and the dream was initiated by the ringing of her phone. The bell was heard and the dream was instantly produced in explanation and association. Future, present, past may be juxtaposed and experienced as a gestalt; like seeing the forest instead of the individual trees. In fact, although dreams may seem to last long time periods, they may be only seconds in length (Frank, 2012, Pagel, 2014, Stickgold & Walker, 2010).

The other explanation is that the ringing of the phone and the fact that Sheryl was calling Katherine, was perceived in dream-time, before it happened. Just as a time-machine traveling at superluminal speeds from the future into the past will pass by an observer only to be followed by its light image (which trails behind at the speed of light), information just seconds or minutes away into the future can be perceived by dream-consciousness in dream-time through entanglement. However, it is not future information traveling at superluminal speeds, but the mind and brain of the dreamer which are accelerating toward that future event in advance of those conscious minds which are still awake.

In dream time, the brain is highly active (Frank, 2012, Pagel, 2014, Stickgold

& Walker, 2010), and certain regions in the limbic system are hyperactive (Joseph 1992, 1996, 2000). During dream-time, brain activity is accelerating which causes a contraction in time-space. The future comes closer to the present during dream time relative to outside observers which may include, upon waking, the conscious mind of the dreamer. However, while in dream-time, in a state of accelerated dream-consciousness, the future may be sensed and it may trigger a complex dream which then leads up to that future event when it arrives in the present thereby waking the dreamer.

Another illustrative example: French physicist Alfred Maury dreamt that he had taken part in the French Revolution and that he had been condemned to death and his head cut off at the exact moment when his bedpost broken and struck him across the neck:

"I was rather,unwell, and was lying down in my room, with my mother at my bedside. I dreamed of,the Reign of Terror; I witnessed massacres, I was appearing before the Revolutionary,tribunal, I saw Robespierre, Marat, Fouquier-Tinville, all the most wicked figures of,that terrible era; I talked to them; finally, after many events that I only partly remember,,I was judged, condemned to death, taken out in a tumbril through a huge throng to the,Place de la Revolution; I mounted the scaffold; the executioner tied me to that fatal,plank, he tipped it up, the blade fell; I felt my head separating from my body, I woke up,racked by the deepest anguish, and felt the bedpost on my neck. It had suddenly come,off and had fallen on my cervical vertebrae just like the guillotine blade."

Certainly it would be expected that a major blow to the head and neck would cause instant waking. But in this instance, it did not. Instead, the dreamer experienced a long and convoluted dream which was initiated by what was about to happen, and which could also be considered a warning of what was about to happen; albeit in the unique dream-language characteristic of dreams. This is not a case of an instantaneous backward dream, but a precognitive dream which provided the dreamer with a glimpse of what lay in store just moments into the future.

A third example related to me by a colleague:

"I had been working in my yard into the late Friday afternoon and was exhausted. It was hot and I stripped off my shirt and lay down in a swinging hammock in my yard to take a nap and instantly fell asleep and began to dream. In the dream I was in a nightclub and there was this exotic beautiful woman with long black hair drinking at the bar. We began drinking together and then we were dancing and kissing and then we were suddenly in my house and we were laying on the floor and I was taking off her clothes and she was getting very excited and aggressive. All at once I could see she had yellow eyes and black skin, but it wasn't skin, but resembled an insect's chitlin. Her arms and hands became claws and her teeth became razor sharp and pointed. She put her claw arms around me very tight as I struggled to escape. She had turned into some demonic insect-creature and pressed her razor sharp claw-hands into my back. I could feel her razor sharp claws knifing me and I felt I was being stabbed in the back. The pain was terrible. It seemed as if her pointed claws were going to completely pierce my back and come out my chest. The pain was so horrific I woke up. But the pain was still there. I got up from the hammock and there was a crippled black bumble bee laying there. The damn thing has stung me on my back."

Dreams that seem to paradoxically lead up to an event which wakes the dreamer are common. These dreams may be relatively brief or become lengthy complicated dreams leading up to some event which then occurs, as if on cue, waking the dreamer who discovers upon waking that someone was knocking on his door, the phone was ringing, it was the alarm clock, a kid was yelling outside the window, and so on, all of which initiated the dream which then led up to the event which caused the dream (Joseph 1992). The dream was produced, so as to explain in the unique language of the dream what was about to happen; and this is because, it already happened in the future. The only other explanation is the dream was produced as an instant gestalt and the dreamer dreamed the dream in accelerated dream-time without any temporal order, and it was upon waking that the dream was reconstructed in a temporal sequential time frame (Joseph 1992).

Be they backward dreams instantly produced as a gestalt, or examples of dream precognition, backward dreams are the most easily comprehended because the conscious mind utilizes temporal sequences to explain what is observed, and may recall the dream in reverse, so it makes temporal-sequential sense; as if the cause led to the effect, when the cause and effect were either simultaneous, or the effect was its own cause.

Joseph Dreams His Death 2000 Years Ago

In the early 1950s, when I [R. Joseph] was a boy of 3, and for many years until around age 7, I had dreams about a little boy playing by the sea shore, by the ocean. And there were crowds of people. Some lying or sitting together on the sand. Others swimming or fishing. And then in the dream the ocean began to recede... the ocean waters drew back back back... and I could see shells and fish flopping on the wet sand where moments before there had been ocean... and ships and small boats lay on their sides... and I ran to where the ocean had been, on the wet sand, picking up shells... and many other people also ran onto the wet sand picking up wiggling fish and laughing and talking in amazement that the ocean had pulled back for miles and miles leaving the sand and ocean floor completely revealed for everyone to see.... and then... and then... and then...

I walked further and further out to where the ocean had been, picking up giant shells some with wiggling living creatures still inside, and gazing in wonder at what the ocean had hidden but which was now revealed... and then I heard screams... women and men and children were screaming... and in my dream, they were all running from the wet sand where the ocean had been toward the dry shore...and people on the shore were also running... everyone was running away and screaming... and I could hear this rumbling roar from behind me... and when I looked back to see why, what they were running from and what was making that roar, I could see the ocean... it was still miles away--but it was a WALL OF OCEAN.. a WALL OF WATER looming up maybe 100 yards perhaps even miles into the sky... and in my dream the wall of ocean was rushing forward, to where the ocean had been minutes before, toward where I was standing with sea shells in my hands... and I started running... like everyone else, running running running... and I could see, over my shoulder, behind me, the roaring wall of ocean water coming closer, and closer... and faster faster faster... and I kept running... everyone was running and screaming...trying to get away... and then the towering WALL OF WATER was just behind me... then looming over me... and then it crashed down upon me... and the little boy that I was, in this dream, drowned.... and then I awoke in my bed... the same boy who drowned, but a different boy...me...

I had this dream over and over for years; the same dream, the source of which was a mystery to me as I had never even imagined that the ocean could actually recede and then rush back to land as I had dreamed. It was not until 20 years later that I learned, for the first time, about Tsunamis and how characteristic it is for people to foolishly run out to where the ocean and been... and then... the ocean comes rushing back as a wall of water drowning everyone who did not immediately run away.

How could I have dreamed so vividly about something 3-year old me knew nothing about in the early 1950s when we didn't even have a television? There were clues in yet other dreams when I was a child, and they were dreams of the same little boy. But it was during ancient Roman times, and I was sitting with my mother who was dressed in royal robes typical of the Roman period. She was singing to me... And down below I could see Roman soldiers marching, and peasant women by a river, washing clothes, and the river was flowing into the ocean. The peasant women, who had with them many naked children, were dressed in clothes I associated with Biblical times, of ancient Egypt; my grandmother would often read to me from a Bible picture book. But in these river-side dreams which began so peaceful, they all ended with incredible earthquakes, like the world was turning up-side down...

How do these two dreams relate? Almost 50 years after I had these dreams, I searched the records for Tsunamis in the Mediterranean sea near Italy and Egypt. On the morning of July 21, 365 AD, an earthquake of great magnitude caused a huge tsunami more than 100 feet high and it inundated and destroyed several towns on the coasts of the Mediterranean, including Alexandria. This is how Ammianus Marcellinus, a Roman historian described it:

> Slightly after daybreak, and heralded by a thick succession of fiercely shaken thunderbolts, the solidity of the whole earth was made to shake and shudder, and the sea was driven away, its waves were rolled back, and it disappeared, so that the abyss of the depths was uncovered and many-shaped varieties of sea-creatures were seen stuck in the slime; the great wastes of those valleys and mountains, which the very creation had dismissed beneath the vast whirlpools, at that moment, as it was given to be believed, looked up at the sun's rays. Many ships, then, were stranded as if on dry land, and people wandered at will about the paltry remains of the waters to collect fish and the like in their hands; then the roaring sea as if insulted by its repulse rises back in turn, and through the teeming shoals dashed itself violently on islands and extensive tracts of the mainland, and flattened innumerable buildings in towns or wherever they were found. Thus in the raging conflict of the elements, the face of the earth was changed to reveal wondrous sights. For the mass of waters returning when least expected killed many thousands by drowning, and with the tides whipped up to a height as they rushed back, some ships, after the anger of the watery element had grown old, were seen to have sunk, and the bodies of people killed in shipwrecks lay there, faces up or down.

Had Joseph dreamed of a previous life from nearly 2000 years ago? Or did he journey to the past, during dream-time, and visit the long ago in the time machine of consciousness?

We have been here before, we will be here again, we will always be, and this is because time and consciousness are a quantum continuum and the distinctions between past present and future are illusions.

REFERENCES

Al-Khalili (2011). Black Holes, Wormholes and Time Machines, Taylor & Francis.

Almheiri, A. et al. (2013). Black Holes: Complementarity or Firewalls? J. High Energy Phys. 2, 062

Bethe, H. A., et al., (2003) Formation and Evolution of Black Holes in the Galaxy, World Scientific Publishing.

Bilaniuk, O.-M. P.; Sudarshan, E. C. G. (1969). "Particles beyond the Light Barrier". Physics Today 22 (5): 43–51.

Bo, L., Wen-Biao, L. (2010). Negative Temperature of Inner Horizon and Planck Absolute Entropy of a Kerr Newman Black Hole. Commun. Theor. Phys. 53, 83–86.

Bohr, N., (1913). "On the Constitution of Atoms and Molecules, Part I".

Philosophical Magazine 26: 1–24.

Bohr, N., (1913). "On the Constitution of Atoms and Molecules, Part I". Philosophical Magazine 26: 1–24.

Bohr, N. (1934/1987), Atomic Theory and the Description of Nature, reprinted as The Philosophical Writings of Niels Bohr, Vol. I, Woodbridge: Ox Bow Press.

Bruno, N. R., (2001). Deformed boost transformations that saturate at the Planck scale. Physics Letters B, 522, 133-138.

Blandford, R.D. (1999). "Origin and evolution of massive black holes in galactic nuclei". Galaxy Dynamics, proceedings of a conference held at Rutgers University, 8–12 Aug 1998, ASP Conference Series vol. 182.

Carroll, S (2004). Spacetime and Geometry. Addison Wesley.

Casimir, H. B. G. (1948). "On the attraction between two perfectly conducting plates". Proc. Kon. Nederland. Akad. Wetensch. B51: 793.

Chodos, A. (1985). "The Neutrino as a Tachyon". Physics Letters B 150: 431.

Einstein, A. (1915a). Fundamental Ideas of the General Theory of Relativity and the Application of this Theory in Astronomy, Preussische Akademie der Wissenschaften, Sitzungsberichte, 1915 (part 1), 315.

Einstein, A. (1915b). On the General Theory of Relativity, Preussische Akademie der Wissenschaften, Sitzungsberichte, 1915 (part 2), 778–786.

Einstein A. (1939) A. Einstein, Ann. Math. 40, 922.

Einstein, A. (1961), Relativity: The Special and the General Theory, New York: Three Rivers Press.

Einstein, A. and Rosen, N. (1935). "The Particle Problem in the General Theory of Relativity". Physical Review 48: 73.

Einstein, A., Lorentz, H.A., Minkowski, H., and Weyl, H. (1923). Arnold Sommerfeld. ed. The Principle of Relativity. Dover Publications: Mineola, NY. pp. 38–49.

Einstein A, Podolsky B, Rosen N (1935). "Can Quantum-Mechanical Description of Physical Reality Be Considered Complete?". Phys. Rev. 47 (10): 777–780.

Eisberg, R., and Resnick. R. (1985). Quantum Physics of Atoms, Molecules, Solids, Nuclei, and Particles. Wily,

Everett, A., & Roman, T. (2012). TIme Travel and Warp Drives, University Chicago Press.

Feinberg, G. (1967). "Possibility of Faster-Than-Light Particles". Physical Review 159 (5): 1089–1105.

Fuller, Robert W. and Wheeler, John A. (1962). "Causality and Multiply-Connected Space-Time". Physical Review 128: 919.

Garay, L. J. (1995). Quantum gravity and minimum length Int.J.Mod.Phys. A10 (1995) 145-166

Ghez, A. M.; Salim, S.; Hornstein, S. D.; Tanner, A.; Lu, J. R.; Morris, M.;

Becklin, E. E.; Duchene, G. (2005). "Stellar Orbits around the Galactic Center Black Hole". The Astrophysical Journal 620: 744.

Geiss, B., et al., (2010) The Effect of Stellar Collisions and Tidal Disruptions on Post-Main-Sequence Stars in the Galactic Nucleus. American Astronomical Society, AAS Meeting #215, #413.15; Bulletin of the American Astronomical Society, Vol. 41, p.252.

Giddings, S. (1995). The Black Hole Information Paradox," Proc. PASCOS symposium/Johns Hopkins Workshop, Baltimore, MD, 22-25 March, 1995, arXiv:hep-th/9508151v1.

Hawking, S. W., (1988) Wormholes in spacetime. Phys. Rev. D 37, 904–910.

Hawking, S., (1990). A Brief History of Time: From the Big Bang to Black Holes. Bantam.

Hawking, S. (2005). "Information loss in black holes". Physical Review D 72: 084013.

Hawking, S. W. (2014). Information Preservation and Weather Forecasting for Black Holes.

Heisenberg, W. (1927), "Über den anschaulichen Inhalt der quantentheoretischen Kinematik und Mechanik", Zeitschrift für Physik 43 (3–4): 172–198.

Heisenberg. W. (1930), Physikalische Prinzipien der Quantentheorie (Leipzig: Hirzel). English translation The Physical Principles of Quantum Theory, University of Chicago Press.

Heisenberg, W. (1955). The Development of the Interpretation of the Quantum Theory, in W. Pauli (ed), Niels Bohr and the Development of Physics, 35, London: Pergamon pp. 12-29.

Heisenberg, W. (1958), Physics and Philosophy: The Revolution in Modern Science, London: Goerge Allen & Unwin.

Jaffe, R. (2005). "Casimir effect and the quantum vacuum". Physical Review D 72 (2): 021301.

Joseph, R (2010a) The Infinite Cosmos vs the Myth of the Big Bang: Red Shifts, Black Holes, and the Accelerating Universe. Journal of Cosmology, 6, 1548-1615.

Joseph, R. (2010b). The Infinite Universe: Black Holes, Dark Matter, Gravity, Acceleration, Life. Journal of Cosmology, 6, 854-874.

Joseph, R. (2014a) Paradoxes of Time Travel: The Uncertainty Principle, Wave Function, Probability, Entanglement, and Multiple Worlds, Cosmology, 18, 282-302.

Joseph, R. (2014a) The Time Machine of Consciousness, Cosmology, 18, In press.

Kerr, R P. (1963). "Gravitational Field of a Spinning Mass as an Example of Algebraically Special Metrics". Physical Review Letters 11 (5): 237–238.

Lambrecht, A. (2002) The Casimir effect: a force from nothing, Physics World, September 2002

Lorentz, H. A. (1892), "The Relative Motion of the Earth and the Aether", Zittingsverlag Akad. V. Wet. 1: 74–79

McClintock, J. E. (2004). Black hole. World Book Online Reference Center. World Book, Inc.

Melia, F. (2003). The Edge of Infinity. Supermassive Black Holes in the Universe. Cambridge U Press. ISBN 978-0-521-81405-8.

Melia, F. (2007). The Galactic Supermassive Black Hole. Princeton University Press. pp. 255–256.

Merloni, A., and Heinz, S., (2008) A synthesis model for AGN evolution: supermassive black holes growth and feedback modes Monthly Notices of the Royal Astronomical Society, 388, 1011 - 1030.

Minchin, R. et al. (2005). "A Dark Hydrogen Cloud in the Virgo Cluster". The Astrophysical Journal 622: L21–L24.

Morris, M. S. and Thorne, K. S. (1988). "Wormholes in spacetime and their use for interstellar travel: A tool for teaching general relativity". American Journal of Physics 56 (5): 395–412.

O'Neill, B. (2014) The Geometry of Kerr Black Holes, Dover

Penrose, R. (1969) Rivista del Nuovo Cimento.

Preskill, J. (1994). Black holes and information: A crisis in quantum physics", Caltech Theory Seminar, 21 October. arXiv:hep-th/9209058v1.

Pollack, G. L., & Stump, D. R. (2001), Electromagnetism, Addison-Wesley.

Rindler, W. (2001). Relativity: Special, General and Cosmological. Oxford: Oxford University Press.

Rodriguez, A. W.; Capasso, F.; Johnson, Steven G. (2011). "The Casimir effect in microstructured geometries". Nature Photonics 5 (4): 211–221.

Ruffini, R., and Wheeler, J. A. (1971). Introducing the black hole. Physics Today: 30–41.

Russell, D. M., and Fender, R. P. (2010). Powerful jets from accreting black holes: Evidence from the Optical and the infrared. In Black Holes and Galaxy Formation. Nova Science Publishers. Inc.

Schrödinger, E. (1926). "An Undulatory Theory of the Mechanics of Atoms and Molecules". Physical Review 28 (6): 1049–1070. Bibcode:1926PhRv...28.1049S. doi:10.1103/PhysRev.28.1049.

Sen, A. (2002) Rolling tachyon," JHEP 0204, 048

Slater, J. C. & Frank, N. H. (2011) Electromagnetism, Dover.

Smolin, L. (2002). Three Roads to Quantum Gravity. Basic Books.

Taylor, E. F. & Wheeler, J. A. (2000) Exploring Black Holes, Addison Wesley.

Thorne, K. (1994) Black holes and time warps, W. W. Norton. NY.

Thorne, K. S. & Hawking, S. (1995). Black Holes and Time Warps: Einstein's Outrageous Legacy, W. W. Norton.

Thorne, K. et al. (1988). "Wormholes, Time Machines, and the Weak Energy Condition". Physical Review Letters 61 (13): 1446.

Wilf, M., et al. (2007) The Guidebook to Membrane Desalination Technology: Reverse Osmosis, Balaban Publishers.

18. The Observer's Now, Past and Future in Physics from a Psycho-Biological Perspective

Franz Klaus Jansen

126 chemin Fesquets, 34820 ASSAS, France

Abstract

The observer in physics makes observations and transforms them into fact and physical laws. Observations are based on perceptions and their transformations, which are influenced by biological and psychological functions. As argued by the philosopher Peirce, one might distinguish between extra-mental reality and its mental representation. An observer creates with his mental functions a mental representation of extra-mental reality due to perception based on specific sense organs. Extra-mental reality and its mental representation exist simultaneously, but are not always in direct contact with each other and can therefore diverge. Only during the NOW, the observer is through his sense organs in direct physico-neural contact with extra-mental reality. After interruption of this contact, observations belong to the past and the observer transforms with mental functions regularities of past observations into physical laws, which can be extrapolated into the far past and future. During the NOW, observations have precise time coordinates, but after interruption of the direct contact, memorized observations undergo transformations into abstract and often timeless concepts in classical and in quantum physics. In normal life, time is the perception of duration and its boundaries. In physics, time is reduced to the relation of its boundaries between different systems or can be completely discarded in timelessness. Whereas the NOW is a direct connection between extra-mental reality and its mental representation, past and future represent pure mental representations based on memorized NOWs. After their transformation, mental representation can predict future potentiality, which does not always correspond to extra-mental reality. Due to this reality-potentiality gap, physical laws created in mental representation need verification in a new experimental NOW, which alone assures direct contact to reality.

Keywords: physical observer; physical now; past; present; future; mental representation; extra- mental reality; time unreality; timelessness; Mc Taggert.

1. Introduction

Time is generally experienced or conceptualized as consisting of a "now" "past" and "future." The philosopher McTaggart (1908) distinguished between three series of time, the A-series as past, present and future, the B-series as earlier or later and the C-series as the order of events. However, he considered time as unreal and wrote "It may be the case that... the distinction of past, present and future -- is simply a constant illusion of our minds" (McTaggart, 1908, p.457). Einstein, came to similar conclusions:

"The distinction between past, present and future is only an illusion" (Einstein 1955).

Some theorists have argued, based on Einstein's theorems of relativity (Einstein 1905a,b,c, 1907, 1910, 1961), that the past, present and future overlap and exist simultaneously but in different distant locations in the dimension known as space-time (Joseph 2014). Experiments on quantum entanglement and what Einstein (1930) called "spooky action at a distance" all call into question the causal distinctions between past, present and future. Time may not even exist, except as a function of perception and the nature of consciousness which imposes temporal sequences on experience (Joseph 2011).

Contemporary physicists like Zeh (1998) also ague that time does not exist: "The quantum theory requires that paths can fundamentally no longer exist. Then any parameter of paths, such as the role of time ... cannot exist either." (Zeh, 1998, p. 15). Then what is time? Do clocks measure time, or is time a manifestation of clocks which are built according to the rules imposed by the conscious mind to account for the experience of change?

As demonstrated by Einstein and others, the experience of time and the dimension described as time-space, are effected by velocity and gravity. However, is what is experienced, time, or velocity and gravity all of which can effect even atomic clocks? The astronomer Barbour (2009, p. 1). writes "Duration and the behavior of clocks emerge from a timeless law that governs change" and Rovelli (2009, p. 1) that "... the best strategy for understanding quantum gravity is to build a picture of the physical world where the notion of time plays no role at all."

Thus, there is a general claim from philosophers, astronomers and physicists, that time does not exist and that the experience of time may be only an illusion of our minds imposed on the quantum continuum by consciousness.

"I regard consciousness as fundamental. I regard matter as derivative from consciousness" (Max Planck, 1931).

The "future" and the "past" are shaped and affected by consciousness which can effect events just by observing them; as illustrated by "entanglement" and Heisenberg's well established Uncertainty Principle (Heisenberg 1927). The Uncertainty Principle holds that we cannot know velocity, position and mass of any particle simultaneously. Moreover, uncertainties propagate into the future; that is small uncertainties becomes larger as distance from the present increases.

Consciousness, therefore, is entangled with the quantum continuum (Joseph 2014).

The role of an observer is an essential part in quantum physics. Von Neumann included the observer as a quantum system (Zeh, 2013, p. 98). Wigner (1962) proposed an active influence of consciousness on the physical world. Zeh (2013, p. 99) himself insisted that the observer always had an essential role, since he performs all observations with physical instruments. In these theories, the observer is only a passive bystander for collecting observations. The recent form of quantum Bayesianism attributes to the observer a more active role, when he makes probability assignments to express his expectations (Fuchs et al. 2013).

However, if consciousness plays an active or passive role is debatable. Quantum physics, as exemplified by the Copenhagen school (Bohr, 1934, 1958, 1963; Heisenberg, 1925, 1927, 1930), like Einsteinian physics, makes assumptions about the nature of reality as related to an observer, the "knower" who is conceptualized as a singularity (Joseph 2014). As summed up by Heisenberg (1958), "the concepts of Newtonian or Einsteinian physics can be used to describe events in nature." However, because the physical world is relative to being known by a "knower" (the observing consciousness), then the "knower" can influence the nature of the reality which is being observed through the act of measurement and registration at a particular moment in time. The same principles must be applied to time. Time is effected by observation.

What is observed or measured at one moment can never include all the properties of the object under observation, and this includes the perception of time. In consequence, what is known vs what is not known becomes relatively imprecise (Bohr, 1934, 1958, 1963; Heisenberg, 1925, 1927). Moreover, as dictated by the "uncertainty principle" energy and mass can be time-independent (Heisenberg 1927, 1958). This is illustrated by evidence of entanglement where effects may occur simultaneously with causes, and take place at faster than light speeds (Francis 2012; Juan et al. 2013; Lee et al. 2011; Matson 2012; Plenio 2007). One might conclude, therefore, that if consciousness plays a passive or active role, time remains an illusion and there is no past, present, or future, as all are merely aspects of the quantum continuum which become subject to the passive or active observation of consciousness which perceives all experience in terms of temporal sequences (Joseph 2011).

From a psychological viewpoint, the observer has a much greater influence, since besides the observation of information, he also affects a transformation of information. Both functions are essential for the establishment of physical laws and are differently influenced by present, past and future. The present is essentially required for observation, the past for memorized observations and their comparison for detecting regularities and the future consists in the extrapolation of past regularities, which are then considered as general physical laws with validity from the past to the future. Thus, the observer's present, past and future exert a special role during the constitution of physical laws, which will be analyzed by distinguishing between the extra-mental reality and its mental representation, which is responsible for the transformation of regularities from past observations into general physical laws. Extra-mental reality concerns all physical factors outside the body and all biological factors within the body, like respiration or heart beats, whereas mental representation has the function to represent the extra-mental reality in the human mind. The NOW is only present when both are in direct contact, whereas the past and the future are pure mental representations no longer linked to the extra-mental reality and require verification in a new NOW.

2. Physical Reality and its Mental Representation

As summed up by the philosopher CS Peirce reality exists independent of the time "... it is out of the mind, is independent of how we think it, and is, in short, the real." (Hookway, 2013, paragraph 3.1). In the same way mental representation could be distinguished from extra-mental reality as different independent entities. Extra-mental reality would comprise all physical events outside the body and all biological events inside the body, whereas mental representation concerns sensation, perception and cognition. The only connection between both realities are sense organs permitting direct physico-neural contact for representing the extra-mental reality within mental representation.

Humans lack the sensory perceptual capability to perceive X-rays, radioactivity, radio waves and others. In the same sense, blind and deaf people have a different representation of the extra-mental reality which is shaped by their sensory experiences. Certain animal species possess additional sense organs permitting a richer representation of extra-mental reality. Pigeons have sense organs for the detection of magnetic fields (Wu & Dickman, 2012), bees perceive ultra-violet light (Frisch, 1963) and some fish species can feel electric fields (Pusch et al. 2008). For these reasons, the representation of extra-mental reality is necessarily incomplete and can therefore only be considered as a model representation.

In addition sense organs only detect a small part of the universe and the finite memory only retrieves part of all encoded observations. The view of the human eye is limited by a perspective, not allowing to see objects at long distances with precision. Hearing and smelling are also limited to certain distances. Nevertheless, science allowed indirect knowledge on imperceptible physical events by transforming them to perceptible manifestations, for instance a radio can transform inaudible radio waves into audible mechanical waves. Thus, the extra-mental reality is necessarily different from its mental representation and can only be modeled with respect to the information provided by sense organs.

Since the mental representation can be different from the extra-mental reality, it has to be verified. David (2009, p. 1) described the correspondence theory of truth and defined that "... truth is a relational property involving a characteristic relation (to be specified) to some portion of reality ...". The correspondence may not always be evident for events lying beyond the perspective of sense organ at physical scales not directly accessible. However, if the correspondence is not verified, one could believe in physical laws established in mental representation, which after extreme extrapolation into the far past or the final future may no longer correspond to their extra- mental reality.

3. Present, Past and Future in Natural Science

Corballis (2014) and Tulving's theory (1983) argue that memory serves not only to remember and reconstruct the past but also creates the future by planning for or anticipating the future episodes all of which contributes to the subjective sense of time. Memory, therefore, serves consciousness by providing a foundation for the perception of time as consisting of a future, past, or present. Memory, however, is therefore subject to observation and observation may effect memory; and which may explain why so many people remember things differently, even eye-witnesses to a crime (Joseph 2014).

The philosopher McTaggart (1908) argued that "We perceive events in time as being present, and those are the only events which we perceive directly. And all other events in time which, by memory or inference, we believe to be real, are regarded as past or future".

Zeh (2013,) argues that "... The observer has always played an essential role in the empirical sciences, simply because they are based precisely on observations performed by humans by physical means."

The acquisition of knowledge through observation by an observer is subjected to its position in time: the present, past and future. The present allows acquiring new knowledge, the past is limited to knowledge already acquired in a former present, whereas the not yet existing future can only be imagined with uncertainty by projection of past regularities into the future. Regularities found in observations allow the conception of physical laws under three basic conditions dependent on present, past and future:

a) observations in the present are the bases for all physical laws (section 3.1),

b) memorized observations of the past are transformed into abstract regularities (section 3.2),

c) abstract regularities are extrapolated into the far past and future (section 3.3).

Although physical laws seem to possess universal validity from the past to the future, the initial acquisition of information by an observer was only possible in a limited present, but the past and future have still important consequences, which will be discussed.

3.1 The "Now" or the Present. Observation consist in a mental perception of information provided by all sense organs communicating by physico-neural contact with the extra-mental reality. Information from extra- mental reality comprises physical events outside the body as well as physiological events inside the body.

Sense organs are an intermediary to extra-mental reality, in which physical stimulation of the sensory surface followed by sensory transduction lead to perception in mental representation (O'Callaghan 2012). For vision, physical factors such as photons are directly transmitted to the retina of the eye, where they activate light sensible neurons by depolarization in a bottom-up direction to specialized brain regions. The ear receives mechanical waves, which induce neurological activations transmitted to other specialized brain regions. Heat activated skin receptors also transmit their information by neurons to the corresponding brain regions. Thus in the present, there is a direct physico-neural information influx between the extra-mental reality and its mental representation in the brain. However, as soon as sense organs interrupt the direct physical contact, for instance by closing the eyes or the ears, any communication with the extra-mental world is broken, whereas the already obtained observations are partially encoded in the episodic long-term memory and after retrieval represent the past.

The direct contact of extra-mental physical factors with biological sense organs lead to sensory transduction with transmission to specific brain regions, where mental representation takes place and explains why this physico-neural contact can only be found in the present. The notion of "NOW" could be psychologically defined and describe time as duration limited by boundaries and unified by a common aspect, which can be extremely short, when hearing the thunder of an unexpected lightning, but can also take minutes to hours when seeing a film or reading a book. It corresponds always to a physico-neuronal information influx, in which extra-mental reality and mental representation are in direct contact. However, when thinking on physical laws, the physico- neural contact can be interrupted. Time is then reduced to its quantitative aspect as relation between boundaries, whereas its qualitative aspect as psychological duration disappears. In the general relativity theory, time is conserved as relation with respect to a reference frame.

3.2 Perception during the NOW. In contrast to pure elementary sensation, during the construction of mental representation from extra-mental reality by perception (O'Callaghan 2012), top down activities are simultaneously activated. They allow binding of the information from different sense organs into a unified multi-modal experience (Lycan 2012), such as simultaneously viewing a fire in the chimney, hearing its sound and feeling its heat. Other cognitive activities are categorization such as grouping animals into classes (Pothos, 2011) or reactivation of visual entities from long-term memory when perceiving faces. In neuroscience visual mental imagery with pure top-down activation mechanisms has to be distinguished from visual percepts including bottom-up mechanisms, which explains why people in general do not confuse visual percepts with visual mental images (Ganis & Schendan, 2008). Mental imagery with pure top down activation no longer necessitates direct elementary sensation from extra-mental reality.

Corballis (2014) distinguishes the psychological present and the past with the concepts of anoetic consciousness, as awareness of the present and noetic consciousness as semantic memory, representing events not tied to the immediate environment and allowing mental time travel between the past and the future. Finally autonoetic consciousness allows episodic memory containing events already experienced by the self and later reminded as the past.

3.3 The Past as Memorized Observation. The NOW allows direct contact by observation between extra-mental reality and its mental representation, which is then encoded in an episodic long-term memory and can later be retrieved as the past. Encoding is an automatic by-product of attending to or processing a stimulus and therefore differs according to the level of attention and processing (Craik & Lockhart, 1972). As soon as observations are memorized, they already represent the past. Thus, immediately after the break down of direct physico-neural contact between extra-mental reality and mental representation, characterized as elementary sensation with sense organs, a partial copy of the prior observations remains. Thereby observations in the present are not lost and can be used for further analyses with cognitive functions. Past observations have the great advantage of preserving copies from multiple observations, which allow their comparison for exploring regularities.

Thus, only the past containing multiple memorized observations allows comparisons, although it is disconnected from any direct physical contact with the extra-mental reality. This complete detachment of memorized observations also allows the transformation of information. In contrast to unchangeable "elementary sensations" in the present, mental cognition is able to modify information of past observations through: 1. association, 2. dissociation or 3. modeling. Besides the representation of extra-mental reality as past observations, their cognitive transformation allows a total independence of mental representation from extra-mental reality. This kind of representation could be called "potentiality" or "possible worlds" as claimed by philosophers like Dennett (2004). Thus, there is in mental representation a gap between its representation of observed reality and its representation of imagined potentiality (i.e. Reality Potentiality Gap or "RePoGap"). This gap is permanently experienced by everybody, when one's imagination does not correspond to one's observation of extra-mental reality.

3.4 Transformation of Past Observations. There are three main transformations of past observations : association, dissociation and modeling. A first transformation by the observer with his cognitive functions is the association of interpretations to perceptions, similar to the model of perception from Bruner (2011). The sun is daily perceived as rising in the east and setting in the west. Although the corresponding interpretation of geocentrism was believed for many centuries, more precise information imposed a different association with the interpretation of heliocentrism for exactly the same perceptions. Thus, insufficient information may induce incorrect interpretations, which have to be changed after more detailed information becomes available.

A second transformation by cognitive functions is the dissociation of certain properties from the complexity of memorized observations. In Galilee's (1638) experiment on the inclined plane, repetitive time measurements had to be compared, but only the relations of the boundaries of time could be used in mathematical calculations and time as duration was dissociated from the relation of its boundaries. Physical laws thereby become invariant with respect to the observed individual time measurements. Thus, our knowledge on the whole universe can be considered as relational and only allows correlations between different systems (Baird, 2013). When only one aspect of highly complex past observations is under study, the other aspects are discarded. Thereby, complexity becomes reduced and looses all other properties, which are not under study.

A third transformation of memorized observations is modeling of past observations with visual models from the macrocosm, such as atoms as billiard balls or with mathematical models by following Galilee. Mathematical models can be of a different nature, either describing, or simplifying or approximating past observations. Galilee's mathematical models directly described the behavior of bronze balls on the inclined plane. Statistical methods simplify the behavior of multiple individual events by calculating one virtual mean value and its standard deviation (sigma) with arbitrary confidence levels such as 95%. In quantum physics probability estimations approximate the characteristics of the behavior of elementary particles. According to the mathematical model applied, past observations are more or less precisely represented by mathematical models.

As expressed by the Heisenberg uncertainty principle (Heisenberg, 1927), the more precisely one physical property is known the more unknowable become other properties. The more precisely one property is known, the less precisely the other can be known and this is true at the molecular and atomic levels of reality (Bohr, 1934, 1958, 1963). Heisenberg's principle of indeterminacy focuses on the relationship of the experimenter to the objects of his scientific scrutiny, and the probability and potentiality, in quantum mechanics, for something to be other than it is. Einstein objected to quantum mechanics and Heisenberg's formulations of potentiality and indeterminacy by proclaiming "god does not play dice."

According to Heisenberg (1925, 1927, 1930), chance and probability enters into the state and the definition of a physical system because the very act of measurement can effect the system. No system is truly in isolation. No system can be viewed from all perspectives in totality simultaneously which would require a god's eye view (Joseph 2014). As summed up by Joseph (2014) "Only if the entire universe is included can one apply the qualifying condition of "an isolated system." Simply including the observer, his eye, the measuring apparatus and the object, are not enough to escape uncertainty. Results are always imprecise. Heinsenberg puts it this way:

"What one deduces from an observation is a probability function; which is a mathematical expression that combines statements about possibilities or tendencies with statements about our knowledge of facts....The probability function obeys an equation of motion as the co-ordinates did in Newtonian mechanics; its change in the course of time is completely determined by the quantum mechanical equation but does not allow a description in both space and time....The probability function does not describe a certain event but a whole ensemble of possible events" whereas "the transition from the possible to the actual takes place during the act of observation... and the interaction of the object with the measuring device, and thereby with the rest of the world... The discontinuous change in the probability function... takes place with the act of registration, because it is the discontinuous change of our knowledge in the instant of registration that changes the probability function." "Since through the observation our knowledge of the system has changed discontinuously, its mathematical representation has also undergone the discontinuous change and we speak of a quantum jump" (Heisenberg, 1958).

The same principles can be applied to the experience of time by the conscious mind (Joseph 2014). The mental transformation of past observations through association, dissociation and modulation, shows that memorized past observations can be completely transformed by cognitive mental functions into virtual concepts, corresponding only partially to the initial observations. Then, the mental representations of physical laws could only be considered as models for extra-mental reality.

3.5 Timelessness of Past Observations. As detailed by Joseph (2014): The wave function describes all the various possible states of the particle. Rocks, trees, cats, dogs, humans, planets, stars, galaxies, the universe, the cosmos, past, present, future, as a collective, all have wave functions. Waves can also be particles, thereby giving rise to a particle-wave duality and the Uncertainty Principle. Particle-waves interact with other particle-waves. The wave function of a person sitting on their rocking chair would, within the immediate vicinity of the person and the chair, resemble a seething quantum cloud of frenzied quantum activity in the general shape of the body and rocking chair. This quantum cloud of activity gives shape and form to the man in his chair, and is part of the quantum continuum, a blemish in the continuum which is still part of the continuum and interacts with other knots of activity thus giving rise to cause and effect as well as violations of causality." As summed up by Joseph (2014) "in a quantum universe all of existence consists of a frenzy of subatomic activity which can be characterized as possessing pure potentiality and all of which are linked and entangled as a basic oneness which extends in all directions and encompasses all dimensions including time (Bohr, 1958, 1963; Dirac, 1966a,b; Planck 1931, 1932, Heisenberg 1955, 1958; von Neumann 1937, 1955). The act of observation be it visual, auditory, tactile, mechanical, digital, is entangled with the quantum continuum and creates a static impression of just a fragment of that quantum frenzy that is registered in the mind of the observer as length, width, height, first, second, and so on; like taking a single picture of something in continual motion, metamorphosis, and transformation. That is, the act of sensory registration, be it a function of a single cell, or the conscious mind of a woman or man, selects a fragment of the infinite quantum possibilities and experiences it as real, but only to that mind or that cell at the moment of registration."

Kubs et al. (1998) demonstrated the direct interaction of instrumental observation on the behavior of elementary particles, when an increasing "which-way detector " changed the interference pattern of electrons. Stapp (2004) conceives an active observer, who has the freedom of choice and intentionally prepares experimental actions, some of which lead to a wave like behavior and others to the particle structure of elementary particles. His theory is based on the interpretation of von Neumann, who included the observer in the quantum system and the collapse of the quantum system was considered as a psycho-physical parallelism (Zeh, 2013 p 98). The observer collects information by observation, thereby inducing the wave function to collapse. Wigner also suggested a participation of consciousness in the physical world (Wigner, 1962). According to Everett, the subjective observer may simultaneously exist in various versions in his multi-world theory. Zeh extended this theory by including the mind of the observer as an essential factor in his multi-mind theory (Zeh, 1970). Besides Stapp, these theories considered the observer as a passive collector of information. Fuchs et al. (2013) gave the observer a more active role by creating with probability assignments a belief in future experimental outcomes and Stapp proposed that the observer by his freedom to choose experiments actively interfered with physical reality (Schwarts et al 2005).

Reducing individual observations only to one property, such as time, space, weight, height or others, allows the elimination of other properties not under study. Besides others, time coordinates can be eliminated, which leads to partial or total timelessness. Partial timelessness can be represented by astronomical constellations only requiring time as relations. The Antikythera Mechanism, a mechanical computer for the calculation of astronomical positions, was used by the ancient Greeks already in the first century BC (Price, 1975) and indicated the positions of the sun, the moon and the planets Venus and Mars. A modern planetarium fulfills the same function, but with a digital computer. Such mechanisms can be turned forwards but also backwards in time for other astronomical positions relative to another time point. Thereby the time arrow is no longer represented and only time relations indicate the corresponding positions of planets. Thus, already classical physical formalism concerning the relation between planets could reduce time only to relations corresponding to partial timelessness.

Time is entangled and is affected by consciousness and relative to and effected by the act of observation and measurement--as predicted by quantum mechanics (Bohr, 1958, 1963; Dirac, 1966a,b; Planck 1931, 1932, Heisenberg 1927, 1958; Neumann 1937, 1955). Complete timelessness is found in quantum physics, when time measurements become uncertain, due to variable outcomes under identical experimental conditions. The uncertainty of time relations only allows probability estimations and corresponds to complete timelessness as claimed by physicists (Zeh, 1998). Nevertheless, complete timelessness can also be found in classical physics, when the time relations are without interest, for instance when only variations are calculated. Already in Galilee's experiments the grouping of individual measurements showed a certain variability of outcomes, which corresponds to a timeless concept even in classical physics.

When timeless values are represented in a graph, they could be interpreted, as if they were in superposition or obtained at an identical virtual time point. Although the physical formalism is completely different, the general idea of superposition of values in classical physics for an identical virtual time point might be seen in analogy to superposition of wave structures in quantum physics. The principle of superposition was applied in the mathematical formalism of the wave function with complex amplitudes by Schrödinger, which differs from weighted sums in classical theory. The wave function also proved to be a better model for human decision making (Pothos & Busemeyer, 2009) and could be interpreted as a superposition of mental functions. Thereby superposition in quantum mechanics seems to be isomorphic to superposition of cognitive mental functions (Jansen, 2008, 2011b).

Highly varying observations can only be extrapolated into the future as timeless group values with their means and variations, but not predict individual time coordinates. Nevertheless, in new measurements, extrapolated mean values will necessarily acquire new individual outcomes with their time coordinates. Since for irregular outcomes only their group behavior is predictable, individual behavior appears to be indeterminist. Thus, the extrapolation of timeless values into the future will acquire new precise time coordinates in new observations.

3.6 The Future as Extrapolation from the Past. Comparison between multiple observations can only be obtained with memorized past observations, since present observations are not finished and future observations are not yet existing. The only way to have a guess of the future is the projection of past events into the future. Patients with a bilateral medial temporal ablation of the brain for the reduction of epilepsy are unable to look neither into the past nor into the future (Berlucchi, 2014). However, the future is of great importance for normal life, and imagining the past is probably not so essential for life as projecting the future (Corballis, 2014). The scientific aim for prediction of the future could be realized by a "physical theory of everything", which covers the past, the present and the future and can be established with past regularities under the condition that they are also reliable in the future. In physics, this could be achieved by the extrapolation of mathematical formalism obtained from the past and projected into the future.

The reliability of any projection from the past into the future essentially depends on the regularity of past events. The revolution of the earth around its axes providing the time unite of one day with 24 hours is highly regular. In contrast, irregular weather conditions in the past projected in the future remain extremely hazardous. Nevertheless, even the extrapolation of apparently regular events, like the revolution of the earth, can also lead to errors at the long term, due to tidal forces of the moon rendering the revolution of the earth more slowly, although only significant in billions of years. Thus, any extrapolation from past events after a relatively short time of observation into the far future of billions of years may become doubtful. The extrapolation to the far past is also uncertain. Under the condition that physical laws are constant, one can calculate that the Big Bang occurred about 14 billion years ago. However, how can the constancy of physical laws and constants be verified over such long time periods of billions of years ? The opposite hypotheses that physical laws could have changed, especially during the first periods after the Bib Bang, would allow another interpretation of the anthropic principle, which indicates that the actual fine tuned universe seems to be required for allowing life to emerge. Magueijo (2004) proposed a change of the speed of light during the early universe, which is in opposition to Einstein's constancy of the speed of light. If physical laws had changed in the past, the actual fine tuned universe could have been obtained through evolution, whereas with constant laws, a fine tuned universe seems to need a prior design.

3.7 Projection of Irregular Outcomes into the Future. Only for extremely regular past observations in classical physics, like ocean tides, individual outcomes will be precisely predictable for the future. The situation is different for the extrapolation of highly varying observations grouped around means with timeless values, which can only predict mean future values. However, in new experiments timeless values necessarily acquire new time coordinates, which could not be predicted with timeless extrapolations. In classical physics mathematical equations do not take into account the variability of experimental manipulation errors and only calculate theoretically modeled outcomes. Thereby the precise practical outcomes induced by manipulation errors are unpredictable. Thus, already in classical physics, there is a limited uncertainty for practical outcomes, although it remains relatively small, not producing practical problems. However, in biology variations can become considerable and sometimes threaten an unambiguous interpretation. The chaos theory based on small initial variations might explain some of such variations.

In quantum mechanics, variations are also considerable, but for different reasons due to Heisenberg's uncertainty principle as well as to instrumental variations. The measurement of location of elementary particles can no longer provide a precise measurement of their velocity and leads to variations. The physical wave function allows the extrapolation of timeless values only as probabilities into the future and the variability of outcomes is mathematically calculated by superposition of timeless values. Even in classical physics, precise time coordinates including manipulation errors cannot be predicted, so that the expected values and their time coordinates remain uncertain. In quantum mechanical experiments the superposition of outcomes cannot be observed, only individual outcomes are found, which correspond to their probable timeless values and seem to appear randomly. Therefore, multiple repetitions are needed for statistically significant outcomes.

Complete knowledge on all past and future events from the initial Bib Bang to the final Big Freeze seems to be achieved by the extrapolation of physical formalism into the far past and the final future. A physical "theory of everything", unifying all physical forces in one unique theory, could be considered as complete knowledge on the whole universe including the whole past and future. Such a view on the universe resembles the philosophical theory of eternalims, already evoked by the Greek philosopher Parmenides and is also called Block-universe (Savitt, 2013). However, the block-universe can only be a model in mental representation and its exact correspondence to extra- mental reality can never be verified for the far past and the final future and necessarily remains a mathematical model with uncertainty.

4. McTaggert's Unreality of Time

The philosopher McTaggart (1908) distinguished between the positions in time, the A-series as past, present and future, the B-series as earlier and later and the C-series as ordering of events. The A- series was explained with the example of the death of Queen Anne, which is for an observer first a future event, then becomes a present and finally a past event. Thus, the same event acquires a different character, which seems to be in contradiction with the unicity of the physical event of the death of Queen Anne happening only once. However, an observer can in his mental representation position the death of the Queen with respect to his own NOW. Then the death could be expected in the observer's future, or happening in his present or was already finished in his past. Thereby the A- series of past, present and future comprises in addition to the unique biological fact a relation to the observer's NOW, whereas the B series concerning earlier and later and the C-series considering an ordering are no longer positioned in relation to the observer, but with respect to each other. Therefore the A, B and C series as relations belong to mental representations.

Mc Taggert argues that the A-series is unreal. The notion of "real" is generally considered to distinguish between the extra-mental and the mental representation world. In this sense, Mc Taggert's seems to interpret the A-series as a mental manifestation, which he considers as unreal and thereby an illusion. There is agreement with Mc Taggert, that the A-series corresponds to mental representation and relations to the personal NOW. However, why should mental representation be an "illusion "? Mental representation reality in the mind can be considered as real and existent in the same sense as the extra-mental world. Thus, there is no illusion, there are two realities with different properties, but not always corresponding to each other.

In mental representation, the notion of time has two aspects, a more qualitative biological and a pure quantitative physical aspect. In biology, time can be considered as a perception of duration with boundaries (Bergson 1992), which is more qualitative and corresponds to the inner time clock, also necessary in biology for the circadian rhythm (Wearden, 2005). Time evaluated with the inner time clock can be considered as perception, similar to visual, auditive or temperature perception depending on specialized sense organs. All sense organs are activated by a physical factor, such as seeing by electromagnetic waves, hearing by mechanical waves and heat feeling by molecular agitation. Eagleman (2009, p 1841) proposed a physical factor for time perception: "the experience of duration is a signature of the amount of energy expended in representing a stimulus, i.e. the coding efficiency." Psychological time perception is opposed to the fixity of physical time and therefore allows a mental time travel between the past, the present and the future (Corbalis 2014).

The physical aspect of time is necessarily only quantitative and therefore restricted to the boundaries of durations, since they can be set in relation to intervals of other systems in extra-mental reality. Thus, the qualitative aspect of time in biology as perception of duration becomes in physics reduced to its boundaries, which can be compared to other time intervals, such as the revolution of the earth, counted as one day with its fractions. The more qualitative biological perception of the inner time clock is not identical to physical relations. For short durations, less than a second, time perception can resemble physical relations, although duration estimations in psychological tests can be shorter or longer than the corresponding physical relations (Eagleman, 2009). This proves that the inner clock is a biological perception of time, which is different from physical relations, but it has biological functions, like the circadian rhythm adapting biological activity to the day and night rhythm. For short durations the inner time clock and physical clocks seem to have good correspondence, but for durations shorter than the flicker frequency or very long in the range of years or centuries, the inner time perception is no longer adapted and only relations to extra-mental systems like clocks can replace time perception in mental representation. The high concentration of information in physical formalism is also unadapted for time representation, however, time reappears, when the abstract formalism of physical laws is applied to new concrete experiments (Jansen 2011, a).

6. Conclusions

The observer creates within his mental functions a representation of extra-mental physical reality. Both exist simultaneously, but are not always in contact with each other and can diverge. Only during the present, the observer is in direct physical contact with extra-mental reality due to "elementary sensation" with physico-neural contact through his sense organs. After interrupting the contact, the observer can with his mental functions transform regularity of past observations to physical theories and extrapolate them to the far past and final future. In the present, during the direct contact with physical reality, all observations have precise time coordinates. Once the direct contact is interrupted, memorized observations undergo important transformations into abstract, often timeless concepts for classical as well as for quantum physics. Thereby, timeless mathematical formalism becomes the bases of physical theories for the prediction of an unobservable past or future. Between the reality of the NOW and the potentiality of the future there is an important gap, the Reality-Potentiality Gap (RePoGap), which can be permanently verified by everybody, when potential projects imagined in mental representation cannot always be realized in extra-mental reality.

Time defined as duration with boundaries exists in both, mental representation and extra-mental reality during direct contact in the NOW. Partial physical timelessness corresponds to the reduction of duration to its boundaries, only considering the relations between systems in physical equations. However, time reappears, when physical laws are again verified in new experiments in a new present. The NOW is the only access of mental representation to extra-mental reality, whereas past and future are only mental representation models for extra-mental reality. Thus, physical formalism for the whole universe can only be considered as a "mathematical model universe".

All physical theories are necessarily based on an observer, who is the only one to collect observations and thereafter to transform them into physical theories. Only when the observer is not considered, a "theory of everything" could give the impression of complete knowledge similar to the philosophical concept of eternalism of Parmenides. However, if the observer is still considered as an important factor in the conception of physical theories, his uncertainty about the unverifiable extrapolation to the far past and the final future has also to be respected. There seems to be a semantic problem with the concept of time. Time perception could only be an illusion, if visual perceptions reduced to physical wave lengths is also considered as illusion. But then every reduction to more basic physical entities should be an illusion and the word losses its original sense. Misinterpretation after unclear sensory experience remains the essential meaning of illusion, whereas any reduction to lower level physical factors should not be considered as illusion. If a future "theory of everything "only considers relations between systems, the notions of present, past and future will disappear in the physical formalism. In this sense Barbour (2009, p.1) might be interpreted when claiming "Duration and the behavior of clocks emerge from a timeless law that governs change". In agreement with Barbour, physical equations essentially consider timeless relations conceived in mental representation, but during the verification of timeless laws in new experiments with a new NOW, time emerges again with duration and boundaries and the behavior of clocks indicates time again.

REFERENCES

Bohr, N. (1958/1987), Essays 1932–1957 on Atomic Physics and Human Knowledge, reprinted as The Philosophical Writings of Niels Bohr, Vol. II, Woodbridge: Ox Bow Press.

Baird, P. (2013). Information, universality and consciousness: a relational perspective. Mind and Matter, 11.1, 21-43.

Barbour, J. (2009). The Nature of Time. arXiv:0903.3489 (gr-qc)

Barbour, J (2008). Youtube, a video on "Killing time " http://www.youtube.com/watch?v=WKsNraFxPwk

Bergson, H. (1992). The Creative Mind. tr., Mabelle L. Andison, The Citadel Press, New York. translation of "La Pensée et le mouvant" [1946].

Berlucchi, G. (2014). Mental Time Travel: How the Mind Escapes from the Present. Commentary on Michael C. Corballis's Essay. Cosmology, 18. 146-150.

Bitbol, M. (2008). Is Consciousness Primary? NeuroQuantology, 6.1, 53-71.

Bruner, J. (2011) in Alan S. & Gary J. Perception, Attribution, and Judgment of Others. Organizational Behaviour: Understanding and Managing Life at Work Vol. 7

Buks, E., Schuster, R., Heiblum, M., Mahalu, D., Umansky, V,. (1998) Dephasing in electron interference by a 'which-path' detector. Nature 391, 871-874.

Chalmers, D.J. (2003) Consciousness and its Place in Nature. in (S. Stich and F. Warfield, eds) Blackwell Guide to the Philosophy of Mind , Blackwell, Oxford, UK. 102 – 142.

Corbalis, M.C., (2014). Mental Time Travel: How The Mind Escapes From The Present. Cosmology, 18. 139-145.

Craik & Lockhart (1972) Levels of Processing: A Framework for Memory Research. J. Verbal Learning and Verbal Behavior, 11, 671-684.

David, M. (2009). The Correspondence Theory of Truth. (Stanford Encyclopedia of Philosophy)

Dennett, D. C. (2004). Freedom evolves. London: Allen Lane.

Eagleman, D. M. and Pariyadath V. (2009). Is subjective duration a signature of coding efficiency? Phil. Trans. R. Soc. B, 364, 1841–1851.

Frisch, C. von (1963). Bees: Their Vision, Chemical Senses, and Language.

Vail-Ballou Press, Inc. Cornell University Press, Ithaca, New York.

Fuchs, C.A., Mermin N.D. and Schack R. (2013). An introduction to QBism with an application to the locality of quantum mechanics. arXiv: 1311.5253v1 (quant-ph).

Ganis, G. and Schendan, H. E. (2008). Visual mental imagery and perception produce opposite adaptation effects on early brain potentials. NeuroImage, 42, 1714–1727.

Hamilton, D. L. (1996). The Geophysical Effects of the Earth's Slowing Rotation. The Mind of Mankind, Suna Press, New York.

Heisenberg, W. (1927), "Über den anschaulichen Inhalt der quantentheoretischen Kinematik und Mechanik", Zeitschrift für Physik 43 (3–4): 172–198.

Hookway, C. (2013). Pragmatism. Stanford Encyclopedia of Philosophy.

James, W. (1907). Pragmatism. In: Pragmatism and The Meaning of Truth. Harvard University Press, 1975. Cambridge, Mass.

Jansen, F. K. (2008). Partial isomorphism of superposition in potentiality systems of consciousness and quantum mechanics. NeuroQuantology, 6.3, 278-288.

Jansen, F.K. (2011a). Isomorphism of hidden but existing time in quantum mechanical formalism and human consciousness. NeuroQuantology, 9.2, 288-298.

Jansen, F.K. (2011b). Isomorphic concepts for uncertainty between consciousness and some interpretations of quantum mechanics. NeuroQuantology, 9.4, 660-668.

Jansen, F.K. (2014). Elementary and memory perception versus cognition with implications for the brain-consciousness problem. Congress : Towards a Science of Consciousness, Tucson AZ.

Joseph (2011). Quantum Physics and the Multiplicity of Mind: Split-Brains, Fragmented Minds, Dissociation, Quantum Consciousness. In Consciousness and the Universed, Penrose, R. (ed). Cosmology Science Publishers.

Joseph (2014) The Time Machine of Consciousness, Cosmology 14, 400-450
Lykan W.G. (2012). Consciousness. in The Cambridge Handbook of Cognitive Science (Frankish K. and Ramsey W M eds) p 213, Cambridge University Press, Cambridge.

Magueijo, J. (2004). Faster than the speed of light: the story of a scientific speculation. Arrow Books, London. ISBN:9780099428084.

McTaggart, J. (1908). The unreality of time. Mind, 17, 457-473.

O'Callaghan, C. Perception (2012) in The Cambridge Handbook of Cognitive Science (Frankish K. and Ramsey W.M. eds) p 76, Cambridge University Press, Cambridge.

Pothos, E. M. and Wills, A. J. (Eds. 2011). Formal approaches in categorization. University Press, Cambridge.

Pothos, E.M. and Busemeyer, J.R. (2009). A quantum probability explanation for violations of 'rational ' decision theory. Proc. R. Soc. B rspb. 2009.0121.

Price, D. J. deSolla (1975) Gears from the Greeks: The Antikythera Mechanism – A calendar computer from ca. 80 BC. Science History Publications, New York

Pusch, R., von der Emde, G., Hollmann, M., Bacelo, J., Nöbel, S., Grant, K., Engelmann, J. (2008). Active sensing in a mormyrid fish: electric images and peripheral modifications of the signal carrier give evidence of dual foveation. J Exp Biol., 211 921-34.

Rovelli, C. (2009). Forget time. arXiv:0903.3832v3 [gr-qc] 27 Mar 2009 (Essay for FQXi). Savitt, S. (2013). Being and Becoming in Modern Physics (Stanford Encyclopedia of Philosophy).

Schwartz, J.M., Stapp,H.P, and Beauregard, M. (2004). Quantum theory in neuroscience and psychology: a neurophysical model of mind/brain interaction. Phil. Trans. Royal Society, B 360(1458) 1309-27 (2005)]

Straulino, S. (2008). Reconstruction of Galileo Galilei's experiment: the inclined plane. Physics Education, 43.3, 316-321.

Trueblood, J.S. and Busemeyer, J.R. (2012). Quantum Information Processing Theory. In: D. Quinones (Vol. Ed.) and N. M. Seel (Ed. in Chief) Encyclopedia of the Sciences of Learning (pp. 2748-2751). Springer, New York.

Wearden, J. H. (2005). Origines et développement des théories d'horloge interne du temps psychologique [Origin and development of internal clock theories of psychological time]. Psychologie Francaise, 50, 7 – 25.

Wigner, E.P. (1962). Remarks on the mind-body question. In: Good LG. The scientist speculates. Heinemann, London , 284-302.

Wu, L.-Q. and Dickman, J.D. (2012). Neural Correlates of a Magnetic Sense, Science, 336. 6084, 1054-1057, http://dx.doi.org/10.1126/science.1216567

Zeh, H.D. (1970). On the interpretation of measurements in quantum theory. Found. Phys.1, 69-76 Zeh, H.D. (1998). Über die Zeit in der Nature. In Evolution und Irreversibilität H.J. Krug & L.Pohlmann, Dunker und Humblot. Berlin.

Zeh, H.D. (2013). The role of the observer in the Everett interpretation. NeuroQantology, 11, 97-105.

19. Synchronicity, Entanglement, Quantum Information and the Psyche

Francois Martin[1], Federico Carminati[2], Giuliana Galli Carminati[3]

[1]Laboratoire de Physique Theorique et Hautes Energies, Universities Paris
[2]Physicist at CERN, Geneva, Switzerland.
[3]Mental Development Psychiatry Unit - Adult Psychiatry Service, Department of Psychiatry, University Hospitals of Geneva, Switzerland

Abstract

In this paper we describe synchronicity phenomena. As an explanation of these phenomena we propose quantum entanglement between the psychic realm known as the "unconscious" and also the classical illusion of the collapse of the wave-function. Then, taking the theory of quantum information as a model we consider the human unconscious, pre-consciousness and consciousness as sets of quantum bits (qu-bits). We analyze how there can be communication between these various qu-bit sets. In doing this we are inspired by the theory of nuclear magnetic resonance. In this manner we build quantum processes that permit consciousness to "read" the unconscious and vice-versa. The most elementary interaction, e.g. between a pre-consciousness qu-bit and a consciousness one, allows us to predict the time evolution of the pre-consciousness + consciousness system in which pre-consciousness and consciousness are quantum entangled. This time evolution exhibits Rabi oscillations that we name mental Rabi oscillations. This time evolution shows how, for example, the unconscious can influence consciousness and vice-versa. In a process like mourning the influence of the unconscious on consciousness, as the influence of consciousness on the unconscious, are in agreement with what is observed in psychiatry.

Key Words: Synchronicity, quantum entanglement, quantum information, consciousness, unconscious.

1 Synchronicity Effects

Synchronicity phenomena are characterized by a significant coincidence which appears between a (subjective) mental state and an event occurring in the (objective) external world. The notion was introduced by the Swiss psychoanalyst Carl Gustav Jung and further studied together with Wolfgang Pauli (Jung and Pauli, 1955). Jung referred to this phenomenon as "acausal parallelism" which are linked by an "acausal connecting principle." Synchronicity effects show no causal link between the two events that are correlated.

We can distinguish two types of synchronicity phenomena. The first one is characterized by a significant coincidence between the psyche of two individuals. An example of this type is when two friends at a distance simultaneously buy two identical neckties without having consulted each other beforehand. The significant coincidence appears as a correlation between the psyche of the two subjects, suggesting some type of psychic communication. There are many examples of such long range correlations between events which are causally unrelated, or subjects who engage in identical behaviors, often simultaneously: twins, relatives, members of a couple, friends, or scientists who make the same discoveries at around the same time.

For example, in March of 1951, a new comic strip appeared in over a dozen newspapers in the United States, featuring a little blond boy wearing a red and black striped shirt. The boy was called: Dennis The Menace. In the United Kingdom, a new character, a little boy wearing a red and black striped shirt was introduced in a comic book, The Beano. He was also named, Dennis The Menace. The creators of both comics claimed it was a coincidence.

The second type of synchronicity phenomena, which is closer to what was advocated by C.G. Jung, happens when the significant coincidence occurs between a mental state and a physical state. In this case the physical state is symbolically correlated to the mental state by a common meaning. They appear not necessarily simultaneously but in a short interval of time such that the coincidence appears exceptional. Jung referred to these events as "meaningful coincidences."

Another more common example goes as follows: You are sitting at home and begin thinking about an old friend who you had not seen in months, when the phone rings, and its him.

Synchronistic events between mind and matter seem difficult to explain in terms of correlations between conscious or unconscious minds. For Jung, synchronistic events are remnants of a holistic reality - the unus mundus which is based on the concept of a unified reality, a singularity of "One World" from which everything has its origin, and from which all things emerge and eventually return. The unus mundus, or "One World" is related to Plato's concept of the "World of Ideas," and has its parallels in quantum physics. Thus, the unus mundus underlies both mind and matter.

As already stressed, in a synchronicity effect, there is no causal link between correlated events localized in space and time. Synchronicity effects are global phenomena in space and time. They cannot be explained by classical physics. However, in the case of a significant coincidence appearing between the psyche of two individuals one can see an analogy with quantum entanglement (Baaquie and Martin, 2005).

Moreover one can possibly see synchronistic events between the mental and the material domains as a consequence of a quantum entanglement between mind and matter (Primas, 2003). For us mental and material domains of reality will be considered as aspects, or manifestations, of one underlying reality in which mind and matter are unseparated (Atmanspacher, 2004).

Synchronicity phenomena, especially those involving a correlation at a distance between several individuals, lead us to postulate non-localized unconscious mental states in space and time. Although different regions of the brain subserve specific functions (Joseph, 1982, 1992), mental states are not exclusively localized in the human brain. They are correlated to physical states of the brain (possibly via quantum entanglement) but they are not reducible to them.

Since we study the analogy between synchronistic events and quantum entanglement, we treat mental states (conscious and unconscious) as quantum states, i.e. as vectors of a Hilbert space (Baaquie and Martin, 2005). Moreover we treat them as vectors of a Hilbert space of information (Martin, Carminati, Galli Carminati, 2009).

2 Quantum information and the Psyche

We try to apply quantum information to some functions of the Psyche. In classical information, the memory boxes are binary system, called bits, which can take only two values: 0 or 1. A quantum bit (in a shortened form qu-bit) can take all values which are superposition of 0 and 1 (more precisely all superpositions of the states $/0 >$ and $/1 >$). In other words, a qu-bit can take simultaneously the values 0 and 1. Quantum information studies the monitoring of qu-bits. It studies also the transfer of quantum information from one qu-bit to another one (especially via two-qubit quantum logic gates).

As an example of a binary psychic system we have considered the phenomenon of mourning (Galli Carminati and Carminati, 2006): either mourning is achieved (qu-bit 0), either it is not (qu-bit 1). So quantum mechanics allow the existence of all superpositions of the state in which mourning is achieved with the state in which mourning is not achieved.

Quantum mechanics rests upon two fundamental properties. First it is based on the superposition principle (superposition of vector states of an Hilbert space). Second it is based on a fundamental phenomenon called quantum entanglement. This phenomenon manifests itself by the fact that a system of two, or several, quantum entangled particles is "non-separable". In technical terms this means that the wave-function of the two-particle system does not factorize into a product of a wave-function for each particle. The quantum system describing the two particle system is a global system, a non-local one. Moreover, in such a system, the particles are heavily correlated. Therefore, if we measure a certain property of one of the two particles, destroying in this way the "non-separability" of the system, we can predict with certainty the corresponding property of the other particle, even if this one is at the other extreme of the universe. However, there are caveats: the quantum specificity indicates that this property is not determined beforehand, i.e. before measurement. Quantum physics is a non-local and non-realistic theory. Quantum entanglement and the property of "nonseparability" are properties that are fundamentally quantum, that do not exist in "classical physics".

Assuming, with Belal Baaquie (Baaquie and Martin, 2005), the existence of quantum entanglement between the unconscious of two or several persons, we have proposed an explanation of correlations at a distance that appears between two (or several) individuals having affective links. This would constitute an explanation of synchronicity of the first type. It would be interesting to measure in a quantitative manner those unconscious correlations at a distance. May be those correlations could activate neural circuits that could be visible in nuclear magnetic resonance imaging (NMRI).

We propose to measure quantitatively the existence (or the non-existence) of such correlations during group therapies or group training, via "absurd" tests (Galli et al., 2008; Martin et al., 2007, 2009). Those experiments are currently in progress.

Quantum information applied to Psyche allows to explain a certain number of mental processes (Martin, Carminati, Galli Carminati, 2009). We suppose that the mental systems first proposed by Freud (1900, 1915a,b), i.e. the unconscious, pre-consciousness, consciousness, are made up of mental qu-bits. They are sets of mental qu-bits.

Specifically, Freud (1900, 1915ab), saw the mind as consisting of three mental realms; the unconscious, preconscious, and conscious mind, with the unconscious being the deepest, most inaccessible region of the psyche and which contains repressed memories and unacceptable feelings, thoughts, and ideas. The preconscious serves as a bridge, or passageway between the unconscious and conscious mind, and lies just below the surface of consciousness. Freud believed that unconscious impulses must pass through the preconscious which acts as a double doorway; one door leading from the unconscious to the preconscious, and the other from the preconscious to the conscious mind. In this way, the preconscious can censor information and prevent unacceptable impulses and ideas from becoming conscious. However, the preconscious is also the depository of information which has been pushed out of consciousness, and which may be shoved so deeply underground, so to speak, that the information becomes completely unconscious. Therefore, although separated, these mental realms interact and can influence one another.

Inspired by the theory of nuclear magnetic resonance (NMR), we have built a model of handling a mental qu-bit with the help of pulses of a mental field. Starting with an elementary interaction between two qu-bits we build two-qubit quantum logic gates that allow information to be transferred from one qu-bit to the other. For example, we build the controlled-NOT (CNOT) gate in which, under certain circumstances, the information is transferred from the control qu-bit to the target qu-bit. We also build swapping in which there is a complete exchange of information between two qu-bits. In those manners we build quantum processes that permit consciousness to "read" the unconscious and vice-versa. The most elementary interaction, e.g. between a pre-consciousness qu-bit and a consciousness one, allows us to predict the time evolution of the pre-consciousness + consciousness system in which pre-consciousness and consciousness are quantum entangled. This time evolution exhibits Rabi oscillations that we name mental Rabi oscillations. This time evolution shows how, for example, the unconscious can influence consciousness and vice-versa.

The pulses of the mental field can be emitted either by consciousness (effects of will or freewill) or by the unconscious (individual, group or collective). As we said, together with quantum entanglement, they can explain the awareness of unconscious components. In this case we can say that consciousness measures the unconscious like an experimental physics device records a microscopic process. As we said, quantum entanglement explains also the influence of the unconscious on consciousness and the reciprocal influence of consciousness on the unconscious. We have studied these two types of influences in the case of mourning and we have seen how they could allow mourning to be achieved with time.

A third mental process, already mentionned above, is the quantum entanglement between two (or several) unconscious psyches. The evolution in time of the state of the two quantum entangled unconscious shows the reciprocal influence of each unconscious on the other one. Then through the interaction of their two unconscious, a psychoanalyst named Alice can help Bob to achieve relief from his mourning.

The fundamental characteristic of the most elementary interaction between two mental qubits, e.g. between a qu-bit of pre-consciousness and a qu-bit of consciousness, is to highlight, as a function of time, oscillations between two quantum states made of two correlated qu-bits; i.e. the states /I1 > /C0 > and /C1 > /I0 > (I for "Insight" or pre-consciousness and C for "Consciousness").

Let us notice that at the level of the brain, there is evidence of an alternating activity of the two hemispheres (Joseph 1982, 1988). This oscillation expresses itself in the phenomenon of binocular rivalry (Blake, 1989). When two images are presented to each of the two eyes of a subject, they enter in "competition" so that one image is visible while the other is not. The same happens when the subject is presented with two superposed images, a nice metaphor to represent the superposition of two quantum states.

3. The Right and Left Hemisphere

Joseph (1982, 1988) proposed that this oscillating activity and the different functions controlled by the right and left half of the brain, could explain some mental phenomenon associated with the conscious and unconscious mind, with the corpus callosum, a major cord of nerves, linking the two brain halves and thus acting as a bridge between these two mental realms. This is similar to Freud's concept of the preconscious linking the conscious and unconscious mind. Further, Joseph (1982, 1988) linked this oscillating activity to dream recall vs dream forgetting, with the right hemisphere (the domain of visual-spatial imagery and social-emotion) producing the dream during high levels of oscillating activity, and the left (the domain of language and verbal thought) forgetting the dream due to low levels of activity.

Mental (Rabi) oscillations are still to be studied. In particular in the case of the "asleep" consciousness, the unconscious + consciousness system (or at least a part of this system) constantly oscillates between the states $/U1 > /C0 >$ and $/C1 > /U0 >$. A pendulum does not measure time. For this we need a system that keeps the memory of the number of the oscillations of the pendulum. This is a function of a clock, which measures time. In a clock the oscillations of the pendulum have a cumulative effect that allows us to keep the memory of the number of oscillations. In the case of the Rabi oscillations of the unconscious (pre-consciousness)+ consciousness system, we have to imagine a system, correlated to the first one, that is subject to cumulative effects and that allows to memorize the mental Rabi oscillations. In this case, it is only thanks to the storage of the mental Rabi oscillations that consciousness or preconsciousness or the unconscious can be modified.

4. The Limbic System

At the level of the brain this memorization can be actuated by the limbic system, and in particular by the hippocampus (Joseph 1992). To be more specific, the limbic system is the domain of our emotions, and is classically associated with the "four F's:" feeding, fighting, fleeing, and sexual behavior. The amygdala and the hippocampus are some of the main structures of the limbic system, with the amygdala playing a major role in emotional memory, and the hippocampus in storing non-emotional memories. So, in some respects, the limbic system could be compared to the unconscious (Joseph 1992). The limbic system is part of the old brain, and is buried beneath the new brain, which consists of "new cortex," i.e. neocortex. It is the neocortex, particularly that of the left hemisphere, which we associate with human thought, language, rational behavior, and the conscious mind. However, it is the limbic system and the right hemisphere which become most active during dream-sleep (Joseph 1988, 1992).

For an asleep consciousness the perturbations coming from the environment are weak. In these conditions, the mental Rabi oscillations may extend over a time that can be long, probably of the order of several minutes, or more. The situation is totally different for an awaken consciousness. Its interaction with the environment, which operates via the sensory system, perturbs the interaction between pre-consciousness and consciousness and therefore interferes with the oscillations that, as a consequence, cannot last very long. The time for the awaken consciousness to receive an external stimulus being of the order of half a second. The Rabi mental oscillations cannot last more than that.

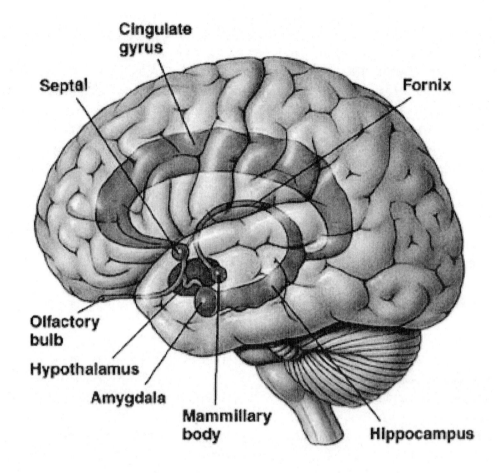

Figure: Limbic System

From a neurological perspective, this can be explained as follows: During dream sleep the left half of the brain is at a low level of activity and it cannot perceive or respond to outside sensory impressions unless they are sufficiently arousing they trigger wakefulness. By contrast, because the right half of the brain and limbic system are at a high level of unconscious-activity during dream-sleep, they can respond to external stimuli (Joseph 1982, 1988). This explains how external stimuli can become incorporated into a dream. A typical example, the dreamer is walking down a strange street when a little boy on a bike rides by ringing a bell. The bell is so loud the dreamer wakes up to discover the alarm clock is ringing. However, upon achieving full awake consciousness, the awake-consciousness may forget the dream; that is, the awake part of the psyche (the left hemisphere) forgets the dream which may remain stored in the limbic system of the right hemisphere. However, later that day, the awake dreamer sees a little boy on a bike ringing his handle-bar bell, and the awake dreamer experiences synchronicity; he remembers his dream.

This same framework can be applied to individuals who engage in the same behaviors. They may respond, unconsciously, to the same stimuli which, for a variety of reasons may not be perceived by the conscious mind. Moreover, these unconscious realms are more closely attuned to the collective unconscious and most probably to the unus mundus, the unified reality from which everything has its origin, and from which all things emerge. Although not perceived by the conscious mind, the unconscious does respond, and then influences the conscious mind of different individuals, who then engage in the same behaviors or come up with the same thoughts or ideas.

5 Conclusions

In summary, some mental phenomena are not explainable in the framework of what we call "classical" mechanics. Let us cite, among others, the phenomenon of awareness, the correlations at a distance between individuals, and more generally the synchronicity phenomena. These three types of phenomena can be explained in the framework of quantum mechanics, particularly, thanks to quantum entanglement for the correlations at a distance between individuals (synchronicity phenomena of type I) and thanks to what we can call the classical illusion of the collapse of the wave-function for the synchronicity phenomena of type II.

Let us notice that the existence of synchronicity phenomena prevents the mental states to be reducible to physical states of the brain. The mental states are correlated to such states, probably via quantum entanglement, but they are not reducible to those states. Therefore this invalidates the materialistic hypothesis.

The projection of our subjectivity in the environment in which we live (synchronicity phenomena of type II), in agreement with quantum mechanics, refutes the local hypothesis ("each individual is in his parcel of space-time") as well as the realistic hypothesis ("the object has a reality well defined independent of the subject who observes it").

As an end let us mention a quantum effect that can have important consequences in mental phenomena, for example for awareness (for the emergence of consciousness). It is the Bose- Einstein condensation, in which each particle looses its individuality in favour of a collective, global behaviour.

References

Atmanspacher, H. (2004). Quantum theory and consciousness: an overview with selected exam- ples, Discrete Dynamics in Nature and Society, 1, 51-73 (2004)

Baaquie, B.E., and Martin, F. (2005). Quantum Psyche - Quantum Field Theory of the Human Psyche, NeuroQuantology, 3, 7-42.

Blake, R. (1989). A neural theory of binocular rivalry, Psychological Review, 96, 145-167

Freud, S. (1900). The Interpretation of Dreams. Standard Edition, 5, 339-622.

Freud, S. (1915a). Repression. Standard Edition, 14, 141-158.

Freud, S. (1915b). Repression. Standard Edition, 14, 159-204.

Galli Carminati, G., and Martin, F. (2008). Quantum mechanics and the Psyche, Physics of Particles and Nuclei, Vol. 39, 560-577.

Galli Carminati, G., and Carminati, F. (2006). The mechanism of mourning: an anti-entropic mechanism, NeuroQuantology Journal, 4, 186-197.

Joseph, R. (1982). The Neuropsychology of Development. Hemispheric Laterality, Limbic Language, the Origin of Thought. Journal of Clinical Psychology, 44, 4-33.

Joseph, R. (1988). The Right Cerebral Hemisphere: Emotion, Music, Visual-Spatial Skills, Body Image, Dreams, and Awareness. Journal of Clinical Psychology, 44, 630-673.

Joseph, R. (1992). The Limbic System: Emotion, Laterality, and Unconscious Mind. The Psychoanalytic Review, 79, 405-456.

Jung, C. G., and Pauli, W. (1955). The Interpretation of Nature and the Psyche, Pantheon, New York, translated by P. Silz (1955); german original: Naturekluarung und Psyche, Rascher, Zurich (1952).

Martin, F., and Galli Carminati, G. (2007). Synchronicity, Quantum Mechanics and Psyche, talk given at the Conference on "Wolfgang Pauli's Philosophical Ideas and Contemporary Science", May 20-25, 2007, Monte Verita, Ascona, Zwitzerland; published in Recasting Reality, pp. 227-243, Springer-Verlag, (2009).

Martin, F., Carminati, F., and Galli Carminati, G. (2009). Quantum information, oscillations and the Psyche, to be published in Physics of Particles and Nuclei (2009).

Primas, H. (2003). Time-Entanglement Between Mind and Matter, Mind and Matter, Vol. 1, 81-119.

20. Consciousness, the Paranormal and Higher Dimensions

Horace W. Crater[1] and Stan V. McDaniel[2]

[1]The University of Tennessee Space Institute Tullahoma, TN

[2]Sonoma State University (Emeritus), Rohnert Park, CA

Abstract:

In the 1800s it was hypothesized by some scientists that the actions of things or beings in a realm of four spatial dimensions, relative to which we might occupy an embedded hypersurface of only three spatial dimensions, might account for some paranormal phenomena perceived by us. That idea was subsequently dismissed. We here consider what issues might be involved if the hypothesis regarding paranormal phenomena were to be re-evaluated in view of the type of contemporary extra-dimensional theory proposed in Randall and Sundrum (Randall, 1999) and Randall (Randall 2005).

Keywords: consciousness, time, quantum physics, paranormal, hypersurface, branes, extra-dimensions

1 Paranormal Phenomena and Extra-Dimensional Theory

In his 1884 book Flatland: A Romance of Many Dimensions, Edwin A. Abbott described how things, including beings like ourselves, who live in a realm with three spatial dimensions (width, length and depth), might appear to those limited to a flat embedded surface (Flatland) having just two spatial dimensions (width and length) and unable to perceive depth. In the 1800s it was argued even by prominent scientists that our realm of three spatial dimensions might be embedded in a universe of four spatial dimensions, and that 4-dimensional beings within that larger spatial realm might be experienced by us as ghosts or spirits. These would perhaps be knowable only by mediums or clairvoyants. (A good historical account of this is to be found in Kaku, 1994).

Although this idea was eventually abandoned, here we explore whether such paranormal phenomena as reincarnation, telepathy, communication with the dead and memories of past lives might fit into an updated analogy based on the theory that our four-dimensional universe (3 dimensions of space plus one of time) may be embedded within a five-dimensional universe (4 dimensions of space plus one of time) as such a universe is proposed in Randall and Sundrum (Randall, 1999) and Randall (Randall 2005). Our examination of the issues involves correlating various unique features of the theory with aspects of such paranormal phenomena. Our aim is not a rigorous verification of the validity of these correlations but rather an attempt at determining their degree of plausibility or implausibility; and if they appear to be plausible, what further experimental determinations may be necessary to raise the level of plausibility.

2 Higher Physical Dimensions

Renewed speculations about "extra" or "higher" dimensions have appeared in many different varieties in the physics literature since the work of Kaluza (Kaluza, 1921) and Klein (Klein, 1926) in the 1920s, and more recently with the advent of modern string theory (Green, 1984); Zwiebach, 2004). Kaluza and Klein showed that by extending Einstein's equation to a universe of five space-time dimensions they could unify the forces of gravity and electromagnetism into a single equation. In string theory, strings were hypothesized as one- dimensional objects within a space which has nine spatial dimensions, (six in addition to length, width and depth). Although infinitesimally small, strings are not points, which have no spatial extension at all.

Advances in string theory in the 1990's brought about the proposal that there could be other structures in space-time with zero thickness in one or more dimensions up to one less than the proposed 9 spatial directions. Thus, for example, the possibility of two-dimensional surfaces with zero thickness was considered. Just as the string was not limited to straight, zero thickness lines, but could have arbitrary curvature and in fact be closed, so the two-dimensional surfaces could be curved and be closed like a spherical surface. The concept of "branes" then followed, being objects that had zero thickness in one or more dimensions--The electron, quark, and other fundamental particles are thought to be true points, 0D objects in 4D space-time, but always accompanied by electromagnetic or chromodynamic fields. They have the effect of giving atoms and nuclei an effective size--angstrom and fermi respectively.

The authors have borrowed the concept of branes from the extended string theory but limit themselves to only one, two, or three extra spatial dimensions. We focus our attention on the Randall-Sundrum model (Randall, 1999, 2005) which proposes just one extra spatial dimension. In that model, the term brane describes our four-dimensional space-time (4D) as an "object" within a five dimensional (5D) space-time, called the bulk. The bulk, in addition to the time dimension, has four spatial dimensions corresponding to coordinates x, y, z and w. The brane has zero thickness in the w dimension and thus in effect has only three measurable spatial dimensions. The brane is an idealization just like the point electron, but although there is no universally accepted and tested theory for branes, like QED for the electron, treating the brane as a 0 w thickness object, as discussed later, gives results of a very profound nature, solving the Hierarchy problem. The brane and bulk are related in that the brane is said to be a kind of boundary of the bulk. As a result there will be a relation between the "size" of the bulk and that of the brane. The bulk must extend in some of its dimensions as far as does its "boundary" i.e. the brane. In the original Randall-Sundrum model (Randall, 1999), the bulk or 5-dimensional realm extends between our brane and a parallel brane (See Fig. 1). The forms of this and the following 5 figures were based on those given in (Randall, 2005).

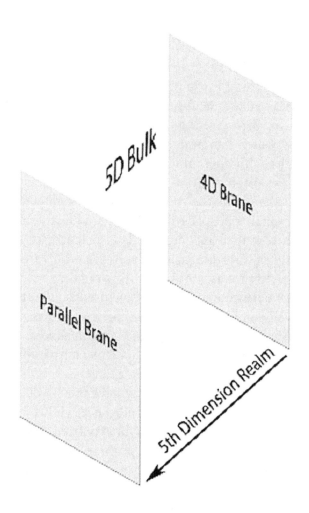

Figure 1. Randall-Sundrum Higher Dimensional Model

Returning for the moment to the "Flatland" idea, we engage in a thought experiment. Consider the model of a hand. (The content of this paragraph first appeared as a contribution of one of the authors (HWC) to a recently published book (Weiss 2012).) Take your hand and place the fingertips on a flat surface (a large enough flat surface would represent a Flatlander's Universe) Now, suppose the impression made by the fingers tips on the flat surface represents five Flatlanders. The Flatlanders are two-dimensional, having only the dimensions of length and width. Their physical interactions would correspond to the tips of your fingers becoming sufficiently near to one another on the flat surface. The fingers, however, represent larger 3-dimensional bodies of which the two-dimensional flatlanders are a kind of extension. In this hypothetical scenario instead of "ghosts or spirits" these 3-dimensional bodies would be part of the Flatlanders themselves, but unseen by them and invisible to their physical science.

This consideration raises a question regarding the mental activities of these apparently divided beings. Since the "fingers" are connected with each other (by belonging to the same "hand"), we might imagine a possibility of the sharing of thoughts from one "finger" to another. This idea need only suppose that the mental activity of the total person is not limited to the two- dimensional body in Flatland but is a capability possessed by the total self comprised of both the Flatland body and the 3-dimensional extension of that body (the "finger"). Another consequence of such a proposal is that the sense of selfhood is divided between the two "bodies" such that the Flatlander, at least, is unable under normal circumstances to be aware of the higher dimensional component of itself. This particular idea will be addressed a bit later on. In the meantime let us refer to the Flatlander as the "ego self" and the addition of the "finger" to the Flatlander as the "total self." As to what the relation between the minds and the bodies of these beings may be, we take no position but leave that as the same question that exists in philosophy and science today and has not yet been resolved.

Now what happens when the two-dimensional Flatlander dies? Lift your finger from the flat surface, leaving behind the two-dimensional "body" of the three-dimensional entity. As time passes, that same finger arches back down toward the plane, and plants itself at a different location. The finger in effect becomes associated with another two-dimensional Flatlander body. Although again the newly "born" Flatlander would under normal circumstances be unaware of the existence of its extended self, if the 3-dimensional finger retains memories of its association with its previous Flatlander body, a phenomenon similar to that of reincarnation and memories of past lives would be implied.

In our thought experiment the physical Flatlander is the action of the "tip" of the three- dimensional "finger" on the surface of Flatland. The two-dimensional flatlander and the three- dimensional "finger" are in some sense a single entity sharing the same consciousness, but the conceptual framework within which the Flatlander is normally constrained renders it very difficult, though perhaps not impossible, for the Flatlander to become aware of the existence of the "finger." Although (in this hypothetical scenario) the self-awareness of any individual Flatlander dissipates upon death, the death of the Flatlander does not bring about the death of its 3-dimensional extended body.

Thus we have in effect a divided self. But by the "fingertip" analogy the lower-dimensional being and its higher-dimensional extension are connected, at the very least by some kind of energy exchange. What then might be the nature of this connection? To what degree might it be a reciprocal relation? (Strangely enough this dilemma is somewhat presaged by the problem encountered by Descartes, who argued that although mind and body are separate "substances" the link between them was through the pineal gland. There was no way to explain how this link might be accomplished, since the two substances were diametrically opposed). And why should the extended higher-dimensional "body" remain after the death of its lower- dimensional component? In what follows we will discuss some of these questions in relation to a version of the theory incorporating the Randall-Sundrum model.

3 Energy Relations of Bulk and Brane

Our investigation focuses on the question whether it is physically coherent to propose that conscious beings, seemingly dwelling only on a brane of zero thickness in the w direction, in fact extend into the w direction (the fourth spatial dimension). As described above, the Randall- Sundrum extra-dimensional concept posits a five-dimensional universe called the bulk, within which is embedded a four-dimensional universe called the brane. Applying this idea to our topic, we ask (a) whether there can be any energy exchange between bulk and brane, and (b) whether there can be enough complexity of structure within the 5D bulk to support the possibility of an extended 5D body of the 4D selves which are limited to the brane. In terms of the "finger- fingertip" analogy, the "fingertips" would be our 4D selves and the "fingers" would correspond to their 5D extended bodies located in the bulk. Also we need to address the issue of how the 5D structures might continue to exist after the death of the 4D selves.

In the models presented in (Arkani- Hamed, 1998) and (Randall, 1999) all energy forms, with one exception, are unable to leave the four-dimensional brane. That one exception is gravity, in the forms of static gravitational fields, gravitational waves and their quanta, the zero mass graviton, and its harmonic excitations, the so-called Kaluza Klein particles (Landsburg, 2006; Chatrchyan, 2012). Since gravity is intimately tied to the curvature of space, it would exist in any extension of space to a higher dimension, and thus in the bulk. We will use the term gravity to refer to any of the above manifestations either in our brane or more generally in the bulk. We will use the term matter to refer to all other energy forms including electrons, quarks, photons, and every quanta of all forms of energy which in the models of Arkani- Hamed (1998) and Randall (1999) are restricted to the brane and do not penetrate the bulk (see Fig. 2).

In the Randall-Sundrum model, the five-dimensional bulk contains only gravitational energy. This would require that any extension of the material bodies of individuals in the brane would necessarily be some kind of structures, or organs, made up purely of gravity (as defined above). The total "body" of an individual would thus include a specifically gravitational component located within the bulk. How might this be possible? We consider two aspects: extension into a higher dimension and the field concept. Somewhat analogous to this is that of the point electron which by virtue of its electromagnetic field extends its influence from zero dimensions to three dimensions. Analogous to this would also be the reciprocal connection between a thin and dense material 2D plane and its gravitational field in the 3D space above and below it. The connection between the material body in the brane and its associated gravitational field in the bulk would also be reciprocal

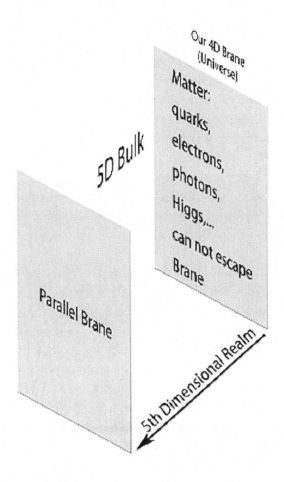

Figure 2. *Matter is confined to our brane*

The third question posed at the end of the last section was "why should the extended higher-dimensional form remain after the death of its lower-dimensional component"? As an analogy, consider that the source of a traveling electromagnetic wave is an accelerating charge. However, when that charge stops accelerating, the traveling electromagnetic field continues on as a pulse. Granted, we are relying on electromagnetic and lower dimensional analogies. But building on analogies is at the very heart of progress in theoretical physics. (Think of the once bizarre concept of de Broglie's matter waves and its progeny the Schrodinger equation.) However, these answers generate in turn further glaring questions. How would it be possible to detect gravitational signals from a higher dimensional space? And, wouldn't gravity's notorious weakness cut off at the start this idea of gravity being the medium through which communication between gravitational "bodies" in the bulk and material bodies in the brane might operate? Even if detectable, how could gravity waves convey information back and forth from the material bodies in the brane (presumably in particular the brains of those individuals) to its purely gravitational extension in the bulk? With these questions in mind we now review aspects of the Randall-Sundrum theory of higher dimensional gravity.

Randall and Sundrum proposed an extra-dimensional extension of Einstein's general relativity for the purpose of solving what is known as the Hierarchy Problem (Randall, 1999). It is known that at a reasonable energy scale the electromagnetic and the weak and strong nuclear forces have approximately the same strength. The gravitational interaction, however, remains in comparison extremely weak. For example, the ratio between the attractive gravitational force between two electrons and their electrostatic repulsive force at equal distances is on the order of 10-41.

In the simplest form of the Randall-Sundrum model they found a resolution of the problem of the relative weakness of the gravitational force by proposing a two brane plus bulk model, in which our locale is the so-called "weak" brane, while on the so-called "strong" brane the gravitational interaction is comparable in strength to the other three interactions--because of this it is also referred to as the "gravity brane", here we call it simply the "parallel brane." Using very simple and plausible assumptions about the Einstein gravitational metric and source terms in the Einstein equations, in particular the tension or stress on the two branes, they then solved the resultant Einstein equations in the intervening "space" between the two branes, i.e. in the bulk. They found that the presence of tension on the branes had a dramatic effect on the strength of the gravitational interaction between the two branes. The strength decreases exponentially from the parallel brane to the weak brane by a factor of about 1016. The distance between the branes was very small (1 or 2 orders of magnitude greater than the Planck length) but the exponential factor explained the dramatic decrease in gravitational interaction. It turns out to be not so much an exponential decrease in the Newton gravitational constant as it is an exponential decrease in the inertial masses of the fundamental matter constituents in the weak brane. Because of the equivalence principle, this means that the gravitational mass of the matter constituents on the weak brane are also exponentially small compared with their counterparts on the parallel brane.

As noted above, in their model the only form of energy in the bulk is gravity as defined above, which includes the ordinary massless gravitons but also harmonic excitations of the gravitons, called Kaluza-Klein particles. In the bulk between the two branes, if ordinary gravitons bounce back and forth between the two branes so that they have an additional kinetic energy due to their motion perpendicular to the weak brane, they in effect turn into higher vibrational modes in a wave description (as with a vibrating string tied between two fixed points, a more energetic excitation will cause the string to have more nodes). If these excited graviton states in the bulk make their way into our brane, then two very counterintuitive circumstances arise. Unlike the hypothetical spin-two graviton (two units of Planck's constant), which is massless, these excited states appear as massive spin-two particles (see Fig.3).

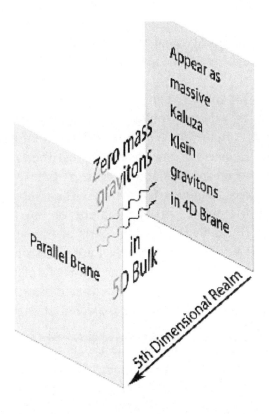

Figure 3. *Imprint of higher dimensional world*

To quote Randall (2005) these Kaluza Klein particles "are the four dimensional (space- time) imprint of the higher dimensional world." How do they pick up this extra mass? Strictly speaking, this comes from solving the 5D Einstein equation in the two brane configuration proposed by Randall and Sundrum [H. Davoudiasi, 1999]. However, one can gain heuristic insight into the origin of the Kaluza Klein masses in our 4D brane without using the 5D Einstein equation by an elementary extension of the Einstein energy mass relation $E = mc^2$. Stated in words, the fourth spatial component of the momentum (perpendicular to the brane) of the graviton in the bulk can only be perceived in the brane as an effective mass.

The second counterintuitive circumstance that arises from the graviton excitations passing from the bulk into the brane, (again derived from the same set of Einstein equations which predict the possible spectrum of higher mode gravitons (KK particles)), is that unlike the ordinary graviton, which couples very weakly to matter with Newton's constant G, the Kaluza- Klein excitations of the graviton would couple to the mass of matter in the brane with a Newton's constant G multiplied by a huge exponential factor of about 10^{16} , allowing it to produce observable effects in ordinary matter. A zero mass graviton in the bulk traveling in the w direction perpendicular to the brane will be detected there in the brane as a spin-two Kaluza Klein particle with non-zero mass. Its appearance would appear to violate energy conservation in the brane. In principle such a massive particle could be detected passively by its decay to ordinary matter particles in the brane.

The same coupling of the KK particles from the bulk to ordinary matter in the brane that allows this decay would also permit the reverse of this process whereby matter particles in the brane collide with one another and produce a KK particle in the brane. Because of the connection between the KK particles and the bulk, the allowed spectrum of energies of the particles would be the same as that observed by the passive mode. In either case their subsequent decays could be detected with a clearly defined decay signature for a particle with spin 2. The model makes a range of predictions of the center of momentum energies of the excitations which will be tested at the new Large Hadron Collider (LHC). In early tests at the lower end of this range, no evidence of these excitations has been found (CMS, 2011). However, the fact that the tests have been and are actually being carried out attests that the expected strength of the interaction would be substantial.

The Einstein geodesic equations and the Einstein field equations show that when matter is restricted to the 4D weak brane, gravity-based energy forms in the bulk are directly affected by and have a direct effect on what takes place in the 4D brane. This provides a possible physical mechanism for the interchange of energy and information between matter-based organisms in the brane and gravitational energies in the bulk. Given the above considerations, we may ask what gravity-based energy forms might there be that could transfer back and forth between bulk and brane, and would they not be overwhelmed by other energy forms?

Since gravity in our brane is incredibly weak in comparison with the other interactions, one might think that any signals between brane and bulk would be overwhelmed by the noise of other interactions. If so it would be impossible to detect in the bulk any gravitational changes associated causally with, for example, human brain activity. But since matter and its interactions are forbidden to manifest directly in the bulk, gravity would not have to compete at all with any matter-based energy forms. Therefore the weakness of ordinary gravity in the brane would not be a factor in the bulk.

However, there are plenty of gravity-based noise sources in the brane that could influence the bulk in addition to ones originating in our brains or nervous systems. If I wave the little finger of my left hand I create a gravitational disturbance perhaps at least as great, and probably much greater, than any gravitational signals coming from my brain or nervous system. But if my (hypothetical) extended self in the bulk behaves like a tuning fork, resonating only with vibrations having a frequency characteristic of the fork, this would provide a way in which that part of the bulk associated with our own 4D selves would not be overwhelmed by other gravitational disturbances either from the brane or within the bulk. This would require, of course, that gravity-based energy forms originating in the brain/brane must have a very well defined frequency.

What about gravitational energy forms entering the brane from the bulk? To be detected by the brains of organisms in the brane they would not only have to compete with other gravitational energy forms but also the myriad of matter-based energy forms. Weak, ordinary zero-mode gravity signals coming from the bulk would be virtually impossible to be noticed because they would be drowned out by the much stronger matter-based reactions. However, this would not necessarily be true of higher mode gravitons propagating into the brane from the bulk. They would indeed be much more likely to be noticeable because they interact with matter by a factor up to 10^{16} times greater than the ordinary zero mode gravitons. This, then, might provide a mechanism whereby whatever system capable of sending a gravity-based energy form with a well-defined frequency should also be capable of receiving such forms and not be overwhelmed by the noise of other energy forms.

So if the human brain is such a system, it would have to have (or be?) a well-tuned receiver of such signals. The question, of course, is whether the brain is such a system and whether, or how, that might be verified or inferred. The 5D Einstein equations provide a derived mechanism for transferring these received higher mode gravity signals to macroscopic matter-based actions. The higher mode signals coming from the bulk would differ from the completely ineffectual zero mode gravity signals coming from elsewhere in the brane or from the bulk. Once these higher mode forms are received, evidently something of the nature similar to that which takes place with an observed quantum state must occur.

Recall that an observation of a quantum state will result in what is known as the "collapse of the wave function." During this (irreversible) process, a macroscopic record (involving many atoms) of the event is made. In the case of the brain then, a quantum event gets magnified to such a state that the brain would be able to detect it. Thus the quantum event might be raised to a level of awareness.

This would, of course, require one to "quiet oneself" in order to limit surrounding disturbances. Such "quieting" may in fact take place in several circumstances: when concentrating on a problem, having an aesthetic experience, sleeping, entering into a deep state of meditation, and perhaps in a psychic trance. Since everyone sleeps, there could be an interchange of information between brane and bulk during the sleep cycle, with the other possibilities being ways of enhancing such exchange. If we extrapolate on such an idea, the possibility of some human individuals being especially sensitive to such possible signals would refer to those historically known as "psychics," clairvoyants, or mystics.

So the bulk, although devoid of any matter, of quanta of any form of energy other than gravitational, would indirectly not be devoid of the influence of all other forms of energy, since the bulk is bounded or encompassed by the brane and the energy forms there would influence not only gravity in the brane but also gravity in the bulk. Likewise, unlike zero mode gravity from the bulk which has only infinitesimal effects, higher mode gravity from the bulk could influence matter in the brane. The possibility of "quieting" any noise which would interfere with energy exchange between human organisms in the brane and gravitational forms in the bulk might then be related to the various methods of ego-transcendence and possibly through the sleep cycle.

4 Structural Characteristics of the Bulk

Generally speaking, complexity of structure is associated with the possibility of the existence of organisms or organs of an organic system. If therefore some entities in the bulk are to be associated, through energy exchanges as discussed above, with organic systems (e.g. brains) in the brane, there would seem to be a requirement for structural complexity of entities in the bulk. We therefore turn our attention to this question.

Gravity waves in the brane (our 4D realm) are generally understood to be created by the accelerated motions of material bodies. Because there is an energy interface between the brane and the bulk, gravity waves in the bulk may also be produced by matter in accelerated motion in the brane. Since the bulk is bounded by two branes, purely gravitational structures in the bulk might then take the form of complex gravitational standing waves (see Fig.4).

Could these waves also, like their electromagnetic counterparts be capable of conveying information? The wave equations for standing sound waves and standing electromagnetic waves in the brane are linear, meaning that the standing waves could be constructed from a linear superposition of two (or more) waves traveling in opposite directions. Without this linearity, information could not be conveyed by the usual linear Fourier superpositions. The obvious problem in trying to extend the concept of standing waves capable of conveying information to gravitational waves in the bulk is that the Einstein equations (in 4D or 5D) are nonlinear. This means that in general if you have two or more solutions of the Einstein equations, then the sum of those solutions will not be a solution of the Einstein equations. This is in contrast to the linear theories in which the sum of two or more solutions of the linear wave equation is itself a solution of that wave equation. Weak gravitational standing waves would be possible in either brane or bulk since they satisfy approximately a linear wave equation. The difference between the two types of linear waves would be that in the 5D bulk there is a 'w' dependence of the wave amplitude and phase whereas in the brane there is no such dependence since 'w' is fixed at 0.

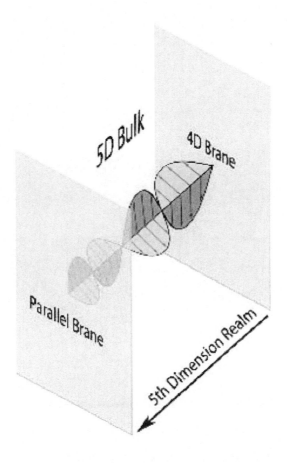

Figure 4: *Gravitational Standing Waves*

Even if the gravitational field is not weak so that the nonlinear terms in the equation would play an important role, a special class of standing waves solutions has been found by Stephani (2003). His testing grounds, however, are not in the context of the Randall- Sundrum model but in the "ordinary" 4D Einstein metric and equations. It would be relevant then to determine if such a class of exact standing wave solutions exists in the 5D Randall- Sundrum model. If that turns out to be the case, there would be no conflict between having stable gravitational standing waves in the bulk capable of conveying information and the nonlinearity of the 5D Einstein equations.

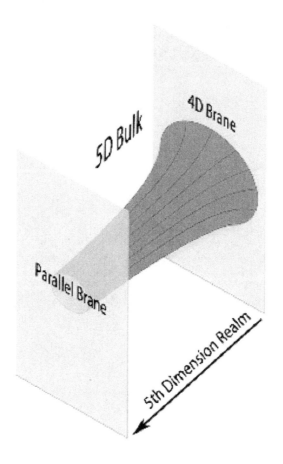

Figure 5. *Corporeal (Brane), Noncorporeal (Bulk)*

There are other factors which may affect the strength and/or complexity of formations in the bulk. In the two-brane Randall-Sundrum model, all massive particles in the parallel brane have an enormously larger inertial mass than they have in the weak brane. Disturbances there could therefore have greater effects within the bulk than disturbances in the weak brane. Also, although solitons and standing waves in the 5D bulk would appear mathematically similar to their counterparts in the 4D brane, their spatial extensions in the x, y, z direction may depend sensitively on the local value of w (the extra spatial dimension). Magnitudes would vary as w varies. Additionally, aside from static gravitational fields and gravity waves, there are also their quanta, the massless gravitons, and of course their excitations. Just what the strength and complexity of gravitational formations in the bulk would be remains for further research. But it is not at all beyond possibility that complex purely gravitational 5D formations capable of dynamically storing and/or transmitting information might exist in the bulk. For an idea as to just how very complex nonlinear standing waves may become, see the studies of wave formations in a fluid medium carried out in Schwenk 1996, and the work of the Institute for Flow Sciences (Institut fuer Stroemungswissenschaften).

Since in terms of the analogy the extended self would have to be made up of 5D complex energy forms in the bulk, and since no ordinary matter inhabits this realm, this provides an interesting match for the oft-stated idea that the "spiritual" realm is not physical (where "physical" is construed as "material"). The bulk is indeed not a "physical" realm in that sense; thus it may be considered "spiritual" in that it contains no matter whatsoever as earlier defined.

We might emphasize this crucial distinction by referring to any entity made up of material substance as a corporeal entity. Then we would say that an entity of pure gravity (in the sense taken here) would be non-corporeal but it would not be non-physical. Using this terminology the speculation would be that each individual has a corporeal and a non-corporeal component (see Fig. 5).

When the 4D corporeal component terminates, the 5D non-corporeal (but still physical) component may remain. If so, the idea of the extended "body" and mind surviving after the death of the corporeal form would be supported (recall that we make no postulation regarding the specific relation of body and mind).

Another aspect of gravity in the bulk that may bear on our investigation is the possibility of information transfer (in the form of energy) from one portion to another of the bulk itself; and therefore if there are extended selves in the bulk, between such extended selves. Again we have a suggestive parallel to various forms of paranormal phenomena. Thinking of claims of telepathy, the theory would allow such communication to take place either indirectly through the brane (by energy transfer from one standing wave (the non-corporeal entity) to the 4D (corporeal) individual and then from there to another individual by ordinary electromagnetic or sound wave communication and from there by gravitational transfer of energy through the brane to the bulk as described earlier), or directly, by complicated connections between standing waves in the bulk or possibly by gravitational solitons (see Fig 6.).

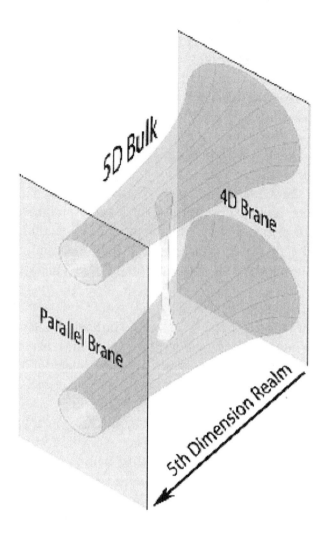

Figure 6: *Gravitational connections*

Gravitational solitons are a feature of the nonlinearity of the vacuum Einstein equation. These are objects that move in the appropriate space-time dimensions with their shape unchanged.

Bizon et al (2007) have studied gravitational solitons in higher dimensional gravity although they did not study the Randall-Sundrum model. Their focus is on the stability of the solitons. They found evidence of stability at the linearized level and beyond for moderate sized perturbations. Also, thinking of "communication with the dead," if the corporeal body of person A dies but the extended self of A in the bulk remains and is capable of exchanging information with the extended self in the bulk of person B, who is alive in the brane, this would suggest something of that nature. Whatever levels of transfer are envisaged, if there is a mechanism for a corporeal individual in the brane (likely through his or her brain) to receive such signals, the soliton or standing wave should be capable of conveying information. Electromagnetic waves are clearly capable of this, so their gravitational counterparts should also be capable of conveying information by similar means.

5 Is Verification Possible?

Based on the above analysis, it is our view that the Randall-Sundrum model, while subject to provisos as noticed frequently above, still provides an intriguing metaphor for the existence of certain paranormal phenomena as well as for the persistent views found in religion, philosophy and psychology asserting a wider concept of the self. In order to raise the level beyond physical metaphors into the realm of potential verification, at least four important studies would have to be undertaken. Four experimental and theoretical requirements that would support the possibility of raising physical metaphors into the realm of potential verification are 1) discovery of KK particles 2) demonstrating theoretically that gravitational standing waves and solitons exist in the "bulk" of the Randall Sundrum theory 3) detecting higher mode gravitational waves originating in the bulk capable of being received by individual human organisms and 4) the identification of a candidate for a specific locus in the human organism of reception and transmission of vibratory effects back and forth from brane to bulk. Below we discuss each of these in detail. Taken together they would constitute necessary but not sufficient conditions for verification.

1. A necessary condition is experimental confirmation of the existence of higher dimensions by the detection of Kaluza-Klein excitation decays in the brane. Because in the theory the bulk is exponentially warped, the KK particles should have a mass on the order of or higher than 10^{12} electron volts (Randall, 2005). At the energies to be available at the LHC, confirmation or falsification should be possible.

2. A second requirement would be theoretical confirmation of the possibility of very complex forms of gravitational wave activity in the bulk, involving standing waves, solitons, gravitons and their excitations. In this respect there is a danger of relying too much on physical intuition from our ordinary 4D space-time, since the extra spatial dimension in the 5D bulk can lead to more complexity. For example, there are very powerful methods (such as conformal mapping) for solving certain equations in 3D (2 space dimensions), and if there is symmetry in the z direction (called axial symmetry) then the added spatial dimension from 3D to 4D space time does not complicate the solutions, and one can use intuition and experience based on the 3D space time. However, in general adding an extra spatial dimension does lead to more complexity. Such would equally be true for the 4D to 5D transition. The potential added complexity of gravitational wave phenomena in the 5D bulk has yet to be investigated.

This second set of requirements will be quite challenging even to the expert general relativist. We have here made a brief foray into this question, but the present paper is limited to a discussion of the possibilities, requirements and issues raised in pursuing the Flatlander analogy in terms of one type of contemporary extra-dimensional theory and does not extend to technical theoretical elaborations along these lines.

It may be objected that it is absurd to imagine that any configuration of purely gravitational field energies in the 5D bulk, however complex, could function as some kind of extension, or organ, of our physical 4D forms. But aside from the point just made (that intuition and experience based on our current paradigm may be inadequate), we submit that our "physical" (i.e. corporeal) bodies are themselves made up of (matter) fields and particles, where the particles are expressions (as quanta) of such fields. It is certainly not clear that this constitutes a radical qualitative difference in the possibilities of organization. Furthermore although the energies making up our own corporeal form are predominantly non-gravitational, they may certainly involve gravitational influences. The reverse case might indeed be made: a complex structure made only of gravitational energies and particles might have capabilities of organization unknown when freed of the presence of the energies constituting "matter," particularly when an additional spatial dimension is a factor. Only more research may determine whether such is a possibility. We note however that this latter point is consistent with the traditional notions of the transcendence of existence beyond the "corporeal."

3. Next, experimental determination of the existence of higher mode gravitational waves originating in the bulk and capable of being received by individual human organisms is required. (Preliminary to this one would first have to detect such received gravitational interactions from the bulk in a passive laboratory setting, without the aid of the LHC!) This would have to include a detailed modeling of gravitational energy exchange mechanisms between bulk and brane. If we are bound to the assumption of mind-brain identity, this would appear to mean localizing a source of such wave frequencies within the human brain.

The idea of biological quantum coherence phenomena based on vibrational effects within active cells, although not directly related to the brain, has been studied by Frohlich [Frohlich,1968]. He has examined biological systems with branches of longitudinal electric modes at frequencies in the microwave range, based on the dipolar properties of cell membranes. In particular he has shown that if energy is supplied above a certain mean rate to such a branch, then a steady state will be reached in which a single mode of this branch is very strongly excited. What is remarkable is that the supplied energy is not completely thermalized but stored in a highly ordered fashion with long range phase correlations which has considerable similarity with the low-temperature condensation of a Bose gas. This is mentioned just to point out that coherent vibratory effects within the biological system of the brain may not be pure speculation. Penrose (1994) has even suggested that there may be a connection between these microwave frequencies and the much lower measured frequencies associated with alpha, beta, theta, and delta brain wave activity.

In regard to a gravity-brain connection, Penrose (1994) has also claimed that consciousness involves processes that may be intimately tied to large scale quantum-coherent phenomena (including state reduction) in the microtubules associated with the synapses branching off nerve pathways, related to the claims discussed above by Frohlich. And he also proposes that quantum state reduction must ultimately be a gravitational phenomenon in spite of the weak interactions involved. This would appear to support the possibility of the effect of gravitational signals on conscious awareness. However, contrary to some of the speculations of artificial intelligence, Penrose also argues that the way that gravitational mechanisms mediate state reduction cannot be modeled by any computational, i.e., algorithmic, procedure.

Returning now to the problem of the weakness of gravity in regard to consciousness and paranormal phenomena, we point out that even gravitational waves produced by large systems are very weak. The Sun-Jupiter rotational system, for example, produces a power output about that of only a 40 watt bulb. Detecting much, much weaker gravity waves is certainly impossible with today's detection devices. This, however, does not imply that such extremely weak signals could not have an impact on the gravitational structures in the bulk. There are two reasons. First of all, no matter-based interfering energy transfers to the bulk can take place; and secondly, some form of frequency resonance could be involved. The extremely weak nature of the coupling of the gravitational field to all matter forms (mass or electromagnetic) makes the determination of a viable mechanism of their generation and reception within the brain the most problematic aspect of our analysis. However, as discussed above the two-brane theory of Randall and Sundrum provides an enormous factor of about 1016 in the strength with which gravitational signals originating in the bulk can affect matter particles in the brane. As stated by Randall (2005), the "KK particles pile up on the weak brane (because their probability function peaks there) and they have all the properties of weak brane particles." Here then is another unexplored avenue of theoretical research, the pressing question being whether Randall's statement about the KK particles from the bulk could theoretically translate into them having effects on brains or bodies in the brane.

4. Finally, verification would require a candidate for a specific locus, or organ, of reception and transmission of vibratory effects back and forth from brane to bulk. One candidate region might be the so-called "god spot" which was thought to be a distinct area of the brain responsible for spiritual experiences. Recent research at the University of Missouri has indicated, however, that experiences thought to be associated with a "god spot" are actually a complex phenomenon involving multiple areas of the brain, not just a single location (News Bureau,

University of Missouri, April 18, 2012). This observation brings into view recent critiques of the mind-brain identity theory in cognitive science, which argue that no sharp demarcation can be drawn between the brain and the entire nervous system. Whether self-awareness can be associated with any specific areas of the brain is unknown with those both arguing for and against the localization hypothesis.

There is also the consideration that mediums and clairvoyants make claims of perceiving information from other dimensions or planes of existence, such as the "astral plane," and also of perceiving one or more spiritual "bodies" of individuals which exist in other such planes or levels of reality. If there were some experimental determination, again, of an organ or region of the body possessed by, or more highly developed in, such individuals, this could also be a candidate for such a focus of reception and transmission between brane and bulk.

Some in the field of cognitive science have proposed a theory of "extended cognition" which attributes mental phenomena to an even larger spatiotemporal structure called a behavioral field which, it is proposed, may be described by Dynamic Systems Theory (DST) (Rockwell, 2007, Chemero 2009). Under such a theory, any source of gravitational forms which might serve as a basis for energy exchange between humans in the brane and gravitational structures in the bulk would be a complex dynamic spatiotemporal field of activity. As such, this latter would perhaps be a more likely source than any single dedicated area of the brain. Such concerns, however, are at the cutting edge of mind-brain research and at present no experiments have been devised or proposed which might detect weak gravitational waves associated with human mental activity, whether localized in the brain or extended to the nervous system or beyond. In fact, although it may be nearly impossible to detect gravity waves in the brain associated with zero mode gravitons from the brane or bulk it remains an open question whether the same could be said for the higher mode excitations from the bulk.

5 Conclusion

Our aim has been limited to an investigation of how the extra-dimensional theory of Randall and Sundrum might apply to an extension of the 3D-4D Flatlander case, by analogy, to a 4D-5D situation. Specifically the theory being investigated is that 5D gravity-based structures in the bulk are non-corporeal but physical extensions (as defined above) of the bodies of 4D individuals in the brane and are engaged in energy exchanges with human individuals, as this updated analogue to the Flatlander case suggests. The requirement of the analogy is that evidence should either be found, or experiments proposed, which might indicate that our personal consciousness may be divided in some way between corporeal forms in the embedded 4D realm and non-corporeal (gravitational) forms in the larger 5D realm, of which (in the Randall-Sundrum model) our 4D space-time constitutes a boundary called a brane. Following up on our detailed exploration of this topic, we identified four experimental and theoretical results whose confirmation would constitute necessary, but not sufficient, conditions for verification of such a theory. Our conclusion, then, is that although the Randall-Sundrum extra-dimensional model is suggestive of that possibility, actual verification of the extension of the Flatlander analogy at the 4D-5D level does not appear to be within the purview of contemporary experimental capability. On the other hand, given the existence of the various possibilities mentioned, the analogy cannot be rejected out of hand as absolutely unverifiable but that the question of what would constitute sufficient conditions remains open.

Acknowledgments The authors would like to thank Dr. Conley Powell and Dr. James Strange for helpful comments on a preliminary version of the paper, to Mr. David Menard for pointing out to us the work of Carr, and to Natallia Kaptur for graphical support on the figures.

REFERENCES

Arkani-Hamed, N., Dimopoulos, S. and Dvali, G Phys. Lett. B429 (1998) 263,hep-ph/9803315.

Antoniadis, I., Arkani-Hamed, N., Dimopoulos, S., and Dvali, G., Phys. Lett. B436 (1998) 257, hep-ph/9804398

Bizon, P. et al (2007) Class.Quant.Grav.24:4751-4776.

Braude, S., "Memory Without a Trace" (2006), European Journal of Parapsychology Volume 21.2, Special Issue, pages 182–202 ISSN: 0168-7263

Carr, B., (2008), "Worlds Apart: Can Psychical Research Bridge the Gulf Between Matter and Mind" Proceedings of the Society for Psychical Research, 59, Part 221.

Chemero, A. (2009). Radical Embodied Cognitive Science. Cambridge, MA: MIT Press, A Bradford Book.

CMS Collaboration, 2011) Phys. Lett. B 697, 434.

Chatrchyan, S. et al. (2012), [CMS Collaboration], JHEP 1204, 061 (2012) [arXiv:1202.639]

Fairvre, quoted in Hanegraaff, W. J. (1998). New Age religion and Western culture: Esotericism in the mirror of secular thought. State University of New York Press.,pp. 398-9.

Frohlich, H., (1968), "Long Range Coherence and Energy Storage in Biological Systems" Journal of Quantum Chemsitry, Vol II, 641-49.

Goodrick-Clarke, N. (2008), The Western Esoteric Traditions, Oxford University Press.

Govinda, Anagarika, (1974) Foundations of Tibetan Mysticism, Samuel Weiser, N.Y.

Green, Michael and Schwarz John, (1984) "Anomaly Cancellations in

Supersymmetric D=10 Gauge Theory and Superstring Theory", Physics Letters B149 pp. 117–22.

Heindel, Max, , (1929) Rosicrucian Cosmo-Conception, Rosicrucian Fellowship. Jung, C. G., (1968), Analytical Psychology, Its Theory and Practice, Random House, Vintage Books.

Jung, C. G., (1981) The Structure and Dynamics of the Psyche, Princeton University Press , Bollingen Series Volume 8, (fifth printing of the 1960 first edition).

Kaku, Michio, (1994) Hyperspace: A Scientific Odyssey Through Parallel Universes, Time Warps, and the Tenth Dimension, Oxford University Press.

Kaluza, Theodor (1921). "Zum Unitätsproblem in der Physik". Sitzungsber. Preuss. Akad. Wiss. Berlin. (Math. Phys.) 966–972.

Kant, I., (1961) The Critique of Pure Reason. MacMillan, London. Translation by Norman Kent Smith of the original 1787 edition.

Klein, Oskar (1926). "Quantentheorie und fünfdimensionale Relativitätstheorie". Zeitschrift für Physik A 37 (12): 895–906.

Landsberg, G. ,(2006), Black Holes at Future Colliders and Beyond: a Topical Review, Phys.G32:R337-R365.

McDaniel, S. V. (2010). Review of Consciousness and Its Objects by Colin McGinn. Journal of Scientific Exploration 24(4), 756-765.

McGinn, Colin, (2004) Consciousness and its Objects. Clarendon Press.

Mitchell, Edgar, (2001), Nature's Mind: The Quantum Hologram. Institute of Noetic Sciences, Lake Worth, FL.

Penrose, Roger, (1994), Shadows of the Mind – A Search for the Missing Science of Consciousness, Oxford University Press.

Randall, L. and Sundrum, R. (1999), Phys. Rev. Lett. 83,3370 [arXiv:hep-ph/9905221].

Randall, Lisa, (2005), Warped Passages: Unraveling the Mysteries of the Universe's Hidden Dimensions. Harper-Perennial.

Rockwell, W. T. (2007). Neither Brain Nor Ghost: A Non-Dualist Alternative to the Mind–Brain Identity Theory. Cambridge, MA: MIT Press, A Bradford Book.

Rothman, T. and Boughn, S. (2006), Foundations of Physics, Vol 36, 1801-1825 [arXiv:gr- qc/0601043]

Schwenk, T, (1996), Sensitive Chaos: The Creation of Flowing Forms in Water and Air, Rudolf Steiner Press, revised edition.

Stephani, H., (2003), General Relativity and Gravitation, Volume 35, Number 3, pp. 467-474(8).

Weiss, B. L. and Weiss, A. E. Weiss (2012) , Miracles Happen, HarperOne.

Weiss, B. (1988), Many Lives, Many Masters. Simon and Schuster, Zwiebach, Barton (2004), A First Course in String Theory, Cambridge

****
****
****

IV. Uncertainty Principle, Parallel Universes, Wave Functions, Entanglement, Violations of Causality, and Paradoxes of Time Travel

****
****
****

21. Multiverse Scenarios in Cosmology: Classification, Cause, Challenge, Controversy, and Criticism

Rüdiger Vaas,
Center for Philosophy and Foundations of Science, University of Giessen, Germany

Abstract

Multiverse scenarios in cosmology assume that other universes exist "beyond" our own universe. These scenarios post an exciting challenge for empirical and theoretical research as well as for philosophy of science. The construct of the multiverse could be necessary to understand why the big bang occurred, why (some of) the laws of nature and the values of certain physical constants are the way they are, and why there is an arrow of time. This paper clarifies competing notions of "universe" and "multiverse"; it proposes a classification of different multiverse types according to various aspects of how the universes are or are not separated from each other; it reviews the main reasons for assuming the existence of other universes including the empirical evidence, theoretical explanations, and philosophical arguments; and, finally, it argues that some attempts to criticize multiverse scenarios as "unscientific", insisting on a narrow understanding of falsification, is neither appropriate nor convincing from a philosophy of science point of view. Key Words: big bang, universe, multiverse, cosmic inflation, time, quantum gravity, string theory, laws of nature, physical constants, fine-tuning, anthropic principle, philosophy of science, metaphysics, falsificationism

1. Introduction

Why is there something rather than nothing? And why is that which is, the way it is? These two questions are among the most fundamental (meta)physical mysteries currently debated in cosmology. The multiverse hypothesis represents, at least in part, an attempt to answer them.

The central tenant of the multiverse hypothesis (henceforth called M) is that our universe is just one among an ensemble, an infinitesimal part of an elaborate structure which consists of numerous universes, possibly an infinite number of universes. Thus M has been conceptualized and described by a variety of terms including "many worlds", "parallel worlds", "parallel universes", "alternative universes", "alternative realities", "alternative dimensions", "quantum universes", and so on.

Some of these "universes" could have a physics or chemistry completely unlike our own, and this has led to additional questions, such as: is our universe fine tuned for life, and if so, why?

No approach can possibly provide an exhaustive or ultimate answer to these questions (Vaas 2006), and neither does M seek to do that. But if empirically confirmed in some way, or rigorously derived theoretically, M would be one of the most radical and far-reaching insights in the history of science. Indeed, it may turn out that M is absolutely necessary for an understanding of why the big bang occurred, why (some of) the laws of nature and the values of certain physical constants are as they are, why this universe appears to be fine-tuned for life, and why there is an arrow of time. M could well be a derivative of the ultimate explanans.

Possibly precisely because of these exciting prospects M is controversial and under attack not just from sceptical scientists, but theologians and critical philosophers of science (reviewed in Vaas 2008a, 2010). This is not surprising and, indeed, it is to be appreciated because extraordinary claims which have the potential to overturn and usher in a new world scientific order, require extraordinary evidence. And considerable evidence remains to be discovered.

This paper discusses the current status of M and provides a classification of different multiverse types, categorized according to the way in which individual universes are assumed to be separated or not separated from another. Then the main reasons for assuming the existence of other universes (empirical, theoretical, and philosophical) are reviewed. It is also argued that criticism of the various multiverse scenarios as "unscientific", and the insistence on a narrow understanding of falsification, are neither appropriate nor convincing from a philosophy of science point of view.

2. Different Notions of "Universe" and "Multiverse"

"The universe is a big place, perhaps the biggest" wrote Kurt Vonnegut, the well-known visionary and author of science fiction. But science is often stranger than fiction, and according to M, the universe is only a tiny part of what exists.

However, this opens up both conceptual and empirical problems which in part have to do with language, and perhaps the limitations of the human mind. Specifically, the term "universe" (or "world"), as it is used today, has many different meanings (Vaas 2004a) such as:

(1) Everything (physically) in existence, ever, anywhere, in totality. According to this defintion there are no other universes.

(2) The observable region of the cosmos that we can observe and which we inhabit (the Hubble volume, almost 100 billion light years in diameter), plus everything that has interacted or will ever interact with this region.

(3) Any gigantic system of causally interacting things that is wholly (or

to a very large extent, or for a long time) isolated from others; sometimes such a locally causally connected collection is called a multi-domain universe, <.i> consisting of the ensemble of all sub-regions of a larger connected spacetime, the "universe as a whole", and this is opposed to the multiverse in a stronger sense, i.e. the set of genuinely disconnected universes, which are not causally related at all.

(4) Any system that might well have become gigantic, etc., even if it does in fact recollapse while it is still very small.

(5) Other branches of the wavefunction (if it never collapses, cf. Wheeler & Zurek 1983, Barrett 1999, Vaas 2001) in unitary quantum physics, i.e. different histories of the universe (e.g. Gell-Mann & Hartle 1990 & 1993) or different classical worlds which are in superposition (e.g. DeWitt & Graham 1973).

(6) Completely disconnected systems consisting of universes in one of the former meanings, which do or do not share the same boundary conditions, constants, parameters, vacuum states, effective low-energy laws, or even fundamental laws, e.g. different physically realized mathematical structures (cf. Tegmark 2004, 2010).

Therefore, "multiverse" (or "world" as a whole) can be used to refer to everything in existence (at least from a physical point of view), while the term "universe" can refer to one of several universes (worlds) within the multiverse.

In principle, these universes – mostly conceived in the meaning of (2), (3), or (4) – might or might not be spatially, temporally, dimensionally, causally, nomologically and/or mathematically separated from each other (see Table 1). Thus, sharp boundaries do not necessarily exist between them.

One might call the whole set of different universes the multiverse. But it could be true that there are even different sets of totally spatiotemporally and strictly causally separated multiverses, e.g. different bunches of chaotically inflating multiverses. In that case it remains useful to have a term with a still broader meaning, namely omniverse or cosmos. Thus, omniverse or cosmos could be taken as the all-embracing term for everything in existence which might or might not be the set of different multiverses, while the multiverse refers to and consists of different universes which are not separated in every respect.

3. Towards a Multiversal Taxonomy

Although most believe that multiverse classifications should be abstract enough to include all possible cosmological scenarios, there is no general agreement as to exactly what that should be. For example, it has been suggested that the multiverse should be categorized with regard to separation/distinction of the different universes (Vaas 2004a; Table 1 is an extension of this). Yet other categorizations include four different levels (Tegmark 2004) or three different types (Mersini-Houghton 2010) (cf. also Ellis, Kirchner & Stoeger 2004). Of course, definitions and taxonomies are just conceptual issues. Nevertheless, they are needed for clarification and to avoid misunderstandings, though categories in-themselves explain and prove nothing. Nevertheless these issues must be discussed and, in the long run, shown, whether they are useful, sufficiently complete, and not too arbitrary.

Multiverse scenarios differ with respect to the kind and degree of separation between the individual universes that they assume and can be categorized accordingly. Note that these aspects of seperation do not necessarily exclude each other. Some multiverse types fit in several categories. For example eternal inflation scenarios describe universes which are spatially exclusive, but could be embedded in a common spacetime; they are not dimensionally separated, only by different vacuum states; they are strictly causally separated with respect to the future (though not in every case because there are models predicting bubble collisions), but not with respect to the past since they share a common mechanism which generates their existence.

However, a classification is no end in itself. As Ernest Rutherford used to provoke, "science is either physics or collecting stamps". So what are the arguments for presuming the existence of other universes?

4. Is Our Universe Fine-Tuned?

Life exists in this universe. But does it exist in other universes, and if so, are those life-forms similar to those which are typical of Earth? We cannot, as yet, answer these latter questions. However, the fact that life exists at all raises its own fundamental questions, such as, why are the physical and chemical features of this universe compatible with life? Why does this universe appear to be "fine tuned," that is, why are the laws and constants of nature and certain boundary conditions narrowly tailored to those constants which are ideal for life (e.g. Carr 2007; Leslie 1989; Vaas 2004b); for indeed, if these fundamental constants varied by just a few degrees, life as we know it would not be possible.

Life as we know it depends crucially on the laws and constants of nature as well as a variety of boundary conditions which allowed intelligent life to evolve. Nevertheless it is difficult to judge how "fine-tuned" this universe really is, both because it is unclear how modifications of many values together might compensate each other and whether laws, constants and initial conditions really could have been otherwise to begin with. It is also unclear how specific and improbable those values need to be in order for information-processing structures – and, hence, intelligent observers – to develop. If we accept, for the sake of argument, that at least some values are fine-tuned, we must ask, "why" and how this can be explained.

In principle, there are many options for answering this question. Fine-tuning might (1) just be an illusion if life could adapt to very different conditions or if modifications of many values of the constants would compensate each other; or (2) it might be a result of (incomprehensible, irreducible) chance, and thus inexplicable (Vaas 1993); or (3) it might be nonexistent because nature could not have been otherwise, and with a fundamental theory we would be able to prove this; or (4) it might be a product of selection: either observational selection within a vast multiverse of (infinitely?) many different realizations of those values (weak anthropic principle), or a kind of cosmological natural selection making the measured values (compared to possible other ones) quite likely within a multiverse of many different values, or even a teleological or intentional selection. Even worse, these alternatives are not mutually exclusive – for example it is logically possible that there is a multiverse, created according to a fundamental theory by a cosmic designer who is not self-sustaining, but ultimately contingent, i.e. an instance of chance.

Digging deeper: Laws, constants and boundary conditions are the basic constituents of cosmology and physics from a formal point of view (besides spacetime, energy, matter, fields and forces or more fundamental entities like strings or spin-networks and their properties with regards to content). An ambitious goal and historically at least a successful heuristic attitude is reduction, derivation and unification to achieve more fundamental, far-reaching and simple descriptions and explanations. While uniqueness is much more economical and predictive, multiple realizations – presumably within a multiverse – have recently been proposed as an opposing (but not mutually exclusive) alternative. This table provides a summary of different approaches, possibilities and problems; it is neither complete nor the only conceivable system.

From both a scientific and philosophical perspective the fundamental theory approach and the multiverse scenario are most plausible and heuristically promising (Vaas 2004a,b).

5. Unique-universe versus multiverse accounts

Unique-universe accounts take our universe as the only one (or at least the only one ever relevant for cosmological explanations and theories). It might have had a predecessor or even infinitely many (before the big bang) and/or a successor or infinitely many (after a big crunch), but then the whole series can be taken as one single universe with spatiotemporal phase transitions. From the perspective of simplicity, parsimony and testability it is favorable to try to explain as much as possible with a unique-universe account. A both straightforward and very ambitious approach is the searching for a fundamental theory with just one self-consistent solution that represents (or predicts) our universe. (Of course one could always argue that there are other, strictly causally separated universes too, which do not even share a common generator or a meta-law; but then they do not have any explanatory power at all and the claims for their existence cannot be motivated in a scientifically useful way, only perhaps by philosophical arguments.)

Future theories of physics might reveal the relations between fundamental constants in a similar way as James Clerk Maxwell did by unifying electric and magnetic forces: he showed that three seemingly independent constants – the velocity of light c, the electric constant eo (vacuum permittivity), and the magnetic constant μo (vacuum permeability) – are connected with each other: c = (μo . eo)-0,5. Indeed some candidates for a grand unified theory of the strong, weak and electromagnetic interaction suggest that most of the parameters in the standard model of particle physics are mathematically fixed, except for these three: a coupling constant (the electromagnetic fine-structure constant) and two particle masses (namely that of down and up quarks) (Hogan 2000). A promise of string theory is to get rid of any free parameter – and if this can be accomplished all constants could be calculated from first principles (Kane et al. 2002). Although at present this remains wishful thinking, it is a direction very worth following and, from a theoretical and historical point of view, perhaps the most promising.

So even without an ultimate explanation, fine-tuning might be explained away within a (more) fundamental theory. Most of the values of the physical constants should be derived from it, for example. This would turn the amazement about the anthropic coincidences into insight – like the surprise of a student about the relationship $ei\pi = -1$ between the numbers e, i and π in mathematics is replaced by understanding once he comprehends the proof. Perhaps the fact that the mass of the proton is 1836 times the mass of the electron could be similarly explained. If so, this number would be part of the rigid formal structure of a physical law which cannot be modified without destroying the theory behind it. An example for such a number is the ratio of any circle's circumference to its diameter. It is the same for all circles in Euclidean space: the circular constant π.

But even if all dimensionless constants of nature could be reduced to only one, a pure number in a theory of everything, its value would still be arbitrary, i.e. unexplained. No doubt, such a universal reduction would be an enormous success. However, the basic questions would remain: Why this constant, why this value? If infinitely many values were possible, then even the multitude of possibilities would stay unrestricted. So, again, why should such a universal constant have the value of, say, 42 and not any other?

If there were just one constant (or even many of them) whose value can be derived from first principles, i.e. from the ultimate theory or a law within this theory, then it would be completely explained or reduced at last. Then there would be no mystery of fine-tuning anymore, because there never was a fine-tuning of the constants in the first place. And then an appreciable amount of contingency would be expelled.

But what would such a spectacular success really mean? First, it could simply shift the problem, i.e. transfer the unexplained contingency either to the laws themselves or to the boundary conditions or both. This would not be a Pyrrhic victory, but not a big deal either. Second, one might interpret it as an analytic solution. Then the values of the constants would represent no empirical information; they would not be property of the physical world, but simply a mathematical result, a property of the structure of the theory. This, however, still could and should have empirical content, although not encoded in the constants.

Otherwise fundamental physics as an empirical science would come to an end. But an exclusively mathematical universe, or at least an entirely complete formal description of everything there is, derivable from and contained within an all-embracing logical system without any free parameter or contingent part, might seem either incredible (and runs into severe logical problems due to Kurt Gödel's incompleteness theorems) or the ultimate promise of the widest and deepest conceivable explanation. Empirical research, then, would only be a temporary expedient like Ludwig Wittgenstein's (1922, 6.54) famous ladder: The physicist, after he has used empirical data as elucidatory steps, would proceed beyond them. "He must so to speak throw away the ladder, after he has climbed up on it." That there is no contingency at all seems very unlikely. So why are some features realized but not others? Or, on the contrary, is every feature realized? Both questions are strong motivations for M.

Multiverse accounts assume the existence of other universes as defined above and characterized with respect to their separation in Table 1. This is no longer viewed as mad metaphysical speculation beyond empirical rationality. There are many different multiverse accounts (see, e.g., Carr 2007; Davies 2004; Deutsch 1997; Linde 2008; Mersini-Houghton 2010; Rees 2001; Smolin 1997; Tegmark 2004, Vaas 2004b, 2005, 2008b, 2010; Vilenkin 2006) and even some attempts to classify them quantitatively (see, e.g., Deutsch 2001 for many-worlds in quantum physics, and Ellis, Kirchner & Stoeger 2004 for physical cosmology). They flourish especially in the context of cosmic inflation (Aguirre 2010; Linde 2005, 2008, Vaas 2008b), string theory (Chalmers 2007, Douglas 2010) and a combination of both as well as in different quantum gravity scenarios that seek to resolve the big bang singularity and, thus, explain the origin of our universe (for recent reviews see Vaas 2010).

If there is a kind of selection, new possibilities emerge within M. One possibility is observational selection (Barrow & Tipler 1986, Leslie 1989, Vaas 2004b). Another is a kind of cosmological natural selection making the measured values (compared to possible other ones) quite likely within a multiverse of many different values (García-Bellido 1995, Smolin 1992, 1997 & 2010, for a critical discussion e.g. Vaas 1998 & 2003). Finally there is teleological or intentional selection (e.g. Ansoldi & Guendelman 2006; Harrison 1995; Leslie 1989; Vidal 2008 & 2010, for a critical discussion e.g. Vaas 2004b, 2009ab).

The strongest version of M is related to the principle of plentitude or principle of fecundity (advocated e.g. by Richard Feynman, Dennis Sciama). According to this principle everything is real, if it is not explicitly forbidden by laws of nature, e.g. symmetry principles. As Terence H. White wrote in his novel The Once and Future King (1958): "everything not forbidden is compulsory". But the question remains: What is forbidden, i.e. physically or nomologically not possible and thus not "allowed" by natural laws? (This is a slippery slope, as Paul Davies 2007 argued: could there even be universes containing magic, a theistic God, or simulations of every weird fantasy? Otherwise some restrictions are necessary!) And is it really true that everything which is physically or nomologically possible is also realized somewhere? Answers to these questions are not known. (It is also unclear whether "metaphysically possible" makes truly sense in contrast to both "logically possible" and "physically possible", cf. Meixner 2008.)

6. Why (Should) We Believe in Other Universes (?)

There are – or could be – at least three main reasons for assuming the existence of other universes: empirical evidence, theoretical explanation, and philosophical arguments (Table 3). These three reasons are independent from each other, but ideally entangled. As far as there is at least some connection with or embedding into a theoretical framework of physics or cosmology, M is part of the scientific endeavour, not only of philosophy. This is also the case in the absence of empirical evidence, if a theoretical embedding exists. And philosophical arguments might at least motivate scientific speculation.

Many cosmologists and philosophers alike argue that M does not belong to science because it cannot be falsified and it can be tested. This criticism is not valid.

7. Falsificationism is Both Too Much and Not Enough

"Scientific statements, refering to reality, must be falsifiable", Karl R. Popper (1930-1933, 1935). Falsifiability has been one of the most important and successful criteria of science. Popper understood it as a demarcation criterium of science (in contrast to metaphysics, logic, pseudoscience...). But what is usually meant here is falsifiability of theoretical systems, or of parts of such a system, not of single statements.

So there is an important distinction: Scientific laws on the one hand must be falsifiable. Take for example Newton's law – it can be tested, was tested rigorously indeed, and is still under investigation (at very large and very small scales). Hypothetical universal existential statements on the other hand need not and cannot be falsified, but must be verified. Take for instance the discovery of the last two naturally occurring stable elements: Hafnium, atomic number 72, was detected by Dirk Coster and George de Hevesy in 1922 through Xray spectroscopy analysis, after Niels Bohr had predicted it, or its properties. (Actually Dimitri Mendeleev had already predicted it implicitly in 1869, in his report on The Periodic Law of the Chemical Elements). Similarly, Rhenium, atomic number 75, was found by Walter Noddack, Ida Tacke, and Otto Berg in 1925, after Henry Moseley had predicted it in 1914.

In science verification is obviously extremely important. But falsification is not sufficient to disprove an idea in controversial and hypothetical situations even if there are concise predictions. That is, "absence of evidence is not evidence of absence." Otherwise fictive ghosts or unicorns would also be part of science, for we cannot know a priori whether they exist or not, but we can imagine ways to detect them; that is to verify their existence in principle. So what is missing here? It is theoretical embedding. To be reasonably part of science, hypothetical universal existence statements must not only be verifiable, they must also be part of a sufficiently confirmed or established scientific theory or theoretical framework. That was the case in the Hafnium and Rhenium examples, where Mosley and Bohr had their theoretical models about the atomic numbers and the properties of the atoms, explaining regularities in the periodic table of the chemical elements.

Statements about the existence of other universes are not like statements about scientific laws. The latter must be falsifiable, while the former should be taken as universal existential statements which cannot be falsified, but must be verified. So ultimately a multiverse scenario might only be accepted, strictly speaking, if there is empirical evidence for it, i.e. observational data of another universe or its effects. A weaker argument for M would be if a – falsifiable, rigorously tested – theory predicts the existence of other universes, and this theory is well established according to the usual scientific criteria. Still weaker are philosophical reasons; whether they could suffice if they are stronger than alternative statements is a controversial issue and lies at – or beyond – the boundaries of physics and cosmology.

8. Research Programs and Systematicity

From a philosophy of science perspective an exaggerated falsificationism is not useful. As Imre Lakatos (1976 & 1977) pointed out, the scientific endeavour usually takes place in the form of research programs (which include not only the main assumptions and theoretical ideas but also methodological issues) rather than in respect of single hypotheses or theories. And refutations are not a straightforward sign of empirical progress, and this is because research programs grow in a permanent ocean of anomalies.

First, data are theory-dependent, not just empirical; they might simply be false or interpreted wrongly. Thus, theories should not been thrown away too quickly. For example the measured anomalies in Uranus' orbit were not a falsification of Newton's law of gravity but an indication of Neptune's existence and the starting point for its discovery.

Second, theories are often ahead of data. Thus, theorists should make testable predictions of course, and observers and experimenters should obtain data. Supersymmetry models, for instance, were theories in search of applications initially, and physicists (and even mathematicians) learned a lot from them although there has still not been a single supersymmetric particle discovered (yet). So testability, a falsifiable prediction, is important, but not necessarily at least at the initial stages of theory building. Thus, theories must be given a chance to develop, to be purged of errors, to become more complete.

What Lakatos advocated was, therefore, a sophisticated falsificationism, referring to a (quasidarwinistic) struggle between theories and data interpretation. Given initial theoretical or empirical contradictions, anomalies or data deviances occur. Nevertheless, it is reasonable to keep the theory for a while, especially its "hard core" (at least if there is no alternative – an experimentum crucis is very rarely accomplished). Instead of killing the theory, the "protective belt" of auxiliary hypotheses should be modified first. Often they are taken as responsible for failed predictions too. Of course this effort to save the core could lead to immunization strategies which would in the end expel the theory from science. Furthermore, falsification is often difficult to achieve because core commitments of scientific theories are rarely directly testable and predictive without further assumptions. That is, a theory grows or becomes modified with the discovery of additional evidence.

Over time and with the accumulation of evidence both pro and con, some research programs are more successful than others. Therefore, ad hoc hypotheses to save a hard core could led to program degenerations – especially if they are problem shifts not pointing to other fruitful areas.

A progressive research program is characterized by its growth, along with stunning novel facts being discovered, more precise predictions being made, new experimental techniques being developed. By contrast, a degenerating research program is marked by lack of growth, or by an increase of the protective belt that does not lead to novel facts.

Cosmology provides a lot of examples for these complex interplays between competing theories, data acquisition and interpretation, immunization ("epicycles" are proverbial now), and even paradigm changes. The most prominent were geocentrism versus heliocentrism, metagalaxy versus island universe, and steady state versus big bang. Universe versus multiverse seems to be the next challenge in this direction.

Though the demarcation criteria for science have sometimes been criticized (Laudan 1988) and are somewhat fuzzy indeed, it is usually rationality that rules. And there are many well established criteria for successful research programs, especially the following: many applications; novel predictions; new technologies; answering unsolved questions; consistency; elegance; simplicity; explanatory power/depth; unification of distinct phenomena; and truth (but how can we know the latter – only via the criteria mentioned above?).

These criteria are also useful in analysing modern theoretical cosmology beyond the falsifiability doctrine. Are statements about the "cause" of the big bang and about other universes unscientific if they cannot provide falsifiable predictions (yet)? No. At least not if they are seen as part of a research program which is otherwise well-established and at least partly confirmed by observations or experiments. And indeed (not all, but at least) some of the just-mentioned criteria are fulfilled by the ambitious big bang and multiverse scenarios: many applications? well, no; novel predictions? perhaps yes, partly; new technologies? definitely not (yet); answering unsolved questions? yes; consistency? hopefully; elegance? depends on taste; simplicity? often yes; explanatory power/depth? certainly yes; unification of distinct phenomena? yes indeed; truth? nobody knows, but this is of course the main source of the controversies.

Last but not least there are other approaches to science. For example science can, negatively, characterized by comparing it with pseudoscience.

Indicators of serious science:

   – no vague, exaggerated, obscure claims
   – no undefined, vague or ambiguous vocabulary
   – embedding in established scientific theories
   – embedding in established scientific research program
   – logical (internal) coherence and consistence
   – open source: no secret data, methods, knowledge…
   – Occam's razor
   – methodological reflexivity
   – no questionable "factoids" (Norman Mailer)
   – no reversal of the burden of proof
   – testability (verification, falsification)
   – rigorously derived predictions
   – no overemphasis of verifications, anecdotes, rumours, ignorance…
   – not belief, faith, hope, obedience, but observations, measurements, arguments, mathematical reasoning, inference to the best explanation…
   – replication, reproduction of measurements, calculations…
   – statistical significance, double-blind studies …
   – distinction between correlation and causality
   – progress, self-corrections, revisions, error analysis
   – publications in scientific journals etc. (peer reviewed)
   – quotations of scientific literature, no dubious references
   – no selective quotes of obsolete or questionable experiments
   – demarcation of popular science
   – demarcation of pseudoscepticism
   – systematicity

Science can be positively defined as a specific sort of systematicity according to the following nine criteria: descriptions, explanations, predictions, the defense of knowledge claims, epistemic connectedness, an ideal of completeness, knowledge generation, the representation of knowledge, critical discourse (Hoyningen-Huene 2008). By this criteria, M should also be taken as a serious part of science (Vaas 2008a).

9. Outlook

Perhaps in a hundred years cosmologists will look back at the scientists of today and ask how we could have been so blind as not to see or accept the signs of other universes, or how we could have been so crazy in our beliefs in (a science of) other universes. Right now however it is an open issue, and therefore not unreasonable to defend and advance a scientific analysis of M. At least in principle there are some possibilities both for a verification of other universes understood as hypothetical universal existential claims and for theoretical embeddings of those claims. This should remind us of what Steven Weinberg (1977) wrote long ago: "our mistake is not that we take our theories too seriously, but that we do not take them seriously enough."

Acknowledgments: It is a pleasure to thank Angela Lahee and especially André Spiegel for many comments and suggestions. I am also grateful to the people attending and discussing my talks about multiversal issues, especially at the Debate in Cosmology: The Multiverse conference (Perimeter Institute, Waterloo/Canada, September 2008) and the Challenges in Theoretical Cosmology conference (Tufts Institute, Talloires/France, September 2009).

References

Aguirre, A. (2010). Eternal Inflation: Past and Future. In: Vaas, R. (ed.). Beyond the Big Bang. Springer, Heidelberg.

Ansoldi, S., Guendelman, E.I. (2006). Child Universes in the Laboratory; arXiv:gr-qc/0611034

Barrett, J. A. (1999). The Quantum Mechanics of Minds and Worlds. Oxford University Press, Oxford.

Barrow, J.D., Tipler, F.J. (1986). The Anthropic Cosmological Principle. Oxford University Press, Oxford.

Carr, B. (2007). The Anthropic Principle Revisited. In: Carr, B. (ed.). The Universe or Multiverse? Cambridge University Press, Cambridge, pp. 77–89.

Chalmers, M. (2007). Stringscape. Physics World 20, 35–47.

Davies, P.C.W. (2004). Multiverse cosmological models. Mod. Phys. Lett. A19, 727–744; arXiv:astro-ph/0403047

Davies, P. (2007). Universes galore: where will it all end? In: Carr, B. (ed.). The Universe or Multiverse? Cambridge University Press, Cambridge, pp. 487–505.

Deutsch, D. (1997). The Fabric of Reality. Allen Lane, London, New York.

Deutsch, D. (2001). The Structure of the Multiverse; arXiv:quant-ph/0104033

DeWitt, B.S., Graham, N. (eds.) (1973). The Many-Worlds Interpretation of Quantum Mechanics. Princeton, Princeton University Press.

Douglas, M. (2010). The String Landscape: Exploring the Multiverse. In: Vaas, R. (ed.). Beyond the Big Bang. Springer, Heidelberg.

Ellis, G.F.R., Kirchner, U., Stoeger, W.R. (2004). Multiverses and physical cosmology. M.N.R.A.S. 347, 921–936; arXiv:astro-ph/0305292

García-Bellido, J. (1995). Quantum Diffusion of Planck Mass and the Evolution of the Universe. In: Occhionero, F. (ed.). Birth of the Universe and Fundamental Physics. Lecture Notes in Physics 455. Springer, Berlin, pp. 115–120; arXiv:astro-ph/9407087

Gell-Mann, M., Hartle, J. (1990). Quantum Mechanics in the Light of Quantum Cosmology. In: Zurek, W.H. (ed.). Compexity, Entropy, and the Physics of Information. Addison-Wesley, Redwood City, pp. 425–458.

Gell-Mann, M., Hartle, J. (1993). Time Symmetry and Asymmetry in Quantum Mechanics and Quantum Cosmology. In: Halliwell, J., Perez-Mercader, J., Zurek, W. (eds.). Physical Origins of Time Asymmetry. Cambridge University Press, Cambridge, pp. 311–345; arXiv:gr-qc/9304023

Harrison, E.R. (1995). The natural selection of universes containing intelligent life. Quart. J. Royal Astr. Soc. 36, 193–203.

Hogan, C.J. (2000). Why the Universe is Just So. Rev. Mod. Phys. 72, 1149–1161; arXiv:astro-ph/9909295

Hoyningen-Huene, P. (2008). Systematicity: The Nature of Science. Philosophia 36, 167– 180.

Kane, G.L., Perry, M J., Zytkow, A.N. (2002). The Beginning of the End of the Anthropic Principle. New Astron. 7, 45–53; arXiv:astro-ph/0001197

Lakatos, I. (1976). Proofs and Refutations. Cambridge University Press, Cambridge.

Lakatos, I. (1977). The Methodology of Scientific Research Programmes: Philosophical Papers Volume 1. Cambridge University Press, Cambridge.

Laudan, L. (1988). The Demise of the Demarcation Problem. In: Ruse, M. (ed.). But Is It Science? Prometheus, Buffalo, pp. 337–350.

Leslie, J. (1989). Universes. Routledge, London 1996.

Linde, A. (2005). Particle Physics and Inflationary Cosmology. Contemp. Concepts Phys. 5 1–362; arXiv:hep-th/0503203

Linde, A. (2008). Inflationary Cosmology. Lect. Notes Phys. 738, 1–54; arXiv:0705.0164

Meixner, U. (2008). Modalität. Klostermann, Frankfurt am Main.

Mersini-Houghton, L. (2010). Selection of Initial Conditions: The Origin of Our Universe from the Multiverse. In: Vaas, R. (ed.). Beyond the Big Bang. Springer, Heidelberg.

Popper, K. (1930-1933). Die beiden Grundprobleme der Erkenntnistheorie. Mohr Siebeck, Tübingen 1994, 2. ed.

Popper, K.R. (1935). Logik der Forschung. Mohr Siebeck, Tübingen 1989, 9. ed.

Rees, M. (2001). Our Cosmic Habitat. Princeton University Press, Princeton.

Smolin, L. (1992). Did the universe evolve? Class. Quant. Grav. 9, 173–191.

Smolin, L. (1997). The Life of the Cosmos. Oxford University Press, Oxford.

Smolin, L. (2010). Cosmological Natural Selection: Status and Implications. In: Vaas, R. (ed.). Beyond the Big Bang. Springer, Heidelberg.

Tegmark, M. (2004). Parallel Universes. In: Barrow, J., Davies, P.C.W., Harper jr., C.L. (eds.). Science and Ultimate Reality. Cambridge University Press, Cambridge, pp. 459–491; arXiv:astro-ph/0302131

Tegmark, M. (2010). The Mathematical Universe: Eternal Laws and the Illusion of Time. In: Vaas, R. (ed.). Beyond the Big Bang. Springer, Heidelberg.

Vaas, R. (1993). Die Welt als Würfelspiel. In: "Gott würfelt (nicht)!" Evangelische Akademie Baden, Karlsruhe, pp. 108–162.

Vaas, R. (1998). Is there a Darwinian Evolution of the Cosmos? – Some Comments on Lee Smolin's Theory of the Origin of Universes by Means of Natural Selection. Proceedings of the MicroCosmos – MacroCosmos Conference, Aachen; arXiv:gr-qc/0205119

Vaas, R. (2001). Why Quantum Correlates Of Consciousness Are Fine, But Not Enough. Informação e Cognição 3 (1), 64–107. http://www.portalppgci.marilia.unesp.br/reic/viewarticle.php?id=16

Vaas, R. (2003). Problems of Cosmological Darwinian Selection and the Origin of Habitable Universes. In: Shaver, P.A., DiLella, L., Giménez, A. (eds.). Astronomy, Cosmology and Fundamental Physics. Springer, Berlin, pp. 485–486.

Vaas, R. (2004a). Time before Time. Classifications of universes in contemporary cosmology, and how to avoid the antinomy of the beginning and eternity of the world. arXiv:physics/0408111

Vaas, R. (2004b). Ein Universum nach Maß? Kritische Überlegungen zum Anthropischen Prinzip in der Kosmologie, Naturphilosophie und Theologie. In: Hübner, J., Stamatescu, I.- O., Weber, D. (eds.) (2004). Theologie und Kosmologie. Mohr Siebeck, Tübingen, pp. 375–498.

Vaas, R. (2005). Tunnel durch Raum und Zeit. Kosmos, Stuttgart.

Vaas, R. (2006). Das Münchhausen-Trilemma in der Erkenntnistheorie, Kosmologie und Metaphysik. In: Hilgendorf, E. (ed.). Wissenschaft, Religion und Recht. Logos, Berlin, pp. 441–474.

Vaas, R. (2008a). Phantastische Physik: Sind Wurmlöcher und Paralleluniversen ein Gegenstand der Wissenschaft? In: Mamczak, S., Jeschke, W. (eds.). Das Science Fiction Jahr 2008. Heyne, München, pp. 661–743.

Vaas, R. (2008b). Hawkings neues Universum. Kosmos, Stuttgart.

Vaas, R. (2009a). Gods, Gains, and Genes. On the Natural Origin of Religiosity by Means of Bio-cultural Selection. In: Voland, E., Schiefenhövel, W. (eds.). The Biological Evolution of Religious Mind and Behavior. Springer, Heidelberg, pp. 25–49.

Vaas, R. (2009b). Life, the Universe, and almost Everything: Signs of Cosmic Design? arXiv: 0910.5579

Vaas, R. (ed.) (2010). Beyond the Big Bang, Springer, Heidelberg

Vidal, C. (2008). The Future of Scientific Simulations: from Artificial Life to Artificial Cosmogenesis. In: Tandy, C. (ed.). Death And Anti-Death. Ria University Press, Palo Alto, pp. 285–318; arXiv:0803.1087

Vidal, C. (2010). Computational and Biological Analogies for Understanding Fine-Tuned Parameters in Physics. Foundations of Science; arXiv:0912.5508

Vilenkin, A. 2006. Many Worlds in One. Hill and Wang, New York.

Weinberg, S. (1977). The First Three Minutes. Basic Books, New York, p. 131.

Wheeler, J.A., Zurek, W.H. (eds.) (1983). Quantum Theory and Measurement. Princeton University Press, Princeton.

Wittgenstein, L. (1922). Tractatus Logico-Philosophicus. Kegan Paul, Trench, Trubner & Co., London.

22. Classical Anthropic Everett Model: Indeterminacy in a Preordained Multiverse

Brandon Carter
LuTh, Observatoire de Paris, France.

Abstract

Although ultimately motivated by quantum theoretical considerations, Everett's many-world idea remains valid, as an approximation, in the classical limit. However to be applicable it must in any case be applied in conjunction with an appropriate anthropic principle, whose precise formulation involves an anthropic quotient that can be normalised to unity for adult humans but that would be lower for infants and other animals. The outcome is a deterministic multiverse in which the only function of chance is the specification of one's particular identity.

Key Words: Consciousness, quantum entanglement, Many Worlds, Multiverse

1. Introduction

Before the twentieth century, classical probabilistic models - such as those developed by Maxwell and Boltzmann for the treatment of many particle systems - were commonly considered as approximations of an objective de-terministic reality of which the details were unknown or at any rate too complicated to be tractable. However since the advent of quantum theory, it has come to be widely recognized that - as Berkeley had warned - such an objective material reality may not exist. A purported refutation of the bishop's scepticism had been provided by Johnson's famous stone kicking experiment (Deutsch, 97), but the learned doctor might not have remained so cockily confident if, instead of a tamely decoherent stone, he had tried kicking the closed box containing Schroedinger's superposed live-and-dead cat.

According to our modern understanding, classical probabilistic models should be considered as approximations, not of illusory material reality, but of more elaborate quantum theoretical models, whose interpretation is to a large extent subjective rather than objective. A complete understanding would therefor require a theory of the sentient mind - as distinct from, though correlated with, the physical brain.

The question of the relationship between our physical brains - the object of study by neurologists - and the thoughts and feelings in our "conscious" minds was already a subject of philosophical speculation long before the development of quantum theory. As very little substantial progress had been achieved, it was natural that some people should wonder whether a resolution of the mystery of quantum theory might provide a resolution of the mystery of the mind. A more common opinion has however been expressed by Steven Weinberg (1995), who wrote "Of course everything is ultimately quantum mechanical: the question is whether quantum mechanics will appear directly in the theory of the mind, and not just in the deeper level theories like chemistry on which the theories of the mind will be based ... Penrose may be right about that, but I doubt it."

I am inclined to share this common opinion, and will proceed here on that basis, not just because of the relatively macroscopic (multiparticle) nature of the neurons constituting the brain, but because quantum theory is not really essential for what is commonly considered to be the crux of the mind to matter relationship, namely what is known as the "collapse" of the "wave function" which is supposed to result from an observation of the kind exemplified by Schroedinger's gedanken experiment in which a cat in a box is liable to be killed by a pistol triggered by a Geiger counter.

2. The Trouble with the Traditional Doctrine

According to the "Copenhagen" interpretation, the relevant "wave func tion" collapses either to a pure state in which the cat is unambiguously alive, or else one in which it is unambiguously dead, when a human "observer"opens its box. The trouble with the Copenhagen interpretation is that it denies "observer" status to the occupant of the box, which is questionable even in the case of a humble cat, and would clearly be quite inadmissible if the cat were replaced by another human.

However as well as the underlying symmetry between the person at risk and the person who observes, the point I want to emphasize here is that the issue is not essentially quantum mechanical, because it subsists even if one goes over to the (decoherent) classical limit. In the human case, an analogous classical experiment can be - and historically has been - done with the Geiger triggering mechanism replaced by use of an old fashioned Russian roulette revolver. The classical analogue of the "collapse of the wave function" would be the Bayesian reduction of the corresponding classical probability distribution, from an a priori configuration, in which the outcome is uncertain, to an a posteriori configuration in which the subject of the experiment is either unambiguously alive or else unambiguously dead. To the question of which protagonist has the privilege of making the observation whereby the definitive "collapse" occurs, it is traditionally presumed that Bishop Berkeley's reply would have been been "God!". However physicists (since the time of Laplace) have tried to avoid such ad hoc invocation of a "deus ex machina", and (in the spirit of Ockham's razor) are therefore inclined to prefer the alternative reply that is expressible succinctly as "None!". Such negation was originally proposed by Everett, and was advocated - but not adequately elucidated - first by Wheeler and subsequently by DeWitt (1973). By thus denying the Copenhagen doctrine of the occurrence of "collapse" as an objective physical process - rather than merely a subjective allowance for new information as in the familiar classical case of Bayesian reduction - Everett got off to a good start. However his attempt to provide a positive interpretation of the meaning of the "wave function" was not entirely successful.

Part of the trouble arose merely from misunderstanding, due to injudicious choice of wording, whereby what I would prefer to refer to as alternative "channels" were called "branches", thereby conveying the misleading idea of a continual multiplication of worlds (Leslie, 1996), whereas (since Everett's idea was that evolution remains strictly unitary) the "worlds" in question are strictly conserved, having neither beginning nor end: what changes is only the resolution of distinction between different "channels", which may become finer (or coarser!) as observational information is acquired (or lost!). A more serious - since not merely semantic - problem by which many people have been puzzled is what Graham (1973) has called the "dilemma" posed by Everett's declaration that the alternative possible outcomes of an observation are all "equally real" though not (if their quantum amplitudes are different) "equally probable". As I have argued previously (Carter, 2004), and will maintain here, the resolution of this dilemma requires the invocation of an appropriate anthropic principle.

3. The Concept of Reality

It was recognised long ago by Berkeley, and has been emphasized more recently by Page (1996), that the only kinds of entities we know for sure to be real are our mental feelings and perceptions (including dreams). The material world in which we have the impression of living is essentially just a theoretical construct to account for our perceptions. In the dualist (Cartesian) picture that used to be widely accepted, this material world was supposed to have a reality of its own, on par with the realm of feelings and perceptions. However under closer scrutinary such separate material reality has turned out to be illusive, so we find ourselves glimpsing a more mysterious but apparently unified quantum picture. Following the approach initiated by Everett (DeWitt, 1973; Graham, 1973), diverse attempts to sketch the outlines of such a unified picture have been made, albeit with only rather limited success so far, by various people (Deutsch, 1999; Wallace, 2003; Reaves, 2004), and in particular - from a point of view closer to that adopted here - by Page (1996) and the present author (Carter, 2004).

Assuming, as remarked above, that mental processes have an essentially classical rather than quantum nature, this essay has the relatively modest purpose of attempting to sketch the outlines of a simpler, more easily accessible, classical unification that may be useful pedagogically and, in appropriate circumstances, as an approximation to a more fundamental quantum unification that remains elusive. The picture proposed here is based on the use of an appropriate anthropic principle in conjunction with the Everett approach, which is relatively well defined in the classical limit, so that the notions of "equal reality" and "unequal probability" can be clarified in a coherent manner.

Deutsch (1999), Wallace (2003), and Greaves (2004) have developed an alternative approach that attempts to do this in terms of the kind of probability postulated in decision theory, on the debatable supposition that the relevant observations are performed by "rational agents". The essentially different approach advocated here is based on probability of a kind proportional to the amount of perception that is "real", in the sense not of Deutsch (1997) but of Page (1996) - as based on sentience rather than rationality. Following a line of thought originated by Dyson (1979), I have suggested (Carter, 2004, 2007) that the relevant amount of perception should in principle be measured by the corresponding Shannon type information content, but in practice that does not tell us much, as it leaves us with the unsolved question of which of the many processes going on in the brain are the ones that actually correspond to sentient perception. This fundamental question does not matter so long as we are concerned only with the standard, narrowly anthropic, case of adult humans, for whom (as in the example of the next section) it can reasonably be assumed that such processes go on at roughly the same average rate. However for more general applications it would be necessary to face the intractible problem of estimating the relevant anthropic quotient q, meaning an appropriate correction factor that might be larger than unity for conceivable extraterrestrials, but that would presumably be smaller for extinct hominids, and much smaller for other animals as well as for infants of our own species. The easiest non-trivial case to deal with would presumably be that of ordinarily senile members of our own species, as their mental processes are similar to those of adults in their prime except for a reduction in speed that can be allowed for by a factor q that should be clinically measurable (and of practical interest for therapeutic purposes).

4. Russian Roulette: A Historical Example

It is customary (Greaves, 2004) to demonstrate the application of such principles by idealized gedanken experiments in which, if there are just two protagonists, their initials are commonly taken to be A for Alice and B for Bob (while to illustrate merely logical, rather than physically conceivable possibilities, it is common (Bostrom, 2002) to consider examples that are not just idealised but frankly fantastic, in which case the protagonists are referred to as "Adam and Eve"). However to emphasise that I am concerned with what is "real" I shall take as a (simplified and approximate, but not artificially idealized) example an experiment that is not merely hypothetical, but that really occurred as a historical event during the XXth century, with a principle protagonist whose initial was actually not A but G.

To illustrate the basic idea, I propose to consider a modified Schroedinger type experiment in which G - an unbalanced adolescent at the time - voluntarily and crazily took the role of the cat, in a solitary game of Russian roulette. The role of the external observer was taken by his big brother (the owner of the revolver) to whom I shall refer by the letter B. Having first heard about it privately from someone who had been neighbor at the time, I read about it many years later in published memoirs of G, who not only survived the experiment but recovered his mental equilibrium and lived to a ripe old age - at least in our particular branch-channel of the multiverse. To keep the arithmetic simple, I shall postulate that the revolver was just a five-shooter, of the compact kind that is most convenient as a concealed weapon. (In reality it may well have been a six-shooter of the kind familiar in cowboy movies, but it can safely be presumed that it was not what was originally used by the reputed inventors of Russian roulette, namely Czarist officers, whose standard service revolvers were actually seven-shooters.) The protocol of the potentially suicidal game is to load just one of the cartridge chambers and then to whirl it to a random position before pulling the trigger. In such a case, starting from initial conditions that are imperceptibly different, there will be five equally likely outcomes, of which four will be indistinguishable for practical purposes, whereas the other one will be fatal.

According to the traditional single-world doctrine of deterministic classical physics (as still taken for granted at the time of the incident in question) only one of the five possible outcomes would have actually occurred. However according to the Everett type many-world doctrine, a complete description will involve many separately conserved "strands" (commonly but misleadingly referred to as "branches") meaning single worlds of all the five types, in a multiverse consisting of five equally numerous sub-ensembles or "channels", one for each qualitatively distinct possibility. Such sub-ensembles will be characterized by a physical measure given by the fraction p of the total number of strands, which in this case is $p = 1/5$ for each one. Since the four possibilities in which G survives would have been effectively distinguishable (by an examination of the weapon) only for a very short time after the experiment, it will in practice be sufficient for most subsequent purposes to use a coarser representation in which they are regrouped into a single larger multistrand "channel", which will thus have measure $p = 4/5$. When Everett refers to things as "equally real" it is clear that he should be understood to have in mind the individual (single world) strands, rather than their weighted groupings into broader "channels".

The stage at which the original presentation of the Everett approach becomes unclear is when it is suggested that the physical weighting introduced as described should somehow be interpreted as a probability, despite the fact that (as the classical limit of evolution that is strictly unitary in the quantum case) the behavior of the many worlds involved is entirely deterministic, so that when their initial configurations have been specified no uncertainties remain.

To give a meaning to the concept of probability in this context, the purely materialistic framework of the classical many-world system described so far needs to be extended to include allowance for the role of mind. For the simplified classical model considered here, it will be good enough to do this in the usual way, by supposing that mental feelings and perceptions correspond to physical states of animate brains that are roughly localizable on time parametrized world lines of the animals concerned within the single world "strands".

5. Anthropic Quotient

Within the foregoing framework, the incorporation of probability into the model is achieved by an appropriate application of the anthropic principle. In the simple (weak) version that is adequate for the present purpose, the anthropic principle (Carter, 2005, 2010) prescribes that the probability of finding oneself on a particular animate world line on a single strand within a small time interval dt is proportional to q dt, where the "anthropic quotient" q, is normalized to unity in the average (adult) human case. This coefficient q is interpretable as a measure of the relative rate of conscious sentient thought (which might be very low compared with the rate of subconscious but perhaps highly intelligent information processing, such as could be performed by an insentient computer). Whereas it might be higher than unity for conceivable extraterrestrials, q would presumably be lower for other terrestrial species (such as chimpanzees) as well as for infants and senile members of our own species. On short (diurnal) time scales the anthropic quotient of an individual would fluctuate between high waking levels and low dreaming values, and it would of course go to zero at and after the instant of death, as also before conception (though perhaps not before the instant of birth).

In the CAE (classical anthropic Everett) model set up in this way, the meaning of the weighting fraction p of a channel constituted by an ensemble of very similar single-world strands is now clear. It does not directly determine the total probability of finding oneself in that channel, but it does determine the probability dP of finding oneself within a time interval dt on a world line of a particular kind (such as that of G, or alternatively that of B in the example described above) within the channel in question, according to the specification dP p q dt (with the proportionality factor adjusted so that the total probability for all possibilities adds up to unity).

Let us see how this works out in the simple example of the roulette gamester G and his brother B, as shown in the figure, on the assumption that both can be considered as average adults characterized by q = 1. To keep the figures round, let us take it that in the first channel, with $p1 = 4/5$, both roulette gamester G and his brother B survived 6 times longer (to an age of about 90) than G did in the second (fatal) channel, with $p2 = 1/5$, where the life of B would have been unaffected (while that of G would have been truncated at about age 15). This can be seen to imply that one is 20 per cent more likely to find oneself to be B than G. In the former case, one will have a 20 per cent chance of being in the fatal channel, and thus of witnessing the death of one's younger brother. In the latter case, that is to say conditional on being G, one will have a 20 per cent chance of finding oneself in the time interval before the game, and thus with only a 4 per cent chance of being in what will turn out to be the fatal channel.

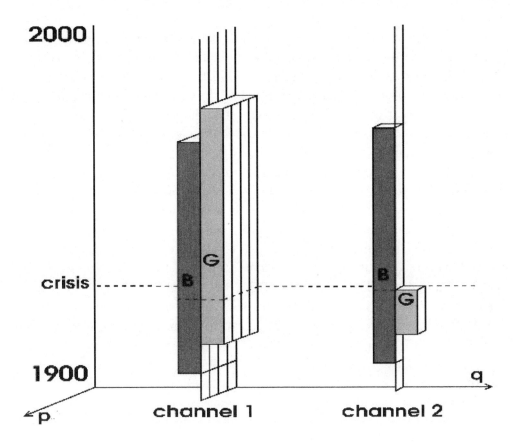

Figure 1: Crude anthropic biograph of XXth century roulette gamester G (pale shading) and his brother B (dark shading) using the vertical direction for time, while the thickness of a worldline in the sideways direction measures subjective anthropic probability weighting per unit time, as specified by the anthropic quotient q which is set to zero before birth and after death, and is taken here to have a uniform unit (average) value during life - whereas in a less crude version it would taper off at the beginning (infancy) and the end (senility). For each of the (Everett type) channels, the 3rd dimension - out of the page or screen - measures

the number of "strands", representing the objective physical probability p (the square of a corresponding quantum amplitude) which is conserved. In such an anthropic diagram, the probability of finding oneself to be in a particular state of a particular person during a particular time interval is proportional to the relevant volume (the time integral of the product pq of the anthropic and physical probability measures). In channel 1 - the one we know about historically, because we are on it ourselves - both brothers survived through a complete life span until old age, the younger naturally outliving the elder. In channel 2 , for which the life of G was truncated after only one 6th of its natural span, it is supposed that the subsequent life of B would not have been substantially affected.

If B and G had been the only sentient inhabitants of the world it can be seen that the a priori odds against channel 2 would have been 48 to 7 which is almost 7 to 1. However when account is taken of all the rest of the population (who would not have been significantly affected by the outcome of the roulette game) it can be seen that the a priori odds against finding oneself in channel 2 (and thus deprived of access to G's later literary output) would actually have been barely greater than 4 to 1 (the value given by the ratio $p1/p2$ of the naive physical probabilities designated by p). A more complete picture, allowing for the many other inhabitants of the world, would of course require a much finer decomposition involving far more than two qualitatively distinct channels. Indeed a complete multibiography just of G alone would probably require many more channels to allow for the vicissitudes of his later life, which extended not just through the Second World War but even through the Cold War. In particular - to be fully realistic - an adequate multi-history of the latter would presumably require the inclusion of non-neglibly weighted channels in which an incident such as the Cuban missile crisis terminated in the catastrophic manner envisaged by Shute (1957).

6. Commentary

Although the interpretations - and perhaps the ethical implications - are different, there is no effectively observable distinction between what is predicted by the deterministic many-world CAE model presented here (in which only one's identity is unforeseeable) and what is predicted by the corresponding classical model of the ordinary single-world type (in which the material physical outcome depends on chance). It might therefore be argued that the traditional single-world model should be preferred on the grounds that it is simpler, or less ontologically "bloated". It is however to be recalled that a classical model cannot claim to represent ultimate reality, but merely provides what is at best an approximation to a more accurately realistic quantum model, a purpose for which the traditional single world-model is not so satisfactory.

Another point to be emphasized is that the ontology in question involves only mental feelings and perceptions. As foretold by Berkeley, but contrary to what used to be taught by "positivists" such as Mach, matter, as incorporated in physical fields over spacetime, should not be considered to have objective "reality", but has the status merely of mathematical machinery (that might be replaced for predictive purposes by an equivalent action at a distance formulation based on Green functions).

Having recognized that the relevant ontology does not involve matter but only mind, one is still free to entertain different opinions about how extensive or "bloated" (Leslie, 1983) it may be. The anthropic measure characterized by the coefficient q merely determines the relative probability of the perceptions in question, but but not the absolute number of times they occur. If ontological economy is a desideratum, it might seem preferable to postulate the actual occurrence only of a fraction of the perceptions admitted by the theory. On the other hand for those concerned with economy only in the sense of Ockham's razor, and particularly for those who are unhappy with the concept of probability except when it can be prescribed in terms of relative frequencies, the most attractive possibility would presumably be to suppose that all the perceptions admitted by the theory actually occur (in the indicated proportions). Although it is more ontologically extravagant, the latter alternative has the advantage of conforming to the requirement that was expressed in metaphorical language by Einstein's edict that "God does not play dice". However that is not for us mere mortals to judge: as far as scientific observation is concerned there is no way of telling the difference.

A more mundane issue (with ethical implications concerning protection from inhumane treatment) is the evaluation of the appropriate anthropic quotient q for non-human terrestrial animals (such as the cat considered by Schroedinger) and particularly for infants of our own species. It is to be presumed that q should be of the order of unity for extinct hominids such as homo erectus, whose integrated population time is at most comparable with our own (Carter, 2010). However the observation (Standish, 2008) that we do not belong to the far more numerous populations of animals of other, less closely related, kinds suggests that their anthropic quotients should be much lower, and hence, by analogy, that the same may apply to infants.

Acknowledgement The author is grateful for stimulating discussions with John Wheeler, Roger Penrose, and Bryce DeWitt on various past occasions, and also for more recent discussions with John Leslie and Don Page.

References

Bostrom, N. (2002). Anthropic bias: obsrvation selection effects in science and philosophy (Routlege, New York).

Carter, B. (2004). Anthropic interpretation of quantum theory, Int. J. Theor. Phys. 43, 721-730. [hep-th/0403008]

Carter, B. (2007). Microanthropic principle for quantum theory, in Universe or Multiverse, ed B. Carr (Cambridge U. Press. 285-319.

Carter, B. (2010). Hominid evolution: genetics versus memetics. [arXiv:1011.3393]

Deutsch, D. (1997). The Fabric of reality (Penguin, London).

Deutsch, D. (1999). Quantum theory of probability and decisions, Proc. Roy. Soc. A455, 3129-3137 [quant-ph/9906015].

DeWitt, B.S. (1973). The many-universes interpretation of quantum theory, in The many worlds interpretation of quantum theory, ed. B.S. De Witt, N. Graham (Princeton University Press, 1973) 167-218.

Dyson, F.J. (1979). Time without end: physics and biology in an open system, Rev. Mod. Phys. 51, 447-460.

Graham, N. (1973). The measurement of relative frequency, in The many worlds interpretation of quantum theory, ed. B.S. De Witt, N. Graham (Princeton University Press, 1973) 229-253.

Greaves, H. (2004). Understanding Deutsch's probability in a deterministic multiverse, Studies in the history and philosophy of modern physics 35, 423-456. [quant-ph/0312136].

Leslie, J. (1983), Cosmology, probability, and the need to understand life, in Scientific Explanation and Understanding, ed. N. Rescher (University Press of America, 1983) 53-82.

Leslie, J. 1996, A difficulty for Everett's many-worlds theory, International studies in the philosphy of science 10, 239-246.

Page, D. (1996), Sensible quantum mechanics: are probabilities only in the mind?, Int. J. Mod. Phys. D5, 583-596. [gr-qc/9507024]

Shute, N. (1957), On the beach (Ballantine, New York).

Standish, R. K. (2008). Ants are not Conscious. [arXiv:0802.4121]

Wallace, D. (2003). Everettian rationality: defending Deutsch's approach to probability in the Everett interpretation, Studies in the history and phi- losophy of modern physics 34, 415-439 [quant-ph/0303050].

Weinberg, S. (1995). Reductionism Redux, New York Review of Books XLII Oct. 5, 39-42.

23. Cosmology, The Uncertainty Principle, Wave Function, Probability, Entanglement, and Multiple Worlds

Rhawn Gabriel Joseph

Cosmology.com / BrainMind.com

Abstract:

In quantum mechanics the cosmos as a whole can be likened to a quantum continuum which is continually in flux and is thus indeterminate except at the moment of perception and registration by an observing consciousness or measuring apparatus. Because of this continual fluctuation and the limitations of conscious perceptual capacities and through a phenomenon known as "entanglement," it is only possible to make predictions about what may be observed; and these predictions can only be based on probabilities and a probability distribution. When quantum mechanics are applied to the concept of "time" then what is conceptualized as "past" "present" and "future" is also best described in terms of probabilities. Time is uncertain and not deterministic. Causes may occur simultaneously with or even after effects become effects, as demonstrated by entanglement. The experience of time or the existence of an object in space, are also manifestations of the wave function. As the wave propagates through space it effects the continuum both locally and at a distance simultaneously as demonstrated by entanglement, where even choices made in the future can effect the present. If time has a wave function, then the present can effect not just the future, but the future can effect the present and the past, as time is a continuum. Time is entangled. If considered as a unity with no separations in time and space except at the moment of conscious observation, then to effect one point in time-space is to effect all points which are entangled in spacetime. Time and events occurring in time, through entanglement, and as a manifestation of the quantum continuum, can therefore change the future and the past and events occurring in time simultaneously. The present and the future may change the past as all are interconnected, thereby giving rise to paradoxes where the past may be changed such that it becomes a different past. This paradox, however, can be resolved through Everett's conception of Many Worlds. The past which is changed, is just one past among many. Hence, in terms of the "grandfather" paradox, for example, one may travel back in time but the "grandfather" they kill would not be their "grandfather," but the "grandfather" of their doppelganger who exists in an alternate world as there are innumerable worlds each with their own probable existence and space-time.

Keywords: Time Travel Paradoxes, Everett's Multiple Worlds, Uncertainty Principle, Wave Function, Probability Function

TimeSpace in Relativity

In 1904, Lorentz introduced a hypothesis that moving bodies contract in their direction of motion by a factor depending on the velocity of the moving object. Time can therefore also contract such that the future and the present come closer together. He also argued that in different schemes of reference there are different apparent times which differ from and replace "real time." He also argued that the velocity of light was the same in all systems of reference. In 1905 Albert Einstein seized on these ideas and abolished what Lorentz called "real time" and instead embraced "apparent time." In his theories of special relativity, Einstein promoted the thesis that reality and its properties, such as time and motion had no objective "true values" but were "relative" to the observer's point of view (Einstein, 1905a,b,c). Einstein's conceptions of reality and time, therefore, differed significantly from that of Newton.

Time is relative to the observer (Einstein 1905a,b,c, 1906, 1961). Since there are innumerable observers, there is no universal "past, present, future" which are infinite in number and all of which are in motion. There is more than one "present" and this is because time is not the same everywhere for everyone, and differs depending on gravity, acceleration, frames of reference, relative to the observer (Einstein 1907, 1910, 1961). Time is relative and there is no universal past. No universal future. And no universal now. The "past" in another galaxy overlaps with the "present" on Earth. The "present" in another galaxy will not be experienced on Earth until the future. There is no universal now (Einstein 1955). Time is relative, and so too are the futures, presents, and pasts, which overlap and exist simultaneously in different distant regions of space-time. Time is relative, and the "present" for one observer, in one location, may be the past, or the future, for a second observer on another planet.

Time has energy. As defined by Einstein's (1905b) famous theorem $E=mc^2$, and the law of conservation of energy and mass, mass can become energy and energy can become mass. Space-time is both energy and mass which is why it can be warped and will contract in response to gravity and acceleration (Einstein, 1914, 1915a,b; Parker & Toms 2009; Ohanian & Ruffini 2013). Time and space are linked, thereby forming a fourth dimension, timespace. Time, and conceptions about the past, present of future are therefore illusions, as there is no "future" or "past" but rather there are different locations in space which relative to an observer appear far away or nearby. However, when considered from the perspective of quantum mechanics, timespace is a continuum, a unity, and time does not exist independent of this continuum, except as an act of perceptual registration by consciousness or mechanical means.

Einstein's theories did not replace Newtons. Instead Einstein came up with a new closed system of definitions and axioms represented by mathematical symbols which were are radically different from those of Newton's mechanics. For example, space and time in Newtonian physics are independent, whereas in relativity they are combined and connected by the Lorentz transformations. Moreover, although Newtonian mechanics could be applied to events where velocities are small relative to the velocity of light, Newtonian physics cannot be applied to events which take place near light speeds whereas Einstein's physics can.

By contrast, it is at light speed and beyond, and for objects and particles smaller than atoms where Einstein's theory breaks down and this was recognized in the early 1920s (Born et al. 1925; Heisenberg 1925, 1927). The phenomenon of electricity, electromagnetism and atomic science required a new physics and radically different conceptions of cause, effect, and time.

The Uncertainty Principle: Cause, Effects, Time, and Probability

In 1925 a mathematical formalism called matrix mechanics posed a direct challenge to Newton and Einstein and conceptions of reality (Born et al. 1925; Heisenberg 1925). The equations of Newton were replaced by equations between matrices representing the position and momentum of electrons which were found to be unpredictable. Broadly considered, atoms consist of empty space at the center of which is a positively charged nucleus and which is orbited by electrons. The positive charge of the atom's nucleus determines the number of surrounding electrons, making the atom electrically neutral. However, it was determined that it was impossible to make precise predictions about the position and momentum of electrons based on Newtonian or Einsteinian physics, and this led to the Copenhagen interpretation (Heisenberg 1925, 1927) which Einstein repeatedly attacked because of all the inherent paradoxes. Matrix mechanics is referred to now as quantum mechanics whereas the "statistical matrix" is known as the "probability function;" all of which are central to quantum theory.

As summed up by Heisenberg (1958) "the probability function represents our deficiency of knowledge... it does not represent a course of events, but a tendency for events to take a certain course or assume certain patters. The probability function also requires that new measurements be made to determine the properties of a system, and to calculate the probable result of the new measurement; i.e. a new probability function." Since time is also a property of a system, as events take place in time, then time also, is subject to the probability function.

Quantum physics, as exemplified by the Copenhagen school (Bohr, 1934, 1958, 1963; Heisenberg, 1925, 1927, 1930), like Einsteinian physics, makes assumptions about the nature of reality as related to an observer, the "knower" who is conceptualized as a singularity. As summed up by Heisenberg (1958), "the concepts of Newtonian or Einsteinian physics can be used to describe events in nature." However, because the physical world is relative to being known by a "knower" (the observing consciousness), then the "knower" can influence the nature of the reality which is being observed through the act of measurement and registration at a particular moment in time. Moreover, what is observed or measured at one moment can never include all the properties of the object under observation. In consequence, what is known vs what is not known becomes relatively imprecise (Bohr, 1934, 1958, 1963; Heisenberg, 1925, 1927). Time, therefore, including what is conceptualized as the "now" also becomes imprecise, as well as relative to an observer as predicted by special relativity.

As expressed by the Heisenberg uncertainty principle (Heisenberg, 1927), the more precisely one physical property is known the more unknowable become other properties. The more precisely one property is known, the less precisely the other can be known and this is true at the molecular and atomic levels of reality. Therefore it is impossible to precisely determine, simultaneously, for example, both the position and velocity of an electron at any specific moment in time (Bohr, 1934, 1958, 1963).Time, itself, becomes relativity imprecise even when measured by atomic clocks which slow or speed up depending on gravity and velocity (Ashby 2003, Chou et al. 2010; Hafele & Keating 1972a,b,)--exactly as predicted by Einstein and Lorenz.

Heisenberg's principle of indeterminacy focuses on the relationship of the experimenter to the objects of his scientific scrutiny, and the probability and potentiality, in quantum mechanics, for something to be other than it is. Time, too, therefore, would have potentiality, including what is believed to have occurred in the past (Joseph 2014). Einstein objected to quantum mechanics and Heisenberg's formulations of potentiality and indeterminacy by proclaiming "god does not play dice."

In Einstein's and Newton's physics, the state of any isolated mechanical system at a given moment of time is given precisely. Numbers specifying the position and momentum of each mass in the system are empirically determined at that moment of time of the measurement. Probability never enters into the equation. Therefore, the position and momentum of objects including subatomic particles are precisely located in space and time as designated by a single pair of numbers, all of which can be determined causally and deterministically. However, quantum physics proved that Einstein and Newton's formulation are not true at the atomic and subatomic level (Bohr, 1934, Born et al. 1925; Heisenberg 1925, 1927), whereas experiments with atomic clocks proves that even "moments in time" can vary (Ashby 2003, Chou et al. 2010; Hafele & Keating 1972a,b,).

According to Heisenberg (1925, 1927, 1930), chance and probability enters into the state and the definition of a physical system because the very act of measurement can effect the system. No system is truly in isolation. No system can be viewed from all perspectives in totality simultaneously which would require a god's eye view. Only if the entire universe is included can one apply the qualifying condition of "an isolated system." Simply including the observer, his eye, the measuring apparatus and the object, are not enough to escape uncertainty. Results are always imprecise. Time itself, is relatively imprecise depending on gravity, velocity and the observer's frame of reference.

As determined by Niels Bohr (1949), the properties of physical entities exist only as complementary or conjugate pairs. A profound aspect of complementarity is that it not only applies to measurability or knowability of some property of a physical entity, but more importantly it applies to the limitations of that physical entity's very manifestation of the property in the physical world. Physical reality is defined by manifestations of properties which are limited by the interactions and trade-offs between these complementary pairs at specific moments in time when those moments are also variable. For example, the accuracy in measuring the position of an electron at a specific moment in time requires a complementary loss of accuracy in determining its momentum; and momentum can contract time and the distance between the present and the future. Precision in measuring one pair is complimented by a corresponding loss of precision in measuring the other pair (Bohr, 1949, 1958, 1963); which in turn may be related to variations and fluctuations in time. The ultimate limitations in precision of property manifestations are quantified by Heisenberg's uncertainty principle and matrix mechanics. Complementarity and Uncertainty dictate that all properties and actions in the physical world are therefore non-deterministic to some degree--and the same applies to time and even what is considered cause and effect.

Bohr (1949) holds that objects governed by quantum mechanics, when measured, give results that depend inherently upon the type of measuring device used, and must necessarily be described in classical mechanical terms since the measuring devices functions according to classical mechanics. The measuring device effects the outcome and the interpretation of that outcome as does the observer using that device. "This crucial point...implies the impossibility of any sharp separation between the behaviour of atomic objects and the interaction with the measuring instruments which serve to define the conditions under which the phenomena appear...." (Bohr 1949). Time, however, is also determined by measuring devices, which may fluctuate depending on gravity and velocity, including the velocity of the object being measured--exactly as predicted by relativity.

Evidence obtained under a single or under different experimental conditions cannot be reduced to a single picture, "but must be regarded as complementary in the sense that only the totality of the phenomena exhausts the possible information about the objects." In consequence, the results must be viewed in terms of probabilities when applied to the nature of the object under study and its current and future behaviors in time. Bohr (1949) called this the principle of complementarity, a concept fundamental to quantum mechanics and closely associated with the Uncertainty Principle. "The knowledge of the position of a particle is complementary to the knowledge of its velocity or momentum." If we know the one with high accuracy we cannot know the other with high accuracy at the same time (Bohr, 1949, 1958, 1963; Heisenberg, 1927, 1955, 1958); and this is also because, there is no such thing as "the same time."

Central to the Copenhagen principle is the wave function and the probability distribution, i.e. the results of any experiment can only be stated in terms of the probability that the momentum or position of the particles under observation may assume certain values at a specific time. The probability distribution is a prediction for what may occur in the future, that is, within a predicted range of probabilities. When the experiments are performed many times, and although subsequent observations may differ, they are expected to fall within the predicted probability distribution. This also means that nothing is precisely determined at any particular moment in time (Bohr, 1949, 1963; Heisenberg, 1927, 1930, 1955).

Time and the measuring devices used to calculate time, are relative, and even moments in time may be stretched or contracted relative to an observer's frame of reference. There is no universal now. Thus, even what is described as "now" or the future or the past, must also be subject to a probability function. Time cannot be known precisely, even when measured by atomic clocks (Ashby 2003, Chou et al. 2010; Hafele & Keating 1972a,b,). Thus, even what is considered cause and effect" must be subject to a probability function as the moments embracing the "cause" may overlap and occur simultaneously with or even preceded the "effect" due to the stretching and contraction of local time.

These are not just thought experiments. There is considerable evidence of what Einstein (1955) referred to as "spooky action at a distance" and what is known in quantum physics as "entanglement" (Plenio 2007; Juan et al. 2013; Francis 2012). It is well established that causes and effects can occur simultaneously and ever faster than light speed (Lee et al. 2011; Matson 2012; Olaf et al. 2003); a consequence of the connectedness of all things in the quantum continuum.

For example, photons are easily manipulated and preserve their coherence for long times and can be entangled by projection measurements (Kwiat et al. 1995; Weinfurter 1994). A pump photon, for example, can split light into two lower-energy photons while preserving momentum and energy, and these photons remained maximally entangled although separated spatially (Goebel et al 2008; Pan et al. 1998). However, entanglement swapping protocols can entangle two remote photons without any interaction between them and even with a significant time-like separation (Ma et al., 2012; Megidish et al. 2013; Peres 2000). In one set of experiments entanglement was demonstrated even following a delayed choice and even before there was a decision to make a choice. Specifically, four photons were created and two were measured and which became entangled. However, if a choice was then made to measure the remaining two photons, all four became entangled before it was decided to do a second measurement (Ma et al., 2012; Peres 2000). Entanglement can occur independent of and before the act of measurement. "The time at which quantum measurements are taken and their order, has no effect on the outcome of a quantum mechanical experiment" (Megidish et al. 2013).

Moreover, "two photons that exist at separate times can be entangled" (Megidish et al. 2013). As detailed by Megidish et al (2013): "In the scenario we present here, measuring the last photon affects the physical description of the first photon in the past, before it has even been measured. Thus, the "spooky action" is steering the system's past. Another point of view...is that the measurement of the first photon is immediately steering the future physical description of the last photon. In this case, the action is on the future of a part of the system that has not yet been created."

Hence, entanglement between photons has been demonstrated even before the second photon even exists; "a manifestation of the non-locality of quantum mechanics not only in space, but also in time" (Megidish et al 2013). In other words, a photon may become entangled with another photon even before that photon is created, before it even exists. Even after the first photon ceases to exist and before the second photon is created, both become entangled even though there is no overlap in time. Photons that do not exist can effect photons which do exist and photons which no longer exist and photons which will exist (Megidish et al. 2013); and presumably the same applies to all particles, atoms, molecules (Wiegner, et al 2011).

As demonstrated in quantum physics, the act of observation, measurement, and registration of an event, can effect that event, causing a collapse of a the wave function (Dirac 1966a,b; Heisenberg 1955), thereby registering form, length, shape which emerges like a blemish on the face of the quantum continuum. Likewise, a Time Traveler or particle/object speeding toward and then faster than light and from the future into the past will affect the quantum continuum. By traveling into the future or the past, the Time Traveler will interact with and alter every local moment within the quantum continuum and thus the future or the past.

Entanglement proves that effects may precede causes, and causes and effects may also take place simultaneously. In the quantum continuum, determinism and causes and effects do not always exist and this is because, as Einstein proclaimed: "The distinction between past, present and future is only an illusion."

In quantum mechanisms, although every deterministic system is a causal system, not every causal system is deterministic (Heisenberg (1925, 1927; 1958). Rather, causality is the relationship between different states of the same object at different times whereas what is "deterministic" relates to what may occur, and is better described in terms of probabilities.

According to the Copenhagen interpretation (Bohr, 1949, 1963; Heisenberg,

1958), it is the act of measurement which collapses the wave function. It is also the measurement and observation of one event which triggers the instantaneous alteration in behavior of another event or object at faster than light speeds; i.e. entanglement (Plenio 2007; Juan et al. 2013; Francis 2012). For example, two particles which are far apart have "spin" and they may spin up or down. However, although they are far apart, an observer who measures and verifies the spin of particle A will at the same time effect the spin of particle B, as verified by a second observer. Measuring particle A, effects particle B and changes its spin. Likewise observing the spin of B determines the spin of A. There is no temporal order as the spin of one effects the spin of the other simultaneously, faster than the speed of light. Even distant objects are entangled and have a symmetrical relationship and a constant conjunction (Bokulich & Jaeger, 2010; Plenio 2007; Sonner 2013).

Because the future can effect the past or present, the relationship of cause and effect and energy or mass over time is uncertain and can be described only by probabilities (Born et al 1925, Heisenberg 1925, 1927). Time is uncertain. Temporal succession may have no probable connection with what precedes or follows (Heisenberg 1958). In quantum mechanics, one can know the connection between two events only by knowing the future state--thus one must wait for the future to arrive, or look back upon the future state of similar systems in the past. If one knows the properties of an acorn at an earlier time t1 one still cannot deduce the properties of the oak tree at time t2. This may be possible only in isolated systems (Bohr, 1949; Heisenberg 1958). Thus time must also be isolated. However, unless the entire universe is included in the measurement, then the system, which includes time, is not truly isolated.

The Probability and Wave Function

Quantum mechanics is mechanical but not deterministic and causal relationships are never teleological and not always deterministic. In quantum physics, nature and reality are represented by the quantum state. The electromagnetic field of the quantum state is the fundamental entity, the continuum that constitutes the basic oneness and unity of all things. The physical nature of this state can be "known" by assigning it mathematical properties and probabilities (Bohr, 1958, 1963; Heisenberg, 1927). Therefore, abstractions, i.e., numbers and probabilities become representational of a hypothetical physical state. Because these are abstractions, the physical state is also an abstraction and does not possess the material consistency, continuity, and hard, tangible, physical substance as is assumed by Classical (Newtonian) physics. Instead, reality, the physical world, is a process of observing, measuring, and knowing and is based on probabilities and the wave function (Heisenberg, 1955).

Consider an elementary particle, once its positional value is assigned, knowledge of momentum, trajectory, speed, and so on, is lost and becomes "uncertain." The particle's momentum is left uncertain by an amount inversely proportional to the accuracy of the position's measurement which is determined by values assigned by measurement and the observing consciousness at a specific moment in time relative to that observe and the measuring device. Therefore, the nature of reality, and the uncertainty principle is directly affected by the observer and the process of observing, measuring, and knowing, all of which are variable thereby making the results probable but not completely certain (Heisenberg, 1955, 1958):

"What one deduces from an observation is a probability function; which is a mathematical expression that combines statements about possibilities or tendencies with statements about our knowledge of facts....The probability function obeys an equation of motion as the coordinates did in Newtonian mechanics; its change in the course of time is completely determined by the quantum mechanical equation but does not allow a description in both space and time" (Heisenberg, 1958).

"The probability function does not describe a certain event but a whole ensemble of possible events" whereas "the transition from the possible to the actual takes place during the act of observation... and the interaction of the object with the measuring device, and thereby with the rest of the world... The discontinuous change in the probability function... takes place with the act of registration, because it is the discontinuous change of our knowledge in the instant of registration that changes the probability function." "Since through the observation our knowledge of the system has changed discontinuously, its mathematical representation has also undergone the discontinuous change and we speak of a quantum jump" (Heisenberg, 1958).

Einstein ridiculed these ideas: "Do you really think the moon isn't there if you aren't looking at it?"

Heisenberg (1958), cautioned, however, that the observer is not the creator of reality: "Quantum theory does not introduce the mind of the physicist as part of the atomic event. But it starts from the division of the world into the object and the rest of the world. What we observe is not nature in itself but nature exposed to our method of questioning." Nevertheless, the act of knowing, of observing, or measuring, that is, interacting with the environment in any way, creates an entangled state and a knot in the quantum continuum described as a "collapse of the wave function;" a knot of energy that is a kind of blemish in the continuum of the quantum field. This quantum knot bunches up at the point of observation, at the assigned value of measurement and can be entangled.

The same principles would also apply to time, and to time travel. The act of moving through time would effect time and all local and even more distant events. Traveling through the past or the future would effect every moment of that future; however, exactly what those changes may be, are indeterministic and can only be described by a probability function.

In the Copenhagen model, objects are viewed as quantum mechanical systems which are best described by the wave function and the probability function. "The reduction of wave packets occurs when the transition is completed from the possible to the actual" (Heisenberg, 1958).

The measuring apparatus and the observer also have a wave function and therefore interact with what is being measured. The effect of this is obvious when its a macro-structure measuring a micro-structure vs a macro-structure measuring a macro-structure.

Moreover, according to the uncertainty principle, it is not possible to restrict any analysis to position or moment without effecting the other, and this is because the very act of eliminating uncertainty about position maximizes uncertainty about momentum (Heisenberg 1927). Uncertainty implies entanglement. Likewise, eliminating uncertainty about momentum maximizes uncertainty about position. Instead, one must assign a probability distribution which assigns probabilities to all possible values of position and momentum.

Therefore, no object, or particle, or quanta, or quantum, or moment in time, has its own eigenstate (inherent characteristic). Although every object appears to have a definite momentum, a definite position, and a definite time of occurrence, the object is in flux and it can't have a position and momentum at the same time as there is no such thing as "the same time." Time is also in flux. Therefore, when applied to time, then time, including the future and the past, can only be defined by a probability function. This means, the future and the past may change and that whatever is believed to have taken place or which will take place is best described in terms of probabilities.

Time and Quantum Physics: The Future Can Lead to the Past

In contrast to Newton and Einstein, quantum mechanics concerns itself with the dynamical change of state and its probability coupled with the Schrödinger (1926) time equations which are both time dependent and time independent for particles and waves. The state-function specifies the state of any physical system as a specific time t. The Schrödinger time equations relates states at a series time t1 to a later time t2. In quantum mechanics, the Schrödinger (1926) equation is a partial differential equation that describes how the quantum state of a physical system changes with time. Like Newton's second law ($F = ma$), the Schrödinger equation describes time in a way that is not compatible with relativistic theories, but which supports quantum mechanics and which can be easily mathematically transformed into Heisenberg's (1925) matrix mechanics, and Richard Feynman's (2011) path integral formulation.

Therefore, time, in quantum physics, is not necessarily relative or even a temporal sequence, and the same is true of future and past. As summed up by Heisenberg (1958), "in classical theory we assume future and past are separated by an infinitely short time interval which we may call the present moment. In the theory of relativity we have learned that the future and past are separated by a finite time interval the length of which depends on the distance from the observer..." and where the past always leads to the future. However, "when quantum theory is combined with relativity, it predicts time reversal;" i.e. the future can lead to the past.

Time Is Entangled

Time cannot be separate from the continuum except when perceived as such by an observing consciousness or measuring device, thereby inducing a collapse of the wave function of time; experienced as the present, past, or future.

Time, be it considered a dimension known as timespace, or as a perceived aspect of the quantum continuum, is also subject to entanglement, as all aspects of time are interconnected and indistinguishable until perceived thereby inducing a collapse of the wave function. "A" future can therefore effect "a" past and change it through entanglement and by effecting the wave function.

Given faster than light entanglement, spooky action at a distance and the reality of the wave function, then the laws of physics must allow for information and effects to be conveyed faster than light speed and from the future to the past. If time is considered as a gestalt and a continuum and not a series of fragments, then the future and past are coextensive.

The quantum continuum is without dimensions and encompasses space and time in its basic unity of oneness. Everything within the quantum continuum can be effected by local effect and distant effects simultaneously at and beyond light speeds. Therefore, the future, and the "present" being part of this continuum can effect the past by effecting the wave function of the past, present, future, and thus, the space-time continuum, as all are entangled.

Light can travel to the future and from the past relative to the observer's frame of reference. However, light and time are not the same. The speed of light, and time, be it past or future, are not synonymous, though both may be affected by gravity (Carroll 2004; Einstein 1961). Even the ticking of atomic clocks is effected by gravity as well as velocity. Time is subject to change, including what is described as "now" as there is no universal "now." Moreover, just as light has a particle-wave duality and can physically interact with various substances, time also can be perceived and therefore must have a wave function if not a particle-wave duality. Time, be it "past" "present" or "future" can be changed.

Time-space is interactional, and can contract to near nothingness and then continue to contract in a negative direction such that the time traveler can journey into the past.

Gravity, Acceleration, Relativity, and the Quantum Mechanics of Time Contraction

Time has energy. As defined by the law of conservation of energy and mass and Einstein's (1905b) theorem $E=mc^2$, mass can become energy and energy can become mass. Space-time is both energy and mass which is why it will contract in response to gravity and acceleration (Einstein, 1914, 1915a,b; Parker & Toms 2009; Ohanian & Ruffini 2013).

Time is perceived. Time is experienced. Time is "something," it exists, and therefore it must have energy and a wave function which is entangled with motion, velocity, gravity, the observer, and the quantum continuum which encompasses space-time.

Time is associated with light (Einstein 1961). Light has a particle-wave duality and travels at a maximum velocity of 186282 miles per second. However, time is not light, and light is not time. Rather, light can carry images reflected by or emitted from innumerable locations in space-time and can convey or transport information from these locations which may be perceived by an observer and experienced as moments in time. For much of modern human history time has been measured by celestial clocks such as the phases of the moon, and the tilt and rotation of Earth and Earth's orbit around the sun which marks the four seasons and the 24 hour day (Joseph, 2011b). Time is a circle and may be segmented into years, months, weeks, days, hours, minutes, seconds, nanoseconds as measured by various clocks from sundials to atomic clocks. However, time, even when measured by atomic clocks, can flow at different rates and speeds such that the "future" and the "past" can overlap and exist simultaneously with the same moment in time, and this is because there is no universal now.

Atomic clocks tick off time as measured by the vibrations of light waves emitted by atoms of the element cesium and with accuracies of billionths of a second (Essen & Parry, 1955). However, these clocks are also effected by their surroundings and run slower under conditions of increased gravity or acceleration (Ashby 2003; Hafele & Keating 1972a,b) In 1971 Joe Hafele and Richard Keating placed atomic clocks on airplanes traveling in the same direction of Earth's rotation thereby combining the velocity of Earth with the velocity of the planes (Hafele & Keating 1972a,b). All clocks slowed on average by 59 nanoseconds compared to atomic clocks on Earth. Time, like the weather, is effected by local conditions. Under accelerated conditions and increased gravity, time slows down; the same conditions which would enable a time traveler to accelerate toward the future and from the future into the past.

It has been demonstrated that atomic clocks at differing altitudes will eventually show different times; a function of gravitational effects on time. The lower the altitude the slower the clock, whereas clocks speed up as altitude increases; albeit the differences consisting of increases of a few nanoseconds (Chou et al. 2010; Hafele & Keating, 1972; Vessot et al. 1980). "For example, if two identical clocks are separated vertically by 1 km above the surface of Earth, the higher clock gains the equivalent of 3 extra seconds for each million years (Chou et al., 2010). The speeding up of atomic clocks at increasingly higher altitudes has been attributed to a reduction in gravitational potential which contributes to differential gravitational time dilation.

A predicted by Einstein, clocks run more slowly (time contraction) near massive objects whereas time dilates and runs more quickly as gravity is reduced. Increases in altitude and reductions in gravity speed up the clock, whereas decreases in altitude and increases in gravity slow the clock down (Hafele & Keating, 1972; Vessot et al. 1980).

Time must have energy and energy can be converted into mass. Acceleration expands mass (as energy is converted to mass) and increases gravity which contracts time and mass. Increases in gravity can squeeze space-time into smaller spaces such that there is more time in a smaller space. According to Einstein's famous equation: $E = mc^2$, where E is energy, m is mass and c is the speed of light, mass and energy are the same physical entity and can be changed into each other (Einstein 1905a,b,c 1961). Because of this equivalence, the energy an object acquires due to its motion will increase its mass. In other words, the faster an object moves, the greater the amount of energy which increases its mass, since energy can become mass. This increase in mass only becomes noticeable when an object moves very rapidly. If it moves at 10% the speed of light, its mass will only be 0.5 percent more than normal. But if it moves at 90% the speed of light, its mass will double. And as mass increases it also shrinks and its gravity increases. This is because increased mass increases gravity which then pulls on the mass making it shrink toward the center of gravity, all of which contributes to the collapsing and contraction of space time (Carroll 2004; Einstein 1913, 1914, 1915a,b).

A similar principle applies to time travel. By accelerating toward light speed, space-time contracts (Lorentz 1982; Einstein 1961; Einstein et al. 1923), and the distance between the future and the present and distant locations in space time shrinks and are closer together.

Speed, that is velocity, per se is not effected by time travel. Velocity does not contract or dilate. Hence, since space-time contracts as one accelerates (and although time slows down), and as velocity is not effected then one can traverse and journey across this shrinking space more quickly, and cover the distance between the "now" and the "future" more rapidly because they are closer together--and this would be possible only if the "future" already exists, albeit in a different location in spacetime. Distant locations in space-time are no longer so far apart; the result of increased speed and gravity.

The relationship between time dilation and the contraction of the length of space-time can be determined by a formula devised by Hendrik Lorentz in 1895. As specified by the Lorentz factor, γ (gamma) is given by the equation $\gamma = $, such that the dilation-contraction effect increases exponentially as the time traveler's velocity (v) approaches the speed of light c. Therefore, for example, at 90% light speed 2.29 days on Earth shrinks to just one day in the time machine and 7 days in the time machine at this speed, would take the time traveler 16 days into the future. The distance between the present and the future has contracted so that the future arrives in 7 days instead of 16.

Consider for example, 30 feet of space which contracts to 10 feet. Those inside the time machine need only walk 10 feet whereas those outside the time machine must walk 30 feet. Likewise because the time traveler's clock runs more slowly, and since more time is contracted into a smaller space, it might take him 10 minutes to get 30 minutes into the future. By contrast, it takes those outside the time machine longer to get to the future because it is further away and as their clocks are running faster and it takes more time. At 99.999999% the speed of light, almost two years pass for every day in the time machine. At 99.99999999999999 % of c, for every day on board, nearly twenty thousand years pass back on Earth. However, upon reaching light speed, time stops. It is only upon accelerating beyond light speed, that time runs backwards and the contraction of space-time continues in a negative direction. One must accelerate toward the future to reach the past.

The shrinkage of space-time has given rise to the famous "twin paradox" (Langevin 1911; von Laue 1913). If one twin leaves Earth and accelerates toward light speed, that twin will arrive in the future in less time than the twin left behind on Earth. Because it took less time, the time traveling twin does not age as much whereas the twin left on Earth ages at the normal rate. Because time-space has contracted, and since it takes less time to get to distant locations which are now closer together, the time traveling twin arrives in the future in less time than her twin on Earth. Hence, the time traveling twin will be younger.

Not just spacetime, but the mass of the object traveling toward light speed also contracts. The amount of length contraction can be calculated and determined by the Lorentz Transforms (Einstein 1961). For example, a 100 foot long time-space ship traveling at 60% the speed of light would contract by 20% and would become 80 feet in length. Presumably, its diameter would remain the same, though the likelihood is that all surrounding space including the diameter of the time machine would contract. If the time-space ship accelerates to 0.87 light speed, it will contract by 50%.

"Length contraction" can be expressed mathematically by the following formula: $E = mc^2/\sqrt{(1-v^2/c^2)}$, which is similar to the equation for time dilation (if one replaces the value of v for 0). As the value of v (velocity) increases, so does an object's mass which requires more energy to continue at the same velocity or to accelerate. Since energy can become mass, mass increases even as the object shrinks and contracts, thereby increasing its gravity which exerts local effects on the curvature of space-time. Not just the time machine, but space-time in front and surrounding the time machine also contracts. Eventually, the time traveler may shrink to the less than the width of a hair--at least from the perspective of outside observers. At near light speed, the time traveler's length would contract to the size of an atom. Once it shrinks in size smaller than a Planck Length, it will have so much mass and energy that it can blow a hole in spacetime and be propelled at superluminal speeds (Joseph 2014)--however once it exceeds light speed, length contraction and the contraction of time continues in a negative direction. Time reverses, and the direction of travel is into the past. One must accelerate to light speed, which takes the time traveler far into the future, and then to superluminal speeds to journey backwards in time, and this means the future leads to the past.

Although seemingly paradoxical, Einstein's theories of relativity (despite his posting of a cosmic speed limit) predicts that the only way to travel into the past is to exceed the speed of light. Upon accelerating toward light speed, space-time contracts and the space-time traveler is propelled into the future. However, it is only upon accelerating into the future and then beyond light speed that the contraction of space-time continues in a negative direction and time flows in reverse. It is only at superluminal speeds that time reverses and one can voyage backward in time. Einstein's general theory of relativity predicts that the future leads to the past. Likewise, as shown by Gödel 1949a,b), Einstein's field equations predict that time is a circle; and this violates the laws of causality (Buser et al. 2013).

Because the present leads to the future which leads to the past, past, present and future are linked in spacetime. The future can therefore effect the past and effects may take place before the cause.

Time, and time-space are embedded in the quantum continuum and can effect as well as be effected by other particle-waves even at great distances; a concept referred to as "entanglement." Time and space-time are entangled.

Probabilities and The Wave Function of the Time Traveler

According to quantum mechanics the subatomic particles which make up reality, or the quantum state, do not really exist, except as probabilities (Born et al. 1925; Dirac 1966a,b; Heisenberg 1925, 1927). These "subatomic" particles have probable existences and display tendencies to assume certain patterns of activity that we perceive as shape and form. Yet, they may also begin to display a different pattern of activity such that being can become nonbeing and thus something else altogether.

The conception of a deterministic reality is rejected and subjugated to mathematical probabilities and potentiality which is relative to the mind of a knower which registers that reality as it unfolds, evolves, and is observed (Bohr 1958, 1963; Heisenberg 1927, 1958). That is, by measuring, observing, and the mental act of perceiving a non-localized unit of structural information, injects that mental event into the quantum state of the universe, causing "the collapse of the wave function" and creating a bunching up, a tangle and discontinuous knot in the continuity of the quantum state.

Therefore, quantum mechanics, as devised by Niels Bohr, Werner Heisenberg, Dirac, Born and others in the years 1924–1930, does not attempt to provide a description of an overall, objective reality, but instead is concerned with quanta, probabilities and the effects of an observer on what is being observed. The act of measurement causes what is being measured to assume one for many possible values at specific moments of time, and yields the probability of an object or particle to be moving at one speed or direction or to be in one position or location, vs many others at a specific moment in time. Thus, it could be said that the act of observation causes a wave function collapse, a discontinuity in the continuum which is interpreted as reality and cause and effect. However, time too, is subject to measurement and can therefor yield different values by being measured. Observing and measuring time causes time to have certain values.

Central to quantum mechanics is the wave function (Bohr, 1963; Heisenberg, 1958). All of existence has a wave function, including light and time. However, quantum physics is also based on the fact that matter appears to be a duality, and can be both a wave and a particle; that is, to have features of both, i.e. particle-like properties and wave-like properties (Niel Bohr's complementary principle). Therefore, every particle has a wave function which describes it and which can be used to calculate the probability that a particle will be in a certain location or in a specific state of motion, but not both at certain moment of time. Again, however,time also has a wave function. Every aspect of existence can be described as sharing particle-like properties and wave-like properties and this would necessarily have to include the experience of time. Time can be perceived, therefore time must have energy, and energy has a particle wave duality.

The wave function is the particle spread out over space and describes all the various possible states of the particle. Likewise, the wave function would describe all the various possible states of time, including past, present, and future. According to quantum theory the probability of findings a particle in time or space is determined by the probability wave which obeys the Schrodinger equation. Everything is reduced to probabilities, including time. Moreover, these particle/waves and these probabilities are entangled.

Reality and the experience of time, are manifestation of wave functions and alterations in patterns of activity within the quantum continuum which are entangled and perceived as discontinuous, and that includes the perception of past, present, future. The perception of a structural unit of information is not just perceived, but is inserted into the quantum state which causes the reduction of the wave-packet and the collapse of the wave function. It is this collapse which describes shape, form, length, width, and future and past events and locations within space-time (Bohr, 1963; Heisenberg, 1958).

In quantum physics, the wave function describes all possible states of the particle and larger objects, including time, thereby giving rise to probabilities, and this leads to the "Many Worlds" interpretation of quantum mechanics

(Dewitt, 1971; Everett 1956, 1957). That is, since there are numerous if not infinite probable outcomes, each outcome and probable outcome represents a different "world" with some worlds being more probable than others and each of which may be characterized by their own unique moments in time. "Many Worlds" must include "Many Times."

For example, an electron may collide with and bounce to the left of a proton on one trial, then to the right on the next, and then at a different angle on the third trial, and another angle on the fourth and so on, even though conditions are identical with one exception: they occur at different moments in time. This gives rise to the Uncertainty Principle and this is why the rules of quantum mechanics are indeterministic and based on probabilities. The state of a system one moment cannot determine what will happen the next moment, because moments in time, and thus time itself has a wave function and a probability function. The wave function describes all the various possible states of the particle (Bohr, 1963; Heisenberg, 1958) and that includes the experience of time, including the eternal now.

Wave Functions: The Past, Present and Future Exist Simultaneously

Only when the object can be assigned a specific value as to location, or time, or moment, does it have possess an eigenstate, i.e. an eigenstate for position, or an eigenstate for momentum, or an eigenstate for time; each of which is a function of the "reduction of the wave function;" also referred to as wave function collapse (Bohr, 1934, 1958, 1963; Heisenberg, 1930, 1955, 1958). Wave function collapse, which is indeterministic and non-local is a fundamental a priori principle of the Copenhagen school of quantum physics and so to is the postulate that the observer and the observed, and the past, present, and future, become entangled and effect one another.

Wave function collapse has also been described as "decoherence" which in turn leads to the "many-worlds" interpretation and the thought experiment known as "Schrödinger's Cat'" i.e. is a cat in a sealed box dead or alive? According to the Copenhagen interpretation, there is a 50% chance it will be dead and 50% chance it will be alive when it is observed, but one cannot know if it dead or alive until observed (measured). However, if there are two observers, one in the box with the cat the other outside the box, then the observer in the box knows if the cat is dead or alive, whereas the observer outside the box sees only a 50-50 probability (Heisenberg 1958).

The wave function describes all the various possible states of the particle. Rocks, trees, cats, dogs, humans, planets, stars, galaxies, the universe, the cosmos, past, present, future, as a collective, all have wave functions.

Waves can also be particles, thereby giving rise to a particle-wave duality and the Uncertainty Principle. Particle-waves interact with other particle-waves. The wave function of a person sitting on their rocking chair would, within the immediate vicinity of the person and the chair, resemble a seething quantum cloud of frenzied quantum activity in the general shape of the body and rocking chair. This quantum cloud of activity gives shape and form to the man in his chair, and is part of the quantum continuum, a blemish in the continuum which is still part of the continuum and interacts with other knots of activity thus giving rise to cause and effect as well as violations of causality: "spooky action at a distance."

Since mass can become energy and energy mass, the "field" is therefore a physical entity that contains energy and has momentum which can be transmitted across space. Likewise, since time can be perceived it must have energy and energy mass as well as momentum which can be transmitted across space. Therefore, "action at a distance" may be both distant and local, a consequence of the interactions of these charges within the force field they create in conjunction with the force field know as "time."

Because time has a wave function which interacts with the continuum which includes time, then effects can be simultaneous, even at great distances, and occur faster than the speed of light (Plenio 2007; Juan et al. 2013; Francis 2012; Schrödinger & Dirac 1936), effecting electrons, photons, atoms, molecules and even diamonds (Lee et al. 2011; Matson 2012; Olaf et al. 2003; Schrödinger & Born 1935). Since time has a wave function and is entangled, then effects may precede the cause since time is a continuity, and this explains why effects may take place faster than light.

If considered as a unity with no separations in time and space, then to effect one point in time-space is to effect all points which are entangled; and those entangled connections includes time and consciousness (Joseph 2010a). And this gives rise to the uncertainty principle because all are interactional (Heisenberg, 1927) and there is no universal "now." Everything effects everything else and thus time in the "future" can effect "time" in the "past" via the wave function which propagates instantaneously throughout the continuum.

Likewise, the intrepid time traveler, journeying into the past, is also a wave function; consisting of particles and waves which interact locally with other local waves and creating additional blemishes in the quantum continuum. By traveling into the past or the future, the time traveler would come into contact with and change and alter the wave function of other blemishes in space-time. Hence, speeding into the past would therefore change the past, or rather, local events in that past, even if the Time Traveler sat still and did nothing at all except go with the flow. The wave function of the observer effects the wave function of what is observed and the wave function of immediate surroundings. The backward traveling time traveler effects each moment of "local" space-time as she travels through it. The wave function of the time traveler moving through time would spread out over space, becoming vanishingly small until disappearing.

By traveling into the past, the time traveler changes the past locally and perhaps even at a distance, depending on his actions. Likewise, since the future, present, and past are entangled, events taking place in the future, can effect and alter the past, thereby violating causality such that the past the time traveler visits may no longer be the past he was familiar with.

The probability function and entanglement when applied to the space-time continuum indicates that the, or rather "a" past may be continually changed and altered to varying degrees. This may also explain why memories of the past do not always correspond with the past record (Haber & Haber, 2000; Megreya & Burton 2008). Although blamed on faulty memory, perhaps the past has been and is continually and subtly being altered through entanglement.

As demonstrated in quantum physics, the act of observation, measurement, and registration of an event, can effect that event, causing a collapse of a the wave function (Dirac 1966a,b; Heisenberg 1955),. Likewise, a Time Traveler or particle/object speeding toward and then faster than light and from the future into the past will affect the quantum continuum. By traveling into the future or the past, the Time Traveler will interact with and alter every local moment within the quantum continuum and thus the future or the past. However, the past which is changed, always existed, albeit, as a probability; one past world among infinite worlds each with their own past, presents, and futures.

Everett's Many Worlds

Since the universe, as a collective, must also have a wave function, then this universal wave function would describe all the possible states of the universe and thus all possible universes, which means there must be multiple universes which exist simultaneously as probabilities (Dewitt, 1971; Everett 1956, 1957). And the same would be true of time. Why shouldn't time have a wave function?

The wave function of time means there are infinite futures, presents, pasts, with some more probable than others.

As theorized by Hugh Everett the universal wave function is "the fundamental entity, obeying at all times a deterministic wave equation" (Everett 1956). Thus, the wave function is real and is independent of observation or other mental postulates (Everett 1957), though it is still subject to quantum entanglement.

In Everett's formulation, a measuring apparatus MA and an object system OS form a composite system, each of which prior to measurement exists in well-defined (but time-dependent) states. Measurement is regarded as causing MA and OS to interact. After OS interacts with MA, it is no longer possible to describe either system as an independent state. According to Everett (1956, 1957), the only meaningful descriptions of each system are relative states: for example the relative state of OS given the state of MA or the relative state of MA given the state of OS. As theorized by Hugh Everett what the observer sees, and the state of the object, become correlated by the act of measurement or observation; they are entangled.

However, Everett reasoned that since the wave function appears to have collapsed when observed then there is no need to actually assume that it had collapsed. Wave function collapse is, according to Everett, redundant. Thus there is no need to incorporate wave function collapse in quantum mechanics and he removed it from his theory while maintaining the wave function, which includes the probability wave.

According to Everett (1956) a "collapsed" object state and an associated observer who has observed the same collapsed outcome have become correlated by the act of measurement or observation; that is, what the observer perceives and the state of the object become entangled. The subsequent evolution of each pair of relative subject–object states proceeds with complete indifference as to the presence or absence of the other elements, as if wave function collapse has occurred. However, instead of a wave function collapse, a choice is made among many possible choices, such that among all possible probable outcomes, the outcome that occurs becomes reality.

Everett argued that the experimental apparatus should be treated quantum mechanically, and coupled with the wave function and the probable nature of reality, this led to the "many worlds" interpretation (Dewitt, 1971). What is being measured and the measuring apparatus/observer are in two different states, i.e. different "worlds." Thus, when a measurement (observation) is made, the world branches out into a separate world for each possible outcome according to their probabilities of occurring. All probable outcomes exist regardless of how probable or improbable, and each outcome represent a "world." In each world, the measuring apparatus indicates which of the outcomes occurred, which probable world becomes reality for that observer; and this has the consequence that later observations are always consistent with the earlier observations (Dewitt, 1971; Everett 1956, 1957).

Predictions, therefore, are based on calculations of the probability that the observer will find themselves in one world or another. Once the observer enters the other world he is not aware of the other worlds which exist in parallel. Moreover, if he changes worlds, he will no longer be aware that the other world existed (Everett 1956, 1957): all observations become consistent, and that includes even memory of the past which existed in the other world.

The "many worlds" interpretation (as formulated by Bryce DeWitt and Hugh Everett), rejects the collapse of the wave function and instead embraces a universal wave function which represents an overall objective reality which consists of all possible futures and histories all of which are real and which exist as alternate realities or in multiple universes. What separates these many worlds is quantum decoherence and not a wave form collapse. Reality, the future, and the past, are viewed as having multiple branches, an infinite number of highways leading to infinite outcomes. Thus the world is both deterministic and non-deterministic (as represented by chaos or random radioactive decay) and there are innumerable futures and pasts.

As described by DeWitt and Graham (1973; Dewitt, 1971), "This reality, which is described jointly by the dynamical variables and the state vector, is not the reality we customarily think of, but is a reality composed of many worlds. By virtue of the temporal development of the dynamical variables the state vector decomposes naturally into orthogonal vectors, reflecting a continual splitting of the universe into a multitude of mutually unobservable but equally real worlds, in each of which every good measurement has yielded a definite result and in most of which the familiar statistical quantum laws hold."

DeWitt's many-worlds interpretation of Everett's work, posits that there may be a split in the combined observer–object system, the observation causing the splitting, and each split corresponding to the different or multiple possible outcomes of an observation. Each split is a separate branch or highway. A "world" refers to a single branch and includes the complete measurement history of an observer regarding that single branch, which is a world unto itself. However, every observation and interaction can cause a splitting or branching such that the combined observer–object's wave function changes into two or more non-interacting branches which may split into many "worlds" depending on which is more probable. The splitting of worlds can continue infinitely.

Since there are innumerable observation-like events which are constantly happening, there are an enormous number of simultaneously existing states, or worlds, all of which exist in parallel but which may become entangled; and this means, they can not be independent of each other and are relative to each other. This notion is fundamental to the concept of quantum computing.

Likewise, in Everett's formulation, these branches are not completely separate but are subject to quantum interference and entanglement such that they may merge instead of splitting apart thereby creating one reality.

Changing the Past: Paradoxes and the Principle of Consistency

Entanglement and "spooky action at a distance" prove that effects can occur faster than the speed of light (Lee et al. 2011; Matson 2012; Olaf et al. 2003), such that effects may take place simultaneously with or before the cause, such that the effect causes itself and may be responsible for the "cause;" a consequence of entanglement in the quantum continuum Likewise, a Time Travel can also effect the present and change the future of the past, or rather, "a" past or "a" future.

Since the time traveler and his time machine are comprised of energy and matter their presence and movement through time-space will also warp and depress the geometry of space-time thereby creating local and distant effects. Time travel would effect each local moment of time-space leading from one moment and location in time (e.g. the present) to another location, i.e. from the present to the future and from the future into the past, and these effects can occur simultaneously and at superluminal speeds.

Many physical systems are very sensitive to small changes which can lead to major change. Unless the past and the future are "hard wired" and already determined, then the very act of voyaging to distant locations in time will alter every local moment of that time continuum. In terms of "Many Worlds" the time traveler is continually creating or entering new worlds which exist in parallel. Each "world" becomes most probable the moment he interacts with the quantum continuum, including simply by passing through time.

As detailed by quantum mechanics (Dirac 1966a,b; Heisenberg, 1955), shape and form appear as blemishes and bundles of energy in the quantum continuum, the underlying quantum oneness of the cosmos, emerging out of the continuum but remaining part of it. According to the Copenhagen interpretation (Bohr 1934, 1963; Heisenberg, 1930, 1955), all quanta are entangled and therefore any jostling of one quanta can create an instantaneous ripple which can effect local as well as distant objects and events through intersecting wave functions.

The space-time continuum is part of that basic oneness and is the sum of its parts including what can and can't be observed. And this includes distant locations in space-time corresponding to all possible futures, presents, and pasts.

As pertaining to time travel, as the traveler journeys through the quantum continuum of space-time he will jostle and affect all the particles (or waves) he contacts as he passes through time, and these will effect particles and waves elsewhere in space-time, thus altering the very fabric of every local and more distant moments of space-time. In the "Many worlds" interpretation, the time traveler is not really changing the future or the past but is engaging in actions which cause branching and splitting, which leads him to a future and a past which exists in parallel with innumerable other futures and pasts. He is not changing the past, but entering a different past which always existed as a probability.

As predicted by the Many Worlds interpretation, if the Time Traveler did make a significant impact in the past, then the alteration of the past would effect the entire world-line of history related to that event, including the memories of everyone living since that event and all those who retain any knowledge of that event; such that no one would realize anything has changed.

Minds, consciousness, the brain, memory, are also part of the quantum continuum and can be altered by changes in it (Joseph 2010a). The act of observation can change an event and an event can alter the observing mind. If the past were changed, we would not know it had changed because everything related to that event would have changed, from the writing of books to documentary films about the event. The alteration of the quantum continuum is not limited to just that event but can alter the entire continuum, including the quantum composition of the brain and memories of everyone who has lived since that event (Everett 1956, 1957).

The Principle of Self-Consistency

Many theorists have argued that it is impossible to change the past. Igor

Novikov and Kip Thorne (Friedman et al. 1990) called this the "self-consistency conjecture" and "the principle of self-consistency" and various paradoxes have since been proposed to support this contention such as: "what if you killed your grandmother before she gave birth to your mother? If you did, then you could not be born and could not go back in time to kill your grandmother! Presumably these paradoxes are supposed to prove it is impossible to travel back in time.

In some respects these "paradoxes" are the equivalent of asking: "What if you went into the past and grew wings?" And the answer is: "You can't." The time traveler can not go back in the past and grow wings, or an extra pair of hands, or develop super powers, and so on. Nor could the time traveler kill anyone in the past who, according to the past record, did not die on the date he was killed.

Just as in "real life" there are boundaries which prevent the average person from engaging in or making world-altering decisions, these same limitations would apply in the past. Therefore, according to the principle of self-consistency, it is impossible to change the past, and if any changes were made, they may be "local" rather than global, and thus completely non-significant and not the least memorable--just like daily life for 99.999999999% of the 7 billion souls who currently dwell on Earth and who live and die and are quickly forgotten except by a few other insignificant souls who are also quickly forgotten as if they never even exists. Any changes made in the past may be so insignificant as to be meaningless.

Just as it is impossible to determine position and momentum of a particle, the past may also be subject to imprecision such that by establishing certain facts, makes other facts less certain The past may also be subject to the Uncertainty Principle, which may explain why historians, eye-witnesses, and husbands and wives may not always agree about what exactly happened in the past or just moments before.

The Principle of Self-Consistency, however, holds that the past is hard wired and cannot be altered, and reverse causality is an impossibility (Friedman et al. 1990). By contrast, reverse causality (also referred to as backward causation and retro-causation) is based on the premise that an effect may occur before its cause, such that the future may effect the present and the present may effect the past. A "cause" by definition must precede the effect, otherwise the effect may negate the cause and the effect! For example, the if a man went back in time and killed his grandfather he would negate his own existence making it impossible to go back in time and kill his grandfather. On the other hand, if he did kill his "grandfather" it might turn out that his paternal lineage leads elsewhere, i.e. "grandmother" had an affair and another man fathered his own father. Thus killing his "grandfather" has no effect on his existence and does not interfere with his ability to go back in time to kill his grandfather. In this instance, the effect does not nullify the cause; which is in accordance with the principle of self-consistency. The past can't be altered and if it is, the result is not significant.

If the past is "fixed" and hard-wired and can't be altered, then although the time traveler may go back in time with the intention of killing his grandfather, or Hitler, or Lee Harvey Oswald, the result would be that he would be unable to do so; his gun would misfire, the bullet would miss, or he never got close enough to the intended victim to do the deed. The past is hard wired and can't be changed.

If the past can't be altered, then this also implies that the future may also be fixed and hard wired and is not subject to alteration. However, if the future is subject to change (as demonstrated by classical physics and the laws of cause and effect), then the future must exist in order to be altered; as predicted by quantum mechanics, entanglement, and Einstein's theories of relativity. If the future may be changed, then why not the past? According to the "Many worlds" interpretation, the past is not changed, instead one changes which past world becomes his reality.

The "Many Worlds" interpretation of quantum mechanics would allow one to kill their mother or commit a murder which had not taken place, in this "world;" but in so doing would be effecting the quantum continuum and contributing to the probability that an alternate world would become the time traveler's world once he commits these crimes.

Paradoxes and Many Worlds

Most time travel "paradoxes" are based on the premise that the time traveler some how gains powers or the will to do things he would never do, or to accomplish what others tried to do and failed. Even if the time traveler wanted to kill his mother before he was born, or assassinate Hitler before he came to power, would he be able to do it? Would he be able to get close enough to shove in that knife or fire that bullet? And if he did, maybe the victims would live. Maybe the knife or the bullet would miss the necessary organ. Maybe he would change his mind at the last moment. Maybe in the struggle someone else would shoot the Time Traveler in the head and he would die instead. Many people tried to kill Hitler and failed.

"Paradoxes" can be reduced to simple probabilities. What is the probability a time traveler would want to go back in time and kill his mother? What is the probability he would succeed? What is the probability others would intervene before he could do the deed? What is the probability that he might be killed in the attempt? ... and so on.

And if he did kill his mother, it would not be "his" mother.

An observer, object, particle, interacts with its environment, with the quantum continuum, changing and altering it. As postulated by "Many Worlds" theory, there is one ultimate reality, but many parallel realities and histories, like the branches of a tree, a hallway with infinite doors, or infinite highways all of which lead out of the city. One highway leads to a past where Hitler won the war. Another highway leads to a past where the Kennedy brothers were never killed.

Yet another takes the time traveler to a world where he was never born.

According to quantum theory and the "many worlds" interpretation, a new highway, a new door, a new branch of the tree appears every time a particle whizzes by or an observer interacts with his environment, makes a decision, or records an observation. Thus, the time traveler may go back in time and kill the mother who dwells in a parallel world or universe, but he would be unable to kill his mother.

The "Many Worlds" Resolution of The Grandmother Paradox Time Traveler "A" goes back into the past and kills his grandmother when she was still a little girl. An observer, object, particle, interacts with its environment, with the quantum continuum, changing and altering it. A time traveler going into the past would change every moment leading to that past simply by traveling through it, so that the past and the grandmother he encounters would be a different past and a different grandmother. As also predicted by the "Many Worlds" interpretation of quantum physics, a time traveler can appear in different parallel worlds. Therefore by killing this grandmother in this past time, Traveler "A" would be preventing the birth of that woman's time-traveling grandson "B", thereby preventing "B" from going into the past and killing the grandmother of the Time Traveler "A."

Multiple Paradoxes. Effects Negating Causes A very wealthy scientist invents a time machine and travels 30 years back into the past to prevent the car accident which killed his very beautiful wife. He arrives in the parking lot of the business where she works and lets all the air out of her tires and disables the engine.

He visits the younger version of himself and gives him the blue print for building a time machine, and a list of 100 stocks and when to buy and sell them. The Time Traveler returns to the future.

When was the time machine invented?

His wife takes a cab to her Lover's apartment and that night they drive to her home and that of her husband (the younger version of the time traveler). The Lover discovers the blue print for the time machine and the list of 100 stocks. The Lover and the wife sneak into the bedroom where her husband (the younger version of the time traveler) is napping and shove a knife through his heart.

Who invented the time machine?

The "Lover" upon killing the younger version of the Time Traveler (with the help of Time Traveler's wife), suddenly finds himself alone with the body, still holding the bloody knife in his hand. However, the Time Traveler's wife (and the blue print for a time machine and list of stocks) have disappeared. Upon his arrest he learns the Time Traveler's wife was killed hours before in a car accident.

Information Exists Before it is Discovered Two research scientists, both bitter rivals, are competing to make a major scientific discovery. Scientist A, who is better funded, makes the discovery first, publishes the results, receives world wide acclaim and receives a Nobel Prize.

Scientist B loses all funding, does not get tenure, and is reduced to living in obscurity and working in his basement lab, where, 20 years later, he invents a time machine. Scientist B makes a copy of the article which won his rival, Scientist A, the Nobel Prize, and goes back in time and gives it to the younger version of himself. To ensure that the true inventor, Scientist A, does not get credit, the time traveler, Scientist B, kills Scientist A.

The younger version of Scientist B publishes the discovery and receives all the credit and the Nobel prize. When the time traveler, Scientist B returns to his own time he is famous and has a Nobel prize on his shelf. When he looks at the scientific journal where the original article appeared, he sees the same article but with himself listed as the author. He no longer understands why he went back in time to kill his rival.

Who made the discovery?

Another scientist after laboring his entire life makes a major discovery which brings him wealth and world wide acclaim. However, he is old and sick and unhealthy and is unable to savor the honors, women, and riches which are now his for the asking but he is too old to enjoy. So, he invents a time machine, takes a copy of his notebook describing the discovery, goes back 50 years in time and gives it to his younger self, and explains: "here are the answers you are searching for. You are going to be rich and famous."

So where did the discovery come from?

Science is replete with examples of scientists who independently make the same discoveries although they were working independently of each other and often not knowing of the other's work (Merton, 1961; 1963; Hall, 1980). Examples include the 17th-century independent formulation of calculus by Isaac Newton, Gottfried Wilhelm Leibniz and others; the 18th-century discovery of oxygen by Carl Wilhelm Scheele, Joseph Priestley, Antoine Lavoisier and others; In 1989, Thomas R. Cech and Sidney Altman won the Nobel Prize in chemistry for their independent discovery of ribozymes; In 1993, groups led by Donald S. Bethune at IBM and Sumio Iijima at NEC independently discovered single-wall carbon nanotubes and methods to produce them using transition-metal catalysts. And the list goes on.

What this could imply, if the past and future are a continuum, is that the discovery exists before it is discovered, albeit in a distant location of space-time. Or, in terms of multiple worlds theory, one branch leads to a world where the discovery is made by scientist A, a different branch leads scientist B to the discovery. Yet another branch leads to a world where the discovery is not made until 20 years into the future, whereas a different branch leads to a world where it is discovered in just a few days.

Mozart heard his music in his head, already composed--and some have proposed there is a cosmic consciousness which contains all information, and that one need only a brain that can tap into this source to extract this information.

If true, this may explain why discoveries are made simultaneously or why Mozart heard his music "already composed" in his head and then simply wrote it down.

Time Travel Through Many Worlds

As based on a Many Worlds interpretation of quantum physics, traveling backwards into the past would itself be a quantum event causing branching. Therefore the timeline accessed by the time traveller simply would be one timeline among many different branching pasts. Hence, the time traveler from one world/ universe may kill his grandfather in another world/universe. Likewise, in the past of some worlds, Hitler won the war, the Kennedy brothers were never killed, the dinosaurs did not become extinct, mammals and humans never evolved, and so on. All quantum worlds, many worlds, all exist as there is an infinity of possible universes and worlds, each of which differs in some manner from the other, from the minute to the major.

However, by changing (or choosing) his past, the Time Traveler would not just be making this past "World" more probable, but may cause all pasts to become unified. That is, the other pasts disappear as they are subsumed by and merge to become this one unified past.

Therefore, according to the Many Worlds interpretation, by changing the past, and by creating a single unified past, then once the merging occurs, all "memories" of earlier branching events will be lost. No one will ever remember that there was any other past and no observer will even suspect that there are several branches of reality. As such, the past (and the future) becomes deterministic and irreversible, and this effects the wave function of time, such that the past shapes the future, and conversely, the future can shape the past.

Therefore, if a time traveler journeys to the past, his passage will either change the past so that those in the future can only remember the past that has been altered since this past is the past which leads up to them. Or, the past was never really altered and always included the Time Traveler's journey into the past. That is, this altered past has always existed even before he journeyed to it and this is because he traveled to and arrived in the past before he left. Thus everything he does, from the moment he left for the past, has already happened. The past, like the future is irreversible and has been hard wired into the fabric of space-time.

According to the Copenhagen model, one may predict probabilities for the occurrence of various events which are taking place or which will take place. In the many-worlds interpretation, all these events occur simultaneously. Therefore, the time traveler is not changing the past, but choosing one past among many: "new worlds" which always existed as probabilities.

REFERENCES

Bohr, N., (1913). "On the Constitution of Atoms and Molecules, Part I". Philosophical Magazine 26: 1–24.

Bohr, N., (1913). "On the Constitution of Atoms and Molecules, Part I". Philosophical Magazine 26: 1–24.

Bohr, N. (1934/1987), Atomic Theory and the Description of Nature, reprinted as The Philosophical Writings of Niels Bohr, Vol. I, Woodbridge: Ox Bow Press.

Bohr. N. (1949). "Discussions with Einstein on Epistemological Problems in Atomic Physics". In P. Schilpp. Albert Einstein: Philosopher-Scientist. Open Court.

Bohr, N. (1958/1987), Essays 1932-1957 on Atomic Physics and Human Knowledge, reprinted as The Philosophical Writings of Niels Bohr, Vol. II, Woodbridge: Ox Bow Press.

Bohr, N. (1963/1987), Essays 1958-1962 on Atomic Physics and Human Knowledge, reprinted as The Philosophical Writings of Niels Bohr, Vol. III, Woodbridge: Ox Bow Press.

Born, M. Heisenberg, W. & Jordan, P. (1925) Zur Quantenmechanik II, Zeitschrift für Physik, 35, 557-615.

DeWitt, B. S., (1971). The Many-Universes Interpretation of Quantum Mechanics, in B. D.'Espagnat (ed.), Foundations of Quantum Mechanics, New York: Academic Press. pp. 167–218.

DeWitt, B. S. and Graham, N., editors (1973). The Many-Worlds Interpretation of Quantum Mechanics. Princeton University Press, Princeton, New-Jersey.

Dirac, P. (1966a) Lectures on Quantum Mechanics.

Dirac, P. (1966b). Lectures on Quantum Field Theory .

Einstein, A. (1905a). Does the Inertia of a Body Depend upon its Energy Content? Annalen der Physik 18, 639-641.

Einstein, A. (1905b). Concerning an Heuristic Point of View Toward the Emission and Transformation of Light. Annalen der Physik 17, 132-148.

Everett , H (1956), Theory of the Universal Wavefunction",Thesis, Princeton University.

Everett, H. (1957) Relative State Formulation of Quantum Mechanics, Reviews of Modern Physics vol 29, 454–462.

Friedman, J. et al. (1990). Cauchy problem in spacetimes with closed timelike curves". Physical Review D 42 (6): 1915.

Haber, R. N., Haber, L. (2000). Experiencing, remembering and reporting events. Psychology, Public Policy, and Law, 6(4): 1057-1097.

Heisenberg, W. (1925) Über quantentheoretische Umdeutung kinematischer und mechanischer Beziehungen, ("Quantum-Theoretical Re-interpretation of Kinematic and Mechanical Relations") Zeitschrift für Physik, 33, 879-893, 1925

Heisenberg,W.(1927),"Über den anschaulichen Inhalt der quantentheoretischen Kinematik und Mechanik", Zeitschrift für Physik 43 (3–4): 172–198,

Heisenberg. W. (1930), Physikalische Prinzipien der Quantentheorie (Leipzig: Hirzel). English translation The Physical Principles of Quantum Theory, University of Chicago Press.

Heisenberg, W. (1955). The Development of the Interpretation of the Quantum Theory, in W. Pauli (ed), Niels Bohr and the Development of Physics, 35, London: Pergamon pp. 12-29.

Heisenberg, W. (1958), Physics and Philosophy: The Revolution in Modern Science, London: Goerge Allen & Unwin.

Joseph, R. (2010) Quantum Physics and the Multiplicity of Mind: Split-Brains, Fragmented Minds, Dissociation, Quantum Consciousness. "The Universe and Consciousness", Edited by Sir Roger Penrose, FRS, Ph.D., & Stuart Hameroff, Ph.D. Science Publishers, Cambridge, MA.

Juan Y., et al. (2013). "Bounding the speed of `spooky action at a distance". Phys. Rev. Lett. 110, 260407.

Lee, K.C., et al. (2011)."Entangling macroscopic diamonds at room temperature". Science 334 (6060): 1253–1256. Matson, J. (2012) Quantum teleportation achieved over record distances, Nature, 13 August.

Megidish, E., Halevy, T. Shacham, A., Dvir, T., Dovrat, L., Eisenberg, H. S. (2013) Entanglement Swapping Between Photons that have Never Coexisted. ArXiv.1209.4191v1, 19, Sep, 2012. Physical Review Letters, 110, 210403.

Megreya, A. M., & Burton, A. M. (2008). Matching faces to photographs: Poor performance in eyewitness memory (without the memory). Journal of Experimental Psychology: Applied, 14(4): 364–372.

Olaf, N.. et al. (2003) "Quantum interference experiments with large molecules", American Journal of Physics, 71 (April 2003) 319-325.

Plenio, V. (2007). "An introduction to entanglement measures". Quant. Inf. Comp. 1: 1–51.

Schrödinger E; Born, M. (1935). "Discussion of probability relations between separated systems". Mathematical Proceedings of the Cambridge Philosophical Society 31 (4): 555–563.

Schrödinger E; Dirac, P.A.M. (1936). "Probability relations between separated systems". Mathematical Proceedings of the Cambridge Philosophical Society 32 (3): 446–452.

24. Logic of Quantum Mechanics, Parallel Worlds and Phenomenon of Consciousness

Michael B. Mensky

P.N. Lebedev Physical Institute, Russian Academy of Sciences, Leninsky prosp. 53, 119991 Moscow,

Abstract

The phenomenon of consciousness, including its mystical features, is explained on the basis of quantum mechanics in the Everett's form. Everett's interpretation (EI) of quantum mechanics is in fact the only one that correctly describes quantum reality: any state of the quantum world is objectively a superposition of its classical counterparts, or "classical projections". They are "classically incompatible" but are considered to be equally real, or coexisting. We shall call them alternative classical realities or simply classical alternatives. According to the Everett's interpretation, quantum reality is presented by the whole set of alternative classical realities (alternatives). However, these alternatives are perceived by humans separately, independently from each other, resulting in the subjective illusion that only a single classical alternative exists. The ability to separate the classical alternatives is the main feature of what is called consciousness. According to the author's Extended Everett's Concept (EEC), this feature is taken to be a definition of consciousness (more precisely, consciousness as such, not as the complex of processes in the conscious state of mind). It immediately follows from this definition that turning the consciousness off (in sleeping, trance or meditation) allows one to acquire access to all alternatives. The resulting information gives rise to unexpected insights including scientific insights.

Key Words: Quantum mechanics; quantum reality; Everett's interpretation; consciousness; unconscious; insights; miracles; probability

1 INTRODUCTION

Strange as this may seem, we do not know what is the nature of consciousness, especially of the very strange features of consciousness which resemble mystical phenomena. The most familiar examples of these mysterious phenomena are scientific insights (of course, we mean only "great insights" experienced by great scientists). Some people supposed that the mystery of consciousness may be puzzled out on the basis of quantum mechanics, the science which is mysterious itself.

This viewpoint has been suggested, as early as in 20th years of 20th century, by the great physicist Wolfgang Pauli in collaboration with the great psychologist Carl Gustav Jung. They supposed particularly that quantum mechanics may help to explain strange psychic phenomena observed by Jung and called "synchronisms". Jung told of a synchronism if a series of the events happened such that these events were conceptually close but their simultaneous (synchronous) emergence could not be justified causally. For example he observed causally unjustified, seemingly accidental, appearance of the image of fish six times during a single day. The work of Pauli and Jung on this topic was not properly published and was later completely forgotten, but it became popular in last decades (see about this in Enz, 2009).

The idea of connecting consciousness with quantum mechanics was suggested by some other authors, mostly without referring Pauli and Jung. In the last three decades this idea was supported by Roger Penrose (Penrose, 1991), (Penrose, 1994). He particularly remarked that people manage to solve such problems which in principle cannot be solved with the help of computers because no algorithms exist for their solving. Penrose suggested that quantum phenomena should be essential for explaining the work of brain and consciousness.

Usually attempts to explain consciousness on the base of quantum mechanics follow the line of consideration that is natural for physicists. Everything must be explained by natural sciences, may be with accounting quantum laws. Therefore, in order to explain consciousness, one has to apply quantum mechanics for analysis of the work of brain. For example, the work of brain may be explained as the work of quantum computer instead of classical one. Thus, it is usually assumed, explicitly or implicitly, that consciousness must be derived from the analysis of the processes in brain.

The approach proposed by the author in 2000 does not include this assumption. This approach is based on the analysis of the logical structure of quantum mechanics, and the phenomenon of consciousness is derived from this purely logical analysis rater than from the processes in brain. The actual origin of the concept of consciousness is, according to this approach, specific features of the concept of reality accepted in quantum mechanics (contrary to classical physics) and often called quantum reality.

Quantum reality has its adequate presentation in the so-called Everett's interpretation (EI) of quantum mechanics known also under name of many-worlds interpretation (Everett III, 1957). The approach of the author is based on the Everett's form of quantum mechanics and called Extended Everett's Concept (EEC).

Some physicists, having in mind purely classical concept of reality, consider the Everett's interpretation of quantum mechanics too complicated and "exotic". However, it is now experimentally proved that reality in our world is quantum, and the conclusions based on classical concept of reality, are not reliable. The comprehension of the concept of quantum reality was achieved after long intellectual efforts of genius scientists. Unfortunately, the ideas of Pauli and Jung were not properly estimated and timely used. The first whose thoughts about quantum reality became widely know was Einstein who, in the work with his coauthors, suggested so-called Einstein-Podolski-Rosen paradox (Einstein et al., 1935). Much later John Bell formulated now widely known Bell's theorem (Bell, 1964), (Bell, 1987) which provided an adequate tool for direct quantum-mechanical verification of the concept of quantum reality, the Bell's inequality. Less than in 20 years the group of Aspect experimentally proved (Aspect et al., 1981) that the Bell's inequality is violated in some quantum processes, and therefore reality in our world is quantum.

Most simple and convenient formulation of quantum reality was given even earlier that the Bell's works, in 1957, by the Everett's interpretation of quantum mechanics. It was enthusiastically accepted by the great physicists John Archibald Wheeler and Brice Dewitt, but was not recognized by the wide physical community until last decades of 20th century, when the corresponding intellectual base was already prepared. From this time the number of adepts of the Everett's interpretation grows permanently. Results of this difficult but very important process of conceptual clarification of quantum mechanics justify the appreciation of the Everett's interpretation as the only correct form of quantum mechanics. It is exciting that, as an additional prize, the Everett's interpretation explains the mysterious phenomenon of consciousness.

Quantum mechanics in the Everett's form implies coexisting "parallel worlds", or parallel classical realities. This clearly expresses the difference of quantum reality from the common classical reality. According to the author's Extended Everett's Concept (Menskii, 2000), consciousness is the ability to perceive the Everett's parallel worlds separately, independently from each other. An immediate consequence of this assumption is that the state of being unconscious makes all parallel realities available without the separation. This leads to irrational insights and other "mystical" phenomena. This is the central point of the theory making it plausible. Indeed, it is well known (from all spiritual schools and from deep psychological researches) that the strange abilities of consciousness arise just in the states of mind that are close to being unconsciousness (sleeping, trance or meditation).

2 PARALLEL WORLDS

According to the Everett's "many-worlds" interpretation of quantum mechanics, quantum mechanics implies coexistence of "parallel classical worlds", or alternative classical realities. This follows from the arguments (see details below) including the following points:

• The very important specific feature of quantum systems is that their states are vectors. This means that a state of any quantum system may be a sum (called also superposition) of other states of the same system. All the states which are the counterparts of this sum, are equally real, i.e. they may be said to coexist. This is experimentally proved for the states of microscopic systems (such as elementary particles or atoms).

• However, this should be valid also for macroscopic systems (consisting of many atoms). It follows from the logical analysis of the measurements of microscopic systems. Indeed, let a microscopic system S be measured with the help of a macroscopic measuring device M. If the state of S is a sum of a series of states, then, after the measurement, the state of the combined system (S and M) is also a sum (each its term consisting of a state of S and the corresponding state of M).

• Different states of the measuring device, by the very definition of a measuring device, have to be macroscopically distinct. Therefore, a macroscopic system may be in the state which is a sum (superposition) consisting of the states which are incompatible (alternative to each other) from the point of view of classical physics. However, quantum mechanics requires them to "coexist" (in the form of a sum, or superposition).

• Therefore, classically incompatible states of our world (alternative classical realities) must coexist as a sort of "parallel worlds" which are called Everett's worlds.

Let us now give some details of these arguments. What does it mean that the states of a quantum system are vectors? If vpi are states of some quantum system, then $\psi = \psi1 + \psi2 + \bullet \bullet \bullet$ is also a state of the same system, called a superposition of the states ψi (counterparts of the superposition).

This feature is experimentally proved for microscopic systems (such as elementary particles or atoms), but it has to be valid also for macroscopic systems. This follows from the analysis of measurements with microscopic measured systems and macroscopic measuring devices.

The conclusion following from this analysis is that, even for a macroscopic system, its state ψ may be a superposition of other states of this system, which have evident classical interpretation (are close to some classical states of the system) while the state ψ has no such an interpretation:

$$\psi = \psi1 + \psi2 + ... + \psin ... \quad (1)$$

It is important that the states ψ here may be macroscopically distinct, therefore, from classical point of view incompatible, alternative to each other, presenting alternative classical realities. Nevertheless, it follows from quantum theory that even such macroscopically distinct states ψi may be in superposition, i.e. may coexist. Let us formulate the above situation a little bit more precisely. The quantum system is in the state denoted by the state vector and only this state objectively exists (however, taken as a whole, has no classical interpretation). The counterparts ^ of the superposition are in fact classical projections of the objectively existing quantum state ψ. These classical projections describe images of the quantum system which arise in consciousness of an observer (therefore, they concern the subjective aspect of quantum reality). This status of the classical projections will be made more transparent below.

In the following we shall use ψ for the state of our (quantum) world as a whole. The components ψi of the superposition will be alternative classical states of this world (more precisely, quasiclassical, i.e. the states as close to classical as is possible for the quantum world).

In the Everett's interpretation of quantum mechanics the states ψ are called Everett's worlds. We shall use also the terms "parallel worlds", "alternative classical realities", "classical alternatives" or simply "alternatives". In case if such alternatives are superposed (as in Eq. (1)), we shall say that they "coexist". Of course this word is nothing else than a convenient slang, meaning in fact "to form a superposition" or "to be in superposition". The status of the "coexistence" is connected with the consciousness and subjective perception of the world, which will be explained below.

3 EXTENDED EVERETT'S CONCEPT (EEC)

We see that the alternative classical realities in our quantum world may coexist (as components of a superposition presenting the state of the quantum world). Subjectively however each observer perceives only a single "classical alternative". These two assertions seem to contradict to each other. Are they in fact compatible? We shall show how this seeming contradiction is resolved in the Everett's interpretation (EI) and how it may be taken as a basis for the theory of consciousness and the unconscious if the EI is properly extended.

3.1 Everett's "Many-Worlds" Interpretation One may naively think that the picture of the world arising in his consciousness (the picture of a single classical alternative) is just what objectively exists. However, EI of quantum mechanics (unavoidably following from the logics of quantum mechanics applied to the phenomenon of quantum measurements) claims that it is only the superposition of all alternatives (as in Eq. (1)) that objectively exists.

The seemingly strange and counter-intuitive presentation of objective reality (in the Everett's form of quantum mechanics) as the set of many objectively coexisting classical realities adequately expresses quantum character of reality in our (quantum) world.

The single alternatives (components of the superposition) present various subjective perceptions of this quantum reality in an observer's consciousness. The natural question arises how the multiplicity of the "classical pictures" that may arise in our consciousness may be compatible with the subjective sensory evidence of only a single such picture.

This is the most difficult point of the EI and the reason why this interpretation has not been readily accepted by the physicists. This point may be made more transparent if it is presented in the terms of "Everett's worlds" as it has been suggested by Brice DeWitt.

Thus, all of the separate components of the superposition (classical alternatives, or Everett's worlds) are declared by Everett to be "equally real". No single alternative may be considered to be the only real, while the others being potentially possible but not actualized variants of reality (this might be accepted in classical physics, but not in quantum mechanics, because of the special character of quantum reality).

To make understanding of the EI easier, Brice DeWitt proposed (De-Witt & Graham, 1973) to think that each observer is present in each of the Everett's worlds. To make this even more transparent, one may think that a sort of twins ("clones") of each observer are present in all Everett's worlds. Subjective perception is the perception of a single twin. Objectively the twins of the given observer exist in all Everett's worlds, each of them perceiving corresponding alternative pictures.

Each of us subjectively perceives around him a single classical reality. However, objectively the twins, or clones, of each of us perceive all the rest realities. It is important that all twins of the given observer are equally real. It is incorrect to say that there is "I" and there are my twins, which are not "I". All twins embody me as an observer, each of them can be called "I".

Thus, the concept of "Everett's world" allows to make the Everett's presentation of quantum reality more transparent. We prefer to verbalize the same situation in another way (Menskii, 2000). We shall say that all alternative classical projections of the quantum world's state objectively exist, but these projections are separated in consciousness. Subjective perception of the quantum world by human's consciousness embraces all these classical pictures, but each picture is perceived independently of the rest.

Regardless of the way of wording, the Everett's assumption of objectively coexisting classical alternatives implies that all these alternatives may be accessible for an observer in some way or another. Yet it is not clear how the access to "other alternatives" (different from one subjectively perceived) may be achieved for the given observer. It is usually claimed that the EI does not allow observing "other alternatives". This makes the interpretation non-falsifiable and thus decreases its value.

It turns out however that the EI may be improved in such a way that that the question "How one can access to other alternatives?" is answered in a very simple and natural way. This improvement is realized in the author's Extended Everett's Concept. The (improved) EI becomes then falsifiable, although in a special sense of the word (see below Sect. 3.2).

3.2 Extension of the Everett's Interpretation Starting with the above mentioned formulation (that classical alternatives are separated in consciousness), the present author proposed (Menskii, 2000) to accept a stronger statement: consciousness is nothing else than separation of the alternatives.

This seemingly very small step resulted in important consequences. Finally the so-called Extended Everett's Concept (EEC) has been developed (Menskii, 2005, 2007; Mensky, 2005, 2007, 2010).

The first advantage of EEC is that the logical structure of the quantum theory is simplified as compared with the EI.

The point is that the formulation "alternatives are separated in consciousness" (accepted in one of the possible formulations of EI) includes two primary (not definable) concepts, "consciousness" and "alternative separation". These concepts have no good definitions. One may object that many different definitions have been proposed for the notion "consciousness". This is right, but all these definitions concern in fact mental and sensual processes in brain rather than "consciousness as such", while the latter (more fundamental) notion has no good definition.

After the notions "consciousness" (more precisely, "consciousness as such") and "separation of alternatives" are identified (as it is suggested in EEC), only one of these concepts remains in the theory. Therefore, EEC includes only one primary concept instead of two such concepts in the EI. The logical structure of the theory is simplified after its extension.

Much more important is that EEC gives a transparent indication as to how an observer may obtain access to "other alternatives" (different from the alternative subjectively perceived by him). This very important question remains unanswered (or answered negatively) in the original form of the EI. This is seen from the following argument.

If consciousness = separation (of the alternatives from each other), then absence of consciousness = absence of separation.

Therefore, turning off consciousness (in sleeping, trance or meditation) opens access to all classical alternatives put together, without separation between them. Of course, the access is realized then not in the form of visual, acoustic or other conscious images or thoughts. Nothing at all can be said about the form of this access. However, if we accept EEC, then we may definitely conclude that the access is possible in the unconscious state of mind.

This of course has very important consequences. The access to the enormous "data base" consisting of all alternative classical realities enables one to acquire valuable information, or rather knowledge. This information is unique in the sense that it is unavailable in the conscious state when only a single alternative is subjectively accessible. One may suppose that a part of this unique information may be kept on returning to the usual conscious state of mind and recognized in the form of usual conscious images and thoughts.

Thus, when going over to the unconscious state, one obtains the information, or knowledge, which is in principle unavailable in the usual conscious state.

This information is unique first of all because it is taken from "other" classical alternatives (different from one subjectively observed). There is however something more that makes this information unique and highly valuable. All alternatives together form a representation of the quantum state of the world (vector $^\wedge$ in Eq. (1)). Time evolution of this state vector, according to quantum laws, is reversible. This means that, given at some time moment, this vector is known also at all other times. Therefore, information about "all alternatives together" (i.e. about the state vector of the world) includes information from any time moments in future and past. This information may be thought of as being obtained with the help of a "virtual time machine".

Evidently, this makes "irrational" inspirations (including scientific insights) possible. Here is a simple example. Let a scientist be confronted with a scientific problem and consider a number of hypotheses for solving this problem. Going, by means of the above mentioned virtual time machine, into future and backward, the scientist may find out what of these hypotheses will be confirmed by future experiments or proved with the help of the future theories. Then, on returning to the conscious state, he will unexpectedly and without any rational grounds get certain about which of these hypotheses has to be chosen.

Remark that it is not necessary, for making use of such a virtual time machine, to turn off consciousness completely (although it is known that some important discoveries were made in sleeping, or rather after awakening). It is enough to disconnect it from the problem under consideration. This is why solutions of hard problems are sometimes found not during the work on these problems but rather during relaxation.

Preliminary "rational" work on the problem is however necessary. The deep investigation of all data concerning the problem enables the consciousness to form a sort of query (clear formulation of the problem and its connections with all relevant areas of knowledge). Then the query will be worked out in the unconscious state (during relaxation) and will result in an unexpected insight.

It is clear that not only scientific problems can be solved in this way, but also problems of general character. Quite probable that, besides ordinary intuitive guesses, we meet in our experience examples of super-intuitive insights of the type described above. Anybody knows that many efficient solutions come in the morning just after awakening. This fact may be an indirect confirmation of the ability of super-intuition.

4 PROBABILISTIC MIRACLES

Thus, Extended Everett's Concept (EEC) leads to the conclusion that unconscious state of mind allows one to take information "from other alternatives" that reveals itself as unexpected insights, or direct vision of truth.

Another consequence is feasibility of even more weird phenomenon looking as arbitrary choice of reality. Let us describe this ability in a special case of what can be called "probabilistic miracles".

Consider an observer who subjectively perceives one of the alternative classical realities at the present time moment t0. Let in a certain future moment $t > t0$ some event E may happen, but with a very small probability p. Call it the objective probability of the event E and suppose that this probability is small.

According to the Everett's interpretation of quantum mechanics, at time t two classes of alternative classical realities will exist so that the event E happens in each alternative of the first class and does not happen in the alternatives of the second class. The twins of our observer will be objectively present in each of the alternatives (this is the feature of Everett's worlds, see Sect. 3.1). However, subjectively our observer will feel to be in one of them. With some probability p it will turn out to be the alternative of the first class. The probability p may be called subjective probability of the event E for the given observer.

It is accepted in the Everett's interpretation that subjective and objective probabilities coincide, $p = p$. However, in the context of EEC we may assume that they may differ and, moreover, the observer may influence the value of subjective probability p'. Let us assume that the observer prefers the event E to happen. Then he can enlarge the subjective probability of this event, i.e. the probability to find himself subjectively at time t just in that classical reality in which this rare event actually happens.

Thus, besides the objective probability of any event, there is a subjective probability of this event for the given observer, and the observer may in principle influence the subjective probability. In the above mentioned situation, an event under consideration can happen according to usual laws of the natural sciences, but with small probability. This means that the objective probability of this event is small, it may seem even negligible. It is important that the objective probability is non-zero. One may say that among all alternatives at the moment t few of the alternatives correspond to the pictures of the world in which the event happens, and much more alternatives correspond to the pictures of the world where the event does not happen.

However, according to EEC, an observer can, simply by the force of his consciousness, make the subjective probability of this event close to unity. Then very likely he will find himself at the moment t in one of those classical realities where the event does happen.

The subjective experience of such an observer will evidence that the objectively improbable event may be realized by the effort of his will. This looks like a miracle. However, this is a miracle of a special type, which may be called "probabilistic miracle".

Probabilistic miracles essentially differ from "absolute" miracles that happen in fairy tales. The difference is that the event realized as a probabilistic miracle (i.e. "by the force of consciousness") may in principle happen in a quite natural way, although with a very small probability. This small but nonzero probability is very important. Particularly, because of fundamental character of probabilistic predictions in quantum mechanics, it is in principle impossible to prove or disprove the unnatural (miraculous) character of the happening.

Indeed, if the objectively rare event happens, the person who has strongly desired for it to happen is inclined to consider the happening as a result of his will. Yet any skeptic may insist in this situation that the event occurred in a quite natural way: what happened, was only a rare coincidence. The secret is in the nature of the concept of probability: if the probability of some stochastic event is equal p, then in a long series consisting of N tests the event will happen pN times (very rarely for small p). But it is in principle impossible to predict in which of these tests the event will happen. Particularly, it may happen even in the very first test from the long series of them.

The latter is a very interesting and general feature of the phenomena "in the area of consciousness" as they are treated in EEC. These phenomena in principle cannot be unambiguously assigned to the sphere of natural events (obeying the laws of natural sciences) or to the sphere of spiritual or psychic phenomena (which are treated by the humanities and spiritual doctrines). Impossibility to do this may be called relativity of objectiveness.

Synchronisms studied by Jung may be considered to be probabilistic miracles. One who observes a subject or event which somehow attracts his special attention, involuntarily thinks about it (often even not clearly fixing his thoughts). According to the above said, he may increase the subjective probability of immediately observing something similar or logically connected.

Some Biblical miracles can also be explained as probabilistic miracles. An example is the miracle at the Sea of Galilee where Jesus calmed the raging storm (Matthew 8:23-27). This was completely natural event. Wonderful was only the fact that the storm ceased precisely at that moment when this was necessary for Jesus and his disciples. The probability of "timely" occurring this natural event was of course very small. The miracle was probabilistic.

5 CONCLUDING REMARKS

We shortly followed in this paper the main ideas of Extended Everett's Concept (EEC) about nature of consciousness. Let us briefly comment on the further development of this theory.

All that has been discussed above, makes sense for humans (possessing consciousness) and may be partly for higher animals. However, the theory may be generalized to give the quantum concept of life in a more general aspect. Thus modified theory is meaningful not only for humans, but for all living beings (belonging to the type of life characteristic for Earth). The idea of the generalization is follows (see (Mensky, 2010) for details).

The main point of EEC is the identification of the "separation of classical alternatives" with the human's consciousness. Now we have to identify this quantum concept with the ability of the living beings to "perceive the quantum world classically". This is an evident generalization of consciousness but for all living beings. Instead of "consciousness" in EEC we have now "classical perceiving of quantum reality" which means that the alternative classical realities (forming the state of the quantum world) are perceived separately from each other.

Similarly to what we told about consciousness (in case of humans), this ability of living beings to "classically perceive the quantum world" is necessary for the very phenomenon of life (of local type). The reason is the same: elaborating efficient strategy of surviving is possible only in a classical world which is "locally predictable". Existing objectively in the quantum world, any creature is living in each of the classical realities separately from all the rest classical realities. Life is developing parallely in the Everett's parallel worlds.

Remark by the way that from this point of view "existing" and "living" are different concepts. Important difference is that existing (evolution in time) of the inanimate matter is determined by reasons while living of the living beings is partly determined also by goals (first of all the goal of survival). Let us make some other remarks concerning philosophical or rather meta-scientific aspects of EEC.

This theory shows that a conceptual bridge between the material (described by natural sciences) and the ideal (treated by the humanities and spiritual doctrines) does exist. This bridge is determined in EEC in a concrete way, but the idea of such a bridge is not novel. The creators of quantum mechanics from the very beginning needed the notion of the "observer's consciousness" to analyze conceptual problems of this theory (the "problem of measurement"). In fact, the difficulties in solving these problems were caused by the insistent desire to construct quantum mechanics as a purely objective theory. Nowadays it becomes clear that there is no purely objective quantum theory. Objectiveness is relative (see Sect. 4).

There is a very interesting technical point in relations between the material and the ideal. We see from the preceding consideration that the description of the ideal, or psychic (consciousness and the unconscious), arises in the interior of quantum mechanics when we consider the whole world as a quantum system. This provides the absolute quantum coherence which is necessary for the conclusions that are derived from EEC. Usually only restricted systems are considered in quantum mechanics. The resulting theory is purely material. Ideal (psychic) elements arise as the specific aspects of the whole world. The unrestricted character of the world as a quantum system is essential for this (cf. the notion of microcosm).

All these issues demonstrate the specific features of the present stage of quantum theory. Including theory of consciousness (and the unconscious) in the realm of quantum mechanics (starting by Pauli and Jung and now close to being accomplished) marks a qualitatively new level of understanding quantum mechanics itself. The present stage of this theory can be estimated as the second quantum revolution. When being completed, it will accomplish the intellectual and philosophical revolution that accompanied creating quantum mechanics in the first third of 20th century.

References

Aspect, A., Grangier, P., Roger, G. (1981). Phys. Rev. Lett., 47, 460.

Bell, J. S. (1964). Physics, 1, 195. Reprinted in (Bell, 1987).

Bell, J. S. (1987). Speakable and Unspeakable in Quantum Mechanics. Cambridge Univ. Press, Cambridge.

DeWitt, B. S., Graham, N. (Eds.) (1973). The Many-Worlds Interpretation of Quantum Mechanics. Princeton Univ. Press, Princeton, NJ.

Einstein, A., Podolsky, B., Rosen, N. (1935). Phys. Rev., 47, 777.

Enz, C. P. (2009). Of Matter and Spirit. World Scientific Publishing Co., New Jersey etc. Everett III, H. (1957). Rev. Mod. Phys., 29, 454. Reprinted in (Wheeler & Zurek, 1983).

Menskii, M. B. (2000). Quantum mechanics: New experiments, new applications and new formulations of old questions. Physics- Uspekhi, 43, 585-600.

Menskii, M. B. (2005). Concept of consciousness in the context of quantum mechanics. Physics-Uspekhi, 48, 389-409.

Menskii, M. B. (2007). Quantum measurements, the phenomenon of life, and time arrow: Three great problems of physics (in Ginzburg's terminology). Physics-Uspekhi, 50, 397-407.

Mensky, M. (2007). Postcorrection and mathematical model of life in Extended Everett's Concept. NeuroQuantology, 5, 363-376. www.neuroquantology.com, arxiv:physics.gen-ph/0712.3609.

Mensky, M. (2010). Consciousness and Quantum Mechanics: Life in Parallel Worlds (Miracles of Consciousness from Quantum Mechanics). World Scientific Publishing Co., Singapore.

Mensky, M. B. (2005). Human and Quantum World (Weirdness of the Quantum World and the Miracle of Consciousness). Vek-2 publishers, Fryazino. In Russian.

Penrose, R. (1991). The Emperor's New Mind: Concepting Computers, Minds, and the Laws of Physics. Penguin Books, New York.

Penrose, R. (1994). Shadows of the Mind: a Search for the Missing Science of Consciousness. Oxford Univ. Press, Oxford.

****
****
****

V: THE AFFECT OF CONSCIOUSNESS OBSERVING THE UNIVERSE

****
****
****

25. Consciousness and Quantum Physics: A Deconstruction of the Topic

Gordon Globus
Professor Emeritus of Psychiatry and Philosophy,
University of California Irvine , Irvine, CA

Abstract

The topic of "consciousness and quantum physics" is deconstructed. Consciousness is not only a vague concept with very many definitions but is entangled with unresolved controversies, notably the notorious measurement problem in quantum physics and the qualia problem in philosophy, so the problematic calls for redefinition. The key issue is that of primary "closure"--the nonphenomenality of quantum physical reality--and the action that brings "dis-closure." Dis-closure of the phenomenal world can be understood within the framework of dissipative quantum thermofield brain dynamics without any reference to consciousness. Some unsettling monadological consequences of this view are brought out in the discussion.

Key Words: consciousness, quantum physics, dissipative quantum thermofield brain dynamics, measurement problem, between-two, monadology

1. Introduction

At present there is no agreed upon definition of consciousness--Vimal (2009) identified over forty!--so how could we discuss it in the same breath as the scientific field of quantum physics? A recent issue of The Journal of Consciousness Studies devoted ten articles to the topic of defining consciousness, the editor concluding that we should all try harder to both specify what we mean when referring to "consciousness" and pay more attention to the contexts within which that meaning applies. And we should embrace the resultant diversity ... . (Nunn 2009, p.7) Might a science-based discussion of consciousness and quantum physics be barking up the wrong tree? And if so, how might discussion be redeployed away from consciousness without falling into the dullness of crass materialism?

Since "consciousness" is so ill-defined, we are at the mercy of tacit subtextual meanings. Yet clues might be found in the term's etymology, which gains us a certain detachment. The very term "consciousness" already carries profound biases. It derives from the Latin con-scieri, which is to know-together, and accordingly cognitive-social. Conscientia--conscience--is an internalization of social knowing, viz. a self-knowing and judging. But today consciousness has a much broader meaning than this historical cognitive emphasis. "Consciousness" in present usage is not just a socialized knowing but is also perceptual. We say that we are conscious of the phenomenal world. The supplement to knowing found in the contemporary meaning of "consciousness" encompasses "qualia" too--the conscious experience of colors, sounds, odors, etc. --but this is precisely where there is hot debate. Despite enormous discussion (e.g. Kazniak 2001; Wright 2008) there is no philosophical consensus regarding the qualia problem. So the extension of the original cognitive meaning of "consciousness" to include qualitative experiences brings complications to any engagement with an unsuspecting physics, which ought to make us suspicious.

It should not be thought that substituting "awareness" or "experience" for "consciousness" improves the situation. "Aware" comes from an old English term meaning cautious (cf. "wary"), which is a cognitive activity. "Experience" (cf. "experiment") comes from the Latin experio, to try out, which is cognitive-behavioral. It is noteworthy that the term 'consciousness' does not even appear until the 17th century. If this is something so fundamental as to be related to quantum physics, why should it take so long to be distinguished in philosophical discourse? Were the philosophers of ancient Greece so unwise?

As if the ambiguity and subtext of "consciousness" were not enough, consciousness is already party to a long-standing and still highly contentious problem within quantum physics itself: the "measurement problem," which is typified by Schrödinger's notorious cat. Consistent with the principles of quantum physics Schrödinger's cat seems to be in a superposition state of being dead and being alive, until a conscious observation is made.

Even if it is supposed that consciousness has nothing to do with the outcome--supposed that the wave function readily collapses on its own (Gihradi 2007; Hameroff and Penrose 1996)--the result is not a phenomenal cat, dead or alive as the case may be. Wave function collapse is to near-certainty of location, not to a phenomenal cat. The wave function is a wave of probability and its collapse is still expressed in probabilistic terms ("exceedingly near 1.0" at some point). Any phenomenality depends on the observer's consciousness, and so the measurement problem drags in some meta-physics. Since the tradition of metaphysics runs back through Kant and Descartes to Plato--a tradition that uncommonsensical quantum physics otherwise challenges at every turn--the very topic of consciousness and quantum physics cries for deconstruction.

There is no place for the phenomenal cat in quantum physics itself--that cat right there in the box, dead or alive, after you open it. Quantum field theory is well capable of describing macroscopic objects with sharp boundary structures (Umezawa 1993, Chapter 6). Scale is not an issue for quantum field theory. (There is no need to get to the macroscopic by the fiat of letting Planck's constant go to zero.) But a macroscopic quantum object is not of the same kind as a cat-in-a-box: that would be a colossal category mistake to equate them. Might quantum brain theory ride to the rescue? Many theories have been proposed for how quantum brain mechanisms might generate consciousness and thereby rescue from metaphysics the principle of the causal closure of the physical domain. (Quantum physicists in general have been slow to recognize the importance of quantum brain theory to their endeavor.) But these attempts run into the wasps nest already emphasized: the definability problem for consciousness, the qualia problem, and unyielding controversy over the measurement problem. A fresh start is tried here and the brutal consequences are faced.

2. Dis-Closure

The world presences, "is," exists, has Being, appears ... . Instead of saying that we are "conscious of the world" it is less prejudicial to say that we always find ourselves already amidst one, waking and dreaming both. Being is no easy replacement for consciousness, to be sure ... and the term "Being" may sound more problematic than "consciousness" to the physics ear. For reasons to be brought out, I shall use instead the term "dis-closure."

To speak of the quantum "world," as is sometimes loosely done, is self-contradictory. As already emphasized above, the quantum realm lacks phenomenality, has no appearance, is closed. What is needed is an account of the appearance of Being, presence, or since the fundamental property is closedness, what is called for is dis-closedness.

Dis-closure entails an action--an action on closure--a dis-closure in which Being--a cat in a box--appears. What is called for by the above deconstruction of consciousness in quantum physics is an account of dis-closure. Thermofield brain dynamics provides an explanation of dis-closure that may get free from the problematical consciousness.

3. Thermofield Brain Dynamics

The origins of thermofield brain dynamics go back to the quantum brain dynamics of Umezawa and coworkers in the late sixties (Umezawa 1995). It was recognized that symmetry-breaking in the ground state of the brain--the vacuum state of a water electric dipole field--offers a mechanism for memory. Sensory inputs fall into the ground after dissipating their energy and break the dipole symmetry. The broken symmetry is preserved by boson condensation (Nambu-Goldstone condensates). When the sensory input is repeated, the condensate-trace is excited from the vacuum state and becomes conscious. Jibu and Yasue (1995, 2004) worked this idea into a full-fledged quantum brain dynamics of consciousness.

Vitiello (1995, 2001, 2004) greatly extended quantum brain dynamics to a thermofield brain dynamics by bringing in dissipation. Now the brain is a dissipative system and its vacuum state has two modes: a system mode and an environment mode. The system mode contains the boson memory traces and the environment mode expresses ongoing input. ("Input" should be understood here as both sensory signals and signals the brain generates on its own, that is, other-generated signals and self-generated signals.) Neither mode exists without the other. The vacuum state is "between-two," between other-generated and self-generated signals on the one hand and memory traces on the other. Vitiello proposed that consciousness is not the quantum brain dynamics model of excitation of memory traces from the vacuum but is the state of match between dual modes. Consciousness for Vitiello is between-two.

Notable in the Vitiello model is a new version of ontological duality. The traditional dualities are the two substances of Descartes or the two aspects of a "neutral reality" proposed by Spinoza. Mitigated dualisms include Sperry's (1969) emergent level which is more than the sum of its interacting parts and Huxley's (1898) epiphenomenalism in which the mental is a nomological dangler without causal influence. The between-two is a new idea. The two are indissolubly coupled--no one without the other--and unlike ontological substances or aspects of a neutral substance, what is primary is their between.

Since Vitiello wedded thermofield brain dynamics to consciousness, the same difficulties already detailed arise. But we may alternatively reinterpret thermofield brain dynamics as a theory of dis-closure (Globus 2003, 2009). Dis-closure is between-two.

Phenomenal world appears when the dual modes belong-together, in the sense that a complex number "belongs-to" its complex conjugate. The match between such dual modes is real. Phenomenal world is a function of the brain's quantum vacuum state, dis-closed in the match between other-action, self-action and memory traces.

4. Paying the Dues for Giving-Up Consciousness

We should not expect to get off so easily after jettisoning consciousness for action-cum-disclosure. Something dear to our hearts is exploded: the world-in-common that faithful observers might by and large agree on. Not only do we lose our consciousness but we lose the world too. Now every quantum thermofield brain is dis-closing worlds in parallel. There is no world-in-common that we each represent (re-present) in our own way, nor do we each pick up a common world's sensory offerings according to our individual predilection (Gibson 1979; Neisser 1976), not even a common world that is selected by sensory input from the possibilities we variously bring to it (Edelman 1987). For the present proposal there is no physical reality of an external world, only unworldly macroscopic and microscopic quantum objects. All worlds are between-two.

So Being, which is to replace consciousness, can be precisely specified. Ontologically primary is distinctionless abground, and Being is secondarily dis-closed--appears--in virtue of an action on the abground, an action that unfolds.

That is, the primary ontological condition is closure and Being requires its undoing: dis-closure. The deconstructed topic of "consciousness and quantum physics" is succeeded by the topic of "Being and quantum physics."

This view should not be confused with multiple worlds theory (Greene 2011), which just compounds the difficulties surrounding consciousness already discussed. In multiple worlds theory every possible result of wave function collapse is realized. In one world the Schrödinger cat is found alive by a consciousness and in another world found dead by a different consciousness. For the present account, in contrast, different observers perceive the same result. The worlds dis-closed are multiple yet in agreement. There is consensus to the extent that other-action, self-action and memory are comparable across brains.

The present view might be called "monadological" but in a distinct sense from that of Leibniz. Leibniz did not doubt that there is in fact a transcendent world bestowed through God's love. "God produces substances from nothing," Leibniz (1952, sect. 395) states in the Theodicy. The worlds in parallel of monads are in "pre-established harmony" with the transcendent world God thinks into being. But there is no transcendent world according to the view developed here. There is closure--a distinctionless "abground" (Heidegger 1999) or even "holomovement" (Bohm 1980; Bohm and Hiley 1993)--and multiple parallel phenomenal world disclosures. This is a rather scary thought, to lose the quotidian world-in-common, when you really think about it ...

Other macroscopic quantum objects besides brains also have a matching state of their between-two but the disclosures of, say, an old cabbage, barely change from moment to moment. To use the Kantian phrase, such a macroscopic quantum object "is in itself" but its Being doesn"t amount to much. The brain's genius is that the between-two comes under exquisite control by three influences: other-action, self-action and memory. Complex dis-closures flowingly evolve in waking life.

Three distinct types of brain state bring out some implications of the model. In the case of well-formed slow wave sleep, the between-two disclosure is closer to that of the cabbage. During active REM sleep, however, the between-two revives, though with the participation of other-action (sensory input) strongly inhibited. The between-two becomes a function of only residual self-actions (mainly from the preceding day, Freudian "day residues") and retraces (typically of emotional significance): the dream life is dis-closed. (See Globus (2010) for a detailed illustration of how this works.) Monadological disclosure accordingly varies dramatically in content across waking, dreaming and sleeping but in no case can be transcended. We are windowless monads in parallel and best get on with it! Such a counter-intuitive conclusion is founded in a relentless deconstruction of the role of consciousness in quantum physics. The successor concept to consciousness is "world-thrownness" in virtue of between-two dis-closure.

References

Bohm, D. (1980). Wholeness and the implicate order. Routledge & Kegan Paul, London.

Bohm, D. and Hiley, B. (1993). The Undivided Universe. Routledge & Kegan Paul, London.

Edelman, G. (1987). Neural Darwinism. Basic Books, New York.

Ghiradi, G. (2007). Collapse theories. In Stanford Encyclopedia of Philosophy. http://Plato.Stanford.edu/entries/qm-collapse/

Gibson, J. (1979). The ecological approach to visual perception. Houghton-Mifflin, Boston.

Globus, G. (2003). Quantum Closures and Disclosures: Thinking together Postphenomenology and Quantum Brain Dynamics. John Benjamins, Amsterdam.

Globus, G. (2009). The transparent becoming of world: A crossing between process thought and quantum neurophilosophy. John Benjamins, Amsterdam.

Green, B. (2010). The Hidden Reality. Knopf, New York.

Hameroff, S. Penrose, R. (1996). Conscious events as orchestrated space-time selections. Journal of consciousness studies 3, 36-53.

Heidegger, M. (1999). Contributions to philosophy (from Enowning). P. Emad & K. Maly, trans. Indiana University Press, Bloomington, Indiana.

Huxley, D.H. (1898). Methods and results: Essays by Thomas H. Huxley. D. Appleton, New York.

Jibu, M., Yasue, K. (1995). Quantum brain dynamics and consciousness. John Benjamins, Amsterdam.

Jibu, M., Yasue, K. (2004). Quantum brain dynamics and quantum field theory. In: Brain and being. Globus, G., Pribram, K., Vitello, G. eds. John Benjamins, Amsterdam.

Kaszniak, A. (ed.) (2001). Emotions, qualia and consciousness. World Scientific: Singapore.

Leibniz, G.W. (1952). Theodicy: Essays on the Goodness of God, the Freedom of Man, and the Origin of Evil. A. Farrer, ed., E. M. Huggard, trans. Yale University Press, New Haven.

Neisser, U. (1976). Cognition and Reality. W.H. Freeman, San Francisco.

Nunn, C. (2009). Editors introduction: Defining consciousness. J. of consciousness studies 16, 5-8.

Sperry, R. (1969). A modified concept of consciousness. Psychological review 77, 585- 590.

Umezawa, H. (1993). Advanced Field Theory: Micro, Macro, and Thermal Physics, American Institute of Physics, New York.

Umezawa, H. (1995). Development in concepts in quantum field theory in half century. Mathematica Japonica, 41, 109-124.

Vimal, R.L.P. (2009) Meanings attributed to the term "Consciousness". J. of consciousness studies, 16: 9-27.

Vitiello G. (1995). Dissipation and memory capacity in the quantum brain model. Int J of Modern Physics B 9, 973-989.

Vitiello, G. (2001). My Double Unveiled. John Benjamins, Amsterdam.

Vitiello, G. (2004). The dissipative brain. In: G. Globus, K. Pribram & G. Vitiello, eds. Brain and being. Amsterdam: John Benjamins.

Wright, E. (ed.) (2008). The case for qualia. MIT Press, Cambridge.

26. Consciousness and Quantum Measurement

York H. Dobyns

Department of Electrical Engineering, Engineering Quadrangle, Princeton University, Princeton, New Jersey 08544

Abstract

The quantum measurement problem remains mysterious, with multiple interpretations of the formalism making different assumptions about its nature. The various interpretations also make very different assumptions about the role of consciousness in this transition from superposed probabilities to definite observed events. Some regard it as completely irrelevant, some regard consciousness as essential to complete the transition, and at least one speculative model identifies this transition as the key physical substrate of consciousness itself. Because of this problematic status for consciousness in the physical theory of quantum mechanics, it seems noteworthy that recently published experimental work reports that a specific state of human consciousness has been observed to disrupt remotely the spatial superposition of photon states in a Michelson interferometer, detectably reducing the level of interference between the two beam paths. This suggests that, at the very least, the instrument is serving as a remote detector for the brain state corresponding to the experimentally induced state of consciousness. Moreover, further experimental work in this genre may shed important light on the physical properties of human consciousness and their relation to quantum measurement.

Key Words: Consciousness; Conscious States; Quantum Measurement; Quantum Observation; Interferometry

1. Basics of The Quantum Measurement Problem

It is presumably well-known that the process by which the probability densities computed from quantum theory are converted into definite observational facts remains profoundly mysterious. The conceptual model of this process depends entirely on the interpretation of quantum mechanics favored by the analysts. The role and relevance of consciousness in this process varies enormously among interpretations. Some would regard the process as essentially irrelevant to consciousness except to the extent that it is part of the physical world in which humans and their minds exist. One example of such a view is seen in the "many worlds" or "many views of one world" interpretation (Everett, 1957; Squires, 1987). In this model, both an experiment and its conscious observer continue a deterministic evolution according to the equations of quantum mechanics and there is no probabilistic transition to definite outcomes; the appearance of such a transition to observers is essentially an illusion arising from the fact that the observing instrument correlates each state of the quantum system with a state of the observer that corresponds to having observed the particular quantum state in question, rather than the entire superposition. Other theories argue that so-called wave function collapse is an actual physical process proceeding independently of observation or measurement as such; classical objects composed of huge numbers of quantum particles spontaneously maintain themselves in classical states regardless of anyone's observations (Ghirardi et al. 1986; Joos et al. 2003). In contrast, the view championed by Wigner and various others holds that conscious observation is the fundamental cause of the transition from probabilities to definite outcomes (Von Neumann, 1955; Wigner, 1963, 1964; Stapp, 2001). In general, those holding this view contend that no observation has actually been made until some conscious being has become aware of the results. It is interesting to note that a fundamental relationship between consciousness and quantum measurement is also required by a view almost diametrically opposed to the Wignerian approach. In the speculative model of Penrose, quantum measurement or "wave function collapse" is viewed as a strictly physical process, but this process is fundamental to the existence of consciousness, and only systems that can maintain certain kinds of quantum superposition and collapse them in particular ways are capable of being conscious (Penrose, 1989, 1994).

One of the most commonly used experimental tools for examining quantum superposition and its breakdown is some form of the Mach-Zehnder interferometer, in which a light beam is split into separate paths and then reunited at another beam splitter. By suitably chosen geometry it is possible to arrange that the reunited beam interferes with itself. Such interference can take place only if the individual quanta of the split beam are free to propagate in a superposed state along both paths between the initial and final beam splitters. If a "which-way" measurement intervenes to establish which branch of the apparatus contains a particular photon, the interference at the final beam splitter is lost, a fact that can be established by the detection of a change in the normal interference pattern. An important point is that interference is destroyed by the mere existence of apparatus capable of performing a which-way measurement, whether or not it actually measures anything. As dramatized by the "Elitzur-Vaidman bomb test" thought experiment, the presence of a photon detector in one branch of the interferometer destroys interference even if it fails to detect anything because the photon traveled through the other branch (Elitzur and Vaidman, 1993). This can, of course, be viewed as a simple instance of the general principle that experiments on quantum objects examine only the properties they are designed to examine. An interferometer with a photon detector embedded in one branch of the light path is, by construction, an instrument for establishing which way the initial beam splitter directed the incident photon, and naturally cannot generate interference effects downstream of the detector. The general properties of the Mach-Zehnder interferometer and its sensitivity to which-way measurements are central to the following discussion.

2. Empirical Data Involving Consciousness

When considering the role of consciousness in the physical universe, physicists are somewhat handicapped by the fact that their traditional experimental techniques do not involve human beings as part of the apparatus, or even as subjects of inquiry. Such tests are generally considered to be part of other fields of science. Moreover, specific inquiries regarding consciousness are seldom useful or informative from a physical-science perspective because of the techniques necessarily used in the so-called "soft" sciences such as psychology, although in recent years there has been considerable input to such studies from allied fields such as neurophysiology.

It is therefore unsurprising that experiments in relatively remote and unfamiliar fields gather little notice in the physics literature even on those occasions when they do have significant implications for physics. Nevertheless, these investigations sometimes produce data that are relevant to fundamental physical theories. Since theoretical predictions must be checked against observational data, it seems inappropriate to ignore such data even when they come from unexpected sources.

The particular data in question come from experiments using a Michelson interferometer, which can be considered as a Mach-Zehnder interferometer in which the light paths are overlaid by reflection so that the same beam splitter can be used both to separate and to reunite the beams. It was found that human subjects were apparently able to perform a limited which-way measurement despite the absence of conventional detection apparatus in the light path (Radin 2008). This experiment was a refinement and extension of earlier experimental work by other researchers that had shown mixed and inconclusive results (Jeffers and Sloan, 1992; Ibison and Jeffers, 1998). It is a noteworthy feature of all these investigations that no attempt was made to evaluate the human subjects' success in actually acquiring which-way information; the existence of a which-way measurement was inferred from its physical effects on an interference pattern. While it might seem peculiar to design an interferometry experiment around a human subject's cognitive state, the primary hypothesis was derived from speculations about human capabilities which, while controversial, are supported by an extensive technical literature (Pratt et al. 1940; Rhine, 1971; Targ and Puthoff, 1974; Parker, 1975; Honorton, 1977; Tart et al. 1979; Bem and Honorton 1994; May, 1996; Brown, 2005). For consideration of the physical nature of consciousness the most interesting thing about this experiment is not the history leading to the adoption of its design, but the fact that it seems to have shown detectable physical consequences of a human subject's mental state in a physically separated, isolated, and shielded experimental system.

A brief overview of the Radin (2008) experimental report is necessary before discussion of its theoretical implications can proceed. The primary empirical finding is that a particular state of consciousness induced by human subjects had the effect of performing a which-way measurement, albeit one with fairly low quantum efficiency, on a nearby Michelson interferometer, which was shielded against electromagnetic interference and vibration. (The report's methodology section refers to a "double-steel-walled, electrically and acoustically shielded room" resting on a vibration isolation mat and with further layers of vibration isolation between the room's interior floor and the experimental apparatus. The implication of a separate floor suggests that the experimental space might more appropriately have been called a steel-walled box rather than a steel-walled room.) The refinements to earlier experiments (Jeffers and Sloan, 1992; Ibison and Jeffers, 1998) consisted largely in this superior isolation, and the change from a simple double-slit interference apparatus to the Michelson interferometer, allowing significant spatial separation of the beam paths. The method for measuring the extent of interference in the apparatus was to measure total light intensity in portions of the interference pattern that showed strong differences between the two-path pattern with interference and a one-path pattern without mutual interference.

Unfortunately, the report does not give actual light intensities for these measurements, instead presenting them either in arbitrary units or in statistical figures of merit. In these statistical terms, then, one can say that subjects skilled in maintaining a state of focused attention produced a change of the measured intensity amounting to 4.28 times the measurement uncertainty. Unskilled subjects produced an apparent change of only 0.29 times the measurement uncertainty, while control runs with no subjects, performed immediately after the sessions with skilled subjects, produced an apparent change of 0.46 times the measurement uncertainty. The changes referred to are the changes between the measured light intensity when the subject was, or was not, maintaining a state of focused attentiveness directed at the location of one branch of the interferometer. The classification of "skilled" or "unskilled" subjects is relevant due to the difficulty most untrained people experience in maintaining such focused mental states over significant intervals of time, as discussed in the report.

What makes these empirical findings of particular theoretical interest is the absence of any conventional measuring device in the interferometer beam path. It was noted above that the presence of apparatus capable of conducting a which-way measurement is sufficient to destroy the ability of the two light paths to interfere with each other. In this case, however, there are two conditions, one with full interference and one with reduced interference, in which from a conventional viewpoint no additional measuring apparatus has been introduced. This seems to force the conclusion that the which-way apparatus in this case consists of the specific cognitive state of the human subjects during the periods when they were instructed to maintain focused attention on the apparatus. This conclusion is less peculiar than it might seem at first inspection. On the presumption that a cognitive state must equate to a particular physical configuration of the subject's brain activity, there is a clearly identifiable physical difference between the two experimental conditions. Runs showing evidence of which-way measurement activity correspond to one condition, and the runs lacking such evidence correspond to the other.

It is, of course, somewhat unexpected that whatever physical changes the subjects are inducing in their brains by entering a state of focused attention should have an effect on instrumentation several meters away and heavily shielded. While a detailed physical mechanism is obscure, there is no shortage of roughly analogous situations in known experiments. Two examples seem particularly apropos. In the Aharonov-Bohm solenoid effect, electron beams propagating through a space free of electric and magnetic fields show changes in relative phase from the presence of a magnetic field completely confined within a solenoid in a region of space isolated from the beam paths (Aharonov and Bohm, 1959, 1961). So-called quantum eraser experiments actively rely upon the fact that an interference pattern can be altered or eliminated by remote manipulations of entangled partners of the photons actually participating in the interference (Kim et al. 2000). There is, of course, no reason to expect that Radin's subjects are actually acting as sources of a field-free potential, or have access to particles entangled with the interferometer's photon stream. These specific examples are presented not as plausible mechanisms for the observed effect, but simply as illustrations of the fact that known physical effects are entirely capable of circumventing methods of isolation, separation, or shielding which naïve physical intuition might expect to be adequate to protect an experimental system from outside influences.

3. Conclusions

It is premature to draw overly strong conclusions from a single experiment, not yet replicated by other researchers. (Although the experiment is itself a conceptual replication, the earlier experiments showed conflicting results and must be considered inconclusive.) Nevertheless, if these preliminary findings are confirmed, it would follow that at the very least we now know how to build an instrument to detect remotely the presence of one particular cognitive state in a human being, and that the physical mechanism mediating this detection is not yet understood. The observed phenomenon involves the resolution of a quantum superposition into distinct spatial states with definite locations, apparently in response to a purely cognitive and internal effort by a human subject. This fact suggests that further and more thorough investigations using this experimental paradigm might be able to throw considerable light on the relationship between human consciousness and the process that remains one of the fundamental mysteries of quantum mechanics.

Acknowledgments The author is indebted to Dean Radin for a number of informal presentations and communications without which this work would have remained unknown to him.

References

Aharonov, Y., Bohm, D. (1959). Significance of Electromagnetic Potentials in the Quantum Theory. Phys. Rev., 115, 485–491.

Aharonov, Y., Bohm, D. (1961). Further Considerations on Electromagnetic Potentials in the Quantum Theory. Phys. Rev., 123, 1511–1524.

Bem, D. J., Honorton, C. (1994). Does psi exist? Replicable evidence for an anomalous process of information transfer. Psychological Bulletin, 115, 4–18.

Brown, C. (2005). Remote Viewing: The Science and Theory of Nonphysical Perception. Farsight Press, Atlanta, GA, US.

Elitzur, A. C., Vaidman, L. (1993) Quantum mechanical interaction-free measurements. Found. Phys., 23, 987–997.

Everett, H. (1957). "Relative State" Formulation of Quantum Mechanics. Rev. Mod. Phys., 29, 454–462.

Ghirardi, G. C., Rimini, A., Weber, T. (1986). Unified dynamics for microscopic and macroscopic systems. Phys. Rev. D., 34, 470–491.

Honorton, C. (1977). Psi and internal attention states. In: Wolman, B. B. (Ed.), Handbook of Parapsychology, Van Nostrand Reinhold, New York, pp. 435–472.

Ibison, M., Jeffers, S. (1998). A double-slit diffraction experiment to investigate claims of consciousness-related anomalies. J. Sci. Explor., 12, 543–550.

Jeffers, S., Sloan, J. (1992). A low light level diffraction experiment for anomalies research. J. Sci. Explor., 6, 333–352.

Joos, E., Zeh, H. D., Kiefer, C., Giulini, D., Kupsch, J., Stamatescu, I.-O. (2003). Decoherence and the Appearance of a Classical World in Quantum Theory. Springer, New York, US.

Kim, Y. H., Yu, R., Kulik, S. P., Shih, Y. (2000). Delayed "Choice" Quantum Eraser. Phys. Rev. Lett., 84, 1–5.

May, E. C. (1996). The American Institutes for Research Review of the Department of Defense's STAR GATE Program: A Commentary. J. Sci. Explor, 10, 89–107.

Parker, A. (1975). States of Mind: ESP and Altered States of Consciousness. Taplinger, New York, US.

Penrose, R. (1989). The Emperor's New Mind. Oxford University Press, New

York, US.

Penrose, R. (1994). Shadows of the Mind. Oxford University Press, New York, US.

Pratt, J. G., Rhine, J. B., Stuart, C. E., Smith, B. M. (1940). Extra-Sensory Perception After Sixty Years. Holt, New York, US.

Radin, D. (2008). Testing nonlocal observation as a source of intuitive knowledge. Explore, 4, 25–35.

Rhine, J. B. (Ed.) (1971). Progress in Parapsychology. Parapsychology Press, Durham, NC, US.

Squires, E. J. (1987). Many views of one world — an interpretation of quantum theory. Eur. J. Phys., 8, 171–173.

Stapp, H. P. (2001). Quantum theory and the role of mind in nature. Found. Phys., 31, 1465–1499.

Targ, R., Puthoff, H. E. (1974). Information transmission under conditions of sensory shielding. Nature, 252, 602–607.

Tart, C. T., Puthoff, H. E., Targ, R. (Eds.) (1979). Mind at Large: IEEE Symposia on the Nature of Extrasensory Perception. Praeger Special Studies, New York, US.

Von Neumann, J. (1955). Mathematical Foundations of Quantum Mechanics. Princeton University Press, Princeton, US.

Wigner, E. P. (1963). The problem of measurement. Am J. Phys., 31, 6–15.

Wigner, E. P. (1964). Two kinds of reality. The Monist, 48, 248–264.

27. A Quantum Physical Effect of Consciousness

Shan Gao

Unit for HPS & Centre for Time, SOPHI,
University of Sydney, Sydney, NSW 2006, Australia

Abstract

It is shown that a conscious being can distinguish definite perceptions and their quantum superpositions, while a physical measuring system without consciousness cannot distinguish such nonorthogonal quantum states. This result may have some important implications for quantum theory and the science of consciousness. In particular, it implies that consciousness is not emergent but a fundamental feature of the universe.

Key Words: consciousness, quantum superposition, quantum-to-classical transition, panpsychism

1. Introduction

The relationship between quantum measurement and consciousness has been studied since the founding of quantum mechanics (von Neumann 1932/1955; London and Bauer 1939; Wigner 1967; Stapp 1993, 2007; Penrose 1989, 1994; Hameroff and Penrose 1996; Hameroff 1998, 2007; Gao 2004, 2006b, 2008b). Quantum measurement problem is generally acknowledged as one of the hardest problems in modern physics, and the transition from quantum to classical is still a deep mystery. On the other hand, consciousness remains another deep mystery for both philosophy and science, and it is still unknown whether consciousness is emergent or fundamental. It has been conjectured that these two mysteries may have some intimate connections, and finding them may help to solve both problems (Chalmers 1996).

There are two main viewpoints claiming that quantum measurement and consciousness are intimately connected. The first one holds that the consciousness of an observer causes the collapse of the wave function and helps to complete the quantum measurement or quantum-to-classical transition in general (von Neumann 1932/1955; London and Bauer 1939; Wigner 1967; Stapp 1993, 2007). This view seems understandable. Though what physics commonly studies are insensible objects, the consciousness of observer must take part in the last phase of measurement. The observer is introspectively aware of his perception of the measurement results, and consciousness is used to end the infinite chains of measurement here. The second view holds that consciousness arises from objective wavefunction collapse (Penrose 1989, 1994; Hameroff and Penrose 1996; Hameroff 1998, 2007). One argument is that consciousness is a process that cannot be described algorithmically, and the gravitation-induced wavefunction collapse seems non-computable as a fundamental physical process, and thus the elementary acts of consciousness must be realized as objective wavefunction collapse, e.g., collapse of coherent superposition states in brain microtubules. Though these two views are obviously contrary, they both insist that a conscious perception is always definite and classical, and there are no quantum superpositions of definite conscious perceptions.

Different from these seemingly extreme views, it is widely thought that the quantum-to-classical transition and consciousness are essentially independent with each other (see, e.g. Nauenberg (2007) for a recent review). At first sight, this common-sense view seems too plain to be intriguing. However, it has been argued that, by permitting the existence of quantum superpositions of different conscious perceptions, this view will lead to an unexpected new result, a quantum physical effect of consciousness (Gao 2004, 2006b, 2008b). In this article, we will introduce this interesting result and discuss its possible implications.

2. The Effect

Quantum mechanics is the most fundamental theory of the physical world. Yet as to the measurement process or quantum-to-classical transition process, the standard quantum mechanics provides by no means a complete description, and the collapse postulate is just a makeshift (Bell 1987). Dynamical collapse theories (Ghirardi 2008), many-worlds theory (Everett 1957) and de Broglie-Bohm theory (Bohm 1952) are the main alternatives to a complete quantum theory. The latter two replace the collapse postulate with some new structures, such as branching worlds and Bohmian trajectories, while the former integrate the collapse postulate with the normal Schrödinger evolution into a unified dynamics. It has been recently shown that the dynamical collapse theories are probably in the right direction by admitting wavefunction collapse (Gao 2011). Here we will mainly discuss the possible quantum effects of consciousness in the framework of dynamical collapse theories, though the conclusion also applies to the other alternatives. Our analysis only relies on one common character of the theories, i.e., that the collapse of the wave function (or the quantum-to-classical transition in general) is one kind of objective dynamical process, essentially independent of the consciousness of observer, and it takes a finite time to finish.

It is a well-known result that nonorthogonal quantum states cannot be distinguished (by physical measuring device) in both standard quantum mechanics and dynamical collapse theories (see, e.g. Wootters and Zurek 1982;

Ghirardi et al 1993; Nielsen and Chuang 2000). However, it has been argued that a conscious being can distinguish his definite perception states and the quantum superpositions of these states, and thus when the physical measuring device is replaced by a conscious observer, the nonorthogonal states can be distinguished in principle in dynamical collapse theories (Gao 2004, 2006b, 2008b). The distinguishability of nonorthogonal states will reveal a distinct quantum physical effect of consciousness, which is lacking for physical measuring systems without consciousness. In the following, we will give a full exposition of this result.

Let v1 and v2 be two definite perception states of a conscious being, and v1 + v2 is the quantum superposition of these two definite perception states. For example, v1 and v2 are triggered respectively by a small number of photons with a certain frequency entering into the eyes of the conscious being from two directions, and v1 + v2 is triggered by the superposition of these two input states. Assume that the conscious being satisfies the following slow collapse condition, i.e., that the collapse time of the superposition state v1 + v2, denoted by tc, is longer than the normal conscious time tp of the conscious being for definite states, and the time difference is large enough for him to identify. This condition ensures that consciousness can take part in the process of wavefunction collapse; otherwise consciousness can only appear after the collapse and will surely have no influence upon the collapse process. Now we will explain why the conscious being can distinguish the definite perception states v1 or v2 and the superposition state v1 + v2.

First, we assume that a definite perception can appear only after the collapse of the superposition state v1 + v2. This assumption seems plausible. Then the conscious being can have a definite perception after the conscious time tp for the states v1 and v2, but only after the collapse time tc can the conscious being have a definite perception for the superposition state v1 + v2. Since the conscious being satisfies the slow collapse condition and can distinguish the times tp and tc, he can distinguish the definite perception state v1 or v2 and the superposition state v1 + v2. Note that a similar argument was first given by Squires (1992).

Next, we assume that the above assumption is not true, i.e., that the conscious being in a superposition state can have a definite perception before the collapse has completed. We will show that the conscious being can also distinguish the states v1 + v2 and v1 or v2 with non-zero probability.

(1). If the definite perception of the conscious being in the superposed state v1 + v2 is neither v1 nor v2 (e.g. the perception is some sort of mixture of the perceptions v1 and v2), then obviously the conscious being can directly distinguish the states v1 + v2 and v1 or v2.

(2). If the definite perception of the conscious being in the superposed state v1+v2 is always v1, then the conscious being can directly distinguish the states v1+v2 and v2. Besides, the conscious being can also distinguish the states v1 + v2 and v1 with probability 1/2. The superposition state v1 + v2 will become v2 with probability 1/2 after the collapse, and the definite perception of the conscious being will change from v1 to v2 accordingly. But for the state v1, the perception of the conscious being has no such change.

(3). If the definite perception of the conscious being in the superposed state v1 + v2 is always v2, the proof is similar to (2).

(4). If the definite perception of the conscious being in the superposed state v1 + v2 is random, i.e., that one time it is v1, and another time it is v2, then the conscious being can still distinguish the states v1 + v2 and v1 or v2 with non-zero probability. For the definite perception states v1 or v2, the perception of the conscious being does not change. For the superposition state v1 + v2, the perception of the conscious being will change from v1 to v2 or from v2 to v1 with non-zero probability during the collapse process.

In fact, we can also give a compact proof by reduction to absurdity. Assume that a conscious being cannot distinguish the definite perception states v1 or v2 and the superposition state v1 + v2. This requires that for the superposition state v1 + v2 the conscious being must have the perception v1 or v2 immediately after the conscious time tp, and moreover, the perception must be exactly the same as his perception after the collapse of the superposition state v1 + v2. Otherwise he will be able to distinguish the superposition state v1 + v2 from the definite state v1 or v2. Since the conscious time tp is shorter than the collapse time tc, the requirement means that the conscious being knows the collapse result beforehand. This is impossible due to the essential randomness of the collapse process. Note that even if this is possible, the conscious being also has a distinct quantum physical effect, i.e., that he can know the random collapse result beforehand.

To sum up, we have shown that if a conscious being satisfies the slow collapse condition, he can readily distinguish the nonorthogonal states v1 + v2 (or v1 - v2) and v1 or v2, which is an impossible task for a physical measuring system without consciousness.

3. The Condition

The above quantum physical effect of consciousness depends on the slow collapse condition, namely that for a conscious being the collapse time of a superposition of his conscious perceptions is longer than his normal conscious time. Whether this condition is available for human brains depends on concrete models of consciousness and wavefunction collapse. For example, if a definite conscious perception involves less neurons such as several thousand neurons, then the collapse time of the superposition of such perceptions will be readily in the same level as the normal conscious time (several hundred milliseconds) according to some dynamical collapse models (Gao 2006a, 2006b, 2008a, 2008b). This result is also supported by the Penrose-Hameroff orchestrated objective reduction model (Hameroff and Penrose 1996; Hagan, Hameroff and Tuszynski 2002). In the model, if a conscious perception involves about 109 participating tubulin, then the collapse time will be several hundred milliseconds and in the order of normal conscious time. When assuming that 10% of the tubulin contained becomes involved, the conscious perception also involves about one thousand neurons (there are roughly 107 tubulin per neuron). In addition, even though the slow collapse condition is unavailable for human brains, it cannot be in principle excluded that there exist some small brain creatures in the universe who satisfy the slow collapse condition (see also Squires 1992).

A more important point needs to be stressed here. The collapse time estimated above is only the average collapse time for an ensemble composed of identical superposition states. The collapse time of a single superposition state is an essentially stochastic variable, which value can range between zero and infinity. As a result, the slow collapse condition can always be satisfied for some collapse events with a certain probability. For these random collapse processes, the collapse time of the single superposition state is much longer than the average collapse time and the normal conscious time, and thus the conscious being can distinguish the nonorthogonal states and have the distinct quantum physical effect. As we will see, this ultimate possibility will have important implications for the nature of consciousness.

Lastly, we note that the slow collapse condition is also available in the many-worlds theory and de Broglie-Bohm theory (Gao 2004). For these two theories, the collapse time will be replaced by the decoherence time. First, since a conscious being is able to be conscious of its own state, he can always be taken as a closed self-measuring system in theory. In both many-worlds theory and de Broglie-Bohm theory, the state of a closed system satisfies the linear Schrödinger equation, and thus no apparent collapse happens or the decoherence time is infinite for the superposition state of a closed conscious system. Therefore, the slow collapse condition can be more readily satisfied in these theories when a conscious system has only a very weak interaction with environment. By comparison, in most dynamical collapse theories, the superposition state of a closed system also collapses by itself. Secondly, a conscious system (e.g. a human brain or neuron groups in the brain) often has a very strong interaction with environment in practical situations. As a result, the decoherence time is usually much shorter than the collapse time, and the slow collapse condition will be less readily satisfied in many-worlds theory and de Broglie-Bohm theory than in the dynamical collapse theories. This difference can be used to test these different quantum theories.

4. Implications

Consciousness is the most familiar phenomenon. Yet it is also the hardest to explain. The relationship between objective physical process and subjective conscious experience presents a well-known hard problem for science (Chalmers 1996). It retriggers the recent debate about the long-standing dilemma of panpsychism versus emergentism (Strawson et al 2006; Seager and Allen-Hermanson 2010). Though emergentism is currently the most popular solution to the hard problem of consciousness, many doubt that it can bridge the explanation gap ultimately. By comparison, panpsychism may provide an attractive and promising way to solve the hard problem, though it also encounters some serious problems (Seager and Allen-Hermanson 2010). It is widely believed that the physical world is causally closed, i.e., that there is a purely physical explanation for the occurrence of every physical event and the explanation does not refer to any consciousness property (see, e.g. McGinn 1999). But if panpsychism is true, the fundamental consciousness property should take part in the causal chains of the physical world and should present itself in our investigation of the physical world. Then does consciousness have any causal efficacy in the physical world?

As we have argued above, a conscious observer can distinguish two nonorthogonal states, while the physical measuring system without consciousness cannot. Accordingly, consciousness does have a causal efficacy in the physical world when considering the fundamental quantum processes. This will provide a strong support for panpsychism. In fact, we can argue that if consciousness has a distinct quantum physical effect, then it cannot be emergent but be a fundamental property of substance. Here is the argument.

If consciousness is emergent, then the conscious beings should also follow the fundamental physical principles such as the principle of energy conservation etc, though they may have some distinct high-level functions. According to the principles of quantum mechanics, two nonorthogonal states cannot be distinguished. However, a conscious being can distinguish the nonorthogonal states in principle. This clearly indicates that consciousness violates the quantum principles, which are the most fundamental physical principles. Therefore, the consciousness property cannot be reducible or emergent but be a fundamental property of substance. It should be not only possessed by the conscious beings, but also possessed by atoms as well as physical measuring devices. The difference only lies in the conscious content. The conscious content of a human being can be very complex, while the conscious content of a physical measuring device is probably very simple. In order to distinguish two nonorthogonal states, the conscious content of a measuring system must at least contain the perceptions of the nonorthogonal states. It might be also possible that the conscious content of a physical measuring device can be complex enough to distinguish two nonorthogonal states, but the effect is too weak to be detected by present experiments.

On the other hand, if consciousness is a fundamental property of substance, then it is quite natural that it violates the existing fundamental physical principles, which do not include it at all. It is expected that a complete theory of nature must describe all properties of substance, thus consciousness, the new fundamental property, must enter the theory from the start. Since the distinguishability of nonorthogonal states violates the linear superposition principle, consciousness will introduce a nonlinear element to the complete evolution equation of the wave function. The nonlinearity is not stochastic but definite. It has been argued that the nonlinear quantum evolution introduced by consciousness has no usual problems of nonlinear quantum mechanics (Gao 2006b).

Lastly, it should be noted that the above argument for panpsychism depends on the assumption that the wavefunction collapse or the quantum-to-classical transition in general is an objective physical process. However, the conclusion is actually independent of the origin of the wavefunction collapse. If the wavefunction collapse results from the consciousness of observer, then consciousness will also have the distinct quantum effect of collapsing the wave function, and thus consciousness should be a fundamental property of substance too. In addition, we stress that this conclusion is also independent of the interpretations of quantum mechanics. It only depends on two firm facts: one is the existence of indefinite quantum superpositions, and the other is the existence of definite conscious perceptions.

5. Conclusions

It is widely thought that the quantum-to-classical transition and consciousness are two essentially independent processes. But this does not mean that the result of their combination must be plain. In this article, we have shown that a conscious being can have a distinct quantum physical effect during the quantum-to-classical transition. A conscious system can measure whether he is in a definite perception state or in a quantum superposition of definite perception states, while a system without consciousness cannot distinguish such nonorthogonal states. This new result may have some important implications for quantum theory and the science of consciousness. In particular, it may provide a quantum basis for panpsychism.

References

Bell, J. S. (1987). Speakable and Unspeakable In Quantum Mechanics. Cambridge: Cambridge University Press.

Bohm, D. (1952). A suggested interpretation of quantum theory in terms of "hidden" variables, I and II. Phys. Rev. 85, 166-193.

Chalmers, D. (1996). The Conscious Mind. Oxford: University of Oxford Press.

Everett, H. (1957). "Relative state" formulation of quantum mechanics, Rev. Mod. Phys. 29, 454-462.

Gao, S. (2004). Quantum collapse, consciousness and superluminal communication, Found. Phys. Lett, 17(2), 167-182.

Gao, S. (2006a). A model of wavefunction collapse in discrete space-time, Int. J. Theo. Phys. 45 (10), 1943-1957.

Gao, S. (2006b). Quantum Motion: Unveiling the Mysterious Quantum World. Bury St Edmunds: Arima Publishing.

Gao, S. (2008a). God Does Play Dice with the Universe. Bury St Edmunds: Arima Publishing.

Gao, S. (2008b). A quantum theory of consciousness. Minds and Machines 18 (1), 39-52.

Gao, S. (2011). Meaning of the wave function, Int. J. Quant. Chem. Article first published online: http://onlinelibrary.wiley.com/doi/10.1002/qua.22972/abstract.

Ghirardi, G. C., Grassi, R., Butterfield, J., and Fleming, G. N. (1993). Parameter dependence and outcome dependence in dynamic models for state-vector reduction, Found. Phys., 23, 341.

Ghirardi, G. (2008). Collapse Theories, The Stanford Encyclopedia of Philosophy (Fall 2008 Edition), Edward N. Zalta (ed.), http://plato.stanford.edu/archives/fall2008/entries/qm-collapse/.

Hagan, S., Hameroff, S. R., and Tuszynski, J. A. (2002). Quantum computation in brain microtubules: decoherence and biological feasibility, Phys. Rev. E 65, 061901.

Hameroff, S. R. (1998). Funda-Mentality: Is the conscious mind subtly linked to a basic level of the universe? Trends in Cognitive Sciences 2(4):119-127.

Hameroff, S. R. (2007). Consciousness, neurobiology and quantum mechanics: The case for a connection, In: The Emerging Physics of Consciousness, edited by Jack Tuszynski, New York: Springer-Verlag.

Hameroff, S. R. and Penrose, R. (1996), Conscious events as orchestrated space-time selections, Journal of Consciousness Studies, 3 (1), 36-53.

London, F., and Bauer, E. (1939). La théorie de l'observation en mécanique quantique. Hermann, Paris. English translation: The theory of observation in quantum mechanics. In Quantum Theory and Measurement, ed. by J.A. Wheeler and W.H. Zurek, Princeton University Press, Princeton, 1983, pp. 217-259.

McGinn, C. (1999). The Mysterious Flame: Conscious Minds in a Material World. New York: Basic Books.

Nauenberg, M. (2007). Critique of "Quantum enigma: Physics encounters consciousness". Foundations of Physics 37 (11), 1612–1627.

Nielsen, M. A. and Chuang, I. L. (2000). Quantum Computation and Quantum Information. Cambridge: Cambridge University Press. Section 1.6.

Penrose, R. (1989). The Emperor's New Mind. Oxford: Oxford University Press.

Penrose, R. (1994). Shadows of the Mind. Oxford: Oxford University Press.

Seager, W. and Allen-Hermanson, S. (2010). Panpsychism, The Stanford Encyclopedia of Philosophy (Fall 2010 Edition), Edward N. Zalta (ed.), http://plato.stanford.edu/archives/fall2010/ entries/panpsychism/.

Squires, E. (1992). Explicit collapse and superluminal signaling, Phys. Lett.

A 163, 356-358.

Stapp, H. P. (1993). Mind, Matter, and Quantum Mechanics. New York: Springer-Verlag.

Stapp, H. P. (2007). Mindful Universe: Quantum Mechanics and the Participating Observer. New York: Springer-Verlag.

Strawson, G. et al. (2006). Consciousness and its Place in Nature: Does Physicalism entail Panpsychism? (ed. A. Freeman). Exeter, UK: Imprint Academic.

von Neumann, J. (1932/1955). Mathematical Foundations of Quantum Mechanics. Princeton: Princeton University Press. German original Die mathematischenGrundlagen der Quantenmechanik. Berlin: Springer-Verlag, 1932.

Wigner, E. P. (1967). Symmetries and Reflections. Bloomington and London: Indiana University Press, 171-184.

Wootters, W. K. and Zurek, W. H. (1982). A single quantum cannot be cloned. Nature 299, 802-803.

28. The Conscious Observer in the Quantum Experiment

Fred Kuttner and Bruce Rosenblum

Physics Department, University of California, Santa Cruz,
1156 High Street, Santa Cruz, CA 95064

Abstract

A quantum-theory-neutral version of the two-slit experiment displays the intrusion of the conscious observer into physics. In addition to the undisputed experimental results, only the inescapable assumption of the free choice of the experimenter is required. In discussing the experiment in terms of the quantum theory, other aspects of the quantum measurement problem also appear.

Key Words: Consciousness, quantum, experiment, free-will, John Bell

1. INTRODUCTION

The intrusion of the observer into physics appeared at the inception of quantum theory eight decades ago. With this "quantum measurement problem," the physics discipline encountered something apparently beyond "physics" (Greenstein & Zajonc 1997).

Photons and electrons manifested "wave-particle duality": They exhibited wave properties or particle properties depending on the experimental technique used to observe them. Wave properties imply a spread-out entity, while particle properties imply a not spread-out entity. The contradiction was perhaps acceptable for these not-quite-real objects seen only as effects on macroscopic measuring apparatus (Heisenberg 1971).

Today, quantum weirdness is demonstrated in increasingly large systems (Haroche & Raimond 2006), and interpretations of "what it all means" proliferate (Elitzur et. al. 2006). Essentially every interpretation ultimately requires the intrusion of the conscious observer to account for the classical-like world of our experience (Squires 1994, Penrose, R. 2005).

The quantum measurement problem is often considered a problem of the quantum theory: How to explain the collapse of the multiple possibilities of the wavefunction to a single observed actuality. This is indeed unresolved (Squires, 1993). However, the measurement problem also arises directly from the quantum-theory-neutral experiment, and depends crucially on the assumption of free will of the experimenter. We present a version of the archetypal quantum experiment illustrating the intrusion of the conscious observer into the experiment.

2. THE ARCHETYPAL QUANTUM EXPERIMENT

According to Richard Feynman, "[The two-slit experiment] contains the only mystery. We cannot make the mystery go away by "explaining" how it works. . . In telling you how it works we will have told you about the basic peculiarities of all quantum mechanics" (Feynman, et. al. 2006).

In the two-slit experiment one can choose to demonstrate either of two contradictory things: that each object was a compact entity coming through a single slit or that each was a spread out entity coming through both. Similar experiments have been done with photons, electrons, atoms, large molecules, and are being attempted with yet larger objects such as live viruses (Clauser 2010). We will just refer to "objects."

We present an equivalent version of the two-slit experiment in which one can choose to show that an object was wholly in a single box (Rosenblum & Kuttner 2002). But one could have chosen to show that that same object was not wholly in a single box. By telling the story with objects captured in boxes, one can decide at leisure which of the two contradictory situations to demonstrate for each isolated object. This displays the quantum challenge to our intuition that an observer-independent physical reality exists "out there." We describe quantum-theory-neutral experiments, by telling only what could be directly observed.

The experimenter is presented with a set of box pairs, say twenty pairs of boxes. Each pair of boxes contains a single object. How the box pairs were prepared is irrelevant for these quantum-theory-neutral experiments. Since it's easiest to describe the preparation in quantum language, we do that in the next section.

The "Which Box" Experiment The experimenter is instructed to determine, for this set of box pairs, which box of each pair contains the object. He does this by placing each box pair in turn in the same position in front of a screen that an object would mark on impact. He then cuts a narrow slit first in one box of the pair, and then the other. For some box pairs, an impact occurs only on opening the first box, and then not on opening the second box. For others, the impact occurs only on the second opening. In this "which box" experiment, the experimenter thus determines which box of each pair contained the object, and which box was empty. The experimenter establishes that for this set of box pairs, each object had been wholly in a single box of its pair.

Repeating this with box pairs placed in the same position in front of the screen, the experimenter notes a more or less random spread of marks on the screen.

The "Interference" Experiment The experimenter is presented with second set of box pairs. This time he is instructed to cut slits in both boxes of each pair at about the same time. He does so, positioning each box pair in the same position in front of the screen. (It's an interference experiment, and we so name it. But we make no reference to waves.)

This time the objects do not impact randomly. There are regions where many objects land, and regions where none land. Each object followed a rule specifying the regions in which it was allowed to land.

To investigate the nature of this rule, the experimenter repeats the experiment with different spacings of the boxes of a pair from each other. He finds that the rule each object follows depends on the spacing of its box pair. Each object "knows" the spacing of its box pair. Something of each object therefore had to have been in each box of its pair. The experimenter establishes that–unlike the previous set, for which objects were each wholly in a single box–for this set of box pairs, objects were not wholly in a single box.

The Free Choice Of Experiment The experimenter is reminded that he established that the objects in the first set of box pairs were wholly in a single box, while the objects in the second set of box pairs were not wholly in a single box. Now presented with a third set of box pairs, he is asked to establish whether the objects in this set of box pairs are, or are not, wholly in a single box.

The experimenter arbitrarily chooses to do the "which box" experiment, and thus establishes that this box-pair set had contained objects wholly in a single box. Given another set of box pairs and similar instructions, he chooses the "interference" experiment, and establishes that the objects in this set were not wholly in a single box.

Offered further sets of box pairs, the experimenter finds that each time he chooses to do a "which box" experiment, objects were wholly in a single box. Each time he chooses an "interference" experiment, he establishes a contradictory physical situation, that objects were not wholly in a single box. His free choice of experiment seemed to create the prior history of what had been in the boxes. He's baffled.

If the experimenter's choice of experiment were predetermined to match what was actually in each box pair set, he would see no problem. He recognizes this, but he is certain his choices were freely made. His conscious certainty of his free will causes him to experience a measurement problem with the archetypal quantum experiment. In fact, the free choice of the observation set is generally recognized as an essential aspect of any inductive science.

No experiment in classical physics raised the issue of free will. In classical physics, questions of free will arose only out of an ignorable aspect of the deterministic theory.

We emphasize that in describing the intrusion of the observer into the archetypal quantum experiment we never referred to quantum theory, wavefunctions, or waves of any kind. Even were quantum theory never invented, one could do these experiments, and the results would present an inexplicable enigma (Greenstein & Zajonc 1997).

3. THE BOX-PAIR EXPERIMENT IN QUANTUM THEORY

The Preparation Of The Box Pairs Objects are sent one at a time, at a known speed, toward a "mirror" that equally transmits and reflects their wavefunction. In Figure 1, a wavefunction is shown at three successive times. The reflected part is subsequently reflected so that each part is directed into one of a pair of boxes. The doors of the boxes are closed at a time when the wavefunction is within the boxes.

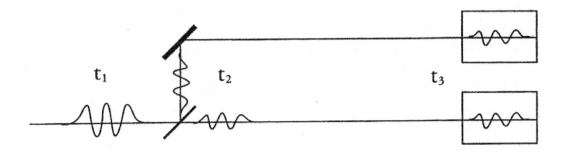

Figure 1. Schematic diagram of the preparation of the box pairs. The object's wavefunction is shown at three successive times.

Dividing a wavefunction into well-separated regions is part of every interference experiment. Holding an object in a box pair without disturbing its wavefunction would be tricky, but doable in principle. Capturing an object in physical boxes is not actually required for our demonstration. A sufficiently extended path length would be enough. The box pair is a conceptual device to emphasize that a conscious choice can be made while an object exists as an isolated entity.

Observation In the box-pairs version of the two-slit experiment, the wavefunction spreads widely from the small slit in a box. In the "which box" experiment, it emerges from each single box and impinges rather uniformly on the detection screen. In the "interference" experiment, parts of the wavefunction emerge simultaneously from both boxes and combine to form regions of maxima and minima on the detection screen.

The Born postulate has the absolute square of the wavefunction in a region giving the probability of an object being "observed" there. In the Copenhagen interpretation of quantum mechanics, observation takes place, for all practical purposes, as soon as the microscopic quantum object encounters the macroscopic screen (Griffiths 1995, Stapp 1972). Macroscopic objects are then assumed to be classical-physics objects viewed by the experimenter. Other interpretations of quantum mechanics, attempting to go beyond practical purposes, consider observation to be more involved with the actual conscious experience of the experimental result.

History Creation Finding an object in a single box means the whole object came to that box on a particular single path after its earlier encounter with the semi-transparent mirror. Choosing an interference experiment would establish a different history: that aspects of the object came on two paths to both boxes after its earlier encounter with the semi-transparent mirror. (As noted above, the question of history creation also arose in the quantum-theory-neutral experiment.) Quantum cosmologist John Wheeler (1980) suggested that quantum theory's history creation be tested. He would have the choice of which experiment to do delayed until after the object made its "decision" whether to come on a single path or whether to come on both at the semi-transparent mirror. The experiment was done with photons and a mirror arrangement much like our Figure 1. Getting the same results as in the usual quantum experiment would imply that the relevant history was indeed created by the later choice of experiment.

For a human to make a conscious choice of which experiment to do takes perhaps a second, in which a photon travels 186,000 miles. Therefore the actual "choice" of experiment was made by a fast electronic switch making random choices. The most rigorous version of the experiment was done in 2007 (Jacques et al., 2007), when reliable single-photon pulses could be generated, and fast enough electronics were available. The result (of course?) confirmed quantum theory's predictions. Observation created the relevant history.

Non-locality and Connectedness When an object is observed to be in a particular location, its probability of being elsewhere becomes zero. Its wavefunction elsewhere "collapses" to zero, and to unity (a certainty) in the location in which the object was found. If an object is found to be in one box of its pair, its wavefunction in the other box instantaneously becomes zero—no matter how far apart the boxes are.

In its usual interpretation, quantum theory does not include an object in addition to the wavefunction of the object. The wavefunction is, in this sense, the physical entity itself. Thus the wavefunction being affected by observation everyplace at once is problematic in the light of special relativity, which prohibits any matter, or any message, to travel faster than the speed of light. The non-local, instantaneous collapse of the wavefunction on observation poses the quantum measurement problem as viewed from quantum theory.

The instantaneous, non-local collapse of the wavefunction provoked Einstein to challenge the completeness of quantum theory with the famous EPR paper (Einstein, et al. 1935). To avoid what Einstein later derided as "spooky action at a distance," EPR held that there must be properties at the microscopic level that quantum theory did not include. However, since EPR provided no experimental challenge to quantum theory, it was largely ignored by physicists for three decades as merely arguing a philosophical issue.

John Bell (1964) proved a theorem allowing experimental tests establishing the existence of an instantaneous connectedness, Einstein's "spooky action." The experiments (Freedman & Clauser, 1972; Aspect et al. 1984) showed that if objects had interacted, what an observer chose to observe about one of them would instantaneously influence the result that an arbitrarily remote observer chose to observe for the other object.

The Bell results included the assumption of the free will of the observers, that their choices of what to observe were independent of each other and independent of all prior physical events. Denying that assumption would be "more mind boggling" than the connectedness the denial attempts to avoid. Such denial would imply, Bell wrote: "Apparently separate parts of the world would be conspiratorially entangled, and our apparent free will would be entangled with them" (Bell 1981).

4. THE ROBOT FALLACY

The most common argument that consciousness is not involved in the quantum experiment is that a not-conscious robot could do the experiment. However, for any experiment to be meaningful, a human must eventually evaluate it. A programmed robot sees no enigma. Consider the human evaluation of the robot's experiment:

The robot presents a printout to the human experimenter. It shows that with some sets of box pairs the robot chose a which-box experiment, establishing that the objects were wholly in a single box. With other sets of box pairs, choosing the interference experiment, it established that the objects were not wholly in a single box.

On the basis of this data, the human experimenter could conclude that certain box-pair sets actually contained objects wholly in a single box, while others contained objects not wholly in a single box. However, a question arises in the mind of the experimenter: How did the robot choose the appropriate experiment with each box-pair set? What if, for example, the robot chose a which-box experiment with objects not wholly in a single box? A partial object was never reported.

Without free will, the not-conscious robot must use some "mechanical" choice procedure. Investigating, the experimenter finds, for example, that it flips a coin. Heads, a which-box experiment; tails interference. The experimenter is troubled by the mysterious correlation between the landing of the coin and what was presumably actually in a particular box-pair set.

To avoid that inexplicable correlation, the experimenter replaces the robot's coin flipping with the one choice method she is most sure is not correlated with the contents of a box-pair set: her own free choice. Pushing a button telling the robot which experiment to do, she establishes what she would by doing the experiment directly, that by her conscious free choice she can establish either of two contradictory physical situations. In the end, the robot argument establishes nothing.

5. CONCLUSION

Extending the implications of quantum mechanics beyond the microscopic realm admittedly leads to ridiculous-seeming conclusions. Nevertheless, the experimental results are undisputed, and quantum theory is the most basic and most battle-tested theory in all of science.

The embarrassing intrusion of the conscious observer into physics can be mitigated by focusing on observation in quantum theory, the collapse (or decoherence) of the wavefunction. However, the inescapable assumption of free choice by the experimenter displays the intrusion of the observer in the quantum-theory-neutral quantum experiment, logically prior to the quantum theory.

The intrusion was less disturbing when confined to never-directly-observed microscopic objects. However, the vast no-man's-land that once separated the microscopic and the macroscopic realms, allowing a tacit acceptance of this view, has been invaded by technology.

Bell's theorem, and the experiments it stimulated, seems to rule out a resolution of the quantum measurement problem by the existence of an underlying structure, somehow involving only properties localized in quantum objects. An overarching structure, somehow involving conscious free will, seems required (Squires 1991).

Acknowledgments: Parts of this article have been taken from the second edition of our book, Quantum Enigma: Physics Encounters Consciousness, with the permission of Oxford University Press.

References

Aspect A., Dalibard J., Roger G. (1982). Experimental Test Of Bell Inequalities Using Time-Varying Analyzers. Physical Review Letters 49, 1804-1807.

Bell, J.S. (1964). On the Problem of Hidden Variables in Quantum Mechanics. Physics 1, 195.

Bell, J. S. 1981. Bertlmann's Socks and the Nature of Reality. Journal de physique 42, 41.

Clauser, J.F. (2010). deBroglie Wave Interference of Small Rocks and Live Viruses. In: Cohen, R.S., Horne, M., Stachel, J. (Eds.), Experimental Metaphysics: Quantum Mechanical Studies for Abner Shimony, Volume One. Kluwer Academic, Dordrecht, The Netherlands, pp. 1-12.

Einstein, A., Podolsky, B., Rosen, N. (1935). Can quantum-mechanical description of physical reality be considered complete? Physical Review 47, 777-780.

Elitzur, A. Dolev, S., Kolenda, A. (Eds), (2006). Quo Vadis Quantum Mechanics. Springer, Berlin.

Feynman, R.P., Leighton, R.B., Sands, M. (2006). The Feynman Lectures on Physics, Vol. III. Addison-Wesley, Reading, MA.

Freedman, S.J., Clauser, J. F. (1972). Experimental Test Of Local Hidden-Variable Theories. Physical Review Letters 28, 938-941.

Greenstein, G., Zajonc, A.G. (1997). The Quantum Challenge: Modern Research on the Foundations of Quantum Mechanics. Jones and Bartlett, Sudbury, MA.

Griffiths, D.J. (1995). Introduction to Quantum Mechanics. Prentice Hall, Englewood Cliffs, NJ.

Haroche, S., Raimond, J-M. (2006). Exploring the Quantum: Atoms, Cavities, and Photons. Oxford University Press, Oxford.

Heisenberg, W. (1971) Physics and Beyond: Encounters and Conversations. Harper & Row, New York.

Jacques, V., Wu, E., Grosshans, F., Treussart, F., Grangier, P., Aspect, A., Roch, J-F. (2007). Experimental realization of Wheeler's delayed-choice gedanken experiment. Science 315, 966-968.

Penrose, R. (2006). Foreword. In: Elitzur, A. Dolev, S., Kolenda, A. (Eds), Quo Vadis Quantum Mechanics. Springer, Berlin, pp. v-viii.

Rosenblum, B., Kuttner, F. (2002) The Observer in the Quantum Experiment. Foundations of Physics 32, 1273-1293.

Squires, E.J. (1991). One Mind Or Many - A Note On The Everett Interpretation Of Quantum-Theory. Synthese, 89, 283-286.

Squires, E.J. (1993). Quantum-Theory And The Relation Between The Conscious Mind And The Physical World. Synthese, 97, 109-123.

Squires, E.J. (1994). Quantum Theory And The Need For Consciousness. Journal of Consciousness Studies 1, 201-204.

Stapp, H.P. (1972). The Copenhagen Interpretation. American Journal of Physics 40, 1098-1115.

Wheeler (1980). Delayed Choice Experiments and the Bohr-Einstein Dialog. In: The American Philosophical Society and the Royal Society: Papers Read at a Meeting June 5, 1980. American Philosophical Society, Philadelphia, PA.

29. Does Quantum Mechanics Require A Conscious Observer?

Michael Nauenberg

Physics Dept. University of Califonia Santa Cruz, CA, USA

Abstract

The view that the implementation of the principles of quantum mechanics requires a conscious observer is based on misconceptions that are described in this article.

Key Words: Quantum Physics, Wave function, Observer, Consciousness

The notion that the interpretation of quantum mechanics requires a conscious observer is rooted, I believe, in a basic misunderstanding of the meaning of a) the quantum wavefunction ψ, and b) the quantum measurement process. This misunderstanding originated with the work of John von Neumann (1932) on the foundations of quantum mechanics, and afterwards it was spread by some prominent physicists like Eugene Wigner (1984); by now it has acquired a life of its own, giving rise to endless discussions on this subject, as shown by the articles in the Journal of Cosmology (see volumes 3 and 14).

Quantum mechanics is a statistical theory that determines the probabilities for the outcome of a physical process when its initial state has been determined. A fundamental quantity in this theory is the wavefunction ψ which is a complex function that depends on the variables of the system under consideration. The absolute square of this function, $\psi2$, gives the probability to find the system in one of its possible quantum states. Early pioneers in the development of quantum mechanics like Niels Bohr (1958) assumed, however, that the measurement devices behave according to the laws of classical mechanics, but von Neumann pointed out, quite correctly, that such devices also must satisfy the principles of quantum mechanics. Hence, the wavefunction describing this device becomes entangled with the wavefunction of the object that is being measured, and the superposition of these entangled wavefunctions continues to evolve in accordance with the equations of quantum mechanics. This analysis leads to the notorious von Neumann chain, where the measuring devices are left forever in an indefinite superposition of quantum states. It is postulated that this chain can be broken, ultimately, only by the mind of a conscious observer.

Forty five years ago I wrote an article on this subject with John Bell who became, after von Neumann, the foremost contributor to the foundations of quantum mechanics, where we presented, tongue in cheek, the von Neumann paradox as a dilemma:

The experiment may be said to start with the printed proposal and to end with the issue of the report. The laboratory, the experimenter, the administration, and the editorial staff of the Physical Review are all just part of the instrumentation. The incorporation of (presumably) conscious experimenters and editors into the equipment raises a very intriguing question... If the interference is destroyed, then the Schrodinger equation is incorrect for systems containing consciousness. If the interference is not destroyed, the quantum mechanical description is revealed as not wrong but certainly incomplete (Bell and Nauenberg, 1966).

We added the remark that "we emphasize not only that our view is that of a minority, but also that current interest in such questions is small. The typical physicist feels that they have been long answered, and that he will fully understand just how, if ever he can spare twenty minutes to think about it." Now the situation has changed dramatically, and interest in a possible role of consciousness in quantum mechanics has become widespread. But Bell, who died in 1990 , believed in the second alternative to the von Neumann dilemma, remarking that :

I think the experimental facts which are usually offered to show that we must bring the observer into quantum theory do not compel us to adopt that conclusion (Davies and Brown, 1986).

Actually, by now it is understood by most physicists that von Neumann's dilemma arises because he had simplified the measuring device to a system with only a few degrees of freedom, e.g. a pointer with only two states (see Appendix). Instead, a measuring device must have an exponentially large number of degrees of freedom in order to record, more or less permanently, the outcome of a measurement. This recording takes place by a time irreversible process. The occurrence of such processes in Nature already mystified 19th century scientists, who argued that this feature implied a failure in the basic laws of classical physics, because these laws are time reversible. Ludwig Boltzmann resolved this paradox by taking into account the large number of degrees of freedom of a macroscopic system, which implied that to a very high degree of probability such a system evolved with a unique direction in time. Such an irreversibility property is also valid for quantum systems, and it constitutes the physical basis for the second law of thermodynamics, where the arrow of time is related to the increase of entropy of the system.

Another misconception is the assumption that the wavefunction ψ describing the state of a system in quantum mechanics behaves like a physical object. For example, the authors of a recent book discussing quantum mechanics and consciousness claim that

In quantum theory there is no atom in addition to the wavefunction of the atom.

This is so crucial that we say it again in other words. The atom's wave-functions and the atom are the same thing; "the wave function of the atom" is a synonym for "the atom". Since the wavefunction ψ is synonymous with the atom itself, the atom is simultaneously in both boxes. The point of that last paragraph is hard to accept. That is why we keep repeating it (Rosenblum and Kuttner, 2006).

If the wavefunction ψ is a physical object like an atom, then the proponents of this flawed concept must require the existence of a mechanism that lies outside the principles governing the time evolution of the wavefunction ψ in order to account for the so-called "collapse" of the wavefunction after a measurement has been performed. But the wavefunction ψ is not a physical object like, for example, an atom which has an observable mass, charge and spin as well as internal degrees of freedom. Instead, ψ is an abstract mathematical function that contains all the statistical information that an observer can obtain from measurements of a given system. In this case there isn't any mystery that its mathematical form must change abruptly after a measurement has been performed. For further details on this subject, see (Nauenberg, 2007) and (van Kampen, 2008). The surprising fact that mathematical abstractions can explain and predict real physical phenomena has been emphazised by Wigner (Wigner 1960), who wrote:

The miracle of appropriateness of the language of mathematics for the formulation of the laws of physics is a wonderful gift which we neither undestand nor deserve.

I conclude with a few quotations, that are relevant to the topic addressed here, by some of the most prominent physicists in the second half of the 20th century.

Richard P. Feynman (Nobel Prize, 1965):

Nature does not know what you are looking at, and she behaves the way she is going to behave whether you bother to take down the data or not (Feynman et al., 1965).

Murray Gellmann (Nobel Prize, 1969):

The universe presumably couldn't care less whether human beings evolved on some obscure planet to study its history; it goes on obeying the quantum mechanical laws of physics irrespective of observation by physicists (Rosenblum and Kuttner 2006, 156).

Anthony J. Leggett (Nobel Prize 2003):

It may be somewhat dangerous to explain something one does not understand very well [the quantum measurement process] by invoking something [consciousness] one does not understand at all! (Leggett, 1991).

John A. Wheeler:

Caution: "Consciousness" has nothing whatsover to do with the quantum process. We are dealing with an event that makes itself known by an irreversible act of amplification, by an indelible record, an act of registration. Does that record subsequently enter into the "consciousness" of some person, some animal or some computer? Is that the first step into translating the measurement into "meaning" meaning regarded as "the joint product of all the evidence that is available to those who communicate." Then that is a separate part of the story, important but not to be confused with "quantum phenomena." (Wheeler, 1983).

John S. Bell:

From some popular presentations the general public could get the impression that the very existence of the cosmos depends on our being here to observe the observables. I do not know that this is wrong. I am inclined to hope that we are indeed that important. But I see no evidence that it is so in the success of contemporary quantum theory.

So I think that it is not right to tell the public that a central role for conscious mind is integrated into modern atomic physics. Or that `information' is the real stuff of physical theory. It seems to me irresponsible to suggest that technical features of contemporary theory were anticipated by the saints of ancient religions... by introspection.

The only 'observer' which is essential in orthodox practical quantum theory is the inanimate apparatus which amplifies the microscopic events to macroscopic consequences. Of course this apparatus, in laboratory experiments, is chosen and adjusted by the experiments. In this sense the outcomes of experiments are indeed dependent on the mental process of the experimenters! But once the apparatus is in place, and functioning untouched, it is a matter of complete indifference - according to ordinary quantum mechanics - whether the experimenters stay around to watch, or delegate such 'observing' to computers, (Bell, 1984).

Nico van Kampem:

Whoever endows ψ with more meaning than is needed for computing observable phenomena is responsible for the consequences. (van Kampen, 1988).

Appendix. Schrodinger's Cat: This cat story is notorious. It requires one to accept the notion that a cat, which can be in innumerable different biological states, can be represented by a two component wavefunction ψ, a bit of nonsense that Erwin Schrodinger, one of the original inventors of quantum mechanics, himself originated. One of the two components represents a live cat, and the other a dead cat. The cat is enclosed in a box containing a bottle filled with cyanide that opens when a radioactive nucleus in the box decays. Thus, this fictitious cat is a measuring device that is supposed to determine whether the nucleus has decayed or not when the box is opened. But according to the principles of quantum mechanics formulated by von Neumann, such a cat ought to be in a superposition of life and dead cat states, yet nobody has ever observed such a cat. Instead, it is expected that a movie camera - a real measuring device - that is also installed in the box containing the cat, would record a cat that is alive until the unpredictable moment that the radioactive nucleus decays, opening the bottle containing the cyanide that kills the cat. For obvious reasons such a gruesome experiment has never been performed. It is claimed that Schrodinger never accepted the statistical significance of his celebrated wavefunction.

References

Bohr, N. (1958). Quantum Physics and Philosophy, Causality and Complementarity in Essays 1958/1962 on Atomic Physics and Human Knowledge. Vintage Books

Bell, J. S., Nauenberg, M. (1966). The moral aspects of quantum me- chanics, in Preludes in Theoretical Physics, edited by A. De Shalit, Herman Feschbach, and Leon van Hove (North Holland, Amsterdam), pp. 279-286. Reprinted in J.S. Bell Speakable and Unspeakable in Quantum Mechanics (Cambridge Univ. Press 1987) p. 22

Bell, J. S. (1987). Introductory remarks at Naples-Amal meeting, May 7, 1984. In: Bell, J.S. Speakable and Unspeakable in Quantum Mechanics. Cambridge Univ. Press, p.170,

Davies, P.C.W., Brown, J.T. (1986). Ghost in the Atom. Cambridge Univ. Press, Interview with J. Bell, pp. 47-48

Feynman, R.P., Leighton, R.B., Sands,M. (1965). The Feynman lectures on Physics vol. 3 (Addison Wesley, Reading) 3-7

Leggett, A. (1991) Reflections on the Quantum Paradox, In: Quantum Implications, Routledge, London, p. 94

Nauenberg, M. (2007). Critique of Quantum Enigma: Physics encounters Consciousness, Foundations of Physics 37, 1612-162

Rosenblum, B and Kuttner, F. (2006). Quantum Enigma, Physics Encounters Consciousness . Oxford Univ. Press, p. 106

van Kampen, N. G. (1988). Ten theorems about quantum mechanical measurements Physica A 153, 97 .

van Kampen, N.G. (2008) The Scandal in Quantum Mechanics, American Journal of Physics 76, 989

von Neumann, J. (1932) Measurement and Reversibility, Chapters V and VI of Mathematische Grundlagen der Quantemmechanik, translated into English by R.T. Mayer, Mathematical Foundations of Quantum Mechanics, Princeton Univ. Press, Princeton (1955) pp. 347-445

Wigner, E. (1984). Review of the Quantum-Mechanical Measurement Problem, Science, Computers and the Information Onslaught, eds. D.M. Kerr et al.. Academic Press, New York, pp. 63-82 Reprinted in "The Collected Works of Eugene Paul Wigner", Part B, vol. 6, Springer-Verlag, Berlin, p. 240

Wheeler, J.A. (1983). Law without law. In: Quantum Theory and Measurement, edited by Wheeler, J.A. and Zurek, W.H., Princeton Univ. Press, p. 196.

Wigner, E. (1960) The Unreasonable Effectiveness of Mathematics, Communications in Pure and Applied Mathematics 13, 1-14.

30. Quantum Physics, Advanced Waves and Consciousness

Antonella Vannini, Ulisse Di Corpo

1Lungotevere degli Artigiani 32 – 00153 ROME - ITALY

Abstract

An essential component of the Copenhagen Interpretation of quantum mechanics is Schrödinger's wave equation. According to this interpretation, consciousness, through the exercise of observation, forces the wave function to collapse into a particle. Schrödinger's wave equation is not relativistically invariant and when the relativistically invariant wave equation (Klein-Gordon's equation) is taken into account, there is no collapse of the wave function and no justification for consciousness as a prerequisite to reality. Klein-Gordon's wave equation depends on a square root and yields two solutions: retarded waves which move forwards in time and advanced waves which move backwards in time. Advanced waves were considered to be unacceptable since they contradict the law of causality, according to which causes always precede effects. However, while studying the mathematical properties of Klein-Gordon's equation, the mathematician Luigi Fantappiè noted that retarded waves are governed by the law of entropy (from Greek en=diverge, tropos=tendency), whereas advanced waves are governed by a law opposite to entropy which leads to concentration of energy, differentiation, complexity, order and growth of structures. Fantappiè named this law syntropy (syn=converge, tropos=tendency) and noted that its properties coincide with the qualities of living systems, arriving in this way at the conclusion that life and consciousness are a consequence of advanced waves.

Key Words: Consciousness, Advanced waves, Syntropy, Feeling of Life, Free Will, Quantum Physics

1. Introduction

The Copenhagen Interpretation of quantum mechanics was formulated by Niels Bohr and Werner Heisenberg in 1927 during a joint work in Copenhagen, and explains the dual nature of matter (wave/particle) in the following way:

* Electrons leave the electronic cannon as particles.
* They dissolve into waves of superposed probabilities, in a superposition of states.
* The waves go through both slits, in the double slit experiment, and

interfere, creating a new state of superposition.

* The observation screen, performing a measurement, forces the waves to collapse into particles, in a well defined point of the screen.

* Electrons start again to dissolve into waves, just after the measurement.

An essential component of the Copenhagen Interpretation is Schrödinger's wave equation, reinterpreted as the probability that the electron (or any other quantum mechanical entity) is found in a specific place. According to the Copenhagen Interpretation, consciousness, through the exercise of observation, forces the wave function to collapse into a particle. This interpretation states that the existence of the electron in one of the two slits, independently from observation, does not have any real meaning. Electrons seem to exist only when they are observed. Reality is therefore created, at least in part, by the observer.

In the paper *Quantum Models of Consciousness* it is argued that quantum models of consciousness can be divided in three main categories (Vannini, 2008):

1. models which assume that consciousness creates reality and that consciousness is a prerequisite of reality;

2. models which link consciousness to the probabilistic properties of quantum mechanics;

3. models which attribute consciousness to a principle of order of quantum mechanics.

Considering the criteria of scientific falsification and of biological compatibility Vannini (2008) notes that:

* Quantum models of consciousness which belong to the first category show a tendency towards mysticism. All these models start from the Copenhagen Interpretation of quantum mechanics and assume that consciousness itself determines reality. These models try to describe reality as a consequence of panpsychism, and assume that consciousness is an immanent property which precedes the formation of reality. The concept of panpsychism is explicitly used by most of the authors of this category. These assumptions cannot be falsified.

* Quantum models of consciousness which belong to the second category consider consciousness to be linked to a realm, for example that of the Planck's constant, which cannot be observed by modern science and which is impossible to falsify or test using experiments.

* Quantum models of consciousness which belong to the third group attribute consciousness to principles of order which have been already discovered and used for physical applications (laser, superconductors, etc.). The order principles on which most of these models are based require extreme physical conditions such as, for example, absolute zero temperatures (-273 C°). These models do not meet the criteria of biological compatibility.

Vannini concludes that only the models which originate from the Klein-Gordon equation, which unites Schrödinger's wave equation (quantum mechanics) with special relativity and are not pure quantum mechanical models, survive the selection of scientific falsification and biological compatibility.

2. Klein-Gordon's Equation

In 1925 the physicists Oskar Klein and Walter Gordon formulated a probability equation which could be used in quantum mechanics and was relativistically invariant. In 1926 Schrödinger simplified Klein-Gordon's equation in his famous wave equation (ψ) in which only the positive solution of Klein-Gordon's equation was considered, and which treats time in an essentially classical way with a well defined before and after the collapse of the wave function. In 1927 Klein and Gordon formulated again their equation (2) as a combination of Schrödinger's wave equation (quantum mechanics) and the energy/momentum/mass equation of special relativity (1).

$$E^2 = c^2p^2 + m^2c^4 \qquad\qquad 1)$$

Energy/momentum/mass equation

Where E is the Energy of the object, m the mass, p the momentum and c the constant of the speed of light. This equation simplifies in the famous $E=mc^2$ when the momentum is equal to zero ($p=0$).

$$E\psi = \sqrt{p^2 + m^2}\psi \qquad\qquad 2)$$

Klein-Gordon's wave equation

Klein-Gordon's wave equation depends on a square root and yields two solutions: the positive solution describes waves which diverge from the past to the future (retarded waves); the negative solution describes waves which diverge from the future to the past (advanced waves). The negative solution introduces in science final causes and teleological tendencies. Consequently, it was considered to be unacceptable.

In 1928 Paul Dirac tried to get rid of the unwanted negative solution by applying the energy/momentum/mass equation to the study of electrons, turning them into relativistic objects. But, also in this case, the dual solution emerged in the form of electrons (e-) and antiparticles (e+). The antiparticle of the electron, initially named neg-electron, was experimentally observed in 1932 by Carl Anderson in cosmic rays and named positron. Anderson became the first person who proved empirically the existence of the negative energy solution; the negative solution was no longer an impossible mathematical absurdity, but it was an empirical evidence. Dirac's equation predicts a universe made of matter which moves forwards in time and antimatter which moves backwards in time. The negative solution of Dirac's equation caused emotional distress among physicists. For example Heisenberg wrote to Pauli: "The saddest chapter of modern physics is and remains the Dirac theory" (Heisenberg, 1928); "I regard the Dirac theory ...

as learned trash which no one can take seriously" (Heisenberg, 1934). In order to solve this situation, Dirac used Pauli's principle, according to which two electrons cannot share the same state, to suggest that all states of negative energy are occupied, thereby forbidding any interaction between positive and negative states of matter. This ocean of negative energy which occupies all positive states is called the Dirac sea.

It is important to note that it appears to be impossible to test the existence of advanced waves in a laboratory of physics:

* According to Fantappiè, advanced waves do not obey classical causation, therefore they cannot be studied with experiments which obey the classical experimental method (Fantappiè, 1942).

* According to Wheeler's and Feynman's electrodynamics, emitters coincide with retarded fields, which propagate into the future, while absorbers coincide with advanced fields, which propagate backward in time. This time-symmetric model leads to predictions identical with those of conventional electrodynamics. For this reason it is impossible to distinguish between timesymmetric results and conventional results (Wheeler & Feynman, 1949).

* In his Transactional Interpretations of Quantum Mechanics, Cramer states that "Nature, in a very subtle way, may be engaging in backwards-in-time handshaking. But the use of this mechanism is not available to experimental investigators even at the microscopic level. The completed transaction erases all advanced effects, so that no advanced wave signalling is possible. The future can affect the past only very indirectly, by offering possibilities for transactions" (Cramer, 1986).

3. The Law of Syntropy

At the end of 1941, the mathematician Luigi Fantappiè was working on the equations of relativistic and quantum physics when he noted that the dual solution of the Klein-Gordon equation explains two symmetrical laws:

$+E\psi$ (retarded waves) describes waves diverging from causes located in the past, governed by the law of entropy;

$-E\psi$ (advanced waves) describes waves converging towards causes located in the future and governed by the law of syntropy.

According to Fantappiè the main properties of retarded and advanced waves are:

1. Retarded waves:

a. Causality: diverging waves exist as a consequence of causes located in the past.

b. Entropy: diverging waves tend towards the dissipation of energy (heat death).

2. Advanced waves:

a. Retrocausality: converging waves exist as a consequence of causes located in the future.

b.   Syntropy:

*   converging waves concentrate matter and energy in smaller spaces (ie this principle is well described by the large quantities of energy accumulated by living systems of the past and now available in the form of coal, petrol and gases).

*   Entropy diminishes. Entropic phenomena are governed by the second law of thermodynamics according to which a system tends towards homogeneity and disorder. The inversion of the time arrow also inverts the second law of thermodynamics, so that a reduction in entropy and an increase in differentiation are observed.

*   Final causes, attractors, which absorb converging waves are observed. From these final causes syntropic systems originate.

*   Because syntropy leads to the concentration of matter and energy, and this concentration cannot be indefinite, entropic processes are needed to compensate syntropic concentration. These processes take the form of the exchange of matter and energy with the environment. For example metabolism is divided into:

o   anabolism (syntropy) which includes all the processes which transform simple structures into complex structures, for example nutritive elements into bio-molecules, with the absorption of energy.

o   catabolism (entropy) which includes all the processes which transform higher level structures into lower level structures, with the release of energy.

Fantappiè noted that the properties of syntropy coincide with the qualities of living systems: finality, differentiation, order and organization.

Other authors suggested the existence of the law of syntropy associated to living systems. For example: Albert Szent-Gyorgyi (Nobel prize 1937 and discoverer of vitamin C) underlined that "One major difference between amoebas and humans is the increase in complexity, which presupposes the existence of a mechanism which is capable of contrasting the second law of thermodynamics. In other words a force must exist which is capable of contrasting the universal tendency of matter towards chaos, and of energy towards heat death. Life processes continuously show a decrease in entropy and an increase in inner complexity, and often also in the complexity of the environment, in direct opposition with the law of entropy." In the 1970s Szent-Gyorgyi concluded that in living systems there was wide evidence of the existence of the law of syntropy, even though he never managed to infer it from the laws of physics. While entropy is a universal law which leads towards the disintegration of all types of organization, syntropy is the opposite law which attracts living systems towards forms of organization which are always more complex and harmonic (Szent-Gyorgyi, 1977). The main problem, according to Szent-Gyorgyi, is that "a profound difference between organic and inorganic systems can be observed ... as a man of science I cannot believe that the laws of physics lose their validity at the surface of our skin. The law of entropy does not govern living systems." Szent-Gyorgyi dedicated the last years of his life to the study of syntropy and its conflict with the law of entropy (Szent-Gyorgyi, 1977).

Erwin Schrödinger talks about the concept of negative entropy. He was looking for the nutrient which is hidden in our food, and which defends us from heat death. Why do we need to eat biological food; why can we not feed directly on the chemical elements of matter? Schrödinger answers this question by saying that what we feed on is not matter but neg-entropy, which we absorb through the metabolic process (Schrödinger, 1944).

Ilya Prigogine, winner in 1977 of the Nobel prize for chemistry, introduced in his book "The New Alliance", a new type of thermodynamics, the "thermodynamics of dissipative systems", typical of living systems. Prigogine stated that this new type of thermodynamics cannot be reduced to dynamics or thermodynamics (Prigogine, 1979).

Hermann Haken, one of the fathers of the laser, introduced a level that he named "ordinator", which he used to explain the principles of orders typical of living systems (Haken, 1983).

4. Experiments

According to the Copenhagen Interpretation no advance effects should be possible, since time flows from the past to the future. On the contrary Fantappiè's syntropy model suggests that life and consciousness are a consequence of advanced waves (Fantappiè, 1942) and should therefore show anticipatory reactions. Is it possible to devise experiments in order to test which of the two models is correct?

In 1981 Di Corpo extended Fantappiè's hypothesis suggesting that structures which support vital functions, such as the autonomic nervous system (ANS), should show anticipatory reactions since they need to acquire syntropy. Consequently, if the Advanced Waves Interpretation is correct the parameters of ANS, such as heart rate and skin conductance, should react before stimuli (Di Corpo, 1981, 2007; Vannini & Di Corpo, 2008, 2009, 2010), on the contrary if the Copenhagen Interpretation is correct no reactions before stimuli should be observed.

Since 1997, anticipatory pre-stimuli reactions in the parameters of the autonomic nervous system have been reported in several studies, for example:

1   The first experimental study was produced by Radin in 1997 and monitored heart rate, skin conductance and fingertip blood volume in subjects who were shown for five seconds a blank screen and for three seconds a randomly selected calm or emotional picture. Radin found significant differences, in these autonomic parameters, preceding the exposure to emotional versus calm pictures.

In 1997 Bierman replicated Radin's results confirming the anticipatory reaction of skin conductance to emotional versus calm stimuli and in 2003 Spottiswoode and May, of the Cognitive Science Laboratory, replicated Bierman and Radin's experiments performing controls in order to exclude artifacts and alternative explanations. Results showed an increase in skin conductance 2-3 seconds before emotional stimuli are presented (p=0.0005). Similar results have been obtained by other authors, using parameters of the autonomic nervous system (McDonough et al., 2002), (McCraty et al., 2004), (May Paulinyi & Vassy, 2005) and (Radin, 2005).

2.   In the article "Heart Rate Differences between Targets and Nontargets in Intuitive Tasks", Tressoldi describes two experiments which show anticipatory heart rate reactions (Tressoldi et al., 2005). Trials were divided in 3 phases: in the presentation phase 4 pictures were shown and heart rate data was collected; in the choice phase pictures were presented simultaneously and the subject was asked to guess the picture which the computer would select; in the target phase the computer selected randomly one of the four pictures (target) and showed it on the monitor. In the first experiment a heart rate difference of 0.59 HR, measured in phase 1 during the presentation of target and non target pictures, was obtained (t = 2.42, p=0.015), in the second experiment the heart rate difference was 0.57 HR (t = 3.4, p=0.001).

3.   Daryl Bem, psychology professor at the Cornell University, studies retrocausality using well known experimental designs in a "time-reverse" pattern. In his 2011 article "Feeling the Future: Experimental Evidence for Anomalous Retroactive Influence on Cognition and Affect" Bem describes 9 well-established psychological effects in which the usual sequence of events was reversed, so that the individual's responses were obtained before rather than after the stimulus events occurred. For example in a typical priming experiment the subject is asked to judge if the image is positive (pleasant) or negative (unpleasant), pressing a button as quickly as possible. The response time (RT) is registered. Just before the image a "positive" or "negative" word is briefly shown. This word is named "prime". Subjects tend to respond more quickly when the prime is congruent with the following image (both positive or negative), whereas the reaction times become longer when they are not congruent (one is positive and the other one is negative).

In retro-priming experiments Bem used IAPS (International Affective Picture System) emotional pictures. Results show the classical priming effect with reaction times faster when the prime is congruent with the image. Considering all 9 experiments, conducted on a sample of more than 1,000 students, the retrocausal effect size is p = 1.34 x 10-11.

4. In the article "Collapse of the wave function?" Vannini and Di Corpo describe 4 experiments which gradually control different types of artefacts and show a statistical significance of prestimuli heart rate effects of p=1/1027

(Vannini & Di Corpo, 2010).

5. How Can These Results Be Interpreted?

Anticipatory pre-stimuli reactions seem to be incompatible with the Copenhagen Interpretation, since Schrödinger's wave equation treats time in an essentially classical way and rejects the possibility of pre-stimuli reactions (effects before causes). Dick Bierman tried to overcome this limit of the Copenhagen Interpretation with his CIRTS model (Consciousness Induced Restoration of Time Symmetry), presented at the PA 2008 conference (Bierman, 2008). This model states that almost all formalisms in physics are time-symmetric. Nevertheless the Copenhagen Interpretation of quantum mechanics, which postulates the collapse of the wave function, introduces a break of time symmetry at the point of collapse. The assumption of CIRTS is that the brain, when it is sustained by consciousness, is such a special system that it partially restores time-symmetry and therefore allows advanced waves to occur. The time symmetry restoring condition is not the brain per se but the brain sustained by consciousness. The restoration of time symmetry is suggested to be proportional to the brain volume involved in consciousness. CIRTS considers consciousness to be a pre-requisite of reality with special properties which restore time-symmetry. However, in CIRTS the rationale behind consciousness is missing and its special properties seem to arise from nothing. Contrary to Bierman's model, Luigi Fantappiè's syntropy model and Chris King's quantumtransactions model describe consciousness as a consequence of the properties of advanced waves: – Fantappiè states that, according to the converging properties of advanced waves, living systems are energy and information absorbers and that the "feeling of life" can be described as a consequence of these converging and absorbing properties of advanced waves. On the contrary it would be difficult to justify the feeling of life as a consequence of diverging and emitting properties which characterize retarded waves. The equivalence "feeling of life = advanced waves" leads to the conclusion that systems based on the retarded solution, as for example machines and computers, would never show the "feeling of life" independently from their complexity, whereas systems based on the advanced solution, as for example life itself, should always have a "feeling of life", independently from their complexity.

According to King, the constant interaction between information coming from the past and information coming from the future would place life in front of bifurcations. This constant antagonism between past and future would force life into a state of free will and consciousness. Consequently consciousness would be a property of all living structures: each cell and biological process would be forced to choose between information coming from the past and information coming from the future (King, 1996). This constant state of choice would be common to all levels of life and would give form to chaotic behaviour on which the conscious brain would feed. King (1996) states that "The chaotic processes which are observed in the neuronal system can be the result of behaviour which is apparently random and probabilistic, since they are non local in space and time. This would allow neuronal networks to connect in a subquantum way with non local situations and explain why behaviour results in being non deterministic and non computational."

The followings are some of the fundamental differences between Bierman's CIRTS model and Fantappiè's syntropy model:

1. Fantappiè focused on the Klein-Gordon's equation and excluded other time-symmetric equations, such as the electromagnetic wave equation. The rational of this choice is that at the quantum level time would be unitary (past, present and future would coexist) whereas at the macro-level time flows forward and advanced waves would be impossible. This conclusion was reached considering the mathematical properties of retarded waves which obey classical causation and propagate from the past to the future, and of advanced waves which obey final causation and propagate from the future to the past. Fantappiè noted that in diverging systems, such as our expanding universe, entropy prevails forcing time to flow forwards and forbidding advanced solutions. On the contrary in converging systems, such as black holes, syntropy prevails, time flows backwards and retarded solutions would be impossible; whereas in systems balanced between diverging and converging forces, such as atoms, time would be unitary, past, present and future would coexist and both advanced and retarded waves would be possible. In the CIRTS model Bierman considers advanced solutions possible also at the macro level, without taking into account the restrictions posed by the law of entropy.

2. Fantappiè argued that, as a consequence of the fact that advanced waves exist at the quantum level, living systems need a way to "extract" advanced waves from the quantum level in order to sustain living functions and contrast the destructive effects of entropy. Fantappiè found this mechanism in water, in the hydrogen bridge, a bond among the hydrogen atom and two electrons, found by Maurice Huggins in 1920, which allows to explains the anomalous properties of water (Ball, 1999). The hydrogen bridge makes water totally different from other liquids, mainly by increasing its cohesive forces (syntropy) and this would be the reason why water is so essential to life, since it allows the flow of advanced waves from the micro to the macro level. Consequently, in the syntropy model advanced waves are not associated to the brain, but are considered a fundamental property of all living systems. On the contrary, CIRTS suggests that advanced waves are mediated by consciousness and therefore should be a consequence of conscious brain activities. Bierman produces evidence in experiments conducted with meditators, but this evidence can be easily read as an increase of the role of the autonomic nervous system during meditation, and not as a consequence of consciousness. It is well known that, while meditating, subjects often experience a state of trance as a consequence of the fact that the aim is usually that of "turning

off the mind".

3.   In the CIRTS model consciousness is a pre-requisite of reality. In the syntropy model the feeling of life is a consequence of the cohesive and unitary properties of advanced waves. According to the syntropy model, any form of life has a feeling of life. Consequently we would have a feeling of life also when no brain activity is observed. This would explain why all forms of life, even the most simple ones, show anticipatory reactions (Rosen, 1985) and why, for example, patients during surgery in a state of anesthetic-induced unconsciousness tend to defend themselves and subjects with no brain activity react and defend themselves when their organs are removed for transplant. According to the syntropy model, the feeling of life does not reside in the brain; however, the brain provides memory which allows us to remember and reason regarding our conscious experiences.

4.   CIRTS associates pre-stimuli reactions to coherence whereas the syntropy model associates pre-stimuli reactions to feelings and emotions. Coherence is a concept which is quite difficult to measure, whereas emotions can be easily measured using the parameters of the autonomic nervous system. Nevertheless Bierman introduces a formula in order to justify why pre-stimuli reactions are lower than post-stimuli reactions. In this formula the volume of the brain affected by coherence is divided by the total volume of the brain. The example reported by Bierman, relative to skin conductance, seems to support this formula. However, when using heart rate measurements pre-stimuli reactions and post-stimuli reactions tend to have the same size of effect. Even though effects vary greatly among subjects and generalization seems not to be appropriate, HR data contradicts Bierman's formula.

6. Conclusion

According to the syntropy model the dual manifestation of the quantum world in the form of waves and particles is not the consequence of the collapse of the wave equation, but the consequence of the dual causality at the quantum level: retarded waves, past causality, and advanced waves, future causality (Cramer, 1986). The advanced waves model does not need the collapse of the wave function and, consequently, does not need a time-symmetry restoration system. Advanced waves would explain not only the dual manifestation particle/waves, but also non-locality and entanglement (De Beauregard, 1977). On the contrary the CIRTS model finds its justification within the Copenhagen Interpretation of quantum mechanics and requires the collapse of the wave function.

The Copenhagen Interpretation was formulated in 1927 and can be considered the expression of the Zeitgeist, "the spirit of the time", since it reflects the idea of men as semi-Gods who, through the exercise of consciousness, can create reality. When Erwin Schrödinger discovered how Heisenberg and Bohr had used his wave equation, with ideological and mystical implications which provided powers of creation to consciousness, he commented: "I don't like it, and I am sorry I ever had anything to do with it" (Schrödinger, 1944).

References

Anderson C.D. (1932). The apparent existence of easily deflectable positives, Science, 76:238. Ball P. (1999). H2O A Biography of Water, Weidenfeld & Nicolson, London.

Bem D.J. (2010). Feeling the Future: Experimental Evidence for Anomalous Retroactive Influence on Cognition and Affect. Journal of Personality and Social Psychology (in press), DOI: 10.1037/a0021524, http://dbem.ws/FeelingFuture. pdf

Bierman D.J., Radin D.I. (1998). Conscious and anomalous non-conscious emotional processes: A reversal of the arrow time? Toward a Science of Consciousness, Tucson III. MIT Press, 367-386.

Bierman D.J. (2008). Consciousness Induced Restoration of Time-Symmetry (CIRTS), a Psychophysical Theoretical Perspective, Proceedings of the PA Convention, Winchester, England, 13-17 August 2008.

Cramer J.G. (1986). The Transactional Interpretation of Quantum Mechanics, Reviews of Modern Physics, 58: 647-688.

De Beauregard C. (1977). Time Symmetry and the Einstein Paradox, Il Nuovo Cimento, 42(B).

Di Corpo U. (1981), Un nuovo approccio strutturale ai fondamenti della psicologia. Ipotesi teoriche ed esperimenti. Dissertation, University of Rome "La Sapienza".

Di Corpo U. (2007). The conflict between entropy and syntropy: the vital needs model. SSE Proceedings, Norway, 132-138.

Dirac P. (1928). The Quantum Theory of the Electron, Proc. Royal Society, London, 117: 610-624; 118: 351-361.

Fantappiè L. (1942). Sull'interpretazione dei potenziali anticipati della meccanica ondulatoria e su un principio di finalità che ne discende. Rend. Acc. D'Italia, 4(7).

Haken H. (1983). Synergetics, an Introduction: Nonequilibrium Phase Transition and Self- Organization in Physics, Chemistry, and Biology, Springer-Verlag.

Heisenberg W. (1928). Letter to W. Pauli, PC, May 3, 1: 443.

Heisenberg W. (1934). Letter to W. Pauli, PC, February 8, 2: 279.

King C.C. (1996). Quantum Mechanics, Chaos and the Conscious Brain. Journal of Mind and Behavior, 18: 155-170.

May E.C., Paulinyi T., Vassy Z. (2005). Anomalous Anticipatory Skin Conductance Response to Acoustic Stimuli: Experimental Results and Speculation about a Mechanism, The Journal of Alternative and Complementary Medicine,

11(4): 695-702.

McCratly R., Atkinson M., Bradely R.T. (2004). Electrophysiological Evidence of Intuition: Part 1, Journal of Alternative and Complementary Medicine, 10(1): 133-143.

McDonough B.E., Dons N.S., Warren C.A. (2002). Differential event-related potentials to targets and decoys in a guessing task, in Journal for Scientific Exploration, 16: 187-206.

Prigogine I. and Stengers I. (1979). La Nouvelle Alliance, Gallimard.

Radin D.I. (1997). Unconscious perception of future emotions: An experiment in presentiment. Journal of Scientific Exploration, 11(2): 163-180.

Radin D.I., Schlitz M. J. (2005). Gut feelings, intuition, and emotions: An exploratory study, Journal of Alternative and Complementary Medicine, 11(4): 85-91.

Rosen R. (1985). Anticipatory Systems, Pergamon Press, USA.

Schrödinger E. (1944). What is Life? The Physical Aspects of the Living Cell, Cambridge University Press.

Szent-Gyorgyi A. (1977). Drive in Living Matter to Perfect Itself, Synthesis, 1(1): 14-26.

Spottiswoode P., May E. (2003). Skin Conductance Prestimulus Response: Analyses, Artifacts and a Pilot Study, Journal of Scientific Exploration, 17(4): 617-641.

Tressoldi P. E., Martinelli M., Massaccesi S., Sartori L. (2005). Heart Rate Differences between Targets and Nontargets in Intuitive Tasks, Human Physiology, 31(6): 646–650.

Vannini A. (2005). Entropy and Syntropy. From Mechanical to Life Science, NeuroQuantology, 3(2): 88-110.

Vannini A. (2008). Quantum Models of Consciousness, Quantum Biosystems, 2: 165-184.

Vannini A. and Di Corpo U. (2008). Retrocausality and the Healing Power of Love, NeuroQuantology, 6(3): 291-296.

Vannini A. and Di Corpo U. (2009). A Retrocausal Model of Life, in Filters and Reflections. Perspective on Reality, ICRL Press, Princeton, NJ, USA, 231-244.

Vannini A. and Di Corpo U. (2010). Collapse of the wave function? Pre-stimuli heart rate reactions. NeuroQuantology, 8(4): 550-563.

Wheeler J.A. and Feynman R. (1949). Classical Electrodynamics in Terms of Direct Interparticle Action. Reviews of Modern Physics, 21: 425-433.

31. The Quantum Physics of God and how Consciousness Became the Universe

R. Gabriel Joseph
Cosmology.com / BrainMind.com

ATOMISTS VS CREATIONISTS

For thousands of years humans have gazed into the heavens pondering the nature of universe, with some arguing the Universe was created, and others championing an eternal, infinite cosmos, in continual flux and change, and with no beginning and no end. This latter view, developed by the Greek "atomists", and the ancient Hindus and Buddhists, was the prevailing theory accepted by most scientists until the 20th century, when the creationists, with the backing of the Catholic Church, came up with a scientific explanation for "the creation" which was eventually accepted by the majority of scientists. Ironically, it was Fred Hoyle, a leading proponent of an infinite universe, who dismissively coined the phrase which popularized the creationist theory. Hoyle called it: "the big bang."

It was in 1927 that Monsignor Georges Lemaître, published what became known as the theory of the big bang. His paper was titled "A homogeneous Universe of constant mass and growing radius accounting for the radial velocity of extragalactic nebulae." Lemaître designed and based his big bang theory on the Biblical story of Genesis. Lemaître hoped to make the Bible scientific and in accord with testable observations. The universe, he said, was created by a creator, as detailed in Genesis, chapter 1: "In the beginning God created the heavens... And God said, Let there be light: and there was light. And God saw the light, that it was good: and God divided the light from the darkness."

Lemaître initially called his theory the 'hypothesis of the primeval atom" and described it as "the Cosmic Egg exploding at the moment of the creation." Today is is known as "The Big Bang."

Lemaître's physics, as Lemaître admitted, had a spiritual foundation. Monsignor Lemaître firmly believed Jesus Christ was God and God created the universe, as advocated by the Catholic Church and as described in Genesis 1. Lemaître was in fact an honorary prelate with the rank of Bishop in the Catholic Church, a professor at the Catholic University of Leuven. and president of the Pontifical Academy of Sciences which is under the direction and authority of the Pope of the Catholic Church. Lemaître's "big bang" theory was in accordance with the teachings of the Church, was supported by the Pope, and backed by the authority of the Bible.

The Universe was created. God created the Universe.

For thousands of years, however, other scientists, philosophers and sages, have argued the universe is infinite and eternal, and that the very foundation of existence, undergoes constant change. For example the Greek "atomists" Democritus, Anaxagoras and Epicurus argued that the universe was infinite; that permanence was an illusion--a manifestation of the act of observing and the limitation of the senses.

As their name suggests, the "atomists" based their reasoning on atomic theory which they originated. Specifically, in the fifth century B.C. Democritus and Anaxagoras proposed that all matter is made up of tiny indestructible units, called atoms. According to Democritus, these atoms move about in space and combine in various ways to give shape and form to all macroscopic objects.

Anaxagoras argued that the fundamental unit of matter, the atom, could neither be created nor destroyed—perhaps the earliest formulation of the law of conservation of mass. All matter was comprised of smaller elements called "atoms"which have always existed and which could not be created. Therefore the essence of existence, including the universe which is made of atoms, has no beginning but has existed for all of time. There was thus no need for a creator god.

The atomists were repeatedly assailed and attacked by Jewish philosophers and religious authorities who described these theories as "heresy." Attacks against the "atomists" continued with the establishment of the Catholic Church who labeled all atomists "heretics" and "blasphemers."

Supporters of the atomists countered: if there is a god, then who created god? The theologians replied: God the creator, became the creator at the moment of creation, just as a carpenter becomes a carpenter at the moment he first builds something. Thus it was argued that god existed before the creation, and it was only at the moment of creation, that god became "god the creator."

Hence, the "creation-event" which gave rise to the universe was created by an all powerful omnipotent Lord God who existed prior to and is responsible for the creation event; exactly as described in Genesis 1. God is self-creating. In fact, similar arguments have been put forth by those supporting the theory of the big bang: the universe did not exist until it was created, and existed as a singularity or as a nothingness prior to the creation event. The universe created itself.

The theory of the big bang creation event, and the argument in favor of god the creator, rely upon similar philosophical arguments. Prior to the big bang there was nothing, or a singularity which for unknown reasons exploded and became the universe. God was the singularity which created the universe, and thus god and the universe are self-creating: the universe became the universe at the moment of creation, and god the creator became "god the creator" at the moment of creating the universe.

Be it God or a "big bang" creation event, both theories rest upon the same belief: something always existed, i.e. "god" and/or the "singularity." And both god and the universe are self-creating. God became god by creating the universe and thus God created God by the act of creation. The Universe became the universe by creating itself and thus the universe created the universe by the act of creation. Be it the Jewish/Christian religion, or the "big bang" theorists, all assume something existed which gave rise to the universe; i.e. god or a singularity.

According to Lemaître, God is that singularity. The universe, therefore, is not just a manifestation of the creative act, but is also god. The universe is god since all things come from God. Every galaxy, stars, planet, human, dog, cat, molecule, atom--all come from God, and in the beginning were one with god-- this singularity. And in the end, all will return to god, becoming one with god. So in the end, is, as the beginning: A oneness from which all existence emanates and returns. The parallels with Hinduism, Taoism, atomic theory, and quantum physics--as will be explained--are striking.

THE HINDU UNIVERSE: THE UPANISHADS / THE BHAGAVAD-GITA

In HinduVedic literature, it is said that Visnu is the primary creator who creates the basic universal shell and provides all the raw materials for what is perceived as the material world.

"In the beginning of the creation, the Lord first expanded Himself in the universal form of the puruṣa incarnation and manifested all the ingredients for the material creation. And thus at first there was the creation of the sixteen principles of material action. This was for the purpose of creating the material universe." -The Bhagavad-gītā

"This form [the manifestation of the puruṣa] is the source and indestructible seed of multifarious incarnations within the universe. From the particles and portions of this form, different living entities, like demigods, men and others, are created." -The Bhagavad-gītā

"Not-being was this in the beginning; From it arose. Self-fashioned indeed out of itself." -Upanishads

"Invisible, incomprehensible, without genealogy, colorless, Without eye or ear, without hands or feet, Eternal, pervading all and over all, scarce knowable, That unchanging one Whom the wise regard as being's womb." -Upanishads

THE TAO

"All things begin from nothing and end in nothing." -Chang Tzu

"This is the Tao--it may be apprehended by the mind, but it cannot be seen. It has Its root and ground of existence in Itself. Before there was heaven and Earth, It was securely existing. From It came the mysterious existences of spirits, from It the mysterious existence of God. It produced heaven. It produced Earth." -Chang Tzu

"From nonexistence we proceed to existence."-Chang Tzu

"Heaven, Earth, and I were produced together; and all things and I are one." -Chang Tzu

"It is from the nameless that Heaven and Earth sprang." -Tao Te Ching

"The nameless Tao was the beginning of Heaven and Earth and was before God." -Tao Te Ching

"There was something undefined and complete, coming into existence before Heaven and Earth; formless, reaching everywhere and in no danger of being exhausted. It may be regarded as the Mother of all things." -Tao Te Ching

THE JEWISH / CHRISTIAN GOD

"Lift up your eyes and look to the heavens:
    Who created all these?
He who brings out the starry host one by one
    and calls forth each of them by name." -Isaiah 40:26

"...when I was being made in secret,
intricately woven in the depths...
Your eyes saw my unformed substance...the days that were formed for me,
when as yet there was none of them" - Psalm 139

"He reveals deep and hidden things;
he knows what lies in darkness,
and light dwells with him" - Daniel 2:22

"The secret things belong to God, but the things revealed belong to us" - Deuteronomy 29:29...

"I am God... declaring the end from the beginning" -Isaiah 46

CONSCIOUSNESS CREATED THE UNIVERSE

But what exactly was that "creative act"? How did non-being produce being? If there is a god, how did "god" create? How did "god the creator" create "god the creator"? The same questions have been asked about the "big bang." What caused it and why?

How do we know something exists?

One answer might be: Consciousness. Consciousness, exists. Consciousness has energy. Energy may become matter and matter, energy. Consciousness is always a consciousness of something. Consciousness requires a duality in order to exist as a consciousness. Self-consciousness, consciousness of consciousness, is also a duality.

As summed up the Heisenberg, one of the founders of quantum mechanics: "the transition from the possible to the actual takes place during the act of observation... and the interaction of the object with the measuring device, and thereby with the rest of the world...Since through the observation our knowledge of the system has changed discontinuously, its mathematical representation has also undergone the discontinuous change and we speak of a quantum jump" (Heisenberg, 1958). In other words, something comes into existence, by becoming conscious of it.

Heisenberg (1958), cautioned, however, that the observer is not the creator of reality, but instead merely registers, at a particular moment, certain isolated fragments of activity within the continuum, the nature of which is determined by our senses which perceives only parts and not the continuum which the part is, part of: "Quantum theory does not introduce the mind of the physicist as part of the atomic event. But it starts from the division of the world into the object and the rest of the world. What we observe is not nature in itself but nature exposed to our method of questioning."

The act of knowing, of observing, or measuring, that is, interacting with the environment in any way, creates an entangled state and a knot in the quantum continuum described as a "collapse of the wave function;" a knot of energy that is a kind of blemish in the continuum of the quantum field. This quantum knot bunches up at the point of observation, at the assigned value of measurement and can be entangled. Consciousness perceives a blemish in the continuum, but which is still part of the continuum, even though it is perceived as distinct.

The universe exists, because there is consciousness of the universe. This also means: consciousness must have come first, creating a quantum jump from singularity to duality. The universe may have become conscious of itself.

If the universe is a conscious universe, then it could be said that the universe came into being when the universe became conscious of itself. Likewise, if there is a "god" then it could be said that God created the universe and became god the creator, by becoming conscious of itself; that is, god became god the creator at the moment god achieved self-consciousness. If there is a a "God" and "god" and the universe are "one" then the god-universe became conscious of itself and thus the universe and god came into existence. Consciousness was the creative act. Consciousness creates by becoming conscious.

In the Upanishads, it is stated: "In the beginning the atman was this universe. He gazed around, he saw nothing there but himself. Thereupon he cried out at the beginning: It is I."

Thus, in the beginning, atman and the universe were a singularity, a oneness. However, upon becoming conscious of its existence, the universe came into existence, but as a duality:

"Not-being was this in the beginning; From it arose. Self-fashioned indeed out of itself." -Upanishads

The act of becoming conscious, created a duality also known as Brahman and Atman:

"Brahman...After he had created it, he entered into it; after he had entered into it, he was: The being and the beyond, Expressible and inexpressible, Founded and foundationless. Consciousness and unconsciousness; Reality and unreality... In truth, there are two forms of Brahman, The formed and the unformed, The mortal and immortal. The abiding and the fleeting, The being and the beyond.... Truly the Brahman is this Atman." -Upanishads

It is the Atman, consciousness/self-consciousness which creates the universe, thereby creating a duality of Brahman and Atman--a universe which is conscious of itself. Brahman is the unknown that needs to be explained, atman is the known through which the unknown finds its explanation. Brahman and Atman became a duality, upon achieving self-consciousness; and this is how "god" and the universe came into being, according to the Upanishads.

Genesis, chapter 1: "In the beginning God created the heavens...And God said, Let there be light: and there was light. And God saw the light, that it was good: and God divided the light from the darkness." What is this light? It is the illumination of consciousness.

THE QUANTUM CONTINUUM: BEING AND NON-BEING

As pointed out by Neils Bohr and Werner Heisenberg, the founders of quantum theory, there are direct parallels between quantum mechanics and Taoism, Buddhism, and Hinduism: "The great scientific contributions in theoretical physics... has.. a relationship between the philosophical ideas in the tradition of the Far East and the philosophical substance of quantum theory." -Werner Heisenberg

Being become nonbeing, and nonbeing becoming being, is a major principle of quantum physics. Form and substance are manifestations of dynamic patterns of energy and electromagnetic radiation that have no material reality. Form and substance, that is, the "particles" they are comprised of, exist only as probabilities. Form and substance have probable realities and can become something else entirely, or cease to exist, returning to the basic oneness of the continuum--the most obvious example of which, is, death and decay. What is, can undergo a transformation from being into nonbeing

Consider the theoretical molecular foundations of matter, e.g., electrons, protons, neutrons, photons, neutrinos, etc., Each of these "particles" consist of yet smaller particles and all are balanced by the existence of anti-particles which are in all respects opposite in charge. However, in some instances, these elements also comprise their own anti-particle. Thus, there is being, and anti-being.

However, according to quantum mechanics, these particles do not really exist, except as probabilities. These "subatomic" particles have probable existences and display tendencies to assume certain patterns of activity that we perceive as shape and form by a conscious mind wielding an measurement apparatus. Yet, they may also begin to display a different pattern of activity such that being can become nonbeing or something else altogether.

Shape and form are a function of our perception of these dynamic interactions within the frenzy of activity which is the quantum continuum. However, we can only perceive what our senses can detect, and what we detect as form and shape are really a mass of frenzied subatomic electromagnetic activity that is amenable to detection by our senses and conscious mind at a particular moment in time. The perception and our consciousness of certain aspects of these oscillating patterns of activity are dependent on our sensory capabilities, which give rise to the impressions of shape and form. If we possessed additional senses, or an increased sensory channel capacity, we would perceive yet other patterns and other realities.

More specifically, this electromagnetic activity is so frenzied, that a particle can exist here, and now there. Although it is neither here nor there, it is perceived by consciousness as a solid object that has shape, form, length, mass, weight, and so on. This is because the rapidity of movement obscures the fact that much of what we perceive are particular patterns of electromagnetic activity that are in frenzied motion.

Mass, as Einstein explained in his famous equation, is energy. That is, mass (M) is equal to energy (E) divided by the speed of light squared ($M=E/C^2$). However, whereas mass can be destroyed, energy cannot. Rather, as mass is destroyed, an equal amount of energy is released back into the electromagnetic continuum. The energy released as a function of destruction, is equal to the mass of the object times the square of the speed of light ($E=MC^2$). Conversely, if we increase the amount of energy, we increase the amount of apparent mass.

Since energy cannot be created, then energy was never created and has existed always.

Mass does not consist of tiny particles that are packed tightly together. Rather, what we perceive as mass (shape, form, length, weight) are dynamic patterns of energy which we selectively attend to and then perceive as stable and static. And, we are perceiving only fragments of the quantum continuum.

This energy that makes up the object of our conscious perceptions, is but an aspect of the electromagnetic continuum which has assumed a specific pattern that may be sensed and processed by our brain. As dictated by quantum mechanics, the universe exists, because we are conscious of it.

Hence, consciousness created the universe. If the universe is self-creating, then the universe became conscious of itself.

THE TAO OF QUANTUM CONSCIOUSNESS

If the universe came into being by becoming conscious if itself, then what is, or was, the singularity, this oneness, before it became conscious of itself?

"The nameless Tao was the beginning of Heaven and Earth and was before God." -Tao Te Ching

According to the Taoists, the basic oneness is not compacted into a single point, but is all pervasive, everywhere, at the same time; and not only do all things emerge from it, but all things return to it, becoming one:

"Tao is forever...All pervading is the Great Tao. It may be found on the left hand and on the right. All things depend on it for their production.. All things return to their root and disappear and do not know that it is it which presides over their doing." -Tao Te Ching

"The Tao passes on in constant flow. Passing on it becomes remote. Having become remote, it returns." -Tao Te Ching

"The Tao produces all things and nourishes them; it produces them and does not claim them as its own; it does all; it presides over all, yet does not control. This is what is called the Mystery of Tao." -Tao Te Ching

"In Tao the only motion is returning. Although Heaven and Earth were produced by being, being was produced by nonbeing." -Tao Te Ching

"Endless the series of things without a name on the way way to where there is nothing. They are called shapeless shapes; Forms without form; are called vague semblances." -Tao Te Ching

"This endless cycle of being emerging from non-being, and returning to its source, is consistent with quantum theory, i.e. the quantum continuum of electro-magnetic activity, from which all existence arises and returns; and similar ideas are repeated in the Upanishads:

"In Him in whom this universe is interwoven; Whatever moves or is motionless, In Brahman everything is lost; Like bubbles in the ocean. In whim in whom the living creatures of the universe Emptying themselves become invisible. They disappear and come to light again. As bubbles rise to the surface." -Upanishads

"After he had created it, he entered into it; after he had entered into it, he was: The being and the beyond... Reality and unreality... The formed and the unformed, The mortal and immortal. The abiding and the fleeting, The being and the beyond. -Upanishads

The central view of Upanishads and the Tao, and which is consistent with quantum mechanics, is the cyclic nature of non-being becoming being, being becoming non-being--ceaseless motion and constant change: "Returning is the motion of Tao... and going far means returning." (Lao Tzu)

This cyclic change of continual motion is also represented by the Chinese concepts of yin and yang: "The yang having reached its end become yin; the yin having reached its end becomes the yang." -I Ching. Book of Changes

Its tao is forever changing -alteration, movement without rest, Flowing through the six empty places, Rising and sinking without fixed law; Firm and yielding transform each other. They cannot be confined within a rule. It is only change that is at work here." -I Ching. Book of Changes

What was the singularity which existed before the universe or the god/universe became the god/universe? The quantum continuum, which is forever changing. At the moment that quantum continuum became conscious of itself, the universe was created: being emerged from non-being.

QUANTUM CONSCIOUSNESS vs EINSTEIN

Einstein ridiculed the implications of quantum theory and its emphasis on consciousness as having any role in the nature of existence: "Do you really think the moon isn't there if you aren't looking at it?"

As theorized by Einstein (1961), and unlike the Copenhagen model of quantum physic, space-time is relative to but independent of any observer. Consciousness and the act of measurement is relative but irrelevant having no effect on the passage of time or events. In relativity, each event, which occurs at certain moments of time, in a given region of space, and are relative to those observers in different regions of space. Each observer chooses a convenient metrical coordinate system in which these events are specified by four real numbers.

In relativity, consciousness is merely relative. In quantum physics, consciousness and the act of observation and measurement constitute a separate reference frame which can collapse the wave function of the quantum continuum and register entangled interactions within the environment. Consciousness by the act of observation or measurement takes a static or series of pictures-in-time which then becomes discontinuous from the quantum continuum (Heisenberg 1958; Planck 1931; von Neumann 2001). These entanglements (Francis 2012; Juan et al. 2013; Plenio 2007), or blemishes in the quantum continuum, may be observed as shape, form, cause, effect, past, present, future, the passage of time, and thus reality; the result of a decoupling of quanta from the quantum (coherent) continuum which leaks out and then couples together in a knot of activity which is observed as a wave form collapse.

As based on the Copenhagen theory of quantum mechanics (Bohr, 1958, 1963; Heisenberg 1955, 1958), what we perceive as reality are a manifestation of wave functions and alterations in patterns of activity within the quantum continuum which are perceived by consciousness as discontinuous. Wave form collapse is always a matter of probability, and is non-local, indeterministic and a consequence of conscious observation, measurement, and entanglement. Consciousness and the act of measurement, therefore, are entangled with the quantum continuum and can after the continuum and the space-time manifold.

In summary, form and substance are comprised of particles which take on specific patterns and which are the result of concentrations of energy that emerge and disappear back into the electromagnetic quantum field; a knot of energy that is a kind of blemish in the continuum of the quantum field which is perceived by a conscious mind.

This reality, therefore, is a manifestation of consciousness and consciousness of alterations in the patterns of activity within the electromagnetic field. The electromagnetic field, this energy, is therefore the fundamental entity, the continuum that is constitutes the basic oneness and unity of all things.

QUANTUM PHYSICS AND PROBABILITY OF EXISTENCE

Einstein and his followers waged war against quantum theory which posed a direct challenge to his theories and those of Newton. For example, the equations of Newton and Einstein were replaced by equations between matrices representing the position and momentum of electrons which were found to be unpredictable. In fact, whereas Newtonian and Einsteinian theories do an admirable job of explaining the macro-world, they completely break down when applied to the sub-atomic world. This is because the patterns that resemble particles, display tendencies to exist and tendencies to no longer exist. Thus measurement becomes uncertain and can only be based on probabilities.

Because particles have only a probable existence it is impossible to predict an atomic event with 100% certainty. This principle, in fact, is called the uncertainty principle, because one can never predict when a particle may exist, and where it may exist when it does exist. Again, these particles exist and do not exist, and are always in motion--which gives rise to the illusion of permanent shape and form when perceived or measured by a conscious mind. It is also these principles which form the crux of quantum electrodynamics, or field theory.

Broadly considered, atoms consist of empty space at the center of which is a positively charged nucleus and which is orbited by electrons. The positive charge of the atom's nucleus determines the number of surrounding electrons, making the atom electrically neutral. However, it was determined that it was impossible to make precise predictions about the position and momentum of electrons based on Newtonian or Einsteinian physics, and this led to the Copenhagen interpretation (Heisenberg 1925, 1927) which Einstein repeatedly attacked because of all the inherent paradoxes. Matrix mechanics is referred to now as quantum mechanics whereas the "statistical matrix" is known as the "probability function;" all of which are central to quantum theory.

As summed up by Heisenberg (1958) "the probability function represents our deficiency of knowledge... it does not represent a course of events, but a tendency for events to take a certain course or assume certain patters. The probability function also requires that new measurements be made to determine the properties of a system, and to calculate the probable result of the new measurement; i.e. a new probability function."

Quantum physics, as exemplified by the Copenhagen school (Bohr, 1934, 1958, 1963; Heisenberg, 1925, 1927, 1930), like Einsteinian physics, makes assumptions about the nature of reality as related to an observer, the "knower" who is conceptualized as a singularity. As summed up by Heisenberg (1958), "the concepts of Newtonian or Einsteinian physics can be used to describe events in nature." However, because the physical world is relative to being known by a "knower" (the observing consciousness), then the "knower" can influence the nature of the reality which is being observed through the act of measurement and registration at a particular moment in time.

And yet, what is observed or measured at one moment can never include all the properties of the object under observation. In consequence, what is known vs what is not known, becomes relatively imprecise (Bohr, 1934, 1958, 1963; Heisenberg, 1925, 1927).

As expressed by the Heisenberg uncertainty principle (Heisenberg, 1927), the more precisely one physical property is known the more unknowable become other properties. The more precisely one property is known, the less precisely the other can be known and this is true at the molecular and atomic levels of reality. Therefore it is impossible to precisely determine, simultaneously, for example, both the position and velocity of an electron (Bohr, 1934, 1958, 1963).

Einstein objected to quantum mechanics and Heisenberg's formulations of potentiality and indeterminacy by proclaiming "god does not play dice."

In Einstein's and Newton's physics, the state of any isolated mechanical system at a given moment of time is given precisely. Numbers specifying the position and momentum of each mass in the system are empirically determined at that moment of time of the measurement. Probability never enters into the equation. Therefore, the position and momentum of objects including subatomic particles are precisely located in space and time as designated by a single pair of numbers, all of which can be determined causally and deterministically. However, quantum physics proved that Einstein and Newton's formulation are not true at the atomic and subatomic level (Bohr, 1934, Born et al. 1925; Heisenberg 1925, 1927).

According to Heisenberg (1925, 1927, 1930), chance and probability enters into the state and the definition of a physical system because the very act of measurement can effect the system; and this is because the observing consciousness and measurement apparatus are also entangled with the quantum continuum and effect it, and vice-verse. No system is truly in isolation, but is contiguous with the quantum continuum. Moreover, no system can be viewed from all perspectives in totality simultaneously which would require a god's eye view; and "god's eye" would also have to observe itself observing. Only if the entire universe is included can one apply the qualifying condition of "an isolated system." By including the observer, his eye, the measuring apparatus and the object, creates uncertainty because every action is entangled with the continuum.

"This crucial point...implies the impossibility of any sharp separation between the behaviour of atomic objects and the interaction with the measuring instruments which serve to define the conditions under which the phenomena appear...." -Bohr 1949.

As determined by Niels Bohr (1949), the properties of physical entities exist only as complementary or conjugate pairs: duality. A profound aspect of complementarity is that it not only applies to measurability or knowability of some property of a physical entity, but more importantly it applies to the limitations of that physical entity's very manifestation of the property in the physical world. Physical reality is defined by manifestations of properties which are limited by the interactions and trade-offs between these complementary pairs. For example, the accuracy in measuring the position of an electron requires a complementary loss of accuracy in determining its momentum. Precision in measuring one pair is complimented by a corresponding loss of precision in measuring the other pair (Bohr, 1949, 1958, 1963). The ultimate limitations in precision of property manifestations are quantified by Heisenberg's uncertainty principle and matrix mechanics. Complementarity and Uncertainty dictate that all properties and actions in the physical world are therefore non-deterministic to some degree.

Bohr (1949) called this the principle of complementarity, a concept fundamental to quantum mechanics and closely associated with the Uncertainty Principle. "The knowledge of the position of a particle is complementary to the knowledge of its velocity or momentum." If we know the one with high accuracy we cannot know the other with high accuracy (Bohr, 1949, 1958, 1963; Heisenberg, 1927, 1955, 1958).

THE WAVE FUNCTION OF REALITY

In quantum physics, nature and reality are represented by the quantum state. The electromagnetic field of the quantum state is the fundamental entity, the continuum that constitutes the basic oneness and unity of all things. The physical nature of this state can be "known" by assigning it mathematical properties and probabilities (Bohr, 1958, 1963; Heisenberg, 1927). Therefore, abstractions, i.e., numbers and probabilities become representational of a hypothetical physical state. Because these are abstractions, the physical state is also an abstraction and does not possess the material consistency, continuity, and hard, tangible, physical substance as is assumed by Classical (Newtonian) physics. Instead, reality, the physical world, is a process of observing, measuring, and knowing and is based on probabilities and the wave function (Heisenberg, 1955).

Central to quantum mechanics is the wave function (Bohr, 1963; Heisenberg, 1958). All of existence has a wave function, including light. Every aspect of existence can be described as sharing particle-like properties and wave-like properties. The wave function is the particle spread out over space and describes all the various possible states of the particle. According to quantum theory the probability of findings a particle in time or space is determined by the probability wave which obeys the Schrodinger equation. Everything is reduced to probabilities. Moreover, these particle/waves and these probabilities are entangled.

The act of conscious observations, by perception, by using a measuring device, interacts with the quantum continuum, because it is part of and entangled with the continuum. By becoming conscious, by focusing the conscious mind (or measuring device) at a particular area of the quantum continuum, triggers a "wave form collapse"--and it is this collapse of the wave function which gives rise to the perception of galaxies, stars, planets, moons, Earth, people, dogs, cats, and molecules.

Wave function collapse has also been described as "decoherence." The wave function describes all the various possible states of the particle. Rocks, trees, cats, dogs, humans, planets, stars, galaxies, the universe, the cosmos, past, present, future, as a collective, all have wave functions. The universe as a whole, has a wave function. If there is a god, then god has a wave function.

Waves can also be particles, thereby giving rise to a particle-wave duality and the Uncertainty Principle. Particle-waves interact with other particle-waves. The wave function of a person sitting on their rocking chair would, within the immediate vicinity of the person and the chair, resemble a seething quantum cloud of frenzied quantum activity in the general shape of the body and rocking chair. This quantum cloud of activity, when perceived by a conscious mind, gives shape and form to the man in his chair, even though the man/chair is part of the quantum continuum. The man/chair is a blemish in the continuum which is still part of the continuum and interacts with other knots of activity thus giving rise to cause and effect as well as violations of causality: "spooky action at a distance."

Reality is a manifestation of wave functions and alterations in patterns of activity within the quantum continuum which are entangled and perceived by conscious observations and measurement. When perceived, the wave function collapses and becomes discontinuous from the continuum, even though it is still part of it. The perception of a structural unit of information is not just perceived, but is inserted into the quantum state which causes the reduction of the wave-packet and the collapse of the wave function. It is this collapse which describes shape, form, length, width, and future and past events and locations within space-time (Bohr, 1963; Heisenberg, 1958).

In quantum physics, the wave function describes all possible states of the particle and larger objects, thereby giving rise to probabilities, and this leads to the "Many Worlds" interpretation of quantum mechanics (Dewitt, 1971; Everett 1956, 1957). That is, since there are numerous if not infinite probable outcomes, each outcome and probable outcome represents a different "world" with some worlds being more probable than others.

In the Copenhagen model, objects are viewed as quantum mechanical systems which are best described by the wave function and the probability function. "The reduction of wave packets occurs when the transition is completed from the possible to the actual" (Heisenberg, 1958).

Likewise, it could be said that the universe underwent a transition from the possible to the actual, at the moment of conscious registration which triggered a wave form collapse.

The measuring apparatus, the observer, and the conscious mind of the observer, also have a wave function and therefore interact with what is being measured. The effect of this is obvious when its a macro-structure measuring a micro-structure vs a macro-structure measuring a macro-structure. According to the Copenhagen interpretation (Bohr, 1949, 1963; Heisenberg, 1958), it is the act of measurement which collapses the wave function. It is also the measurement and observation of one event which triggers the instantaneous alteration in behavior of another object at faster than light speeds; i.e. entanglement. However, that which takes place faster than the speed of light means that an event in the future can travel from the future into the present and then into the past. Therefore, the future can effect the present and the past.

For example, an electron may collide with and bounce to the left of a proton on one trial, then to the right on the next, and then at a different angle on the third trial, and another angle on the fourth and so on, even though conditions are seemingly identical. This gives rise to the Uncertainty Principle and this is why the rules of quantum mechanics are indeterministic and based on probabilities. The state of a system one moment cannot determine what will happen next. Instead, we have probabilities which are based on the wave function. The wave function describes all the various possible states of the particle (Bohr, 1963; Heisenberg, 1958).

THE WAVE FUNCTION OF GOD/UNIVERSE CONSCIOUSNESS

From a singularity, out of nothingness, emerged the universe which emerged upon becoming conscious of itself. By becoming conscious, this caused a "collapse of the wave function" and the universe underwent a transition "from the possible to the actual" (Heisenberg, 1958).

Thus, if the universe became conscious of itself, it collapsed the wave function and the universe was transformed into the actual. If there is a god, and if the universe is god, then god is that quantum consciousness which created itself and the universe, by becoming conscious.

A conscious universe, or rather, a quantum consciousness which is identical with and yet distinct from the quantum continuum, is predicted by quantum physics, the theories of the "atomists" and the "Eastern" philosophies of Hinduism, Buddhism, and Taoism: the act of perceiving, of being conscious, creates an impression of distinction, of unique individuality; when in fact what is perceived are only fragments of the totality which is all.

Some Big Bang theorist like to believe the hypothetical "singularity" that gave rise to the universe, may have initially existed as a solid mass, no larger than a Plank length; with all matter compacted into the smallest of all measurable space. And then it exploded outward. However, as predicted by quantum mechanics, and Newtonian and Einsteinian physics, the gravity would be so immense that instead of blowing outward, it would have blown inward, imploding, creating a hole in the fabric of space-time; at the bottom of which would be a mirror universe. Thus, a universe of matter and a universe of anti-matter, a duality, would have been fashioned by the creative event. Two universes, being and non-being, matter and anti-matter, and each conscious of the others' existence.

This singularity, this basic oneness, from the perspective of quantum mechanics, need not have been compacted, however, but exists as a quantum continuum forever in flux, from which being emerges from non-being at the moment of consciousness of it. That is, when the singularity became conscious of itself, by becoming conscious of the "singularity", this created a fragmentation within the quantum continuum, the basic oneness which is everything. The quantum continuum became discontinuous by the act of becoming conscious. Again, consciousness, to be consciousness, must be consciousness of something; and that something is distinct from consciousness. Even consciousness of consciousness (self-consciousness) creates a duality which may then become a multiplicity (Joseph 2011).

By becoming a conscious observer, fragments of the quantum continuum were observed as distinct from the continuum, and perceived as galaxies, stars, planets, molecules, atoms, particles. And collections of those molecules and atoms also became conscious of themselves as things, and were perceived as having shape, form, with length, width, height, weight, duration, and individual identities. The quantum continuum, as a quantum consciousness, begets not just self-consciousness, but islands of consciousness: consciousness begets itself.

THE CONSCIOUS UNIVERSE

Since the universe, as a collective, must have a wave function, then this universal wave function would describe all the possible states of the universe and thus all possible universes. Hence, there must be multiple universes which exist simultaneously as probabilities (Dewitt, 1971; Everett 1956, 1957).

And if there is a god, the same would be true of "god" and the universe as a whole. "God" and the universe would have a wave function. Therefore, there would be more than one god--and this leads to the Hindu religion with its millions of gods, each of which is actually a manifestation of the one god which is the universe.

Consciousness, too, would have a wave function. In consequence, because the wave function of consciousness is entangled with the quantum continuum it can cause a collapse of the wave function.

If consciousness is energy, then the energy which is the quantum continuum also has the probability of becoming conscious. If the universe, as a whole, is a manifestation of the quantum continuum, as perceived by consciousness, then the continuum could have become conscious of itself, and in achieving self-consciousness, created the universe, which, created itself by becoming conscious.

And if the wave function is consciousness, and if there is a god and that god is the universe, then god/universe became god/universe, when the quantum continuum became conscious.

"In the beginning the atman was this universe. He gazed around, he saw nothing there but himself. Thereupon he cried out at the beginning: It is I." -Upanishads

And from the quantum continuum, through quantum consciousness, the one became the many: galaxies, stars, planets, moons, people, dogs, cats, molecules....

"O Lord of the universe, O universal form, I see in Your body many, many arms, bellies, mouths, and eyes, expanded everywhere, without limit I see in You no end, no middle, and no beginning. You have numberless arms, and the sun and moon are Your eyes. I see You with blazing fire coming forth from Your mouth, burning this entire universe by Your own radiance." -The Bhagavad-gītā

Sūta said: In the beginning of the creation, the Lord first expanded Himself in the universal form of the puruṣa incarnation and manifested all the ingredients for the material creation. And thus at first there was the creation of the sixteen principles of material action. This was for the purpose of creating the material universe. -The Bhagavad-gītā

This form [the second manifestation of the puruṣa] is the source and indestructible seed of multifarious incarnations within the universe. From the particles and portions of this form, different living entities, like demigods, men and others, are created. -The Bhagavad-gītā

In Him in whom this universe is interwoven; Whatever moves or is motionless" -Upanishads

THE QUANTUM PHYSICS OF ALL KNOWING GOD

In a quantum universe all of existence consists of a frenzy of subatomic energetic activity which can be characterized as possessing pure potentiality, and all of which are linked and entangled as a basic oneness which extends in all directions and encompasses all dimensions including time (Bohr, 1958, 1963; Dirac, 1966a,b; Planck 1931, 1932, Heisenberg 1955, 1958; Joseph 2014; von Neumann 1937, 1955). If there is a "god" then that god is that basic oneness.

The quantum continuum is the ultimate reality, an all inclusive oneness which is all things, and which becomes all things at the moment of consciousness--and the same has been said of the Tao, Hindu, Christian, Buddhist, and Jewish god.

It has been said that "god" is all knowing, omnipotent, omnipresent, existing in the future and the past, and in all things and the same can be said of the quantum continuum. And because this frenzied electromagnetic continuum extends in all directions and dimensions, encompassing even what is experienced as time, then the continuum which could be described as "god" would encompass the future, present, and past, and thus, would be eternal and all knowing.

"The Supreme Truth exists both internally and externally, in the moving and nonmoving. He is beyond the power of the material senses to see or to know. Although far, far away, He is also near to all." --Bhagavad Gita, 13:16

The omniscience of God is to be all knowing, to know all things past, present and future, including what is hidden from human sight and knowledge--all is still known by God. God's knowledge originates in himself and is complete--so says the Tao, Apanishads, Bhagavad Gita, and the Christian and Jewish religious texts (see Isa 40:13-14, Job 21:22, Mt 10:30, Dt 29:29).

"Who has directed the Spirit of the Lord
or instructed him as his adviser?
Whom did he consult?
Who gave him understanding?
Who taught him the right way?
Who taught him knowledge?
 Who showed him the path to understanding?" -Isaiah 40:13-14

To be all-knowing is to be knowing of all time--time itself is but a manifestation of the oneness as experienced as a single moment, an eternal "now" by a conscious observer. According to Einstein, time is relative to the observer (Einstein 1905a,b,c, 1906, 1961). Since there are innumerable observers, there is no universal "past, present, future" which are infinite in number and all of which are in motion. However, as all observers are but blemishes in the electromagnetic continuum, knots of energy which perceive themselves as distinct but which are still entangled in the continuum, then the basic oneness of the continuum, consists of all observers and all pasts presents and futures--in which case, there is only one observer: the quantum consciousness which is the universe, and what some have described as Tao, and God. From a god's eye view, the eternal "now" consists of all pasts, presents, futures, which are one.

"....the days that were formed for me, when as yet there was none of them"
- Psalm 139

"God" would thus encompass the past, present, and future, and would have consciousness of all pasts presents futures.

Because space is "isotropic" there is nothing in the law of physics indicating that a particular direction is preferred; down, up, sideways, backwards, its all the same. Why should space-time, or time, be any different? The laws of electromagnetism do not make a distinction between past and future (Pollack & Stump, 2001; Slater & Frank, 2011). Since the past, present and future overlap and are relative to observers and differ according to location, gravity, and speed of movement, then as Einstein stated, the distinctions between them are an illusion.

Like a flowing river, the "present," "past" and "future" are relative to an observer, just as "downstream" is relative to the location of an observer. In quantum physics, the river has no present or past or future, it just is; and this is why events which, from the perspective of an observer, occur in the future, can effect events which take place in the present: the eternal now.

As demonstrated by what is known as "entanglement" (Plenio 2007; Juan et al. 2013; Francis 2012) effects cannot always be traced to an earlier cause, for the cause may occur in the future (Megidish et al 2013). Effects may occur simultaneously with causes, and take place at faster than light speeds (Francis 2012; Juan et al. 2013; Lee et al. 2011; Matson 2012; Plenio 2007). As indicated by entanglement, the future may effect or take place before the past-present (Megidish et al 2013).

GOD AS ENTANGLMENT: PAST PRESENT FUTURE ARE ONE

According to Einstein's theorems of relativity (Einstein 1905a,b,c, 1907, 1910, 1961), the past, present and future overlap and exist simultaneously but in different distant locations in the dimension known as space-time, and as such "The distinction between past, present and future is only an illusion" (Einstein 1955). Quantum physics, the Uncertainty Principle, the "Many Worlds" interpretation of quantum physics, and what Einstein (1930) called "spooky action at a distance" all call into question the causal distinctions between past, present and future.

As predicted by quantum mechanics and relativity, time is a circle--a closed loop with no beginning and no end--time is a continuum, where past, present, future, are linked and entangled. If there is a god, and if that god is the quantum continuum, then from the perspective of the god-continuum, time and god are one and the same, except at the moment of consciousness, which triggers a wave form collapse which is experienced as the eternal "now." God, the quantum continuum, is entangled with the future and the past, as all a basic oneness.

These are not just thought experiments. There is considerable evidence of what Einstein (1955) called "spooky action at a distance" and faster than light "entanglement" (Plenio 2007; Juan et al. 2013; Francis 2012). It is well established that causes and effects can occur simultaneously and ever faster than light speed (Lee et al. 2011; Matson 2012; Olaf et al. 2003); a consequence of the connectedness of all things in the quantum continuum.

For example, entanglement, between photons, has been demonstrated even before the second photon even exists, such that the photon in the future effects the photon in the present; "a manifestation of the non-locality of quantum mechanics not only in space, but also in time (Megidish et al 2013). Time-space is interactional. Time, and time-space are embedded in the quantum continuum and can effect as well as be effected by other particle-waves even at great distances; a concept referred to as "entanglement." Time and space-time are entangled in the continuum which is all things.

Consider photons which are easily manipulated. They preserve their coherence for long times and can be entangled by projection measurements (Weinfurter 1994; Kwiat et al. 1995). A pump photon, for example, can split light into two lower- energy photons while preserving momentum and energy, and these photons remained maximally entangled although separated spatially (Goebel et al 2008; Pan et al. 1998). However, entanglement swapping protocols can entangle two remote photons without any interaction between them and even with a significant time-like separation (Ma et al., 2012; Megidish et al. 2013; Peres 2000). In one set of experiments entanglement was demonstrated following a delayed choice and even before there was a decision to make a choice. Specifically, four photons were created and two were measured and which became entangled. However, if a choice was then made to measure the remaining two photons, all four became entangled before it was decided to do a second measurement (Ma et al., 2012; Peres 2000). Entanglement can occur independent of and before the act of measurement. "The time at which quantum measurements are taken and their order, has no effect on the outcome of a quantum mechanical experiment" (Megidish et al. 2013).

Moreover, "two photons that exist at separate times can be entangled" (Megidish et al. 2013). As detailed by Megidish et al (2013): "In the scenario we present here, measuring the last photon affects the physical description of the first photon in the past, before it has even been measured. Thus, the "spooky action" is steering the system's past. Another point of view...is that the measurement of the first photon is immediately steering the future physical description of the last photon. In this case, the action is on the future of a part of the system that has not yet been created."

Hence, entanglement, between photons has been demonstrated even before the second photon even exists; "a manifestation of the non-locality of quantum mechanics not only in space, but also in time (Megidish et al 2013). In other words, a photon may become entangled with another photon even before that photon is created, before it even exists. Even after the first photon ceases to exist and before the second photon is created, both become entangled even though there is no overlap in time. Photons that do not exist can effect photons which do exist and photons which no longer exist and photons which will exist (Megidish et al. 2013); and presumably the same applies to all particles, atoms, molecules (Wiegner, et al 2011). As dictated by the "uncertainty principle" energy and mass can be time-independent (Heisenberg 1927, 1958).

However, if the future present past are a continuum and the distinctions between them illusions, then the photons in the future already exist, in the future. The future already exists, now.

KARMA: HOW GOD AND THE UNIVERSE CAN BE SELF-CREATING

Since time is entangled with the electro-magnetic continuum; in a continuum, the future can overlap with and even come before the past and catch up with itself in the past, so that an event can be "simultaneous" with or occur before its cause. An event may be able to cause itself.

Thus, the universe-quantum-universe-continuum, could have caused itself--and if there is a god, then god could have created god--the universe could have created itself.

If time is considered from the perspective of space-like intervals and not time-like intervals, then causality can be forward, backward, or simultaneous (Bonor & Steadman, 2005; Buser et al. 2013; Carroll 2004; Gödel 1995). The future and the past become entangled as a continuity in space-time. If "God" is that continuum, made conscious, then the God-continuum can also have knowledge of the future before the future takes place. Likewise, effects in the future can affect the present.

For example, it is believed that "Karma" can affect a person's future, or reincarnated life. However, if there is Karma, then that future life can have a backwards-in-time effect. In other words, someone's "evil deeds" in the future, or in a future life, may cause suffering in the present. God may punish the sinner before they sin, because the sin has already taken place: in the future.

It is well established that objects respond to and can influence and affect distant objects at speeds faster than light. This "spooky action at a distance" has been attributed to "fields," "mediator particles," gravity, and "quantum entanglement" (Bokulich & Jaeger, 2010; Juan et al. 2013; Sonner 2013).

It is believed that an electric "field" may mediate "electrostatic" interactions between electromagnetic charges and currents separated by great distances across space. However, these changes can take place at faster than light speeds. Charged particles, for example, produce an electric field around them which creates a "force" that effects other charges even at a distance. Maxwell's theories and equations incorporate these electrostatic physical "fields" to account for all electromagnetic interactions including action at a distance.

Since mass can become energy and energy mass, the "field" is therefore a physical entity that contains energy and has momentum which can be transmitted across space. Therefore, "action at a distance" may be both distant and local, a consequence of the interactions of these charges within the force field they create. However, the effects can be simultaneous, even at great distances, and occur faster than the speed of light (Plenio 2007; Juan et al. 2013; Francis 2012; Schrödinger & Dirac 1936), effecting electrons, photons, atoms, molecules and even diamonds (Lee et al. 2011; Matson 2012; Olaf et al. 2003; Schrödinger & Born 1935). The effect, therefore, may precede the cause since it takes place faster than light.

Correlation is not causation and it can't always be said with certainty which is the cause and which is the effect and this is because the cosmos is entangled as a basic oneness. According to the Tao, Gita, Upanishads, and so on: that oneness is god.

"Everywhere are His hands and legs, His eyes and faces, and He hears everything." --Bhagavad Gita, 13:14

"He is the source of light in all luminous objects. He is beyond the darkness of matter and is unmanifested. He is knowledge, He is the object of knowledge, and He is the goal of knowledge. He is situated in everyone's heart." --Bhagavad Gita, 13:18

GOD CONSCIOUSNESS AND THE QUANTUM CONTINUUM

The quantum continuum is without dimensions and encompasses space and time in its basic unity of oneness. Everything within the quantum continuum can be effected by local effects and distant effects simultaneously at and beyond light speeds; even the future can effect the present. Therefore, the future, and the "present" being part of this continuum can effect the past-present-future by effecting the wave function of the past, present, future, and thus, the space-time continuum, as all are entangled.

Quantum entanglement is a feature of time and the quantum continuum, this frenzied electromagnetic activity which is all things, encompassing even what some have called "god."

As based on quantum mechanics, it could be said that in space-time all things overlaps and coincide and exist side by side, including time, god, and consciousness. If consciousness is considered as spatial and different aspects of consciousness all all connected to the quantum continuum, then the future, past, and present coexists simultaneously, albeit continually in flux. Thus quantum consciousness, or god-consciousness, can be viewed as the union of all events in the same way that a line is the union of all of its points. God becomes all knowing, and what effects the future, can therefore effect the past as a continuity which is linked and not broken up and into isolated fragments which are separated by artificial time-like intervals. Likewise, when considered as phenomenon taking place in space, then the past can also effect the future as they are entangled as a unity.

If the world-line of cosmic consciousness is conceptualized as a string, then no matter where the string is plucked, the entire string will vibrate.

Since space-time includes "consciousness" then since space-time consists of energy which can become matter. Then consciousness is also interactional, which is why it can be experienced and perceived and why it can perceive. Consciousness can act on matter and time has energy which can become matter, a particle-wave duality which propagates through space. This implies that consciousness can also effect and warp the space-time continuum which includes multiple futures and multiple pasts which share world lines which can overlap and intersect one another. Again, if there is a god, or a quantum consciousness, then this god/consciousness is also a unity which creates singularities by becoming conscious and collapsing the wave function even of events which take place in the future; and this is because the future is entangled with the present, past, and with the continuum which is all things.

"And his mind was afterwards clear as tehe morning, and after this he was able to see beyond his own individuality. that individuality perceived, he was able to banish all thoughts of past and present...." --Chuang Tzu

THE LIMITATIONS OF THE SENSES

"Whatever you see in existence, both moving and unmoving, is only the combination of the field of activities and the knower of the field."--Bhagavad Gita, 13:27

In relativity consciousness is merely relative. In quantum physics, consciousness and the act of observation and measurement constitute a separate reference frame which can collapse the wave function and register entangled interactions within the environment. Consciousness by the act of observation or measurement takes a static or series of pictures-in-time which then becomes discontinuous from the quantum continuum (Heisenberg 1958; Planck 1931; von Neumann 2001). These entanglements (Francis 2012; Juan et al. 2013; Plenio 2007), or blemishes in the quantum continuum, may be observed as shape, form, cause, effect, past, present, future, the passage of time, and thus reality; the result of a decoupling of quanta from the quantum (coherent) continuum which leaks out and then couples together in a knot of activity which is observed as a wave form collapse.

As based on the Copenhagen theory of quantum mechanics (Bohr, 1958, 1963; Heisenberg 1955, 1958), consciousness and reality are a manifestation of wave functions and alterations in patterns of activity within the quantum continuum which are perceived by consciousness as discontinuous--and that ultimate consciousness, the collective consciousness, could be construed as "god."

Wave form collapse is always a matter of probability, and is non-local, indeterministic and a consequence of conscious observation, measurement, and entanglement. Consciousness is entangled with the quantum continuum and can after the continuum and the space-time manifold.

Most religious, in their conceptions of "god" share similar conceptions. Consciousness, the act of observation be it visual, auditory, tactile, mechanical, digital, is entangled with the quantum continuum and creates a static impression of just a fragment of that quantum frenzy that is registered in the mind of the observer as length, width, height, first, second, and so on; like taking a single picture of something in continual motion, metamorphosis, and transformation. That is, the act of sensory registration, be it a function of a single cell, or the conscious mind of a woman or man, selects a fragment of the infinite quantum possibilities and experiences it as real, but only to that mind or that cell at the moment of registration (Heisenberg 1955, 1958).

As demonstrated in quantum physics, the act of observation, measurement, and registration of an event, can effect that event, causing a collapse of a the wave function (Dirac 1966a,b; Heisenberg 1955), thereby registering form, length, shape which emerges like a blemish on the face of the quantum continuum. Thus, it can be said, at the moment the quantum continuum became conscious, achieved consciousness, this triggered a collapse of the wave function, and the universe came into being.

The mind, however, is not a singularity, but a multiplicity. The mind is also limited by its senses. Consciousness cannot perceive what it cannot perceive. Only fragments of the quantum continuum may be perceived by consciousness, and different aspect of consciousness--the multiplicity of mind--may perceive aspects of reality that other regions of the mind cannot perceive. However, they are perceived, because a mind becomes conscious of them.

"These realms are not come from somewhere outside thyself. Theey come from Within... they exist from eternity within the faculties of thine own intellect... issuing from within thine own brain... reflection of thine own thought-forms." --Tibetan Book of the Dead

A radio or television receiver may be capable of receiving radio or television transmissions from hundreds or thousands of stations. These transmissions contain all manner of messages, voices, shapes, images, and information, and continue to be transmitted, even if the radio or television is off. There are other channels and other transmissions even if we have only one channel. This information is out there if we know it or not, and if we receive it or not.

However, we can only receive and perceive these messages, these images if the television, internet, or radio is on. The number of stations and messages we can receive depends on the channel capacity of the radio/television receiver. That we cannot see or hear it without the proper receiver, or if the radio/television is off, does not mean that this information, these images, these sounds, do not exist, or that those who do perceive these stimuli are hallucinating.

The same is true regarding other realities, including those which may contain spirits, souls, gods or demons. What some perceive as a "demon" could well be an entity living in one of the multiple (probable) worlds predicted by quantum mechanics. Or, this same "demon" may be created by the act of observation--collapsing the wave form of the continuum, created by an observing consciousness; even when that consciousness has been liberated from a body which has died.

"No terrible god punishes you. The shapes of frightening monsters who take hold of you, place a rope along your neck and drag you along, are just illusions which you create from the forces within you.... there are no gods, and no demons." --Tibetan Book of the Dead

We can only perceive what we are able to perceive. Perception is also reality. Our senses not only limit and shape our perceptual reality, but the very act of perceiving can alter that reality; a phenomenon known as entanglement. What is observed is effected by being observed, as has also been demonstrated in quantum physics. Likewise, by changing one's perceptions, by changing the observer, can also change the reality that is being perceived; just like changing the channel on the radio or television.

Each conscious mind is entangled with the quantum continuum. Each mind, and each brain housing that mind, come into existence via the collapse of the wave function and the creation of decoherence. The mind is not "one" with the continuum because it represents a collapse of the wave function and is entangled yet separate from the continuum.

In part, the mind is restrained by its senses and perceptual capabilities, and the inhibitory influences that filter out stimuli which may be overwhelming. Our intellectual and perceptual capabilities cannot process what they cannot perceive or comprehend. Language and belief also act as yoke, by shaping perceptions and labeling that which is beyond the norm, as abnormal, unnatural, crazy, and sinful.

However, trance states, isolation, fasting, prayer, meditation, dream states, and LSD, can free the mind of inhibitory restraint, producing not just dream-like hallucinations, but by opening the mind to a fuller range of experience, so that what is concealed may be revealed.

Yet, to enter into this other perceptual reality so that what is hidden is revealed, also entails the temporary annihilation of this world and this reality. Being becomes non-being, and non-being becomes being--which is also the philosophical view of the Tao.

IN THE BEGINNING THERE WAS LIFE

"Material nature and the living entities should be understood to be beginningless."---Bhagavad Gita, 13:20

According to Darwin (1871): "A belief in all-pervading spiritual agencies seems to be universal, and apparently follows from a considerable advance in man's reason, and from a still greater advance in his faculties of imagination, curiosity, and wonder. I am aware that the assumed instinctive belief in God has been used by many persons as an argument for His existence. But this is a rash argument, as we should be thus compelled to believe in the existence of many cruel and malignant spirits, only a little more powerful than man; for the belief in them is far more general than in a beneficent Deity."

Yet, despite, Darwin's rash claims to the otherwise, we are in fact spiritual beings, and there is scientific evidence to support these beliefs. We in fact possess the genetic and neurological capability to experience "gods" demons, spirits, souls, and other realities, for this reality is only one of many.

And, we possess a brain that not only shapes and filters this reality, but which, under certain conditions enables us to perceive at least some of these other probable realities. These same areas of the brain enable humans (and perhaps other animals) to experience the spirit and the soul as they transcend the body to traverse these myriad realms.

However, the spirit or soul, if comprised of energy, remain tethered to the body during life. But upon death, the energy is released to become one with the quantum continuum.

"All things begin from nothing and end in nothing."-Chuang Tzu

"There is no difference between life and death. The destruction of life is not dying and the beginning of new life is not living. There is no differences between life and death."-Chang Tzu

"There is a limit to our life, but to knowledge there is no limit." -Chuang Tzu

"All things return to their root and disappear and do not know that it is it which presides over their doing." -Tao Te Ching

"Tao is forever, and he that possesses it, though his body ceases, is not destroyed." -Tao Te Ching

"And his was mind was afterwards clear as the morning, and after this he was able to see beyond his own individuality. Freed of this he was able to penetrate to the truth-- how the destruction of life is not dying-- that there is no differences between life and death."   -Chuang Tzu

Life, is common to life. Life has "life energy"--what some might call the "soul" or the essence or "spirit of god."

If life is energy, then life/energy cannot be created or destroyed. There has always been life. There will always be life. The universe itself, is alive.

What we perceive as "individuality" is a manifestation of the wave form collapse; an entangled blemish in the quantum continuum. At the moment of death, as being is transformed into nonbeing, the energy which was the mass which was the individual, returns to the quantum continuum, and this is because energy cannot be destroyed. Energy can neither be created nor destroyed.

If life is energy, then life can be neither created nor destroyed. Rather the structural organization that gives form to life, the body, is subject to disintegration and decay. What we call death.

Again, consider Einstein's theorem: i.e. $E=M/C^2$. Although energy cannot be destroyed or created, the destruction and transmutation of matter is something wholly different and is dependent on the organization and stability of the force field which is energy.

Although material forms may become unstable, disintegrate or assume new organization, the constituent fabric that gives rise to matter and its manifest structure, is pure energy -which cannot be destroyed. However, if matter decays, if the body dies, that energy is liberated, although its material form appears to disintegrate and to die.

Birth is being. Death is the return to non-being: a return to the quantum continuum which is all things.

"Tao is forever and he that possesses it, Though his body ceases, is not destroyed." -Lao Tzu

"Thine own consciousness, shining, void, and inseparable from the Great Body of Radiance, hath no birth, nor death, and is the Immutable Light--Buddha Amitabha, the source of life and boundless light." -Bardo Thodol / Tibetan Book of the Dead

Death is generally a gradual process, with some cells and tissues disintegrating in advance of others, and yet other tissues living for hours or even days before the body completely decays.

Presumably, even after death, so long as the body and its brain lives, one's sense of a personal soul and identity remains intact. This personal identity is perceived, after the death of the body, as an out-of-body experience. Moreover, this personal identity, the energy field associated with the dying body, may be perceived by itself, or by others, as a ghost, spirit, or departing soul. Presumably, this ethereal after-death existence and sense of personal identity remains tethered to the body/brain until the body completely dies and decays.

Indeed, the linkage of the personal soul and individual immortality to the body were widespread beliefs and practices among the ancient Egyptians which is why they expended so much effort to preserve the body via mummification. If the body could be preserved, so could one's personal soul and sense of individuality, leading to "immortality".

Others, including the Tibetan Buddhists sought just the opposite, to free the soul from the body and so as to escape the "illusion" of individuality and personal existence.

Therefore, what some experience as their personal soul upon death, may be but a gradual liberation of LIFE that at first retains its bodily links, thus preserving one's sense of individuality; the shadow of one's previous form as the body dies.

As the body is consumed, perhaps so too is the sense of individuality, freeing the soul, one's LIFE, to be embraced by the radiance of all LIFE thereby becoming One with the god/universe: the quantum continuum.

REFERNCES

Bell, J. S. (1964) On the Einstein Podolsky Rosen Paradox, Physics 1, 3, 195–200 (1964)

Bell,J. S. (1966) On the problem of hidden variables in quantum mechanics, Rev. Mod. Phys. 38, 447 Bohr, N. (1934/1987), Atomic Theory and the Description of Nature, reprinted as The Philosophical Writings of Niels Bohr, Vol. I, Woodbridge: Ox Bow Press.

Bohr. N. (1949). "Discussions with Einstein on Epistemological Problems in Atomic Physics". In P. Schilpp. Albert Einstein: Philosopher-Scientist. Open Court.

Bohr, N. (1958/1987), Essays 1932-1957 on Atomic Physics and Human Knowledge, reprinted as The Philosophical Writings of Niels Bohr, Vol. II, Woodbridge: Ox Bow Press.

Bohr, N. (1963/1987), Essays 1958-1962 on Atomic Physics and Human Knowledge, reprinted as The Philosophical Writings of Niels Bohr, Vol. III, Woodbridge: Ox Bow Press.

Bonnor, W. Steadman, B.R (2005). "Exact solutions of the Einstein-Maxwell equations with closed timelike curves". Gen. Rel. Grav. 37 (11): 1833.

Born, M. Heisenberg, W. & Jordan, P. (1925) Zur Quantenmechanik II, Zeitschrift für Physik, 35, 557-615, 1925

Buser, M. et al. (2013). Visualization of the Gödel universe. New Journal of Physics. Vol. 15.

Carroll, S (2004). Spacetime and Geometry. Addison Wesley.

DeWitt, B. S., (1971). The Many-Universes Interpretation of Quantum Mechanics, in B. D.'Espagnat (ed.), Foundations of Quantum Mechanics, New York: Academic Press. pp. 167–218.

DeWitt, B. S. and Graham, N., editors (1973). The Many-Worlds Interpretation of Quantum Mechanics. Princeton University Press, Princeton, New-Jersey.

Dirac, P. (1928). "The Quantum Theory of the Electron". Proceedings of the Royal Society of London. Series A, 117 (778): 610–24.

Dirac, P. (1930) Principles of Quantum Mechanics

Dirac, P. (1966a) Lectures on Quantum Mechanics

Dirac, P. (1966b). Lectures on Quantum Field Theory .

Einstein, A. (1905a). Does the Inertia of a Body Depend upon its Energy Content? Annalen der Physik 18, 639-641.

Einstein, A. (1905b). Concerning an Heuristic Point of View Toward the Emission and Transformation of Light. Annalen der Physik 17, 132-148.

Einstein, A. (1906a). On the Theory of Light Production and Light Absorption. Annalen der Physik 20, 199-206.

Einstein, A. (1906b). The Principle of Conservation of Motion of the Center of Gravity and the Inertia of Energy. Annalen der Physik 20, 627-633.

Einstein, A. (1926). Letter to Max Born. The Born-Einstein Letters (translated by Irene Born) Walker and Company, New York.

Everett , H (1956), Theory of the Universal Wavefunction",Thesis, Princeton University

Everett, H. (1957) Relative State Formulation of Quantum Mechanics, Reviews of Modern Physics vol 29, 454–462.

Einstein A, Podolsky B, Rosen N (1935). "Can Quantum-Mechanical Description of Physical Reality Be Considered Complete?". Phys. Rev. 47 (10): 777–780.

Gödel (1995) Lecture on rotating universes Kurt Gödel: Collected Works (Unpublished Essays and Lectures vol 3) ed S Feferman (Oxford: Oxford University Press)

Heisenberg, W. (1925) Über quantentheoretische Umdeutung kinematischer und mechanischer Beziehungen, ("Quantum-Theoretical Re-interpretation of Kinematic and Mechanical Relations") Zeitschrift für Physik, 33, 879-893, 1925

Heisenberg, W. (1927), "Über den anschaulichen Inhalt der quantentheoretischen Kinematik und Mechanik", Zeitschrift für Physik 43 (3–4): 172–198,

Heisenberg. W. (1930), Physikalische Prinzipien der Quantentheorie (Leipzig: Hirzel). English translation The Physical Principles of Quantum Theory, University of Chicago Press.

Heisenberg, W. (1955). The Development of the Interpretation of the Quantum Theory, in W. Pauli (ed), Niels Bohr and the Development of Physics, 35, London: Pergamon pp. 12-29.

Heisenberg, W. (1958), Physics and Philosophy: The Revolution in Modern Science, London: Goerge Allen & Unwin.

Joseph, R. (2014). The Quantum Physics of Time Travel. Cosmology Science Publishers

Juan Yin, et al. (2013). "Bounding the speed of `spooky action at a distance". Phys. Rev. Lett. 110, 260407.

Langevin, P. (1911), "The evolution of space and time", Scientia X: 31–54

Lee, K.C., et al. (2011). "Entangling macroscopic diamonds at room temperature". Science 334 (6060): 1253–1256.

Matson, J. (2012) Quantum teleportation achieved over record distances, Nature, 13 August

Matthew. F. (2012). Quantum entanglement shows that reality can't be local, Ars Technica, 30 October 2012

Nairz, O. et al. (2003) "Quantum interference experiments with large molecules", American Journal of Physics, 71 (April 2003) 319-325.

Olaf, N.. et al. (2003) "Quantum interference experiments with large molecules", American Journal of Physics, 71 (April 2003) 319-325.

Plenio, V. (2007). "An introduction to entanglement measures". Quant. Inf. Comp. 1: 1–51

Schrödinger, E. (1926). "An Undulatory Theory of the Mechanics of Atoms and Molecules". Physical Review 28 (6): 1049–1070. Bibcode:1926PhRv...28.1049S. doi:10.1103/PhysRev.28.1049.

Schrödinger E; Born, M. (1935). "Discussion of probability relations between separated systems". Mathematical Proceedings of the Cambridge Philosophical Society 31 (4): 555–563.

Schrödinger E; Dirac, P. A. M. (1936). "Probability relations between separated systems". Mathematical Proceedings of the Cambridge Philosophical Society 32 (3): 446–452.

Yin, J. et al. (2013). "Bounding the speed of `spooky action at a distance". Phys. Rev. Lett. 110, 260407.

Printed in Great Britain
by Amazon